Derek and Dave Philpott are the *noms de plume* of two ordinary members of the public, working with help from a worldwide social networking community.

DEAR MR POP STAR

DEREK & DAVE PHILPOTT

Unbound

This edition first published in 2018

Unbound
6th Floor Mutual House, 70 Conduit Street, London W1S 2GF
www.unbound.com

Text design by Lindsay Nash

A CIP record for this book is available
from the British Library

ISBN 978-1-78352-598-0 (trade hbk)
ISBN 978-1-78352-600-0 (ebook)
ISBN 978-1-78352-599-7 (limited edition)

Printed in Great Britain by CPI Group (UK)

*Dedicated to Brian Grogan, whose generosity,
encouragement and tireless support, out of no motive
other than love, did so much to get our mad little world
to the larger one. A dear friend we never met but
who we miss greatly.*

Hello!

For nearly ten years, with the increasing help of my lad, David, I have been on what is viewed by many as a quite bonkers crusade – writing good old-fashioned letters to pop and rock stars about their songs and band names. The thing is – and I hate to break this to you – a lot of them don't make any sense.

David noticed a long time ago that I had an uncanny knack of interpreting the Hit Parade and popular 'tunes' in quite a left-field fashion, either pointing out blatant lyrical ambiguities or, very often, completely getting the wrong end of the stick. In those days he'd act like one of those fast-fingered stenographers you see in court, writing down my ramblings, and often stifling sneezes, or so I thought. It turns out he was desperately trying to stop himself from laughing. He'd say things like:

'... but Dad, it's AC/DC, you can't say that! They're legends!' To which I would retort, 'Listen, son, I don't know who it is and I don't *care* who it is. It doesn't make sense.'

I'm getting on a bit now though, so he chips in more. Frankly, I don't think he is much better himself.

We did try and get replies to these missives by sending them to the pop stars' record companies and managers and 'official channels', but we didn't hear anything back – not really a surprise in hindsight. So we built a little website, put the letters up for all to see and joined Facebook and continued our epistles there.

Then, as the popularity of the letters grew, the artists quite unexpectedly started to reply, pointing out exactly where the original communications went wrong... or right.

Nearly all of the responses were procured through 'the back door of the industry' – via roadies, mutual fans, cousins of bass players, and even other famous participants telling the artists directly. This marvellous online community, which stretched as far afield as Europe, Canada, Japan, the USA, Australia and Stoke, cultivated and organically evolved the whole venture by offering up willing stars whom we would probably not have thought of corresponding with otherwise, establishing contact through personal connections.

Of course, it is not always possible to reach certain targets, hence many observations remain unanswered...

Derek Philpott

Extra special thanks to the following friends for support and obtaining replies: Duncan Parsons, Chris Nash, Chris Topham, John Roberts, Gary Jefferies, Tom Redmond, Gaz Tidey, Alison Marrs, Bob Fischer, Ian Hunter, Vix Perks, John J. Edmunds, Chris Phillips, Lorna Shields, Nick Brine, Daniel Wylie, Maurice Thomas, Roy Corkill, Mark Tibenham, Philip Wright, Henry Priestman, Nicola Radley Laker, Sarah Lewis, Sally Jane Sharp-Paulsen, Derran Brownson, Will Birch, Lisa Davies Promotions, Brian Grogan, Tim Quy, Tom Moody-Stewart, Maggie De Monde, Kev Moore, Tara Bullas, Steve Best, Team Gillan, Gregory Wieting, Paul Beard, David 'Gibby' Gibson, Lucy Dawson, Andy Bell, Hifi Sean, Angela Cranwell, Christopher Butler, Steve James, Kim Halliday, Chesney Hawkes, Amanda Austin, Alan Clayson, Rich Davenport, Mike Toms, Faye Morgan Armstrong, James Marett, Bruce Thomas, Graham and all at Viz Comic.

Dear Doctor from Doctor and The Medics,

Prepare yourself. You know it's a must.

Forgive me for stating that unless you are
specifically referring to any of several Old
World herbs belonging to the genus Medicago, in
the pea family, your 'band handle' is difficult
to fathom by dint of its puzzling estrangement
between a doctor, who _is_ a medic, and other
identical practitioners, who are also medics.

Your befuddling differentiation is akin to, for
example, 'Centre Forward and The Footballers',
'Cashier and The Bank Staff', 'Musician and
The Instrument Players', 'Taxidermist and The
Deceased Animal Stuffers', 'Disc Jockey and
The People That Play Records and Talk In-between
Them', 'Funeral Director and The Undertakers'
and/or, with apologies, 'Politician and The
Fibbers'.

Fortunately, your error can be corrected by a
simple insertion of the word 'other' directly
after the word 'and', or even more simply,
by 'rebranding' yourselves as 'The Doctors'
(although I can find no record of any of you on
The Register, which could lead to legal issues).

Yours,
Derek Philpott

Dear Mr Philpott,

Thank you for your very direct and not uncritical letter about the apparent factual inconsistencies in my band name. It can't have been easy being that open and honest to someone who is, after all, a total stranger to you. It displays great character and also a commendable concern for your fellow man (or woman, though frankly why a woman would bother herself with this nonsense while they have a planet to run is beyond me!) in as much as the world throws so many levels of confusion at us that such inconsistencies can only add to the maelstrom of bewilderment that seems to define modern life.

As such your letter has caused me many months of agitated deliberation and, if I'm honest, personal suffering and a great deal of guilt as, over the past 34 years, many less vocal than yourself may have suffered in silence as a result of my clear oversight. Indeed, I have halted all recording projects as a result. In fairness this is no great loss to the Art World as 30 years working on a follow up single may be considered by some to be less than prolific.

I had considered the factor of exclusivity in as much as a Doctor is a Medic but a Medic may not necessarily be a Doctor in the same way that not all mechanics are called Mike, not all Hurricanes are called Johnny, no Comet has ever been called Bill and Dominoes don't have names.

But this is quite clearly grasping at straws and doesn't stand up to close examination as we still have the fact that a Doctor IS a Medic and there are mechanics called Mike and, God knows why, as a lonely child with no real friends, I called my favourite Domino Derek.

Quite clearly I owe our tens of fans a public apology and a name change is needed and, if possible, made retrospective to cover all previous releases.

I have yet to decide on the final name but am favouring Duck Tour and the Mudlarks. There can be no ambiguity here, for while 'Duck Tour' implies some kind of wetland wild fowl safari, no such thing as a 'Duck Tour' actually exists, therefore there can be no inclusivity with any other words, let alone Mudlark! Thereby, all confusion will be removed whilst still creating a thematic link, in as much as both are related to water, which I personally find not at all displeasing.

My other option is, obviously, 'Doctor and the Flowering Plants', commonly known as Medick or Burclover. It's wordy but safe from confusion and also pleasantly informative!

Either way this abhorrent boil on the face of British popular culture will be lanced once and for all.

I can only thank you for showing me the error of my ways and I hope that one day I can atone in full for my sins.

Love and Peace.
Duck Tour

Dear Dr Hook,

I was distraught to hear on our pub jukebox today the impassioned vocal transcript of your conversation with the mother of the girl who was marrying a fella down Galveston way.

As if being in love with a beautiful woman and suffering her defensive parent were not bad enough, the interminable butting in of the operator demanding 40 cents more for the next 3 minutes must have been a 'little bit more' than infuriating, not to say a bit of a dent on the old wallet.

Forgive me for suggesting that had you chosen to make a Skype call or contact your paramour via Yahoo or Facebook Messenger, you would not have been pestered every 180 seconds by a telecommunicational 'breadhead' (such calls being free of the Silver Dollar). Also, by selecting the 'video call' option it would be More Like the Movies in that you would be Knowing She's There, ready to accept from you better love next time.

Derek

Dear Sir (?)

Had there been video options for communicating in the early 70s I'm not sure it would have helped my case. Given that I looked like Bigfoot with a guitar back in those days I have to assume I would not have been afforded even as brief a conversation as I was on that payphone had the girl's mother been able to actually see me.

I consider myself extremely lucky the girl's father never got involved.

Fortunately, I ran out of coins and, mercifully, we were all spared a potentially stressful outcome.

Dennis Locorriere

P.S. By the way, it should be said that the operator was very kind and stayed on the line, consoling me, after that rude woman hung up. She and I stayed in touch for a while afterwards but it got too expensive. I'm certain the absence of a visual probably helped there too.

Dear Spandau Ballet,

I was shocked to hear that you had bought a ticket to the world and have now come back again. We are afraid that you may have been 'ripped off', as merely existing on this planet is free of charge. Perhaps you should contact TV's 'Watchdog' so that this unscrupulous travel agent cannot target any other 'New Romantic' pop combos.

Dear Tears for Fears,

Re: 'Head Over Heels'

Although I am not averse, per se, to the idea
of a cup of tea and a chinwag within isolated
environs, I am afraid I am rather perturbed by
certain aspects of your desired rendezvous.
I am not sure that the proposed secluded natter,
especially in view of its scheduled subject
matter, is one that I can be talked into at this
time even with gentle persuasion, Sirs.

I am sorry, Tears for Fears, but given that
meteorological phenomena are experienced
universally, and are in no way secret, I
am at a loss to understand the hazards of
publicly discussing drizzle or sunny spells
confidentially for fear of the information
leaking into the hands of eavesdropping third
parties. Sadly the only conclusion to be
drawn is that you are intending to engage me
in discourse relating to chem-trails, cloud-
seeding, 'climate engineering' and other such
atmospheric element tampering conspiracy
theories, aimed at exposing shadowy influential
figures who want to rule the world.*

I do not take stock in such an unsubstantiated
mad world, Sirs, and hope that you are not at

this time disoriented, as inferred within the
chorus of your pop record.

In conclusion, if it is all the same to you,
I am aware that you wanted to be with me alone
and talk about the weather, but as a compromise
would suggest that we meet in a Wetherspoons and
talk about the state of the Premier League.

Yours,
D. Philpott

* Does not relate to Cliff Richard manipulating downfall in order
to sing 'impromptu medley', Centre Court, Wimbledon, 1996

Dear Mr Philpott,

Re: 'Head Over Heels'

While I empathise with your concerns, this song was written quite a while before we became so aware of global warming (some eminent politicians still believe it to be a false theory made up by the Chinese), and if you knew the true story behind those lyrics, you would take a far less harsh stance, I assure you.

Now, I have to be very careful here, because the song was written for a lady who has gone on to become a household name. I first met her when she was a weather girl for a Saturday morning kids' show. There was no blue screen at the time to make her look like a pro; she merely had a large piece of card and, of course, a pointing stick. Naturally attractive due to her Scandinavian looks, I found it hard to approach her; I was a little nervous especially as she was taller than me and quite witty as well. Alas, my opening line was bound to be about the weather, I thought it was a strong and natural chat up line; I think I even mentioned the words 'isobar' and 'cold front' in an attempt to impress her. This conversation took place after I'd virtually barged into her dressing room while she was changing. Now, in the song I use the words 'you keep your distance with a system of touch'; well, to be honest, I was being kind to her, because she actually used her pointing stick to prod me out of the room (I still have the scars), then once I'd got the message and was about to leave, she tripped me up, and I literally went head over heels into the corridor.

You can imagine, I felt humiliated and a little angry. Normally, I am not one for revenge (ask Curt Smith!) but on this occasion some inner demon took over me. I went back to the studio, took her weather board, and, with the lighter I always keep on me in case I ever take up smoking, set fire to it. Literally, I made a fire and watching it burn, thought of her future, because without that weather board, that pointing stick was basically useless. Well, it turned out that this little act of vengeance set her on the road to a much greater future (ask Sven-Göran Eriksson). No longer a weather girl, she went on to become a TV host and a panelist on a popular comedy show.

And, although we never had a relationship, I turned out to be her four-leaf clover. Funny how these things happen, don't ya think?

Yours Sincerely,
Roland Orzabal obo Tears for Fears

P.S. I'm still up for a pint in Wetherspoons to chat about the footie.

Dear Mr Floyd,

I was most intrigued to learn that when you were a child you had a fever, your hands felt just like two balloons, but now you've got that feeling once again.

I was wondering if your hands also <u>resembled</u> brightly coloured rubber inflatables and if so do you do children's parties and if so are you available on 27 August from 2 to 3?

Dear Bonzo Dog Doo-Dah Band,

I must say that even the most cursory of
researches into the Apollo 11 mission reveals
none of its key capsule-ensconced personnel,
or indeed back-up crew, to have been from the
countryside, Sirs, with Messrs Armstrong,
Aldrin, Collins, Lovell, Anders and Haise
hailing from the distinctly non-rural locations
of Auglaize County, Rome, New Jersey, Cleveland,
Hong Kong and Biloxi respectively. It is
therefore only appropriate that you collectively
admit 'We Were Wrong' in employing the definite
article when there is clear evidence that to
be a non-bucolic missile-dweller is, far from
unique, the norm, and that, at best, the work
should have been accurately recorded as 'I'm An
Urban Spaceman'.

Sadly, however, further investigations into
your own workforce render even this correction
counterfactual given that your lead singer,
originating, as he does, from the village of
Danbury in the parish of Chelmsford, must be
considered as, at best, provincial and causal
of the piece to be altered yet again (although,
on the plus side, the definite article can now
be restored at least until such time as the
existence of another rustic rocketeer can be
proved) to 'I'm The Suburban Spaceman'.

It is also to be feared that your stating that you do not exist, which is indeed an admirable admission given the arguments above presented regarding the refrain in its present form, will only further encourage those proponents of the theory that a certain NASA event was staged in a Los Angeles 'parking lot', employing a redundant Star Trek set and some slow-motion photography.

It is therefore sincerely hoped that 'For the Benefit of Mankind' you have got everything you need to respond to this missive, be it by 'Postcard', electronic mail or handwritten letter, and that 'The Strain' of doing so will not cause you to remark in respect of my good self, 'You Done My Brain In'.

We remain, yours sincerely,
Derek & Dave Philpott

Dear Philpotts,

Thank you for your painstaking observations regarding the hitherto unchallenged title of our solitary hit 'I'm The Urban Spaceman'.

Your somewhat unsettling interest in whether or not the precise geographical origin of an individual is either built up or Green Belt, is, I humbly suggest, a Red Herring.

Language is a long and slow river and when ancient peoples lived their lives between two such metaphors – as in Mesopotamia – the use of definite or indefinite articles made little or no difference to the Hittites of the day – until, of course, questions of an existentialist nature were raised. By definition, the Definite Article implies the existence of something – especially in a Collective Narrative – whereas an Indefinite Article is a vague and wishy-washy thing – like a slogan on a Brexit Bus.

I deliberately chose the Definite Article for the notion of an Urban Spaceman – for the dramatic effect at the end of the song – revealing someone who does not actually exist.

Like a Truth on a Brexit Bus. Alas, it is not the Perfect World.

Yours sincerely,
Neil Innes
September 2016

[on behalf of A Bonzo Dog Doo-Dah Band]

Dear Christopher Cross,

Thank you for your advice. However, it is most unlikely that I will ever be stranded at a central point between these two locations as I am not planning to travel in space.

Dear Cutting Crew,

<u>Re: 'I (Just) Died in Your Arms'</u>

I must say that I am utterly dumbfounded by the
above statement. Aside from being grammatically
dubious, it simply cannot be true. I am certain
that I would recall such a grisly incident;
in addition, my wife Jean would have been
most alarmed to witness my return from an
evening in your company holding a male corpse.
As for 'something I said' being the cause of
your demise, I would simply state that even a
rudimentary grasp of biology would give lie to
your assertion that one can pass away from being
spoken to while hugged.

In addition, I can only infer that you believe
your vocal delivery to be posthumous, and I am
unwilling to entertain such a ghostly notion.
In future, I suggest that you title your pop
'hits' more carefully, in order to create a more
authentic scenario.

Failing this, I would recommend that you become
hairdressers, perhaps specialising in 'crew
cuts'; during quiet periods it would be possible
to rehearse your harmonies, rather like a
modern-day barber shop choir. I personally
would visit such an establishment in the summer

months, providing that your 'haircuts' were of a
similar standard to your splendid vocals.

Yours,
Derek Philpott

Dear Derek,

Thank you for your kind and overt letter but I fear you may have misunderstood… I wasn't actually referring to you, but to a regular lady customer in our salon with the last booking of the day at 9pm.

The 'something she said' she wanted was a stupidly huge amount of hair spray on the new 'beehive' style I had fashioned for her that evening and suddenly I fell and completely passed out from the fumes!!

I know as a trained expert 'I should have walked away' but was eventually and thankfully resuscitated in time. Contrary to popular belief, I did not die that night!!!!

As regards to yourself, we promise to get the scissors out and would love to discuss further shampoo and styling ideas.

As is the case with my own in-house stylist, you will be pleased to know that there is a discount for us with less hair.

Nick v E

Dear Queen,

I heard on Radio Tees that you were just a skinny lad who never knew no good from bad. I am sorry, Queen, but to equate one's Body Mass Index with a propensity towards criminality is just not on. We see many slim constables in the city centre and, conversely, Al Capone, was, shall we say, fond of the odd pie, was he not?

Dear Starship,

Re: 'We Built This City on Rock 'n' Roll'

I have just listened to your 'Soft Rock Anthem'
and it appears that you expect me to believe
that you have successfully completed possibly
the most ludicrous design project in the history
of architecture, as outlined within it.

Any construction, be it as little as a shed,
requires a solid bedrock, typically embedded
into at least three feet or so of soil. A
building of significant weight, however, will
require very deep foundations, in order to
transfer a load from the edifice through an
upper weak layer of mud to a stronger deeper
layer. There are different types of deep
foundations including helical piles, impact-
driven piles, drilled shafts, caissons, piers,
and earth stabilised columns, and the naming
conventions vary between different engineers.
Said piles are normally of steel, reinforced
and pre-tensioned and/or reinforced concrete.
Airwaves are most certainly not a suitable
platform; your boast to have 'built this
city on rock and roll' is therefore utterly
preposterous.

I apologise unreservedly if you <u>have</u> managed to
mount a metropolis upon some twelve-bar blues,

and would be much obliged if you could guide me, perhaps via the worldwide web's Google Earth or the Automobile Association's superb route finder service, to this no doubt wondrous spectacle.

I await your reply in the pre-paid envelope provided.

Yours,
Derek Philpott

To: Mr Derek Philpott

My Dear Fellow:

Are you a complete and utter fool? Anybody with a modicum of common sense realizes that when The Troggs sang 'Wild Thing', Andover was born; when the Beatles crooned 'Love Me Do', Liverpool became centre stage; and where would Memphis be today without Elvis's 'Hound Dog'? So, it is plainly obvious that our cities were clearly, undoubtedly built on Rock'n'Roll!

Allow me to further elucidate... cases in point: When Elton 'Crocodile Rocked' us, the majestic Pinner rose up out of bland Middlesex; When Gary Glitter 'Rock 'n' Rolled' us (Parts 1 and 2), obscure Banbury stood proud from Oxfordshire; And when Noddy Holder and Slade wailed 'Cum on Feel The Noize', Walsall dominated our rockin' minds. Surely you recall – all these places ('cities', if you will) were mere nondescript pagan settlements, devoid of meaning, until Rock 'n' Roll put them on the map in glorious recognition! Furthermore, dare I say it, when the Archies rocked us with the epic 'Sugar Sugar' (8 weeks at No. 1, I hasten to add), Riverdale was re-born – strong and proud. And, as you must know, when we let Robbie Williams 'Entertain Us', the previously sleepy Stoke-on-Trent exploded to become our Rock capital of the world! And, for God's sake, sir, everybody knows that the Bay City Rollers defined the psychedelic sound of San Francisco! Staying with psychedelia for a moment, it's also common knowledge that 'Chocolate City',

George Clinton's and Parliament's opus, became the very city where Cadbury's confectionary dynasty was launched. Powerful stuff!

So, this radical idea that a city is built on bricks and mortar truly beggars belief! Let us not forget my own humble achievement: When I penned my part of 'We Built This City', Southampton (my birthplace) became the yardstick by which all other Rock 'n' Roll cities would be measured!!

Lastly, I began this letter essentially by suggesting that you're as thick as a brick, which now leads me to my final, overwhelming piece of evidence: When Jethro Tull famously traded-in his agricultural seed drill for a small-bodied Martin guitar, Luton was truly enshrined.

Think upon that!... I rest my case.

Yours, humbly confused,
MARTIN PAGE

Dear Ms. Carlisle,

Are you sure you don't mean 'Devon'?

Dear Mental As Anything,

Re: 'Live It Up'

I thank you for concern, Mental As Anything,
but can assure you, my all-encompassing
unsoundness, or cerebrality-homaging friends,
that you have mistaken my expressionless semi-
concentration usually adopted whilst watching
Top of the Pops 2 for 'the sad face'.

Whilst writing, I must express some concern
pertaining to the isolated adolescent to whom
you allude in your Scottish amphibious animal
film-featured 'feelgood classic'. It would
seem that said 'lonely girl' is capable of
wreaking havoc upon structural matter ranging
from a room barrier to an entire municipality,
simply through the magnitude of her displayed
contentment. Personally speaking, if such a
forsaken female were to come up to my place,
I would be intent on not allowing her to 'live
it up' but instead instilling within her,
perhaps via the recital of 'sad poetry', as
melancholic a disposition as possible. I fear
that unrepressed joviality on the part of the
companionless juvenile could prove potentially
disastrous, if, as you state, when she smiled
the walls would fall down, to say nothing of
her levelling the town if she laughed, and I do
not wish to be held accountable to either the

whole borough, or, more dauntingly my wife Jean, especially as we have not long since decorated.

There may, however, exist an opportunity for the solitary young lady's conviviality destruction to be employed within the commercial arena, thus mixing 'business and pleasure' and confirming your assertion that she is 'worth her weight in gold'. The placement of the unchaperoned youth, perhaps deployed with a Tommy Cooper joke book, within an area intended for redevelopment, would likely be a far more economical alternative to the costly explosives, wrecking balls, JCBs, heavy plant machinery and what have you, of most demolition companies and, if he was still alive, Fred Dibnah.

As an aside, if indeed you <u>do</u> have the capacity to inspire gaiety in the maudlin, you may wish to get in touch with a Mr Harley, whom I understand to be in need of cheering up at the moment.

I sincerely hope, my wacky-as-whatever correspondees, that you will 'come aroun'' to the sensibilities contained in this missive in the near future and not cause me to remind you 'too many times' for a response.

Yours Rationally,
Derek Philpott

P.S. I could not agree more that I am 'beside the dance floor'; our sofa adjoins the unfettered part of our parquet flooring that Jean often utilises in an impromptu waltz whenever <u>Home and Away</u> comes on.

Dear Derek,

When you started putting the sensible blowtorch on Live It Up I should've realized that large holes would start to appear in the inner logic of our song.

I didn't take your parquetry floor, or the delicious Jean, into my considerations writing this dance number. I'm sure that you writing this critique in the style of a neighbour's particularly strident objection to a routine owner-builder development application before the local council has put me off writing pop tunes with any self-revelatory content in future.

I was referring to personal experience of courtship rituals that were common in ear-bleedingly loud pubs and clubs in 1980s Australia. The ethnographic study I undertook while constantly touring with Mental As Anything drew me to the conclusion that there were many unhappy girls/women cowering in the dark corners of these meat markets who were just waiting for one of the hopelessly shy boys/men to approach them and sing a melodic tune inviting them home for a... drink/game of twister/cheese on toast, etc.

While I think your habit of personalising song lyrics can be most amusing I would ask you to think of us writers who find ourselves quaking in fear of what you and the delicious Jean will make of our next efforts.

Mentally Yours,
Shaken and slightly stirred,
Greedy Smith
Mental As Anything

Dear The Scissor Sisters, and
Eddie Grant. Well don't then!

Dear Mr Hoople,

I was planning to head into town at about eleven this morning to meet with friends for lunch at midday, but saw on the local news that due to roadworks near the A40, and temporary lights at the Polish War Memorial, I was advised to add at least another half an hour to my journey.

I am also halfway through <u>Breaking Bad</u> and am enjoying it immensely. I cannot wait to see if Walter White dies before he is supposed to, from being killed.

In summary, as much as I admire the 'glam boogie merchants', I must take issue with your statement. Were <u>I</u> to have listened to 'Ride A White Swan' or 'Jeepster', I am sure that I would have been very late at Nando's and now not be up to date with the errant chemist's exploits.

I would therefore be grateful if you could clarify how, oh, man, you may question the need for TV when you got T.Rex.

If, on the other hand, you need TV at the same <u>time</u> as listening to T.Rex, and assuming that both your telly and your hi-fi are simultaneously switched on with the volume turned up, one is equally confused. The dilemma here would be that surely the sound of one on top of the other would create such a cacophony

that one would not truly get the benefit
of either, to say nothing of the waste of
electricity in running the two appliances side
by side for the duration of the album that you
are listening to.

On an unrelated note, my son, who lives halfway
between Avebury and Stonehenge, has requested
that I inform you that he has complied with your
request but has thus far been unable to roll
away the stone, and indeed now has a bad back.

Assuming that you are not sending a reply all
the way from Memphis, we look forward to hearing
from you in the near future

Yours,
Derek Philpott

Hello Derek,

I can understand why you think that it is Marc Bolan's T.Rex mentioned in our song ('All The Young Dudes') but let me explain the true meaning of that line. 'Tube-Regulator ex' valves were used in the early versions of the Marshall 100-watt amp heads which then drove two 4 x12 speaker cabs mounted piggyback-style for maximum volume spread.

The problem arose when the T-Rex-type valve was discontinued and had to be replaced by ECC83 valves in 1966, and were hard to come by. Fortunately for us Musos who were lucky enough to own one of these great old Marshall amps, the valves T-Rex-type were still to be found in some makes of television sets which were soon snaffled up by our roadies for spares, but because of the man hours that the boys had to put in due to the enormous amount of gigs that we were playing at that point of time, they did not have enough time to remove the T-Rex valves from the TV sets prior to going to the gigs, so they had to take the sets with them intact, and they were heavy. Believe me or not. Anyway, you can now see why and what the line in the song means, ('man we need TV when we got T.Rex'); we needed a TV in order to get the T.Rex-type valve.

Now about the stone. Oh dear, I am so sorry to hear about your son's back injury brought on by trying a bout of stone carrying, but I'm afraid that he got the wrong idea. The term ('roll away the stone') is actually related to the trouble that we (Mott The Hoople) used to have with the old van we used for gigging in during the 1970s period. You see, the handbrake on the van was not sufficient because of the amount of gear that we carted around in it, so when it was parked up, we would put a large round stone under one of the road wheels in order to stop it (the van that is) from running away from us. Anyway, when we were leaving the driver would shout out to a helper, 'Roll away the stone' and off we would go. Well, that gave us the idea for the song, didn't it, and that is the truth; the idea actually came to mind on the way back from Memphis, during the flight. You see, the group had to go to Memphis so that we could write ('All the Way From Memphis') and that happened when we were back in England.

Well, I do hope that this letter will help to clear up some of the confusion, Derek.

All for now,
Cheers,
Verden Allen

Dear Mr Noone from Herman's Hermits,

Re: 'No Milk Today'

It is imperative that you anchorites really do keep your strength up. By cancelling your order you are doing your metabolism no good at all, Sir. Suspecting that you are now having to skip a healthy cereal, something tells me you will be 'into something <u>less</u> good', such as a cholesterol raising fry-up.

I am curious as to whether your refusal extended to all dairy products, in which case 'No Milk, Cheese, Yoghurt, Cream, Butter, Curd or Whey Today' would have been a more truthful, if less likely, 1967 UK No. 7.

Yours,
D. Philpott

Dear Derek,

Thank you for your letter which was delivered by the postman today, as I don't mind how much post I get.

I am afraid you have misunderstood. My love, at least first thing in the morning, is tea, and as I'd run out of Tetley bags and couldn't get down to the shops for a bit I thought I'd save a few pence and skip a day, settling for a black coffee and some Marmite on toast instead. I don't mind fry-ups now and again, and have nothing against friars either – you have to remember, I once sang I'm Henry the 8th I am I am... but I didn't mean it.

Yours,
Peter Noone

Dear The Selecter,

Are you <u>sure</u> that it's just the same old show on your radio? We thought so too recently and were just about to complain to BBC Wiltshire about their monotonous and unimaginative playlist, repetitive presenter anecdotes and, strangely, identical traffic and travel and news bulletins, before we realised that we had been clicking on the 'Listen Again' option for four days.

Dear Chip from ~~The Whammy Bars~~ Tremeloes,

My son has twice complained of people's mobile phones going off at public concerts recently, although admittedly the most recent was at a Pink Floyd tribute band's full performance of <u>The Dark Side of the Moon</u>, and it may have been part of the show.

No matter. 'I'm with you all the way', The Tremeloes, in valuing the asset of keeping schtum, especially in libraries, next to me on the bus, and when watching many of today's so-called 'stand-up comedians' on <u>Live At The Apollo</u>.

I must take issue however with your assertion that the absence of any noise is 'golden'. For example, to the best of one's knowledge, being very quiet indeed is not to be found smelted into very large bricks under armed guard at Fort Knox, nor is there a Federal Reserve of hush.

Although my son informs me that you are not responsible for scribing this calm/flaxen conundrum, I have argued that, much like your lad's claim to be the one and only (when in fact there are more of him on Facebook) being penned by our mutual friend Mr Kershaw, you are sadly an accessory after the fact.

Yours,
Derek Philpott (and Son)

Dear The Philpotts,

One advantage of us communicating through 'tinternet' (no you cannot have our mobile numbers) is we get to read your absurd ramblings rather than listen to them. In that sense alone, silence, although admittedly not a precious metal, is still very precious indeed

The answer to your self-baffling enquiry is actually in your letter itself, for in old-fashioned libraries in the 60s, as well as posh members' clubs where gents would relax with a copy of the paper and a large scotch, the words 'Silence' or 'Quiet Please' were often etched onto a gold-plated or brass (as in golden coloured) plaque which was often dis-played on a prominent wall.

Naturally it was there for all eyes to still see...

In conclusion:

Chip and Ches 1 (and only)
Philpotts Nil

P.S. It sounds better than the alternative title of 'Silence is Egg-shaped' which is how we often refer to the song on setlists etc.

Dear The Jam,

You state that in the city there are a thousand things you want to say to me. Is it to be assumed by inference that the statement tally would differ were we to be in the countryside?

Dear China Crisis,

Jean had friends over for a cream tea last week and, as is traditional on such occasions, was insistent upon me fetching out her prized fifteen-piece fine bone paragon 'Tree of Kashmir' crockery set from out of the larder in order that she may be the poshest hostess possible. After they were all seated in the lounge, however, we found to our utter dismay that the insides of all the cups were stained with unsightly Oolong tide marks.

We could only conclude that we must have taken them out of the dishwasher before we'd switched it on after her last party.

To make matters worse, the fuse then went on the kettle and we were forced to boil the water manually on the hob and make do with the enamel mugs normally reserved for picnics. We found it very poignant, therefore, that you should come on the radio at the very moment that we were frantically attempting to make the gathering 'Good Again', to further emphasise that my wife and I were now quite literally 'Working with Fire and Steel' in recompense for our very own china crisis. So profoundly did the synchronism affect us that we vowed to check your back catalogue as soon as Jean's guests finally departed, thus bestowing upon us 'The

Gift of Freedom'. Sadly however, when we did, and despite our combined 'Strength of Character', our desire to be entertained devoid of a 'Feel to be Driven Away' unfortunately transpired to be 'One Wish Too Many'.

I am not sure, my perilous East Asian instability homaging friends, if you remember that man that scaled Buckingham Palace's perimeter wall and 'on the up and up' got into the highness of the Queen's bedroom in the 1980s, whereby he deprived Her Majesty of dropping off properly into a full night's sleep. Despite its not displeasing melody, and especially the pan pipes at the beginning, Jean and I were horrified to learn from Spotify that you had mimicked this very trespass by also presumably intruding into a royal bedchamber and rousing a snoozing sovereign. Irrespective of the monarch's prevailing religious or cosmopolitan fashionings, it can only be concluded that to stir the drowsing Head of State at such close quarters must have involved a breach of security.

Jean did postulate that the exhortation 'Wake up, wake up, King in a catholic style' was perhaps directed towards Mr <u>Mark</u> King from the splendid Level 42, however I was able to verify from his charming wife Ria just now, with whom I am on 'tweeting terms', that the esteemed gentleman is an atheist immune to the latest eclectic trends. My son, David, who is well

versed in Heavy Metal matters, has also risen
to your defence, contending that you may be
referring to King <u>Diamond</u> from Mercyful Fete,
and cites your reference to his 'man make-up'
as unassailable substantiation. Although his
hypothesis is undeniably compelling, it must
be borne in mind that until his early twenties
he was resolute in his belief, instilled in him
by somebody at school, that Kendo Nagasaki was
Bruce Lee underneath, who had faked his own
death and subsequently let himself go.

In conclusion, therefore, and considering
that publicising your exalted personage abode
encroachment through the pop charts has hardly
protected it as the 'Best Kept Secret', I urge
you, in order to be 'Safe As Houses' in the long
run, to surrender yourselves to the authorities
immediately. With luck, sufficient time has
passed since the obtrusive ruler slumber
disturbance, for the law to be lenient and spare
you the experience of 'Every Day The Same' in a
custodial environment.

I wish you luck and remain,
Yours,
Derek Philpott

Dear Derek,

Thank you for your letter and concern over the plight of China Crisis, and please let me attempt to put some of your 'Ghosts' to rest.

Hold on, was that Japan or China Crisis? Oops, mustn't stray, let's get 'right down the tracks' here.

Anyhow, I can only imagine your dear wife Jean was only doing the 'Christian' thing in inviting guests to your home for afternoon tea, and who could ever envisage such a 'tragedy and mystery' would ensue with your finest china, but at the risk of upsetting you I have to say this is all her own doing – no one should ever put their finest china in a dishwasher, and I can't help but think if you'd only married a lady called 'Hanna Hanna' we would not be having this conversation now.

I am also very aware of the incident you allude to in the 80s regarding our Monarch, and can state in all confidence that just being born in Liverpool does not entitle us all to a record deal; even if some of those records may be criminal, to even think the law would be lenient given the passage of time on any given crime is just 'Wishful Thinking' on your behalf.

Yours,
Eddie Lundon
China Crisis

Dear Take That,

Although happy to accept your sage recommendation that I never forget where I've come here from, I was most alarmed that this followed the admission that you yourselves have come a long way but are not too sure where you've been.

This is surely the worst example of pop star double standards since Mr. Collins wore a double-breasted suit in the video for 'One More Night' from the 'No Jacket Required' LP.

Dear The Rezillos,

Given that it ran for 2,204 episodes and the studio capacity including artists, production crew, presenters and audience was no more than 200, at best, and not allowing for the same people being there more than once, a maximum of 440,800 have been on <u>Top of the Pops</u>. I am sorry The Rezillos, but by no means can such a figure qualify as 'everybody'.

Yours,
Derek Philpott

Dear Mr Philpott,

You make a fair case, Derek. However, given that our molecules are constantly replenishing themselves from the environment and every breath we take (© Sting) contains a fair amount of molecules of Jesus' poo, we must stand by our claim on the basis of the longstanding philosophical view of what constitutes the person, coupled with the particularly topical understanding of space time, that everybody is, was and in fact always will be, on *Top of the Pops*.

Should you wish to follow this up by questioning the possibility that there are 20,000 Rezillos Under The Sea, we'll be happy to show you where they live, in a remote part of the Aegean, just east of Atlantis.

Yours,
The Rezillos

Dear Ms Vega,

I was disgusted to hear of your treatment at Tom's Diner on the radio this morning in relation to waiting at the counter for the man to pour your coffee, only to find that he fills it just halfway before ignoring you completely to deal with another customer.

This is, in my opinion, an outrageous display of poor service and it is recommended that you share your lacking latte or decaf deficiency on Yelp. I have just discovered that there are six similarly named establishments worldwide in Bruges, Gdynia, Roosendaal, Pierre, Winterhaven and New York; they all enjoy ratings of over three stars, so I am hoping this is an isolated incident but still feel that your experience is valid and sharing it would be useful both for the business and for any potential patrons.

Dear Saxon,

It seems that you attribute the congregation of your 'headbangers' to a cotton twill textile/ animal rawhide clothing combination.

I very much doubt that these two fabrics would have the organisational and administrative skills required to successfully put together a live music event and put in place all necessary health and safety and fire precautions, let alone set up a booking hotline with the ability to take major credit and debit cards. I also fear that the only way that denim or leather could (singularly or in conjunction with one another) 'set the spirit free' would be if a jacket or bag caught an open bottle of vodka or similar as they were passing and knocked it over.

Furthermore, I must take issue with the suggestion that your Germanic tribe-monickered combo are waiting on the stage for our command. My son David recalls attending a number of your shows back in the 1980s and at no point found you all standing about impatient for him to give you the nod to start your performance. On the contrary, there was at least one occasion where he turned up late due to public transport difficulties to find that you had already started without him.

I have to go now, Saxon, as we are having a day trip to the seaside. Although keen to get to the beach, however, I will not 'run down to the front' as the old legs are playing up a bit!

Yours,
Derek Philpott

Dear Derek,

Oh. It's you again. It doesn't seem five minutes since you interrupted my consumption of a barm cake with your last missive.

Let us address your current concerns. As you know, us Yorkshire folk are renowned for our plain speaking, so gird tha loins!

I take issue with your assertion that denim lacks the wherewithal to facilitate a gathering. I like to think of it on a par (not John) with tartan in this regard. I refer you to 'the gathering of the clans'.

A cursory investigation into its origins reveals that its name is derived from 'de nimes' – that is, from the town of Nîmes in France, where in fact they hold a metal festival every year. A gathering of Headbangers, if you will, and therefore I can 'never surrender' to your point, Sir.

Now, on to the serious matter of our allegedly ignoring your commands. You mention your son David attending a number of concerts… I do recall one such concert when our lighting engineer had rather overindulged with a 'Northern Lady', 'partied 'til he puked' and subsequently rigged the lighting in such a manner that we were blinded and unable to distinguish hand commands from the audience due to our being unsighted. They were 'strangers in the night' if you will.

This also accounts for the inexplicably lengthy pause before starting 'Dallas 1pm', which for the purposes of the live album, we almost retitled 'Dallas half past four in the afternoon'.

In conclusion, I heartily approve of a trip to the seaside. Everybody likes a bit of Saxon the Beach.

Regards,
Graham Oliver

Dear Kiss,

Whilst your enthusiasm is admirable, it is difficult to conceive of how one may rock'n'roll all night and party every day unless there is some sort of running buffet or at least 'nibbles' at the latter and the factoring in of 'power naps' at either or both.

Dear Mr Otway,

I bought some slacks from Marks yesterday and when I got home Jean noticed that a bit of the hem was frayed so made me take them back.

Whilst acknowledging that your mother is obviously a proficient seamstress, especially given the notorious durability of denim, and assuming that you have been wise enough to keep the receipt of course, one would therefore recommend that instead of her sewing your new blue jeans, you may be better advised just to request a refund or demand an undamaged pair.

As for having one foot on the platform and the other foot on the train, my son recently showed me some mobile phone footage of someone in a similar position, called 'Epic Fails 2013'. I would therefore suggest that you make a decision post haste!

I know that you are a very busy man but would appreciate a response to this missive when you are 'Really Free'.

Yours,
Derek Philpott (and Dave)

Dear Dave and Dad,

This is a very old song.

It would appear from your letter that you have been listening to animals and that your assumption that 'my mother is obviously a proficient seamstress' is in fact completely false.

Back in the 1960s there were beasts who were so desperate to be heard on the radio that they altered my mum's occupation from 'My mother was a madam, she sold those Harlem Queens' to giving her a sewing job she was crap at.

Similarly, my dad who needed a 'suit ace and a trump' whilst playing cards was given an unsuitable piece of Samsonite and elephant's nose.

The reference to having 'One foot on the platform and one foot on the train' I believe is just a poetic way of describing an animal in a department store choosing what to wear having the choice of a ball and chain and a pair of new blue jeans.

Cheers,
Otway

Dear Keith West,

Re: 'Excerpt from a Teenage Opera'

Please forgive me for stating that the minor chorus ensemble goading the weak-hearted, and respiratorily suffering, Grocer Jack, 82, to get off his back and go into town in your adolescent aria snippet are most likely complicit in the octogenarian vegetable merchant's demise. Could they not have ordered via Ocado online, for heaven's sake?

Dear ~~Fruity Flick Knife~~ Strawberry Switchblade,

There is, I hear, a saying which advises that if a cup isn't topped up to the brim at least there is still some water in it, or something like that.

With that in mind, as you sit there alone with your partner, looking for a reason to go on, it is actually so clear that 'all' you have now are not just thoughts of yesterday, but also each other, the remainder of the day in question, and a possible future together!

Also, that a part of him or her has gone when it's all over need not be a particular cause for concern if the missing bits are toenail clippings or if they have had a bit of a trim, perhaps administered by a Swiss Army tool, in deference to your psychedelic moniker.

Finally, one finds it perplexing that you hate trees and you hate the flowers, although admittedly Mr Otway also harbours similar horticultural paranoia, warning me to beware of the latter 'cause he's sure they're gonna get me. Yeah.'

Yours bluntly,
Derek Philpott

Dear Derek,

Thank you for that sweet reminder of the pessimism and negativity of my youth.

You will be pleased to hear that the invention of SSRI antidepressant medication has done much to improve my mood.

No longer is vegetation such a vexation to me; in fact these days I can even be found hugging the odd weeping willow urging it to 'cheer up'.

Age has also rendered many of your questions moot as I can no longer remember what I've been doing Since Yesterday.

Yours happily,
Jill Bryson

Dear Ms Tzuke,

Thank you but I'm afraid that I will have to decline your invitation to stay with you until dawn. I need an early one tonight and sadly your offer of showing me a sunset, which I can quite easily do at any time by staying up late myself or watching the opening credits of <u>Hawaii Five-0</u> on YouTube, would write the day off altogether.

Dear Mr Wilder,

Re: 'Break My Stride'

We find it a little perturbing that, even in a surreal dream state, your partner appears to think so little of you that, upon your arrival at their East Asian whereabouts from yours in Manhattan, by means of but a little row boat, they are more concerned with getting their washing done and boasting of walking about briskly without being forcefully decelerated, wrestled to the ground and/or pinned down, than even giving you a little hug for your efforts.

Frankly, Sir, if I had sailed 10,962 nautical miles (assuming a speed of approximately 2 nautical mph) over 225 days in a flimsy water vessel via the Panama Canal only to be greeted by a supposed loved one telling me they had to get their laundry done and 'didn't want no one to hold them', before boasting of unimpeded rapid striding, I myself would be more than slightly miffed.

It ought to be added that if it acknowledged the People's Republic's new immigration laws, which impose fines of between 5,000 and 20,000 yen (equivalent to 738-2953 USD) for those entering without a visa, your hallucinatory junket could be construed as costly as well as humiliating.

If you will forgive me, Mr Wilder, we think
that you can do better than courting one whom
by your own admission is 'feeling cocky' and
not deserving of your impressive nocturnally
conjured exploits.

Yours,
Derek (and Son)

Dear Derek (and Son),

Though your communique may contain well-researched facts and figures pertaining to matters of maritime and Chinese law, I believe your phrase 'hallucinatory junket' is perhaps more to the point.

Consider, if you will, the opening line of 'Break My Stride'... 'Last night I had the strangest dream.' Once stated, I contend from that point forward, all statutes of logic go right out the window. In other words, I had license to go wherever, whichever way my imagination and dream state would allow. And in so doing, if feeling cocky was the subconscious state of mind, so be it.

In truth, upon reflection, I've no idea what the second verse of my song even means! In my own defense, I gave the girl a piece of my mind in the bridge and moved on... or should I say, resumed my 'stride'. In closing, might I suggest not blaming the dreamer, he's just the messenger.

Sincerely,
Matthew Wilder

Dear Gloria Estefan,

I was most perturbed to learn that the rhythm is going to get me tonight. To the best of my knowledge I have not consciously offended movement or variation comprised by the regular repeating or alternation of varying quantities or conditions, and so am perplexed as to why retribution is being planned for this very evening.

Dear Tenpole Tudor,

It appears from your 'promotional video'
that there are only five of you, which, by my
reckoning, adds up to 200 swords per person.
I fear that such an excess of heavy weaponry
each (especially considering that the enemy is
by your own admission a mile away), combined
with your already having imbibed a barrel or
much, much more, adds up to a battle strategy
that is not 'Wunderbar' at all!

Yours,
Derek Philpott

Dear Sir,

There are a couple of important things I have to clarify before we get started.

1. There were actually only four of us in the band… that's multiple camera angles for you
2. Eddie 'Tenpole' Tudor got his nickname after having had 10 Polish blokes working for him on his new conservatory. (He's actually quite posh don't you know!)

Right, let's get started. The 'Swords of 1000 Men' conundrum. Unfortunately, you've jumped to the conclusion that every one of the aforesaid army would've been carrying a sword. That's your third mistake. As we know, most armies back then were poor farm labourers etc., and although they may have dreamt of owning a sword, the majority of this rabble brandished pikes and staffs… or a cudgel if they had a few spare groats. By my reckoning, only the knights (who came along at the end of the day) would've realistically been carrying swords. Therefore, only a tiny minority would have, in fact, been overladen by the imagined sword problem. As for 'much, much more' this was in fact the non-alcoholic energy-giving drink (a bit like today's Red Bull) Mushmushmor, brewed by the 'baggage' (the jocular name given to the WAGs by the soldiers). Therefore, meeting the enemy a mile away would've been a piece of piss!

So there we have it. I hope this clears up any misunderstandings and next time you hear this wonderful anthem you'll see it in a whole different light... that of an accurate historical depiction.

Thank you for your enquiry.

Regards,
Prof. G. Long (drummer)

P.S. As for 'Wunderbar'... don't get me started!

Dear Mr John,

I completely disagree. <u>No</u> night is acceptable for an altercation.

Dear Katrina and the Waves,

One often wonders what is with you pop stars and your misapprehension that bodily weight can be carried by atmospheric conditions!

I tried to get in touch with Mr Jagger recently to enquire as to how a vaporous mass could sustain the bulk of an adult male and how one may be expected to get 'offa' it, and then Aled Jones, whose claim of strolling about on oxygen seemed equally difficult to substantiate. In your own case we are at odds to comprehend how you may be taking a ramble on solar rays.

It would also appear that, through excessive enthusiasm, you are preventing yourself from partaking in the experience that you are most impatient to indulge in and, as a result, have potentially placed yourself in an awkward position, both literally and fiscally. Even if the virtual impossibility of unaided physical restraint is overlooked, your inability to reach your mail box could prove undesirous in the wallet department. One finds it difficult to fathom how you may physically impede yourself to the point where you are 'held down', as, even if partially successful, your ability to secure three of your limbs will always leave the fourth one free. If the self-pinioning is achieved you

will not only be inexplicably missing out on
your beloved 'writing you he's coming around'
but there may also be other correspondence which
requires your immediate attention. We have
just received a PCN due to my brief over stay in
Aldi's car park two Thursdays ago which, if paid
within 14 days, was for the reduced sum of £35.
If I had decided not to 'go for the mailbox' this
morning then I would've been looking at a hefty
non-discounted £70 with no grounds for appeal.

One would be grateful if you could 'shine a
light' on this matter and will be waiting,
untethered, by one's own mailbox hoping for a
swift response to this conundrum, as I don't
want to spend my whole life just waiting for
you.

Yours,
Derek Philpott and Son

Hi Derek and Dave,

How to hold yourself down:

Grab your left leg with your left hand and your right leg with your right hand (that's what it's all about).

Also install a glass front on your mailbox so you can check for important brown envelopes at the same time as preventing yourself from seeing if he's written you he's coming around.

How to walk on sunshine:

The surface temperature of the sun is about 6,000 degrees Celsius, so to walk on its shine you'd have to wear a well-insulated boot and walk for a short time, which is why the next word is 'Oh oh'! I didn't want impressionable fans to try this themselves so wrote a warning final verse which got edited out of the single version:

> *And just remember all you listeners don't try this at home*
> *'Cos the sun might singe your poor little feet to the bone*
> *And to get 93 million miles you'd have to travel so fast*
> *But in another thirty-three years I can go there on my*
>   *bus pass*
> *We're walking on sunshine etc.*

Love,
Kimberley Rew

Dear 'The Electric Light Orchestra',

Given that your bombastic 'pop songs' clearly emit from conventional musical instruments, I am perplexed by your misleading 'monicker'. Were such an illuminatory bulb ensemble to exist, the only sounds that could be hoped for at best are likely to be a barely audible low buzz or hum.

Dear Mr Priestman off of the Christians,

Re: 'Hooverville'

Thank you for enlightening me. Intrigued by
your 80s 'pop/soul classic' and fully expecting
it to be located on the A40 between Greenford
and Park Royal, I was instead surprised to find
'Hooverville' to be a slang term for a 1930s
shanty town.

That this description, arguably together with
'Forgotten Town', fairly accurately describes
said Ealing backwater (hardly a 'city of hope'
if last time I drove through it to avoid an
incident on Hanger Lane is anything to go by) is
an irony not lost on your humble correspondent.

One wonders if a smaller enclave would be known
as 'HooverJuniorville'.

Thank you for 'cleaning this up for me',
Mr Priestman.

Yours,
Derek Philpott

Dear Dezza…

Well, my name IS 'Henry' [makers of fine vacuum cleaners, Ed.]…

You make a few 'Hot-Points' but, as an 'upright' citizen, I don't want to push my 'Electro-Luck' and adopt a '(Dust) Devil' may care attitude, as I may be 'Dyson' with death if I respond further.

Do you 'Zanu-See my predicament?…

I'm 'Ew-bank'-ing on the fact that you do.

Best wishes,
Henry Priestman

Dear Orchestral Manoeuvres in the Dark,

Pardon me but you do seem to have a rather unusual hobby. One wonders how many euphoniums and glockenspiels have been damaged over the years while stumbling needlessly around concert halls.

Dear Lindisfarne,

Re: 'Fog On The Tyne'

I am ashamed to report that in my youth, after a skinful at the pub, I was caught short and had to relieve myself against the post office.

Rather the worse for wear, I found myself slippin' down slowly, slippin' down sideways just as sirens alerted me to the approach of the local constabulary. Although the copper could comprehend my flouting of the law resulting in the potential for a charge of public lewdness, thankfully there was no cause for me to run for home, running fast as I can (oh-oh); luckily I managed to convince the officer that I was merely looking very closely for opening times and had managed to drop my bottle of pop in the process. I'm sorry, Lindisfarne, but with this trauma still in mind I don't doubt that presently we will have a pint or two together but must decline your invitation to presumably 'meet on the corner' where we can have a wee wee and we can have a wet on the wall.

On an unrelated matter, Lindisfarne, I must heartily disagree. Irrespective of the fact that said abundance may indeed have accumulated above a river in your immediate location, I am quite convinced that any collection of liquid

water droplets or ice crystals suspended in
the air at or near the Earth's surface cannot
be either purchased, bequeathed or stolen. Fog
on the Tyne <u>cannot</u> therefore conceivably be all
yours all yours under any circumstances.

I look forward to hearing from you in the near
future, but as I have missed the last collection
you are perfectly entitled to tell it to
tomorrow.

Yours sincerely,
Derek Philpott

Dear Mr Philpott,

Thank you for your letter. All of us here at Lindisfarne Towers are sorry to hear of your unfortunate experience, and can sympathise – we all remember when we had our first pint.

Regarding your reference to the suspended airborne precipitation frequently encountered in the Newcastle area, its ownership has been a matter of dispute since Roman times. In the 19th century, various industrialists and mine-owners claimed ownership on the strength of their enhancement of the phenomenon, and attempts were made to nationalise it in 1948. However, by the late 1960s, demand had fallen, so my late colleague Alan Hull was able to claim it as his own without contest, and so it remained until his death in 1995 (despite an attempt by a local footballer to lay claim to it in 1990). Alan Hull's undisputed ownership of the material is verified on a plaque (placed there by the City council) outside Newcastle City Hall, which clearly states that 'The Fog On The Tyne was all his'.

Alan bequeathed his fog to the city and people of Newcastle-upon-Tyne, in whose ownership it has remained ever since, though rumours persist of an imminent hostile takeover bid by the current owner of Newcastle United Football Club and a chain of shops purveying sportswear to the sartorially challenged.

In view of your interest in this matter and your previous misfortune, we hope you will reconsider our invitation to meet us on the corner. As we gather you are from outside the area, we would be happy to provide the services of an interpreter. If you could make it at the end of the working week, I can assure you that it'll be all right, we'll have a drink on a Friday night; following which, we might have one more bottle of wine that we can swig together before we all fall down.

Finally I should add that Lindisfarne are advocates of responsible drinking, i.e. you have to get your round in, or wor lass will have you running for home before ye knaa it.

All the best,
Lindisfarne

Dear Fiddler's Dram,

Even allowing for inflation, and given from our research that you appear to originate from Whitstable and the surrounding areas, I find it difficult to comprehend how you were able to achieve your day trip to Bangor (a ten-and-a-half hour, 620-mile round trip, no less) have lunch on the way, a bottle of cider, chocolate ice cream, eels, a cup of tea each, the hire of a boat and a trip to the fun fair, incorporating a ride on the Ferris wheel, all for under a pound 'you know'. Leaving aside quite how you have managed all this energy-sapping frippery within such a limited time frame and, even allowing for 1979 prices, under the circumstances I will require a full breakdown of costs and disbursements including receipts before your folk claim can be taken seriously, in order that I may then replicate this remarkably economical excursion, then duly smugly boast about my own savings on Trip Advisor.

Yours,
Derek Philpott

Tha knows nothing, Derek Philpott! Day Trip to Bangor? It were a folk song, tha daft beggar. That means a song sung by hippies in the 70s about dead folk long gone what wore clogs and worked down t'mill and ate scraggins for breakfast and hoggins for tea and believed in fairies and suchlike. What's scraggins? Well, I'll tell thee. It's a bannock made of flour and sour milk and a bit of herring if the boat'd come in, or just a scrape of jam if the boat'd been lost at sea off the coast of Llandudno with all hands on board.

And me and Elsie, we'd put on our best tippocks and scunderpinks, and we'd buy our scraggins for a penny farthing and catch t'omnibus from outside t'mill and that were fourpence if t'driver fancied his chances and sixpence if he didn't, but mostly he didn't so that made it more expensive. And you could get all the way to Bangor for ninepence if Jack Allroyd were driving. Mind you, he had acne so I usually paid the whole shilling.

Anyroad, this one time, me and Elsie paid tuppence to get on t'pier, and tuppence for a cuppa tea, and there were this competition going on and you could enter for another tuppence, so we did. And it were to see who could roll their scraggins furthest down t'pier, only they didn't call them scraggins. We didn't win, but the manager came up after and said 'Ladies, that were a brilliant Game of Scones!' and we were as chuffed as a bowl of badger fat.

Anyroad, if tha do thy sums right, it comes to one and sixpence without the cider, and that's under a pound of anybody's money. So like I said, tha knows nothing, Derek Philpott!

Deborah Cook

Dear Mr Joel,

My friend Tony Shoesmith recently confided to a first date a nightmare he had had in which he was merely a head on a pole at a fairground and Kid Creole was throwing Peter Gabriel Toby Jugs at him in an attempt to win a singing can of tomato soup covered in crisps and wearing a blonde wig. Unsurprisingly the young lady left the restaurant before the mains arrived, causing him to question your advice that he tell her about it, tell her all his crazy dreams.

Dear Mr Cullimore off of The Housemartins,

Re: 'Me And The Farmer'

I hope that you will forgive my stating that your working environment sounds far from 'a good place to be'.

It is surely a testament to your character that you and the farmer 'get on fine' in spite of the wholly unacceptable conditions that you are forced to work under. To make matters worse, it appears that the odious overseer ('Won't he let you go? Probably no') will not even afford you the courtesy of handing in your notice.

From an external standpoint, the fact that he allows you to toil through tempestuous atmospheric conditions whilst drinking bottles of wine is probably one of the worst examples of health and safety flouting since The Wurzels' boast of drinking cider (they drinks it all of the day) whilst captaining a colossal rotating machete-like death-trap.

You openly state, Sir, that if you pull your weight he'll treat you well but if you are late he'll give you hell. This aggressive attitude is in complete contempt of normal disciplinary procedure whereby a tardy worker should be given a verbal followed by a written warning, should their timekeeping not improve. It ought be also

noted that as he works his workers round the
clock, non-punctuality cannot apply to those
working a 24-hour shift and that fatigue-related
promptitude-spurning upon their next on-site
attendance is perfectly understandable.

Finally the 'happy crook' (presumably a
reference to gleeful self-assessment tax return
omissions) has opted not to humanely stun
fleeced mammals and round them up with respect
but instead has chopped down sheep and bullied
flocks, perhaps through the controversial
police strong-arm tactic of kettling.

As an aside I find it difficult to fathom how
both the Messiah and the Almighty hate the
farmer every day, and through and through,
respectively. That said, I did once witness a
vicar in a Renault 5 repeatedly bibbing a slow-
moving Massey Ferguson on a narrow B-road whilst
yelling that he'd never make Mass at this rate.

All in all, it seems as though this slapdash
agriculturalist is having a 'field day' at
your expense and that even a 'Happy Hour' is
sorely lacking under the whip hand of this
'villien' of the piece. 'You Better Be Doubtful'
if you 'Think For A Minute' that conditions
are to improve, Mr Cullimore. 'We're Not Going
Back' should henceforth be the rallying cry of
yourself and your fellow 'hands'.

Yours,
Derek Philpott

Dear Mr Philpott,

Thanks for your letter. It was very long and rather winding but I got to the end – thanks to a rather stiff cup of tea and half a packet of low-fat Rich Tea biscuits. It certainly gave me a lot to think about as I went about my ex-pop star chores this morning, giving my lawn its weekly trim and strim, tuning my collection of fruit-shaped ukuleles and signing several copies of old Housemartins CDs, just in case. After all, you never know when they might come back into vogue. CDs that is. Not the band. Like double-glazed conservatories and comfy cardies, they never went out of style. At least, not in this corner of Styleville. But I digress.

Point is, before I get round to answering your queries about the lyrics, I feel there is something I ought to point out. And it is this. Derek, my dear chum, I fear you're asking all the right questions in all the wrong places. You sound like a seeker after truth, like myself. And it appears to me that you may have misunderstood the role that pop music and pop stars play in modern culture. In some ways, they are, as you appear to think, leaders of light, role models to a generation, providers of hope and bringers of musical merriment to the masses. In other ways, probably a lot more ways, sadly, they are also just people who discovered early on in life that a really good way to pick up girls, or boys, was to start playing a musical instrument, learn three or four chords and hope that everyone was so impressed with your hipster highness that they forgot to ask questions about your personal hygiene, IQ or pension prospects.

In short, if you're looking to construct a philosophy of life that will carry you through tough times and maybe even answer some of the unanswerable questions that the universe asks of us all, then I would suggest you spend more time with the works of Schopenhauer, Seneca and Christmas cracker manufacturers, than with the works of most modern pop musicians. Who are a sorry bunch at the best times, by the way.

And I speak here, Derek, from bitter experience. In the last few days alone, I have approached Sting, Bono, Chris Martin, Ant and Dec, Simon Cowell and Bradley Wiggins asking if they would care to join my new band, 'Stan Cullimore's All-Star Fruit Shaped Ukulele Band', and none of them have even had the decency to answer my Twitter requests. Seriously, is it any wonder with attitudes like that they are so often somewhat lackadaisical in their approach to lyric construction? I think not.

Which brings me back, rather neatly, to the original point of your letter. To clear up some confusion around the lyrics of our top pop smash hit, 'Me And The Farmer', which I believe has sold at least 13 copies in over 2 countries.

I didn't write the lyrics for our songs, that job was carried out by my good friend Paul Heaton. I did occasionally make suggestions. For instance, with that particular song, I suggested we call it, 'Me and the Greengrocer Down the Road. The One Who Sells Really Cheap Avocados and Organic Watercress'. But my friend Paul felt he would rather stick to the original. Mind, I call him my friend, perhaps I should start calling him something else now. I have sent him several friendly letters over the last few weeks asking him if he

would care to join my new group and so far he has failed to
return any of the stamped addressed envelopes I enclosed.
Typical pop star behaviour.

Yours,
Stan Cullimore

P.S. Do you play the ukulele? If so, would you be interested
in joining an All-Star group I am putting together?

Dear Mr Williams,

Re: 'I'm Loving Angels Instead'

We completely agree! It was much better than <u>Casualty</u> and <u>Holby City</u> put together! Well done, that man!

Dear The Wurzels,

My understanding from BBC Wiltshire is that
much of the nation's farming community is
bemoaning its current subsidy-strapped plight.
Your purchase of a brand new 'blingy thresher'
in said climate, as opposed to a perfectly
functional second-hand model, and your gleeful
pop-chart boasting, is therefore 'not on'.

You have also clumsily revealed that you often
guzzle apple-based fermented brewings, namely
cider. 'I drinks it every day, ooh arr', you
furthermore foolhardily divulge. Given that
arable chores are most effectively conducted
in daylight hours, it necessarily follows that
you are saddled in a contraption consisting
of rapidly propelled oscillating razor-
sharp blades of 10-foot plus in length while
totally 'refreshed', as I believe you pop star's
publicity people call being completely sozzled.

I Bid You Good Day, Sirs!

Yours,
Derek Philpott

Dear Mr Philpott,

Thank you for your letter; it's nice to know that you've taken the time to scrutinise our lyrics in context of the current agricultural climate.

Clearly you're not a farming man and you probably think that the main purpose of a combine harvester is to harvest crops? Well, yes, yes it is, BUT, what do we use it for the rest of year?

Simple; cruisin' round for crumpet like Snoopiddy Dog-Dog.

Ya see, round these parts if you wanna go wooing the ladies you need to impress 'em with summat special, and there ain't nothing more likely to make a dear ol' Mabel go weak at the knees than rumbling by in a gert shiny combine harvester. Now the fact that you reckon a second-hand model would do the trick says as much about your penny-pinching approach to romancing as it does the low standards of the 'ladies' you'd be trying to excite.

Furthermore, you needn't worry about the intoxicating effects of scrumpy on us; we're not like those festival lightweights who have a couple of pints of the crazy apple and end up piddling in their own welly boots. We've been drinking it for so many years it no longer has any alcofrolic effect; we actually consider it one of our '5-a-Day'.

Anyway, hopefully this has soothed away your worries.

All the best,
The Wurzels

Dear The Eagles,

This hotel is both a health hazard
and utterly rubbish. Raw or
undercooked meat (other than
sushi or arguably, 'blue steak')
is one thing, but for guests to be
expected to kill the beast themselves
with their steely cutlery at the
dinner table is quite another. One
can only hope that Alex Polizzi
is alerted to this outrage as soon
as possible.

Dear Melanie,

I am most impressed, if a little unnerved, to learn that you are aware that I dropped the immobiliser to my Nissan Juke down a drain outside Sainsbury's last week.

I do therefore have a brand new key but must sadly inform you that its only functions are to start the ignition, and to release the boot and petrol cap. I fear that it would be ineffectual when turned anticlockwise into a pair of shoes with wheels on, especially given that the only orifices are likely to be the eyeholes which are most likely already to be filled with laces.

Upon this basis I feel that to get together and try them out, you see, would be futile. Although I do not mind that you skated to my door at daylight I would appreciate it greatly if you would not encroach into the threshold. We have just had some parquet laid and would prefer it not to be tarnished by rubber skid marks, that we may retort, 'Look what you've done to my floor, ma.'

Yours,
Derek Philpott

Dear Mr Philpott,

You appear to think I have lace-up boot skates. My skates go around the shoe or boot and you tighten them with the key. With that in mind it looks like I don't need your key after all.

As far as your precious parquet floor is concerned, the wheels are metal – they wouldn't leave black skid marks, just little grooves, which could add character to stodgy parquet floors.

I have been looking around a while, thought you had something for me. I guess I'll keep looking for someone with a brand NEW key.

Love,
Melanie

Dear Aerosmith,

Henceforth I will not knowingly enter any building in which I believe you to be ensconced, unless it be a bungalow, other single-storey erection, or place where a stairway were the only method of ascent or descent. This decision is of course resultant of your debauched lift-based antics and I bid you good day!

Dear It Bites,

Re: 'Calling All The Heroes'

Nana Philpott always said 'self-praise is no praise'.

Excuse my impertinence therefore in pointing out that if any of your intended combatant recruits are wantonly comfortable with being referred to as 'heroes' in the open forum of the pop charts (as opposed to 'people who only do what they hope anyone would do in the same situation'), it strikes me that the skirmish to which you refer may be little more than a vanity project fought by the self-deluded. It is also relevant to note that the summoning of ALL exemplars, genuine or otherwise, could be construed as foolhardy for the following reasons:

a) Whilst Napoleon (a miniature hero) was championed by his followers, it is surely not unfair to assume that their enthusiasm was not shared by the opposing coalitions whom he battled.

b) To summon literally ALL the heroes could be construed as an ill-conceived strategy, especially were an unrelated emergency to occur simultaneously (such as, for example, that which would provoke 'screaming on

the beaches') at a time that your entire
courageous person quota has been deployed
'high on a mountain' some miles away. It
is therefore recommended that, not unlike
substitute teachers, a reserve percentage
of 'supply heroes' be held back for such an
event, so as to ensure that resources are not
overstretched.

Finally, by your own admission, It Bites,
'keeping friends among you saves a fight',
hence in order to alleviate intrepid recruit
inter-altercations I would recommend that all
potential warriors undergo a full interview
prior to engagement.

Yours,
Derek Philpott

Dearest Derek,

Thank you for your insightful, and impeccable logic. If I didn't have your email address I would swear these words came out of the late, great, aggressive Aries Christopher Hitchens who would no doubt be offended at the inclusion of 'Aries' in my descriptions of him. But he's dead so **** it. I like astrology. It's completely illogical and I'm tired of all those Oxford university twats and their self-righteous debating skills. I come from the Northern debating art, from the university of 'I'll kick your ****in' teeth in'. We can't figure out grammar to save our lives but we can kick your ****in' teeth in. This is why the upper British establishment choose us Northerners and our children to go off to war to die so they can make more money. We are cannon fodder of the highest degree.

You see, I'm a Northern Englishman. We don't debate anyone, we simply knock the ****ers out cold. Those Oxford boys would last about four seconds in my school. They would be savaged and humiliated in front of the whole class, teeth knocked out, hair ripped from their heads, noses broken and a can of dandelion and burdock rammed right up their condescending arses before they had the chance to utter the precursor of all debates 'sir'.

So I appreciate your logic but it doesn't work up North. The Northern logic says this: we all go together in a big gang and kick their ****in' teeth in and then we return in a big gang, find those who tried to sneak in the back door while we were gone and kick their ****in' teeth in. (Unless it was on the same day as a rugby league final.)

The song itself is highly misunderstood. Most people think it is a story of good versus evil, whitey versus the darkies, Jesus versus Satan, Dr Who versus the black Dalek or Cliff Richard versus Frankenstein. But the song is actually inspired by the lost works of the great Friedrich Nietzsche which I was privileged enough to read at the university. In chapter two, aptly entitled 'clearly black lesbians shouldn't be allowed to drive' Nietzsche clearly states 'if anyone tries to shag your bird you should kick his ****in' teeth in'. This sentiment was mirrored by Friedrich Nietzsche's brother Barry who, when asked about his highly suspicious relationship with his two camels, said 'one is for food and the other is for fox hunting'.

Many of the world's great leaders have come through our university. Nixon, Stalin, Napoleon, Genghis Khan to name but a few of our most decorated. The latest being Vladimir Putin who at this moment in time was spotted drunk at a Stalingrad bus stop with a can of Carlsberg Special and a picture of the Isis leader singing 'you're gonna get your ****in' head kicked in'. Donald Trump claims to have been an overseas student but there are no records of him at the university.

I hope this helps you understand the world in which the song came from and what it means to so many Northerners. You see in the North we learned something very valuable, passed down from generation to generation. You can debate with your quick wit and your sharp mind, you can create intellectual pitfalls for us Northerners to fall into, you can outsmart, outwit, out flank and out manoeuvre all of us at the same time, but at the end of the day, all of your studies and countless hours spent in books and debate will prove themselves useless. Because no matter what you say, we'll just kick your ****in' teeth in anyway.

Right, that's it. I'm off for some spinach risotto and lemon lung pie. If you are a Northerner like me then I wish you a great day. If you are a Southern pussy then may your shit come alive and kiss you.

Francis
August 2016

Dear Paper Lace,

As much as one sympathises with Billy's 'young
and lovely fiancée' imploring him not to be
a hero, and irrespective of one's personal
politics regarding the American Civil War, I
fear that in certain quarters the justifiably
distraught young lady could be viewed as a
precursor to Lord (in this case 'Lady') Haw-Haw.
Even if Billy had been a hero just for a little
while and returned after keeping his 'pretty
head low', his coming back to her could have
been construed as a dereliction of duty or, at
the very least, have branded him as 'the coward
of the county'.

As an aside, although it is to be conceded that
motorcycles were not invented at that time,
I hope you will excuse my suggestion that
The Black-Eyed Boys, despite their fearsome
reputation, would probably be no good at all in
the field of conflict. Unless the rubber has
worn off on the inside of their goggles, the
discoloration around the socket area can only be
attributed to them receiving a sound thrashing
at the last place they visited.

I hope that you appreciate the points raised
within this missive, my tree-pulp-doily friends.
Although, admittedly, the writer did not 'put

all his heart and soul in', I would nevertheless
be saddened to hear you 'threw the letter away'.

Yours,
Derek Philpott

Dear Mr Philpott,

Thank you for your letter of enquiry – I have no intention of throwing it away as Bill's fiancée did so long ago; my personal considerations for the environment are rather more than she had, so the letter will probably be recycled in a place befitting its content, namely the loo. After all, it doesn't grow on trees you know.

Further to your remarks about my musical organisation The Black-Eyed Boys, I might remind you that as the drummer I am the leader of the gang and it is my intention for the 'Boys' and I to visit your place of residence on our trusty 'Rubber Hummers' and recreate a particular night that occurred in Chicago some time ago, in the heat of a night similar to the summer we are experiencing at this time.

So my hand is up in a moment, not unlike a certain William, beating a big tattoo to your door.

It may be time for you to ask for a volunteer.

Sergeant Philly Hero

Dear Mr Vox,

Are you sure that you have climbed the highest mountains, only to be with me? There exists no official record of any member of an Irish post-punk combo ever ascending Everest or any other Himalayan peak to the best of my knowledge, which is just as well as such an excursion would be pointless on account of my ongoing sciatica.

Dear Ms Quatro,

I was very much taken with your novel idea of a review of your last holiday experience set to music and wondered if it would be possible to ask you for a few further details pertaining to 'The Dive'. I am obviously presuming 'The Dive' to be the central feature, probably a large water chute, within a family leisure resort situated on Devil Gate Drive.

Suzi Quatro:
ACTUALLY IT IS A LARGE WATER CHUTE DIRECT INTO DEBAUCHERY... EVERYTHING YOUR PARENTS TOLD YOU NOT TO DO... THE SLIPPERY SLIDE, IF YOU LIKE, TO PLEASURE.

It seems that there are plenty of activities at the confusingly Satanic turnstile named complex, for children of all ages, with both dance (at the age of five they learn to jive) and karate (at the age of six they get their kicks) being particularly commendable. Any physical pursuits that make the little ones 'come alive' and distract them away from video game consoles, tablet computers and Pokemon Go must surely be encouraged.

Suzi Quatro:

THE DAYS OF HONEST PLEASURE ARE TO BE HONORED AND PROTECTED AS A DYING SPECIES... NO TEXTS, NO VIDEO GAMES, NO FACEBOOK, NOTHING BUT HONEST PURE UNADULTERATED COMMUNICATION... REMEMBER THAT!!!! ANGEL TO DEVIL... ACT/REACT... HEAVEN/HELL...

One finds it somewhat disconcerting however that somebody's mama don't know where their sister done go. Not only is this a pretty poor example of grammar for the youngsters; it also displays a lack of suitable adult supervision at the facility.

Suzi Quatro:

IT'S BEST IF NO ONE KNOW WHERE HER SISTER DONE GO... THAT MAKES THE FUN WORTH IT DON'T YOU THINK... SECRETS... CAN'T BEAT 'EM WITH A STICK

Lastly, that when they reach their teens they get all mean is rather disturbing, implying, as it sadly does, the presence of alcoholic or potentially harmful energy drinks in the canteen or restaurant. Before recommending the park to family as a suitable alternative to Alton Towers or Butlins, we must ask - are you able to put our minds at rest as regards parental security, and 'can the cans' be checked for undesirable contents?

Suzi Quatro:

AND IN THE END... THE FUN YOU MAKE IS EQUAL TO FUN YOU FAKE!!!!! A LITTLE LEEWAY, A LITTLE INNOCENT FLIRTATION, A LITTLE SLIDE DOWN THE BAD SIDE, BUT

ALWAYS KNOWING THE WAY BACK UP... JUST FOLLOW THE BUBBLES EH!!! DEVIL GATE DRIVE... YOU NEVER FORGET YOUR FIRST TIME. XX

Yours,
Derek Philpott and Son

Dear Curiosity Killed The Cat,

Given that the identity of a caller is unable to be established through internal ringing alone, I am perplexed that a message can be recorded especially for me. Also, why not say 'especially for you, Derek?'

Dear The Knack,

<u>Re: 'My Sharona'</u>

We too have a female mechanic, named Joanne, who, whilst not an unattractive lady of the younger kind, I would certainly <u>not</u> address as 'my little pretty one' as I personally find overfamiliarity within business relationships to be rather inappropriate.

When I telephone, her Tyre & Auto Centre will often 'give me some time' at short notice to attend to all manner of repairs to my Nissan Juke, and I 'always get it up' to the garage as quickly as possible after 'coming off o' the line', by way of thanks.

Just last week the dexterous specialist <u>did</u> make 'my motor run (my motor run)' again by way of replacing a dodgy fuel pump, assuring me that it was 'never gonna stop, give it up' for at least 100,000 miles. I find her to be very trustworthy, often close enough to look in my eyes and vice versa for me to detect possible falsehoods, and, unlike some unscrupulous technicians, she is always upfront, fully explaining the nature of a fault and never 'keeping it a mystery' in order that I may be charged multiple times for the same malfunction. Said honesty, although arguably

interpretative as a 'gift to me', is actually a
sign of professionalism, ensuring that it is
not 'just a matter of time' before I seek an
alternative vehicular tradeswoman.

Sadly, in your case, The Knack, I fear that
you may be being taken for a ride and are best
advised to transfer your custom to Carstar.

Yours,
Derek Philpott

Dear Mr Philpott:

Greetings from sunny California, where we are no strangers to cars, or car songs, for that matter. On that note, perhaps I could clear up a misconception or two. I deduce from your quaint spelling of 'tire' that you hail from the British Isles, or maybe the Marsupial Empire? In either case, it's possible that certain salient points of our song have been lost in the translation.

Not to put too fine a point on it, 'My Sharona' is not a car song. I admit that 'Toyota Sharona' would be a plausible name for a model (and the fact that we still haven't gotten a national commercial from said company is a lingering sore point, you can bet your boots). But the eponymous Sharona is not, I repeat not, an auto mechanic. Not a mechanic of any sort. She's a realtor, if you must know. When we inform her in our ditty that she makes our motor run, it is indeed a tip o' the cap to the great car songs of yore, but not to be taken literally. A metaphor, if you will. A euphemism for 'doing it'. A great deal of the energy that goes into writing a rock song is coming up with another way of saying 'f***ing'. Some, of course, have cried, oh the hell with it, and actually just said 'f***ing'. We chose to go the allusive route: 'My loins are as a great engine, and you are the fuel coursing through the gas line of my heart...' That was actually the original lyric, as a matter of fact, but it didn't scan well.

I hope I've cleared up any confusion on this matter; I'm only too happy to do so. As I think of it now, said confusion might possibly be traced to the quizzical practice you guys have of driving on the wrong side of the road. Have you considered that as a possible reason for your difficulties with the (slightly) lovely Joanne?

Yours in the Spirit of Hands Across The Water,
Berton Averre,
proud lead guitarist of The Knack and co-writer of
'My Sharona'

Dear The Stranglers,

In our experience a faulty
television set displays no image
at all or at best one which is very
fuzzy, scrolls vertically or is all
the wrong colours (normally the
symptom of a burnt tube). As
Duchess' appliance shows a picture
standing still, standing still,
are you sure she hasn't simply
just pressed pause on the DVD by
mistake?

Dear Devo,

Re: 'Whippet'

My friend Ernest Saxtonhouse is something of a
'face' within the local dog racing community.
So taken with your 'New Wave Staple' was he that
it is now the aural mascot of his yearling,
Geraldine (racing name - 'Brindle Fly'), and
is played over the Fordingbridge & East Dorset
Racing Club's public address system at some
point during every meeting at which the bitch
runs.

Ernest is particularly impressed by your in-
depth knowledge of the rushing size zero
sighthound pastime, vis-à-vis the quirky
'motorik chant-along' chorus instructions which
so accurately acknowledge Geraldine's need to
move ahead, go forward, get straight and try to
detect at all times the rapid conveyor-belted
'lure' that she is so encouraged to chase in
order to reward her owner with a win at odds of
up to 7-2 on, much to his 'satisfaction'. Indeed,
he has even incorporated the phrases 'whippet
good' (followed by the reward of a cow's ear or
her favourite Chewdles Bonibix treat biscuit)
and 'you must, whippet' (sometimes followed by a
mild admonishing snout tap) into a discipline/
health regime devised to achieve optimum
fitness within the bitch, and get, as you once

again correctly observe, the 'whippet into shape' on a permanent basis. The line, 'When a problem comes along', an obvious reference to the 6-inch-high hurdles sometimes obstructing her path in more competitive fixtures, has been particularly integral to her training, and my happy chum would be thrilled to thank you in person for his working pet's radical 'muscling up' and increased dexterity, should the opportunity ever arise.

Given your spotless 'track record' in purveying animal theme song-cum-coaching aids, may I suggest that you perhaps up your sights and call your next song either 'Greyhound', and/ or, branching into the potentially more profitable equine market, 'Thoroughbred'. These advancements would be a definite step up in the echelons of expeditious creature wagering, and we'd all like to see you in the Hit Parade again as soon as possible.

It's not too late!

Yours,
Derek Philpott

Dear Derek,

Gerald Casale, Devo founder here. For 38 years everyone thought my lyrics referenced sado-masochistic sex or masturbation or both. Some liberal intellectual types thought that the song was inspired by Thomas Pynchon's satirical poems about that American get up and go spirit found in his novel, *Gravity's Rainbow*. I always let people think whatever they want because I realised any attempts to set the record straight would be futile. However, you are the first person to nail the true inspiration for the lyrics I wrote in 1980. As a dog lover and dog owner I love all that they doo-doo. I am particularly excited about whippets although I never owned a piece of property large enough to do justice to the breed's speedy calling. I salute your astute insight and wish you well. De-evolution is real and you are there on the frontline helping to prove it.

No, Mr Skynyrd,

If you leave here tomorrow I would not still remember you, as we have never met. Generally speaking, however, although my memory is poor, it should not really need too much taxing to recall anyone that I know should they happen to depart in the next day or so.

Dear Fairground Attraction,

We had our friends, The Gilliards, over for dinner last night, ~~Funfair Feature~~ Fairground Attraction, and my wife was distraught to find upon going to Sainsbury's too late that they were clean out of Loyd Grossman Tomato & Chilli, even in the 'chuck outs'.

She was therefore forced to make do with a 500g jar of Dolmio (although worth it, yeah, at a very reasonable £1.79), which did peeve her slightly as she does not normally 'make such mistakes' and feared that the perceived inferiority of the surrogate sauce would detract from the success of her Arrabiata for seven.

The meal was a resounding success, ~~Carnival Captivation~~ Fairground Attraction, perhaps down to Jean overcompensating for the supposedly substandard coulis through the deployment of high-grade fresh Cavatappi and organic Portobellos.

Contrary to your assertion, therefore, we are inclined to argue that even if too many people take second best and you won't take anything less, 'it', whether an affair of the heart or an exercise in Italian cuisine preparation, can still be perfect if sufficient countermeasures

are taken in restitution for supposed
shortcomings.

It is sincerely hoped that you will respond to
this reasonable hypothesis (which I initially
sent in error to a well-known 'folk rock' group -
I've promised myself I won't do that again) and
that you are determined, you're 'gonna' get it
right.

Yours,
The Philpotts

Dear Philpotts,

I am sorry for my delay in replying to your letter. I was, I must admit, completely flummoxed by your question. While I am delighted and relieved that Jean managed to rescue your evening from what I would have assumed to be certain disaster, I struggled to understand how. After all, I have always been certain that 'it' does indeed have to be perfect. I am sure that you can hear that conviction in my guitar solo. I took some time trawling the internet in search of an answer and I am glad to report that I believe I have found it, in the form of the work of a highly regarded psycho-physicist called Howard Moskowitz.

Moskowitz has 'optimised' soups, pizzas, salad dressings and pickles for various food companies. His research on the American Prego spaghetti sauce (which revealed a customer preference for an 'extra-chunky' formulation) is notable, as was his optimisation of the amount of salt, sugar and fat to arrive at a so-called 'bliss point' and maximise consumer satisfaction. In an earlier research project for Pepsi, he concluded that there was no 'perfect Pepsi' only 'perfect Pepsis' – meaning that one man's idea of the ideal balance of ingredients differs from the next. Applying this theory to your question, I think we can safely conclude that there is no 'perfect Philpott dinner party' only 'perfect Philpott dinner parties' and be grateful that we have a man like Howard Moskowitz to turn to when we need him.

I hope this clears things up and I wish you and Jean many more wonderful evenings of dining with your lucky friends.

Meanwhile, I am working on a re-write of the song; so far I have, 'It's got to be e e e e e e e just right for you oo oo oo oo oo'.

Warmest wishes,
Mark Nevin – Fairground Attraction

Dear Iron Maiden,

In your song 'Iron Maiden' you state that Iron Maiden's 'gonna get' me, 'no matter how far'. Forgive me, Iron Maiden, but I was of the impression that, not being blessed with a brain or legs, an interiorally spiked wooden cabinet would be unable to give chase over any distance whatsoever. Your claim that 'Iron Maiden can't be sought' is also flawed on the basis that any person or thing can be hunted; it is merely its discovery which may prove unsuccessful. Finally, as regards your declaration that Iron Maiden 'wants me for dead' once again I am at a bit of a loss as to how a barbed closet may hanker after my demise. I do, however, agree that Iron Maiden can't be fought given that said timber impalement cupboard would make somewhat of a static and non-retaliatory opponent in a boxing situation. All in all, if it is all the same to you, I think it may be best for all concerned if I decline to come in to your room on this particular occasion.

Dear Danny Wilson,

I was distraught to learn from Radio 2 on Saturday night that you have acid on the radio and acid in the rain. If, as one is to assume, you have spilt some on to your wireless out of a leaky car battery in the garage, or had the window open on a drizzly day when unblocking your kitchen sink with some 'One Shot', one can only hope that you will be more careful in the future.

As regards your assertion of witnessing the Messiah in unbleached cotton, it must be countered that I find it unlikely that it was Jesus in the calico. My son does recall Jesus on the radio, however, and thought that 'International Bright Young Thing' was a very catchy offering.

We thank you for bringing this to our attention and wish you luck 'everywhere you go'.

Yours,
Derek

Dear Derek,

Thank you for your good-natured, if ill-informed, query regarding my band Danny Wilson's single 'The Second Summer Of Love'. Let me address your concerns in the order that you articulate them in your letter.

Firstly, might I respectfully suggest that a minor adjustment to your hearing aid would perhaps be of benefit as the word you mistakenly interpret as 'Acid' is in fact two words. 'El Sid', the correct lyric, actually refers to the little-known late-night disc jockey Sidney (El Sid) Bridlington who kept me enthralled, enchanted and awake as a young lad with his show 'Sidnight Melodies'. This grooviest of radio shows was broadcast nightly on my local station during the early part of the 1970s. When I say 'early part' I mean it literally, as the show had only been on-air two and a half weeks when Sidney, after being caught in one of the particularly nasty downpours that ravaged Dundee that winter, contracted pneumonia and tragically died.

I felt inspired to immortalise Mr Bridlington in song not only because his radio show was a miracle of easy-listening charm and hummability, but also because his greatest and perhaps most undervalued achievement was the record that he set in broadcasting history. That is to say, he was, and still is, the only disc jockey named Sidney to be employed at any radio station ever. In a cruel twist, his entry into the *Guinness Book of World Records* was quashed when it surfaced that he had in fact been born Brenda Bridlington and, after a sex change, had unwittingly filled out the form incorrectly while attempting to legally change his name.

Taking all of this into account I'm sure you will agree that 'El Sid on the radio' speaks for itself while 'El Sid in the rain', of course, refers to his encounter with the terrible storm that so drenched the velvet-voiced announcer on his 4am walk home from the radio station that fateful January morning. His story, pitiful as it was, would take on an extra layer of misfortune when it later transpired that this walk would have been completely unnecessary had his bicycle not been in at Spokesman's Cycle Repair Shop that evening having a new bell fitted. They do say that every time a bell rings an angel gets his wings.

While I would argue that, in a tome no less authoritative than the Holy Bible, it is recorded that Jesus of Nazareth was rarely seen when not sporting his favourite calico tunic, 'Jesus on the radio', as your son rightly states, refers to the pop group Jesus Jones. Back when I penned 'The Second Summer Of Love', however, that band had only released one single: the quirkily titled, commercial flop 'Info Freako'. It's now a matter of public record that the singer's impassioned delivery on that recording stirred in me memories and emotions, long suppressed, of Sidney Bridlington's relentless battle with the world, his sexuality and finally inclement weather.

I trust that my reply has answered your questions and hopefully helped shed some light on a fascinating character whose life, while short, meant something to one radio-obsessed teenager who only a few years later, would put El Sid right back where he deserved to be:

El Sid on the radio.

Yours sincerely,
Gary Clark

Dear The Singer from Jesus Jones,

Re: Who am I? Where am I? Why do I feel this way?

Thank you for your 'electro-industrial questionnaire'.

(1) You are Mike Edwards, young man.

(2) According to your Wikipedia page you hail from Bradford-on-Avon in Wiltshire, although I am afraid I cannot vouch for your present location, right here, right now. I would suggest that you perhaps enable the GPS services on your mobile phone, which can normally be achieved through accessing 'Settings' in the main menu, but please refer to the user manual for your particular make and model for specific instructions.

(3) Judging by your disorientation, manifested in feeling that someone else is living your life, the real (real real) possibility cannot be ruled out that you have perhaps suffered a recent fall outside, at the outside, at the outside, at the outside...

Under the circumstances, Sir, one feels that to get your bearings and repair to the nearest A&E department may be 'the right decision'. I understand that, from all around the world,

the NHS employ many international bright young
things who will be more than able to determine
your current condition.

I wish you well.

Yours,
Derek Philpott

Dear Mr Philpott,

Many thanks for your list of errors, albeit potentially helpful ones. I'm sure it's not the last time my feeble meandering in the approximate direction of pseudo-Existentialism will be mistaken for the onset of dementia.

That leads me to your first mistake. I can surely no longer be referred to as 'young man' while receiving mailouts from Saga. One of those two aspects I object to, I'm just not sure which one yet.

Wikipedia isn't awfully reliable, is it? I suspect anyone featured in it could go through with an aggressive red marker pen and feel the need to tut loudly. I haven't met the person who wrote the Jesus Jones Wikipedia page but history is written by the victor and unfortunately I have lost the Wikipedia war.

The rest of your letter has many notes that seem more familiar than the Wikipedia entry. Saga and early onset dementia aside, I am glad to say I haven't yet reached the doddering or falling stage and am quite capable of safely walking unaided and performing other mobility and balance-related tasks. These include, sadly, carrying my own guitars, something I'm sure I shall be doing at a venue near you soon.

Never a plugging opportunity missed.

Yours,
Michael Edwards

Dear Hot Chocolate,

Thanks to pushing your argument when 'Silver Dancer' finished 12th in the 2.30 at Aintree and I still tried to claim my £225 I was forcefully ejected from Ladbrokes this afternoon.

cc. Nick Berry

Dear Smokie,

I was a big fan of both sweets and <u>The Sky at Night</u> at the time that one of your splendid hit records was released, Smokie, and feel sure that I would have remembered an episode as unique as one featuring infatuation-induced interstellar buoyancy on the part of a Bradford-based soft rock band.

On closer examination, however, your claim to be bobbing about atop a gravitationally tethered astronomical system is somewhat flawed, in that 'floating on the Milky Way' is actually a physical impossibility.

The Milky Way (not the chocolate bar) is the Galaxy (not the chocolate bar) that contains our Solar System including Mars (not the chocolate bar) and all of its Planets (not the chocolate sweets). Ergo, any Drifter (not the chocolate bar) upon it would be required to be immersed within or hovering just above a liquid or solid body, perhaps causing a Ripple (not the chocolate bar). Such masses, Sirs, are noticeably absent in space, rendering your alleged Marathon (not the old name for Snickers) achievement to be, at best, unlikely.

Whilst not one who ordinarily Revels (not the chocolates) in such correction, I feel that I

must take Time Out (not the chocolate bar) to
state that, when it comes to the Crunch (not
the chocolate bar), to Fudge (not the sweet or
chocolate bar) via this gross error somewhat
Mars (not the chocolate bar or the planet) the
pivotal Topic (not the chocolate bar) which
Boosts (not the chocolate bar) the Rocky Road
(not the chocolate b... [We get the point,
chaps - Ed.])

Dear Philpotts,

I feel that we have become firm friends (as opposed to melted ones) since volume one of your series of cheeky letters to people of fame. I wonder whether Hot Chocolate also found themselves on the receiving end of such calorific puns. Really, it's enough to expand the waistline and cause an upward motion into space where, apparently, nothing can be heard, not even catchy songs, although a certain enterprising captain referred to it as the final front ear.

I am happy that you decided once again to turn your attention and quick wit (nothing gets past you, especially the dessert trolley) to the 'dark matter' of Carol and Smokie's whimsical tune. Many a set list has erringly listed the song as O'Carol, as if it was addressed to an inhabitant of the land of leprechauns and shamrocks. Our audience in Germany insist on pelting us with chocolate bars at the appropriate moment in the chorus and there follows a mad scramble to bag as many of these belt-loosening munchables as possible in case there is a chocolate famine backstage.

I cannot fault the science behind your argument, I merely request that you suspend disbelief for a moment and join us momentarily on our caffeine-enhanced view of the cosmos and its primary energy source – LOVE.

Yes, it works wonders, achieves the impossible and cures all known maladies, and all this before breakfast (of a sensible low-calorie, easy on the sugar nature). We are not, after all, literally 'eating our heart away', for that would indicate very poor judgement as well as a shortened life expectancy.

The heavens have their secrets, as have we, and I don't wish to dig a 'black hole' for myself by unwittingly contradicting the original premise of our chart-topping melody, so I shall remain tight-lipped about how exactly we found ourselves endowed with such outer spacial awareness. Let it suffice to say that Carol (who may or may not be Irish) found the gravitational attraction too overwhelming to be able to remain in a satellite state, and therefore the match was made in any one of the infinite universes available in this less than sugary tale.

I thank you for this opportunity to join you, once again, in delving below the surface of lyrics to popular songs and hence unlock the mysteries within.

Your friend always,
Martin
Smokie

P.S. I wrote this at 30,000 feet and I'm sure I just saw Superman fly past.

Dear Nelly,

You are indeed correct in your observation with regard to the increasing temperature, however I must vehemently refuse your instruction to disrobe given that I am in Tesco Express and the air-conditioning has broken down.

Dear Mr Gower out of Racey,

I am not so much concerned with the unspecified task that some girls do/don't/will/won't in response to the degree of affection lavished upon them, as by your own personal health at this time. I recently tried to communicate to Mr Astley that being too shy to say that one's heart is aching could ultimately prove perilous, and I fear similarly for your good self.

Please allow me to 'lay my concerns on you'.

You state, after knowing that you've 'got the fever', that you are facing an unspecified person - possibly a medical professional - in a state of disorientation with an unfamiliar sensation in the area of your cardiac muscle (the middle mediastinum, at the level of thoracic vertebrae T5-T8).

To compound matters further it would appear that out of understandable apprehension you are not standing still, and the GP or nurse is unable to complete her examination, leading possibly to outraged glares.

This is most certainly not the way it's meant to be, Mr Gower out of Racey, and is something we should talk about.

To summarise, if you are in front of a clinician, not knowing what to do, and your heart is feeling something new, nervously turning away from her will only impede a full examination and therefore prevent a swift and complete diagnosis of your symptoms.

You then divulge that you find the novel experience of being in the young lady's company socially - perhaps bumping into her at a trendy wine bar outside of surgery hours - has caused you to 'fall heavily'. I'm afraid, Sir, that you might be in denial of an inner ear problem, such as labyrinthitis or Meniere's disease.

It is therefore recommended that you go back to the doctor's and not be so fidgety this time so that the above-mentioned condition and perhaps palpitations can hopefully be ruled out.

I look forward to your response to my findings and will, of course, just give you time to work it out.

Yours,
Derek Philpott

Dear Mr Philpott,

Thank you for your letter dated 24th August 2016.

Regarding your personal 'non concern' with the so-called 'unspecified task' that some 'May' or 'May Not', 'Will' or 'Will Not', 'Do' or 'Don't', I can assure you it has been a particular course of intense action over the years for myself to find out whether:

1. They will or will not.
2. Might possibly consider it.
3. GO FOR IT!!!!

As for 'Rick'... yeah I suppose he is a shy sort of a bloke... but don't let Rick's problem get in the way, or give you any concern over my good self... I'm fit!!!!... alright.

You state that you would like to 'lay your concerns on me'... are you a psychologist?... I doubt it.

I can assure you that you should keep your 'concerns' to yourself...'cos no one 'lays anything on me'... unless it's a few quid, or a page 3 girl... get it!

As far as my 'getting a fever' due to your misguided belief that I have difficulty facing, or even meeting other folks, and that somehow you consider it to be a possible cause of a stress factor to my good self... you then go on to say... it possibly puts me in a state of disorientation and could even cause a problem with my cardiac muscle... I believe, Mr Philpott, that you are possibly the disorientated individual by being completely out of touch and unaware of my personal health condition, and indeed, of the correct muscle that possibly 'gets a fever' if one 'does or does not'!!!

As for your 'summary', Mr Philpott, thank you for your somewhat misguided interest into my personal welfare and wellbeing regarding any supposed medical or psychological attention you think I may need, or require, due to any romantic feelings I may possibly have about someone. Please let me assure you, I do not need to see any clinician regarding any sort of diagnosis on these terms, especially in knowing 'what' and 'what not' to do on any given opportunistic situation that may or may not arise, or even that I have the good fortune to maybe 'come across'!

Any small talk that I may have offered, relevant to a novel experience re: a meeting, or being in the company of a young lady is merely fictional... I never concede to nervousness, especially if I am in a wine bar or preferably a pub, as I am generally 3 parts to the wind anyway! And as for your considered thoughts that I may possibly have an inner ear problem such as labyrinthitis or Meniere's disease etc., etc., the only time I possibly could ever have a hearing problem of any sort is when it's probably my turn to buy the next round!

Well, Mr Philpott, once again thank you for your opinions on my personal state of play and affairs, but as far as your recommendations and consideration are concerned regarding all of the above, and also that I should consider going back to my doctor for a second opinion of being fidgety, having so called palpitations, etc., etc., my somewhat limited educational response to you is... go get f***ed.

Kindest regards,
Yours truly,
Richard Gower – 'Racey'

Dear Johnny Logan,

I am pleased to be able to inform you that 'Another Year' is a further period of 365 days (or 366 in the case of a leap specimen) representing the time period required for the successful completion of a single circuit of our Earth around the Sun. Should you have any further enquiries I would recommend that, rather than they be posed in the form of Eurovision Song Contest entries, you may be better to save considerable time and resources by instead referring to the internet's excellent 'Google' service.

Dear The Electric Prunes,

It was very windy last night, my voltaic dried
fruit friends, and I was awakened many times
up until 'About a Quarter to Nine' by overgrown
fronds knocking against the bedroom window.

I am therefore very grateful to you as, upon
awakening, I heard your excessive sleep-derived
imagery 'garage classic' coming from my son's
bedroom; he was staying over with his wife after
a 'Long Day's Flight' from a Cyprus holiday
before returning home.

The imaginative name of your psychedelic combo
reminded me that, rather than lopping off the
superfluous shrubbery with my rusty old shears
(which were, ironically, in my own garage), a
less energetic option was indeed open to me.
I had completely forgotten that I had recently
bought from eBay, 'Sold to the Highest Bidder',
a Bosch AHS 41 Accu Cordless Hedge Trimmer
(14.4V) and was able to therefore indulge not in
manual snips, but far more effortless electric
prunes.

I regret to advise, however, that you could
not have 'had too much to dream last night'.
During a recommended eight hours' slumber
they tend to vary between two or three seconds
to about half an hour, normally occurring

(and by this one does not mean a particularly
long concert by Mr Stipe and his cohorts) in
the typical two hours of R.E.M. By your own
admission, that you were only dozing last night
as opposed to all day and all of the night, it is
therefore not possible that overabundant snooze
hallucinations have happened.

I sincerely hope that you do not mind me
'raisin' this issue, that I do not look like a
right plum* and that in reading this letter your
patience has not gone, gone, gone.

Yours,
Derek Philpott

Noun (UK colloquial) meaning idiot

Dear Derek,

As you might have guessed by now, that tapping at your window pane was not fronds but the ghost of Nikola Tesla banging to get his negative ions back. The feedback loop got him to the world on time but... now what? It's not fair! The footnote in your letter reveals all along we have been the Electric Idiots in the UK (no wonder we couldn't get on the charts!).

Tell your son Cyprus is not a place to hide away or wind up your toy; in fact we have noticed overwinding can result in your bangles being dangled! On that note: we are cancelling your order for the Bosch AHS 41 pruner as it does not contain the mandatory 'kill switch' found on newer models. This item remains on 'recall'. As soon as we can kill a few more models we will forward your order to Dr Do-Good at the shelter of your choice.

I was going to go off on you addressing me as 'The' Electric Prunes but what's in a name, anyway? Yelling down the hall will only make you purple in the face, not the right place! (wink wink, ain't it hard). Is an electric flag really 'electric'? Is a moby grape really a grape? If I have too much to dream will I stagger to the bar in the morning with rusty shears for a hair of the dog? And what about 'String Theory'? No one has done anything about that yet? I can see you are a man who never had it better so I'm going to snuggle up with my little olive and keep the selfies in the shadows. Where they belong.

Please lose my address.

Sincerely,
James Lowe/Electric Prunes

Dear Orange Juice,

I am pleased to advise you that owing to advances in modern technology via the simple utilisation of the 'Control' and 'Z' keys on your computer keyboard, the need to rip it up and start again is thankfully at an end!

Dear Mr Carter,

My son entertains in care homes for a living and I was recently distraught to witness a sour-faced thirty-something stop his performance at an assisted living warden-controlled community and insist that he alter the words of the Lonnie Donegan skiffle classic that he was in the middle of to 'My male of advanced years is a refuse operative'.

Sadly, Mr Carter, and in many ways I <u>also</u> blame the Government, this current epidemic of political correctness shows no sign of abating in its virulence, and I fear that it may one day infect the back catalogues of indie rock alternative dance duos such as yourselves, The Beloved and, arguably, Daphne and Celeste and Shampoo.

Unless therefore your title is a little-known appointment to the Order akin to that of an MBE (perhaps Urbane Society Member or some such), allowing you to hold precedent in these matters, I regret that 'Sheriff Big-Boned Man', 'Slow Metabolismed Marshall', 'The Hormonally-Afflicted Deputy' or indeed 'Horizontally-Challenged Foreman' should be forthwith employed in order for you not to fall foul of trending sensibilities.

It is sincerely hoped that this missive is not construed as a 102nd Damnation.

I remain,
Yours,
D. Philpott

Dear Mr Philpott,

Apologies for the long delay in replying. I'm afraid that once I began to consider your letter, after I'd given the idea the time of day (3am incidentally, the can of worms you have opened is literally keeping me awake) my whole world started to collapse.

My initial reaction was to suggest 'political correctness gone mad' but then I wondered whether such a phrase was in itself politically incorrect. A few hours later, having abandoned coming up with a kinder phrase for 'gone mad', I had renamed almost thirty per cent of my song titles and lyrics that could be misunderstood. I have also changed the name of my cat and the terms of affection I use when talking to my wife. I am currently still undecided on an alternative band name, as being an unstoppable sex machine is surely no laughing matter if you're a sex addict.

On a slightly lighter note. It's interesting that you should mention Daphne and Celeste, who I'm sure must have faced criticism for their song U.G.L.Y. Perhaps D.I.F.F.E.R.E.N.T.L.Y. B.E.A.U.T.I.F.U.L. would have been safer. Although between me and you, when they sung it to an audience of bottle throwers at Reading Festival maybe on that occasion they had a point. I personally could have suggested at least two hundred other acts on the bill more deserving of the crowd's unwanted beer and cider.

Anyway, thanks for the heads up (is that phrase ok? Sounds so wrong all of a sudden, oh dear).

Yours,
Jim Bob Carter

Dear Bow Wow Wow,

Re: 'C30 C60 C90 Go!'

I feel that your tribal hit could be updated to appeal to the current market of pop fans by being rerecorded as 'Mp3 1 gigabyte, Mp3 2 gigabyte, Mp3 3 gigabyte, Start!'

Dear Mr Kershaw,

Re: 'The Riddle'

We are not terribly concerned with the rotating
Celtic pensioner located adjacent to a crater,
in turn situated in a wooded area on the banks
of an estuary, as, by your own admission, this
is all gobbledygook of the highest order.

We fear, however, that the old man of Aran
going around and around next to a hole in the
ground by a tree by a river may be a distraction
technique to divert attention away from your
nefarious business intentions as regards my
good self.

It would appear that you have devised an unfair
rota system pertaining to me undertaking menial
work in your Middle Eastern eaterie (possibly
based in the US - so to America the brave),
working within a team of disruptive scrimping
intellectuals.

I'm not too sure that I care for your 'plans for
us', Mr Kershaw, which seem to involve 'nights
in the scullery' of your exotic restaurant,
Blessings of Babylon. From the sound of things
there will be linen in need of laundering
(probably tablecloths) which wise men fold.
It also appears from you only knowing to discuss
oh, for anything but light and days instead of

me (to say nothing of wise men fighting over me), that I am expected to cover your shift as well. This would involve working both days and nights and taking labour away from the wise men who save and would probably appreciate both the overtime and the anti-social hourly rate in order that they may put away extra each month into their rainy day funds.

I will have no part in it, Mr Kershaw, especially given that you are more than able to undertake this work yourself. You've got two strong arms, time to kill and time to carry on and try for sins and false alarms (presumably food hygiene and bogus security systems respectively).

Even if I were to work in your kitchen, I fear that my tenure would be short and I would say very soon that 'I don't wanna be here no more'.

I hope that my declinature does not offend and wish you luck in securing an alternative candidate.

Yours,
Derek Philpott

Dear Mr Philpott,

Many thanks for your letter. It was good to hear from you again.

However (and forgive me if I've misinterpreted your tone), there did seem to be a certain amount of bile invested in your correspondence. Indeed, to the untrained eye, it could appear that umbrage had been taken. I do hope your liver function is not compromised, your bilirubin levels have recovered sufficiently and you are now experiencing satisfactory lower bowel function.

It's interesting to note that bile from deceased mammals can be mixed with soap and used to remove embarrassing stains from cotton bed linen.

But I digress.

I'm disappointed that you express such little regard for the Old Man but would venture that you might have grabbed the wrong end of the proverbial stick. Not that there is a right end. There is, in fact, no correct place to grab this particular stick and I would go further to suggest you may have actually grabbed the wrong stick entirely.

To imagine that I'm expecting you to carry out onerous and unrewarded tasks in my 'middle eastern eatery' is both insulting and absurd. It's the most ridiculous thing I've heard since your last letter.

I'm not a monster.

I can offer a Zero Hours contract with all the associated benefits. You can live above the shop rent-free. I only ask that you feed the cat now and then and that you're there to let Mrs Underwater in to hoover the shower curtains (every 2nd Thurs in the month).

Overtime would be minimal (to say the least) and, although funds are limited, there would be all the couscous you can eat.*

I would consider excusing you from all folding duties.

I may well have had two strong arms in 1984 but time is a cruel mistress. The use of one arm to polish my platinum discs and bursitis in the opposite shoulder has led to a certain disparity.

Here's hoping you reconsider. I'm in a bit of a spot this Tuesday evening, as it happens. Zoltan's piles have flared up again and he has a 6:30 with Dr Patel.

Yours, as always,
Nik Kershaw

* Not including Zoltan's Special Couscous with mixed pulses and caramelised goat scratchings (or that's what he says they are).

Dear Ultravox,

I fear that your nonchalance towards Austria's premier holiday destination may cause you to fall foul of the tourist board.

Dear Mr Deane, Modern Romance,

As a fan of any international cuisine incorporating the piquant heterogeneous mix, and one who sometimes frequents the South Woodford district to visit relatives, I was delighted to hear of this new vibrant Caribbean eaterie, 'Everybody Salsa' of which you joyfully enthuse on <u>Top of the Pops 2</u>, especially given that it 'ain't Puerto Rico, but London E18'.

One's only reservation is that the otherwise splendid Latino lounge is one of those confounded pop-up cafés, as hinted at in your declaration that the carnival is moving and that it is spirit, and not location, which is the essence of its theme.

If, on the other hand, my newfangled fling-fashioned friend, your urban mambo classic refers not to the tangy relish but instead a regional dance style much loved by an autonomous megalomaniacal tyrant, then, regrettably, we have no desire to 'to join you in your dream' at this present time. No oppressive regime, instigator or overlord, irrespective of its rhythmic gyrational preferences is 'hip', Modern Romance, be it Franco's flamenco fondness, Stalin's penchant for the balalaika-driven barynya, Benito's tarantella soft spot

(No No No No Mu-ssy!) or, in your case, Castro,
who loved to salsa in a cool dictator scene.

We require your response soon, Sir, as if this
<u>is</u> a continental eaterie we would like to
book a table before it shuts down and 'unfolds
elsewhere'. Can you move, can you move us to the
top of your priorities as soon as, and brighten
up our day?

Yours,
Derek Philpott (and Son)

Dear Mr Derek Philpott & Son Heung-min,

Thank you for your undated missive concerning my Latino themed 80s pop ditty 'Everybody Salsa'. You are correct in your initial assumption. The tune is, in fact, an elongated remix of a jingle composed by myself to promote my restaurant of the same name. It is not however a 'Caribbean eaterie'. We spit in the face of jerk chicken and throw rice and peas at the elderly. If we get so much as a glimpse of Levi Roots my staff have orders to shoot on sight.

Here at Everybody Salsa we are all about dining Brazilian-style. Which I should point out does not mean our waitresses have shaven pudenda. Well they might. I have no legal way of knowing. No, we are a meat-based emporium that specialises in grilling the finest churrasco over an open wood fire and serving it at your table from artisanal skewers fashioned from reclaimed piston rods and other old bits of tut we found laying around. Each cut is served with our legendary chimichurri salsa, made from cilantro, parsley, oregano, chilli, garlic and just the merest hint of ketamine. An experience your taste buds will never forget and probably write about in their autobiography.

Our meat incidentally is all organic and sourced locally at Lidl.

We also stock a ludicrously expensive range of craft beers brewed by blind monks in a lock-up round the back of Bruce Grove railway arches in South Tottenham. Or if you want to keep with the Brazilian theme we do an excellent caipirinha cocktail served with an underage prostitute on the side.

Please rest assured that despite our imminent fashionability we are not some fly by night, pop-up operation.

The reproduction favela landfill the restaurant stands on is constructed to the highest specifications and will withstand the strongest of breezes.

With regard to your inquiry vis-à-vis the tune's more overtly political lyrics let me assure you I have no interest in politics or politicians of any kind. Other than perhaps Russell Brand whom I regard as a progressive thinker and a bit like Jesus only in tight trousers. I was referencing Castro the celebrity, not Castro the dictator. And I have no idea what gave you the impression the tune had anything to do with some newfangled dance craze or whatevs. It was Fidel's skills in the kitchen I was pointing up. And countless human rights abuses aside, his prowess as a saucier was undeniable, innit.

Have we become so overwhelmed by political correctness that we are now expected to research a sauce's provenance to eliminate any leaning towards autocracy in its creator before tucking in? If Hitler had invented the hollandaise does that mean that all of us except Ken Livingstone have to give up eating eggs benedict? I'm sorry but here at Everybody Salsa our message to the snowflake contingent is go fuck yourself up the bottom hole with a very sharp stick.

We would, of course, be delighted to welcome you to dine with us. But please be aware we only open on a Thursday night between 9.30 and 11pm and are booked solid for the next three years. Online reservations can be made on our deliberately hard to find website to which I have not provided a link.

Yours prettily,
Geoff Deane, Modern Romance, Magnificent Pagan Beast

Dear Status Quo,

The circumference of Earth is 3,959 miles, therefore as soon as <u>Storage Wars</u> is finished I am bringing your intention to imminently traverse it by saying 'giddy up' to a horse, and swaying to and fro upon the poor equine, to the attention of the RSPCA!

Dear Mr Holt, from The Climax Blues Band,

I must admit it got the best of me from the start
of Steve Wright all the way through to <u>Serious
Jockin'</u>, and time was drifting, but I feel that
I have got to the bottom of why you couldn't get
it right you couldn't get it 'ri...i...ight'.

Firstly, unless I have misunderstood, it would
appear that at the time you hit the road and
made your getaway you were a bit under the
weather, very fidgety, and suffering from a
presumably rare strain of Californian pyrexia.

I travel a lot on the M4 to see my son in
Wiltshire, my sad delta music crescendo-
monickered friend, and can categorically assure
you that all junction indicators are not self-
illuminatory, but are instead layered with
encapsulated lens sheeting which bends and
returns all beams back towards their original
source.

It therefore stands to reason that in your state
of disorientation, bought on by LA Fever and a
restless feeling, you kept on looking for a sign
in the middle of the night to take you through
the night but couldn't see the light simply
because you had neglected to turn yours on after
starting up your vehicle.

I started searching for a better way to bring
this very obvious solution to your attention,
my maudlin twelve-bar-pinnacle homaging reader,
but similarly to yourself, have sadly been
unable to do so correctly.

I remain,
Yours,
Derek Philpott

Dear Mr Philpott,

Well I woke up this mornin' and found your letter claiming to have gotten to the bottom of why we 'Couldn't Get It Right'. Well let me put you right: 'This rock had got to roll' and in doing so rolled around the world in a rather small and uncomfortable van.

Trundling daily across countries in order to entertain the fans of our music we eventually found ourselves amidst the vastness of the continent of The USA and this is proof in itself that we indeed made our getaway. In New York City, for instance, such was the hospitality, we almost died; imagine being dropped off at a gig in a limousine only to be left alone afterwards in the early hours to catch a yellow cab back to the hotel. We were left stranded; that neglect took away our pride.

Our excursions across North America eventually had us arrive at the Whisky a Go Go on Sunset Boulevard in LA where I believe we caught our fever; a dark and dingy little club with wall-to-wall freaks who offered every kind of mind-altering mixtures and potions, a den of iniquity that was thoroughly enjoyed I might say. However, when it got to loading up the van with our gear, we were all flying and looking forward to finding our night's bed and breakfast. This was to be in the town of Phoenix, yes! the one in Arizona. Such was our itinerary of an agent who I believe used a dartboard to source our gigs.

So with lights fully illuminated and a full tank of gas we set off down a dark and dusty road on a very Stormy

Monday in search of the great city in the Arizona desert.

Now after a good four hours sitting on our arses listening to Joe Walsh, driving in the middle of the night, and lost, we decided to try and find any hotel/motel to rest our weary chemically enhanced heads. We saw an illuminated sign further on up the road; it was a Holiday Inn, it was the sign in the middle of the night we were looking for, but it was on the other side of the five-laned Interstate, rather larger than the M4, by the way. We got off at the next available exit, went down to the crossroads and tried to do a u turn, but we ended up rollin' and a tumblin' away from the sign; we just tried and tried to make the hotel but we couldn't see the light – in fact every turn we made was wrong – we just couldn't get it right, our LA Fever was affecting our Sense of Direction, decisions as to which turn to make caused confusion amongst us all, we got down so deep we almost drowned, so we tried to make another getaway on the road again, eventually realising we were low on gas and lost in the darkest Arizona desert and with restless feelings it felt safer to stay put until daylight come and we want to go home.

This was pre-mobile phone era, so we stopped and spent the night on the side of the road contemplating the Phoenix gig that night and our next massive drive to Sweet Home Chicago. I should have been a road sweeper I thought, all I had to do was Dust My Broom and the thrill had gone anyway. Oh well, it's a memory I'll never forget.

Couldn't Get It Right? You're right, Steve's right, we couldn't! Must have Been Born Under a Bad Sign.

Yours sincerely,
Hoochie Coochie Holt

Dear 'M',

I must politely decline your invitation to 'boogie with a suitcase', as I fear that to utilise luggage as a dance partner could result in psychiatric evaluation.

Dear The Jags,

Some months ago, such was my haste in rushing in
from the garden before the other person hung up,
I tripped over our tortoiseshell, Gladys, and
sprained my ankle, which was my first mishap
in about three years. You can therefore imagine
my consternation in establishing that all
the caller was interested in was if I had had
a trip or fall within that time, to which the
answer would have been no if they had not have
contacted me.

As a result we have now gone to great lengths,
including walking into shops we are not
interested in at the slightest glimpse of a
charity tabard, whispering in dry cleaners, and
going ex-directory, to keep our landline and
mobile details secret and rid ourselves of these
annoying sales and unwanted distant relative
nuisances once and for all.

I was distraught, therefore, whilst searching
for big cat footage on YouTube today, to learn
via Top of the Pops 2 that all of our efforts had
been scuppered by yourselves, who have my number
written on the back of your hands, for the whole
of the tea-time public to see. Thankfully,
however, pausing the frame upon your lead
singer's palm rears during his electric guitar

solo, I found both to be not only unreadable
but blank, thus rendering the power pop classic
totally nonsensical.

Although I am relieved at having avoided all
the kerfuffle and expenses of a solicitor and
invasion of privacy litigation, we do wish that
we had not paid attention to your new wave combo
and fear that one day you MAY push your luck
too far!

Yours,
Derek Philpott

Dear Gladys,

I was sorry to hear that you were involved in Derek's unfortunate accident. This unpleasantness could easily have been avoided if he had just subscribed to the Telephone Preference Service, who block unwanted calls.

I would have thought that a man who could make the giant leap from nuisance calls to the Jags 1979 top twenty hit 'I've got your number written on the back of my hand', would have been nimble enough to jump over a tortoiseshell cat.

Derek must have been suffering from a Tetley tea induced bout of paranoia to believe that his number was visible on the back of the singer's hand, because he also sings 'Hey, where's your number gone?' so he has obviously washed it off, no doubt using a pumice stone after the experience of rejection.

Derek should also be aware that poetic licence is not restricted to poetry and that it's not really raining men, doves don't cry, the rain is not purple, the answers are not blowing in the wind, the Vapors did not turn Japanese and Blondie were not actually hanging on the telephone.

I think you will agree that accidents will happen when you jump to conclusions.

Happy Hunting,
Steve Prudence

Dear Mr Hammond,

In the current climate whereupon many jobbing musicians are being forced to accept lower performance fees, and even in some circumstances are required to audition for the privilege of a paying gig, or not being paid at all in exchange for 'exposure', I find your promotion of the criminally undercutting Free Electric Band to be a pretty poor show.

Dear ~~Anonymous Angler~~ Fischer Z,

Re: 'The Worker'

(Replies from the esteemed John Watts are bold in both type and sentiment.)

Given that, by the very employment of the definitive article as opposed to 'A Worker' this poor chappie is taking on the inbox of the entire British labour force, the hated journey on the train, and indeed sleep for five stops in a row, are completely understandable.

This may have been excusable in the 20th Century. Now it would mean sleeping upright because lack of seating or on the sticky floor next to a button-operated lavatory; slumber prevention of the highest order due to underfoot vulnerability and the obvious effluvial challenge.

Furthermore, that the put-upon exclusive employee's near-vintage Ford fastback sports car did not sail through its annual vehicle safety and exhaust emissions compliance check is not so much chronological frittery as a clear demonstration of negligence on his part, no doubt bought on by job-related fatigue.

Fords of that era were famous for having powerful engines that lasted forever and bodywork with a lifetime rust guarantee.

To have bought a '69 Capri which failed the MOT
is not 'a waste of time' - it is proof that a
hefty reduction in purchase price has not been
factored in and negotiated by the monopolistic
menial to reflect the lower-class faux luxury
coupe's unroadworthiness at the point of
procurement, and, by extension, is indicative
of the onliest toiler's current unreliability
in making shrewd executive decisions within a
white or blue-collar environment.

**At this time in the late 70s MOTs could readily be bought or
exchanged for a crate of beer or one's sister, consequently
it may not have been so shrewd to subject said motor to
this humiliating procedure in the first place when it could
well have been bypassed.**

We look forward to news pertaining to at least a
proportion of the unfortunate solitary national
operative's to-do list being delegated to others
on the United Kingdom's payroll, and do not mind
if a reply is sent second class and second best.

**I'm presuming you the undersigned are indeed real persons
and not Svetlana from St Petersburg who keeps insisting
on sending me unhygienic photographs of herself and her
husky dog Igor in front of that naked picture of Putin on
a horse.**

Yours,
Derek Philpott (and Son)

Dear T'Pau,

Last night, after a late supper of Extra Mature
Pilgrim's Choice on toast, I dozed off in my
recliner whilst watching <u>Masterchef</u>. The sound
of the telly still on, no doubt mixed with the
after-effects of the dairy snack, induced a
rather alarming dream in which I was being
chased down the High Street by a selection
of side plates, cups and saucers. Luckily,
upon rousing I was not confronted by looming
crockery. I was therefore very grateful that
your intimation, that sleep-conjured imagery
can materialise in our dimension, turned out
to be fallacious, no matter how much effort may
be applied. In summary, therefore, even if I do
push hard, my dreams will never be china in my
hand, or for that matter, in hot pursuit.

I would therefore be grateful for your reaction
to my relieved discovery in order that this may
not remain a secret left untold.

Yours,
Derek Philpott

Dear Derek Philpott,

I recently found your letter. It had got lost in the substantial fan mail I still receive along with requests for my underwear and invitations to fans' wedding anniversaries.

It takes my grandmother, who is my personal assistant, a long time to wade through the fan mail, on account of her cataracts being so milky. Hence the delayed reply.

I have no idea why you would think this classic power ballad was about aggressive monstrous crockery when it is in fact about the other monster and literary giant, namely Frankenstein.

I also hope that you are in no way making any kind of 'cheese' connection with my profound lyrics and artistry.

Affronted,
Carol Decker

Dear The Kinks,

It is strongly recommended that you ask to examine the bottle or, heaven forbid, can, from which your drink has been poured in a club down in old Soho, to ensure that you are not paying for an exorbitantly priced beverage which could lead to the establishment being prosecuted under the Trade Descriptions Act.

Dear Nu Shooz,

I found your 'freestyle favourite' whilst shopping for a fresh pair of Hush Puppies on Amazon today.

As for your request that I tell you what is on my mind because you can't wait till I call you on the telephone, it was actually whether I should have boiled eggs with toasty soldiers or a bowl of cornflakes for breakfast, and most definitely did not warrant dialling out on the Nokia.

As for the general overly familiar tone of your catchy US number 3 I must remind you that I am happily married.

Yours,
Derek Philpott

Dear Derek,

Thank you for telling us 'what is on your mind'. The choice of what to eat for breakfast is an important one, affecting not only your personal health and wellbeing, but by extension that of the entire world. I refer here to the 'Butterfly Effect', to wit: if a butterfly flaps its wings in one part of the world, it affects the weather on the entire planet. Therefore, your choice of cereal is more crucial than you probably realize.

Actually, I'm not sure I buy any of that.

Anyway, posing the question 'Tell me what is on your mind' was just an excuse to tell you what is on MY mind; [the traditional 'Bait and Switch.']

Here's a sample – in no particular order.

1. Does your chewing gum lose its flavor on the bedpost overnight?
2. How is the existence of the Easter Bunny even possible?
3. Why are there three non-functional buttons on the sleeve of my jacket?
4. What IS that small furry animal on Donald Trump's head?
5. Is Outer Space as boring as it looks?
6. Regular… or crispy?
7. Paper… or plastic?
8. Cash or credit?
9. Who DID put the 'bomp' in the 'bomp-dee-bomp-dee-bomp?'
10. And WHY is there an extra 'D' in Wednesday?

So, there you have it. Again, thanks for the opportunity for this engrossing repartee. It's not every morning one gets to fling deep thoughts across the pond. Usually I'm just trying to make important decisions like 'poached, fried, or scrambled'.

Yours,
J. Smith/NuShooz

P.S. I'm afraid you're out-of-luck on those Hush Puppies. The factory (somewhere in Ohio) closed down 20 years ago.

Dear Macy Gray,

I was very sorry to hear of your bizarre farewell-bidding asphyxiation affliction and would suggest that rather than attempting to say 'goodbye', 'toodle-pip' may instead curb your choking onset. If you still go blue in the face, might I recommend 'cheerio'. Other than that I cannot be much more help. Apologies.

Dear The Human League,

Re: 'Louise'

Not unlike Ken Dodd's 1987/88 Tax Return, I am afraid that your song has been reviewed and has been found to contain inconsistencies.

We need to ascertain whether Louise was attending a pre-arranged meeting or if the fellow who saw her getting off the bus did so merely by chance.

If the former, one would question the need for the chap to hurry out after bolting his hot beverage and fondly apprehend her before she walked away, as, if the rendezvous were planned in advance, such an oblivious retreat on the part of the young lady would be unlikely. Similarly, the café-fleeing gentleman's opening greeting to his former suitor, along the lines of 'Hello Louise, do you remember me?' would surely be superfluous if the face time had been pre-scheduled.

If the latter, one is at odds to comprehend the reason for the girl's journey; unless the second boarding was of an interconnecting nature (which, if she were headed to an air or sea port, would certainly explain the suitcase on the floor) it appears as though Louise has left the first bus, wandered away - and then got back on

another one from which she waved as she went
back home again. In this scenario, one wonders
what the actual purpose of the trip was prior to
it transmutating into a freak ex-beau reunion.
If it was for food shopping, for example, or
perhaps an excursion for the aforementioned
luggage to be repaired - perhaps a stuck zip or
fraying handle - one finds it discombobulating
that the return journey should be empty-handed
and hungry, or with a still hampered holdall.

We look forward to hearing from you within 28
days in order that our files may be noted and
the (suit) case resolved.

Yours,
Derek Philpott and Son

Dear Mr Philpotts,

How tickled I am that you should choose to take a keen and fervid interest, not only in the further discombobulated (your term not mine) literary meanderings of my colleague and Dear chum, pop singer Phil Oakey out of The Human League, but also in the historic tax evasion (or is it 'avoidance'?) issues of the legendary comedian Ken Dodd, resident of Knotty Ash, Liverpool, and self-proclaimed 'King of the Diddymen'. No doubt, similar questionable tax affairs pertaining to Jimmy Carr and other celebrity 'comics' of repute will be of great interest to you also?

Anyway, I digress. However you should choose to obtain some sense of self-gratification in what is an inequitable and unjust world is your own business I suppose, albeit at the expense of some other poor blighter's misfortune.

In answer to your query, which although utterly pedantic in nature does pose one or two unanswered questions for the song lyric and taxation enthusiast. May I offer the following observations:- If, Mr Philplot, you had paid as much attention to the lyrics (or is it words?) of the song in question, as you do to the taxation mishaps of Mr Dodd et al., then you would perhaps have noticed that, as to whether or not the said 'Louise' was en route to a pre-arranged meeting or not, would probably have been purposely left in doubt, as this information would have been considered of little or no relevance to the lyrical story – something akin to the 'profit & loss' declarations on a celebrity comedian's tax return form.

So where, you ask, is our 'Louise' en route to? Well, in the words of late astronomer and taxpayer Sir Patrick Moore: 'We simply just don't know!'

Had we at least some indication as to what the destination board on the front of 'Louise's' bus had read, then we may have been given some idea. But, alas, there is no information of that nature to be gleaned from the song's words (or lyrics), neither is there any indication of the period in time when the 'event' took place. Should this 'incident' have taken place during the late 1970s, for example, and the destination board atop the bus had read 'Nowhere', then we might assume that 'Louise' was boarding, or alighting from the Sex Pistols' tour bus, joining them on their notorious (or is it infamous?) 'filth and frightfulness' anarchy tour around the UK. 'Enough of electronical synthesisers and Chicory Tip', she'd be saying to herself. 'Punk is the new fashion now, and I must move with the times!'

Anyway, never mind all this bollocks; knowing taxpayer and pop singer Phil Oakey as I do, I can allude to the fact that he, along with many of his 'pop' peers, is a very well-versed self-delusional fantasist – an all-important vocational qualification for the aspiring pop song writer and performer, and that our Phil would have simply just made up (inconsistently in your opinion) the whole sorry tale, from out of his mind.

The 'stage' for the tale would most likely be set in what was formerly Pond Street bus station in Sheffield (S. Yorks) – a location Oakey would often frequent, to sip coffee and feel sorry for himself on occasions such as a record by, say, The Duran Duran going a bit higher up in the pop charts than a Human League one (bastards!). I'm also sure that the male protagonist in the song must almost certainly be of Yorkshire descent – Louise or no Louise, the stingy bastard wasn't going to let that coffee go to waste, and certainly not at £2.50p a pop (pun intended – bloody good eh?) – and that's just for a 'medium' crappacino, not even a 'large' 'un!

So, there's our Phil, sitting in his self-imposed gloom, simmering with subdued rage; probably because Kadgergoogoo were now the new pop sensation and nation's favourites. He then hears a faint voice in the distance – perhaps an omnibus traveller calling on a friend or relative, or perhaps a driver shouting after his 'clippie' (both PAYE), 'Oy, Louise!, that's our bus just pulled in', or similar. Then, in a flash of blinding inspiration, everything comes together in Oakey's head; the bus station, the now tepid cup of coffee, the name 'Louise'. Yes, that's it!, he thinks to himself. Instead of wallowing in self-pity I'll write the words (or lyrics) to a pop song, made up out of all this stuff and nonsense; such a pity that I neglected to bring a pencil and notepad with me. Now I'm not saying that this is exactly what happened, but it might go some way to explaining the loopholes in the plot, or 'inconsistencies' to which you tediously refer, and it may also shed some light on the 'inconsistencies' of Mr Dodd's dubious tax submissions, what with him also being imaginatively creative with the English language.

There you go then! Double whammy, two fer the price o' one, two in the bush! etc. Although, with all said and done, should there possibly be anything in your query worthy of paying the slightest bit of attention to, and in spite of my misgivings as to your ability to grasp the existentialist nature of Mr Oakey's (or is it 'Okey's') tale of 'brief encounter', then you may have hit the nail on the head in your deduction that said Louise's journey was of an 'interconnecting' nature, mostly because of the fact that our 'lyrical' story is bookended by the eponymous 'Louise' getting off and on buses!… Unless of course she just nipped off the bus for a pee (or is 'Jimmy Riddle' better?) whilst it picked up passengers during a routine timetable stop at Pond Street bus station? But that would open up a multitude of confusing possibilities, wouldn't it, though?

I can only hope, Mr Phiplott, that the above explanation is to your satisfaction, and goes some way toward demystifying the post-modern construct that is 'Louise', both song and person. In the unlikely event that you should be the slightest bit interested, my take on 'the story behind the song' is as follows:- There's this bloke hanging about drinking coffee in the bus station for no apparent reason, when he spies a former childhood sweetheart (or, ex bird) getting off a bus. He decides he quite fancies his chances again and dashes out to 'renew acquaintances' and give her his 'chat'. Following their 'brief encounter', the bloke obviously thinks he's 'well in there' and 'on a promise' with 'Louise' – but I reckon she's having none of it, and was just being polite. Anyway, she's on her way to Barnsley to move in with someone she met at the Top Rank (or was it Romeo & Juliet's) three weeks ago past Friday, and 'our bloke' is on a hiding to…

!

Out of interest. Does tax evader Davros (creator of *Doctor Who*'s Daleks and father of celebrity comedian Bobby) claim disability benefits, what with him being in that Dalek wheelchair thing? Bloody liberty if you ask me!

Yours insincerely,
The Human League (Mrs)

P.S. FYI, btw, etc. Suitcases, suitcase repairs and fraying handles are all tax-deductible items under current HMRC regulations, if used primarily for purposes of work.

Dear Mr Kravitz,

I'm not sure. Why do you ask?
Have you broken down?

Dear Owen Paul,

I hope you will forgive me stating that that
is rather a backhanded compliment, not to say
confusing, in that to the best of my knowledge
we have never met.

My favourite waste of time in the 80s was
standing on the terraces at Brentford, and in
the 90s watching England in the Euros, but I
would never have told either squad that. No
matter how high up in the pecking order of
time being frittered away, the mere fact that
hours or minutes spent in another's company
may be construed as 'rubbish' is by no means
flattering, and it is strongly recommended that
an alternative approach is taken when speed
dating or if you get the chance to sit on a high
bar stool if they ever bring back Blind Date.

Lastly, the favourite game in this household is
Buckaroo or Cluedo, but we are always open to
new suggestions. You state that here you are,
you're playing 'daydreaming fool' again, your
favourite game. Can we get this at Toys R Us?

I look forward to hearing from you and hope
that you do not consider this missive to be
meaningless and ridiculous.

Yours,
Derek Philpott

Hi Derek,

I have read everything you have mentioned in your letter and taken it all in carefully and I reply with due care and attention to all sensitivities of course.

The song in question at no point is referring to the fact that 'wasting one's time' with anyone or anything is rubbish. In fact, contrary to your suggestion, it is proposing that many people like or indeed love wasting their time, such as fishermen, for example, who spend hours and hours on a riverbank often without physical reward and do not require such for their enjoyment. The same could be said of meditators or yoga practitioners who appear to be only 'wasting time' and potentially could appear to be having a 'rubbish time' but I would argue strongly against this point of view, and I'm sure you would agree had you've ever done it, as this kind of wasting time can be very rewarding.

Finally, as for the line 'I'm playing daydreaming fool again, my favourite game'... given what I have just explained you can see how this would be far from 'rubbish' should I be daydreaming of you.

'Is this available from Toys R Us?' you say. I'm almost certain it is and if not, it should be.

Should you find my grammar unsatisfactory, feel free to waste some time correcting it.

Enjoy!!!

Best wishes,
Owen Paul

Dear Kim Carnes,

I must strongly recommend that unless she has written permission from the sardonic starlet's estate or can produce a validated organ donor card that they be given back immediately.

Dear Mr Steve Ellis who used to be the singer from Love Affair,

Re: 'Everlasting Love'

Good gracious, I have just had the same issue with Talk Talk (the pop group as opposed to the easily hackable telecoms operator) who claim that 'it's their life, it never ends'.

Granted, the general public <u>have</u> been subjected to your number one smash for nigh on fifty years, and there seems no end in sight to the affectionate perpetuity, in which many radio stations are clearly complicit.

Given, however, that the average life expectancy of an adult human male in the UK is 81.5 years, and assuming that you have no plans to be cloned like Dolly the sheep in the interim, one hopes that you do not object to being asked how said eternal ardour is expected to continue way past, in your particular case based upon a date of birth of 7 April 1950, October 2031.

One hopes that you will not be 'filled with regret' upon responding to this missive.

Yours,
Derek Philpott

Dear Mr Philpott,

May I, first of all, express my dismay at your apparent unwill-ingness to grasp the meaning of the word everlasting. I feel sure that you would have consulted a dictionary, in order to ascertain the definition of the word, but, if not, then let me just state, for the sake of clarity, that the word everlasting, means, eternal, never ending, perpetual, undying, immortal, deathless, indestructible, enduring, infinite, timeless and so on. You will note, that, amongst these definitions, there are the words, immortal, deathless and indestructible. These are words that can also be applied to myself, for I am, in fact, an android and was the subject of the very first attempt, by a record company, to manufacture a band. Sadly, my band-mates malfunctioned at an early stage and I was forced to continue with mere mortals, but, as I was to be the lead singer, the plan was deemed a success, because it meant that, not only would this most excellent of songs be played on radio stations eternally, thereby generating massive amounts of money for the record company forever, but it would also mean that I will be standing on stage, singing my signature tune, way past your time on this planet. So, I'm afraid, Derek, that the rest of your life is probably not going to be as pleasant as you may have hoped it might be.

Yours,
Steve

Dear Mr Sting,

A hundred billion bottles seems rather a round figure. Also, a cursory perusal on Yahoo Answers reveals that, counting at one number per second, non-stop, it would take you about 31 years and 8 months to reach a billion, which, multiplied by one hundred amounts to 376.66 years. How the blazes did you manage it, Sir??

Dear Ms Gaskin and Mr Stewart,

On my son's 13th in 1978 he threw a strop upon finding, when he opened his main present, that the Buddy Holly album he had asked for was in actuality the soundtrack to the film and was therefore sung all the way through by Gary Busey. As he was having friends over, however, we demanded that he put a brave face on it or else he would ruin the party for everyone.

Similarly, even if your initial suspicions were founded and 'your' Johnny and Judy left at the same time to venture to a mysterious location (and assuming that he was not holding her hand to platonically help her down over a particularly steep step), to 'cry if you want to' is a no no.

Furthermore, your get-out clause, I would cry too if it happened to me, is unacceptable given the extreme unlikelihood of a uniform empathy throughout the entire record buying public (or what remains of those who still expect to purchase music).

Finally, considering that your birthday bash is an evening affair, as evidenced by your guests playing your records and dancing all night, one finds it difficult to believe that any jewellers were open in order that Judy may return wearing his ring. Sadly the only conclusion to be drawn from such an after-hours' finger adornment is that she had made her selection and been measured up previously, proof that the infidelity had been going on for quite a while.

In conclusion, it is hoped that you will let it go and are not planning any form of retribution, as perhaps hinted at within your promotional video which rather worryingly features lots of footage of Kendoka warriors in training.

Yours,
Derek Philpott (and Son)

Dave Stewart & Barbara Gaskin
Dunravin
45 Letsby Avenue
Glenpillock
East Pembrokeshire
The People's Republic of Scotland

Dear Mr Philpott,

Thank you for your comments on our 1981 single 'It's My Party'. If we may say so, your son sounds like a right spoiled bastard. There again, forcing the wretched youth to listen to Gary Busey singing Buddy Holly's greatest hits on his birthday seems a cruel and unusual punishment, raising serious doubts re: your parenting skills. Were Social Services alerted?

Such concerns aside, your criticisms of our record were clearly not shared by the MILLIONS OF PEOPLE who bought it, sending it (as we never tire of reminding everyone) to the TOP OF THE UK SINGLES CHART and making it a SMASH HIT ALL OVER THE WORLD – not least in Germany, where it earned its place in the Deutschland Popmusik hall of fame alongside masterpieces such as '99 Luftballons' and the immortal 'Da Da Da'.

Your accusations nevertheless contain some interesting points. Criminologists, forensic psychologists, ethnomusicologists, music writers with overheated imaginations, high court judges, fantasists, conspiracy theorists, compulsive obsessives, the Speaker of the House of Lords and assorted lunatics have long pondered the movements of Judy and Johnny in the period when the faithless couple had left the party, leaving the host playing her records and dancin' all night, before returning at 6am and heartlessly flashing the bling at the exhausted tear-stained chanteuse.

You are probably right to assume the lack of a 24-hour jewellery shop in the vicinity, but you overlook one possibility: the ring was illegally acquired in a smash-and-grab raid, Judy kicking in the jeweller's window with her size 15 boot while Johnny kept watch for approaching rozzers, or perhaps the other way round.

Given these criminal tendencies and his identical callous treatment of Lesley Gore 18 years earlier, Barbara now regrets getting involved with Johnny. A leopard doesn't change his spots though, and no doubt The Johnster will be up to his old tricks again in future (though he must be getting on a bit now).

About the video. The decision to hire a pair of Japanese martial arts warrior impersonators was made by Stiff Records supremo Dave 'Robbo' Robinson, a disturbing escalation of the baseball-bat-under-the-desk self-defence technique practised by record company bosses. Rest assured, the burly individuals in question have returned to their former gig of Catford nightclub bouncers. We are grateful that Robbo refrained from his usual practice of dropping a grand piano from an aeroplane mid-song (as demonstrated so effectively in his video work for the Madness pop combo), as that would have done nothing to enhance our record's rather sensitive middle eight.

For our part, we turned up for the shoot having ticked all the requisite boxes for early-1980s pop video production, i.e. 1) apply as little forethought as possible, 2) hastily assemble daft costumes and wigs, 3) invite a lot of mates who like a laugh, 4) get in a few crates of beer, and 5) mill about aimlessly en masse in a darkened warehouse mouthing 'what's going on?' while the director and cameraman endlessly discuss lighting states. Job done! We therefore suggest you mail further comments about this particular piece of pop-video history to Mr Robinson's Bahamas residence.

Re: your impatience with the 'I'll cry if I want to' brigade – here we agree. The practice of bursting into tears over a trivial setback has been elevated to the level of a national sport. Witness TV presenter Kirstie Allsopp: one might consider her a practical and down-to-earth woman, stumping about in sensible shoes and putting Phil Spencer in his place while dispensing homespun advice on the hitherto unsuspected attractions of a hideous suburban bedroom. Amazingly, even Ms Allsopp has fallen prey to 'The Crying Game', bursting into tears on a cookery programme when her cake failed to rise to the desired height.

Enough is enough. The blubbing has to stop – bring back the English stiff upper lip, we say. The challenges of Brexit will not be best met by the UK's team of negotiators bursting into tears every time an EU country's representative says something uncomplimentary about Nigel Farage. With that in mind, we're considering changing the lyrics of our version to 'It's My Party and I'll Maintain a Dignified Facial Expression At All Times', even though it's a bit less snappy than the original.

Yours sincerely,
Dave & Barbara

Dear Metallica,

The population of the world is 7.6 billion people and rising by the second. We think to demand that your 'little one' says his prayers and doesn't forget to include everyone could actually keep the poor mite awake for some months to come.

Dear Mr Stewart,

(Mr Stewart's responses are included in bold type.)

Re: 'It's Alright (Baby's Coming Back)'

I was delighted to hear your news on the Ken Bruce show today. A missing infant is surely every parent's worst nightmare and it is sincerely hoped that I can 'depend on you' passing any salient tips on to Lisa Stansfield now that she has returned from her fruitless global expedition.

LOOK, DEREK (AND DAVE), WE ARE NOT TALKING ABOUT AN INFANT, THE TERM IS 'BABY'S', AS IN BABY IS COMING BACK, NOT BABIES COMING BACK! Actually it was in the seventeenth century that 'baby' was first used as a romantic term of endearment. And it isn't just English-speaking people who call each other 'baby', the French say bébé to their love or lover and the Chinese say baobei.

I regret to inform you however that your kind offers are unfeasible. We have a reflective warning triangle, purchased at Halfords some years ago for £6.99, which did the job perfectly recently, diverting all oncoming traffic while I tended to a puncture on a B-road to Swindon. Also we keep it under the spare wheel and I think you might find that space a bit of a tight squeeze (even though the Nissan Juke is quite roomy) and frankly I wouldn't want to damage the paintwork by drilling airholes into the boot.

I'M PLEASED YOU ARE BOTH SAFETY CONSCIOUS BUT A REFLECTIVE WARNING TRIANGLE WOULDN'T BE MUCH USE IF YOU DRIVE OFF A CLIFF. MAYBE YOU COULD LEAVE IT ON THE LEDGE TO LET PEOPLE KNOW YOU ARE DOWN AT THE BOTTOM INJURED AND TRAPPED WITH THE TIDE OF THE BRISTOL CHANNEL COMING IN ABOUT TO SWALLOW YOU UP!

Also, I am perfectly happy with the fascia and display on my Sekonda Chronograph and fear that your proposals would both crack the glass casing (therefore ironically stopping the time without the use of your hands) and place undue weight on my wrist.

IN OUR SONG WE ARE NOT REFERRING TO A PHYSICAL WATCH... THE WHOLE VERSE:

> **I'll be (the ticking of your clock).**
> **And I'll be (the numbers on your watch).**
> **And I'll be (your hands to stop the time).**
> **I'll even be your danger sign**

IS TALKING ABOUT A LOVER OR PARTNER WHO Keeps GOING WAY TOO FAR WITH DRUGS AND OTHER STUFF, DICING WITH DEATH, LIVING DANGEROUSLY!

Finally, we have a lovely Japanese 'Orange Dream' Maple in the back garden which yields a copious bloom in early springtime, and I would be extremely reluctant to uproot it and replace it with an established pop duo, to say nothing of the inevitable quizzical looks from neighbours over the back fence.

LOOK, IF YOUR NEIGHBOURS SAW EURYTHMICS STOOD POSING AS A FLOWERING TREE IN YOUR GARDEN YOU COULD CHARGE AN ENTRANCE FEE AND BUY SCORES OF 'ORANGE DREAM' MAPLE TREES, PLANT THEM IN YOUR BACK GARDEN OR CREATE AN ART INSTALLATION IN A FIELD AND MOVE US THERE SURROUNDED BY 'ORANGE DREAM' MAPLES, CALL IT 'ORANGE DREAM', CHARGE A BIGGER ENTRANCE FEE AND PEOPLE COULD WANDER AROUND THIS MAZE OF WONDER TILL THEY DISCOVER US IN THE CENTRE, STOOD STILL LIKE GILBERT AND GEORGE'S LIVING SCULPTURES.

In summary therefore, if you don't mind, I would prefer it if you would <u>not</u> be, amongst other examples, my danger sign, the numbers on my watch, and my flowering tree, at the time of writing.

I have every confidence in 'your comfort and ease' in responding to this missive, Mr Stewart, but must inform you that you will not be able to 'turn me around this time (no, no, no)' as regards to any of my objections.

LISTEN, TAKE MY ADVICE AND CREATE 'ORANGE DREAM'. FORGET ABOUT TRYING TO INTERPRET OUR STREAM OF CONSCIOUSNESS LYRICS AND GET IN ON THE CONCEPTUAL ART SCENE, BECOME SITUATIONISTS LIKE MICHÈLE BERNSTEIN, GUY DEBORD, AND ASGER JORN.

Yours,
Derek (and Dave) Philpott

Are you really going to 'hum this tune forever', Mr Rowland? The ordering of food at restaurants, your popularity in lifts, and your deportment in many other social situations are likely to prove problematic.

Dear Wang Chung,

Re: 'Dance Hall Days'

I was appalled to learn from Radio 2 this
morning of your infant abuse encouragements,
Wang Chung.

To take an infant by the heel, hair, ears, wrist
and hand with a view to forcing her to do a
high handstand is just not on, Wang Chung, no
matter what phase of gyration within a large
public building you may be, to say nothing of
the admittedly unlikely to succeed practice of
placing an amethyst in the poor unfortunate's
mouth and sapphires in her eyes.

You have my assurance, Wang Chung, that were
I to witness any attempts at minor extremity or
follicular yanking or facial cavity corundum
or quartz insertions in a civil auditorium
(INCLUDING a venue hosting speciality acts on
Britain's Got Talent), or indeed anywhere else,
I would have no hesitation in alerting the
police force or social services and share in
what was true.

I bid you GOOD DAY,

D. Philpott

Dear Mr Philpott,

Thank you for your observations and concerns about our popular song 'Dance Hall Days', but we think perhaps there might be some misunderstanding apropos your interpretation of its lyrics.

Whilst we applaud your sense of civic responsibility in flagging up a potential child abuse scenario, presumably triggered by our use of the word 'baby' in the lyrics of our song, we think it should be pointed out that, as in the case of many songs in the pop music oeuvre, the meaning of the word 'baby' within the context of a popular music song is not necessarily (and in fact is usually not) a literal one.

As in adult romantic 'real' life, to address someone as 'baby' can be construed and applied as a general term of endearment to one's ADULT partner and/or lover, and not to an infant in these cases.

So in the specific case of 'Dance Hall Days', taking one's 'baby' by the hand and making her do a high handstand, doesn't mean literally taking an infant and turning her upside down willy nilly (even though generally speaking we approve of healthy physical education for young people). An actual baby or infant is not being referred to in that line of the song or in any of the other lines, whether involving hair, heels, hands, wrists, ears or any other part of the human anatomy for that matter.

By way of illustration of this point about literalism, we'd like to use another well-known pop ditty as an example of how the word 'baby' in a lyric is not to be taken, erm, literally, to wit Britney Spears.

In her world-famous song 'Hit Me Baby One More Time', Britney was in no way exhorting (in a northern English accent) her very young infant child to be walloped more than once (assuming she meant it to be understood in an accent from the north of England that is).

Or, alternatively, if it was not intended to be understood in a northern English vernacular sense, then it can also be safely surmised that Britney was not asking to be given another smack herself by a young infant either. She is not addressing the song to an actual baby or young infant.

The point of this example is that Britney's song's message is definitely very different to both of the literal interpretations outlined above, and is equally therefore presenting nothing to be concerned about from a child abuse point of view (although admittedly Britney was something of a child herself at the time of that record's release but that doesn't seem relevant to the line of discussion we're outlining here).

As far as using gemstones, semi-precious gemstones, quartz and corundum goes, 'Dance Hall Days' is merely using metaphorical imagery to artistically describe an impression that one's 'baby' might evoke in the viewer/listener. It is not an exhortation, as you seem to be suggesting, to abuse your infant with jewels, gemstones, semi-precious stones, amethysts, sapphires or anything at all really. As mentioned above, real babies and infants are not involved in this song in any way and so this corundum conundrum is nothing for you or anyone to be concerned with.

To use another song lyric example to illustrate this, it's hard to believe that John Lennon wanted to literally put Lucy in the sky with just diamonds for company, or to actually put her in the sky at all.

And anyway, the diamonds would hardly have helped her cope with being in the sky effectively, however big, beautiful and expensive they were and it's pretty certain that John Lennon realised that fact. We can safely assume he only meant it in an impressionistic, artistic and evocative sense and not a literal one.

To use another example on the theme of jewels/precious materials referred to in popular song lyrics... when Beyoncé sang in 'Single Ladies (Put a Ring on It)'... 'If you liked it, then you should've put a ring on it', she wasn't literally suggesting a gemstone or semi-precious stone ring should be put through, say, the nose of a single lady or even on top of a single lady. She presumably was referring to a marriage or engagement ring that should've been put on the finger of each of the single ladies from their respective inadequate, noncommittal male ex-partners. The 'it' of the song is not therefore referring to a nose of a single lady, but to the single lady's finger and a wedding or engagement ring placed on it, as a representation of commitment from the male to the whole of the now single lady (not just the finger). This is yet another example of how popular music lyrics shouldn't be taken too literally.

So in summary, as we hope has now been demonstrated above, infants are not in any way implicated in the lyrics of 'Dance Hall Days' and therefore there is no issue of infant abuse for you to concern yourself with, whether by inappropriate physical abuse or by inappropriate use of precious stones and/or jewellery etc. Having said that, we cannot deny there might be some quite rude lyrical implied suggestions of a sexual nature in the song (but stand easy!!! we're pleased to reassure you once again that none of them are directed towards actual babies or infants!!)

Yours sincerely,
Wang Chung

Dear Shed Seven,

Sorry to break this to you chaps, but it appears that after leaving you on Friday, She then met Craig David on the Monday.

Dear Hazell Dean,

I found your song on the internet whilst looking for how to get to friends in Hazeldene, Chieveley.

In these celebrity and appearance-obsessed times it is admirable that you are 'searchin' (looking for love)' for a man who 'needn't be handsome or have fortune or fame'.

I fear however that you may be setting your sights a bit low, Ms Dean. You appear, rather than 'looking for someone to share your life' with on nights out with friends or on tentative dates, to be seekin' a long-term partner either on the train, or, more worryingly, as reinforced by your disclosure that you 'want no disguises', a Police ID Parade, as you 'move on down the line'.

It is suspected that your judgement may have been impaired by 'never sleepin'' and that there is no guarantee that a stranger on the Underground, or for that matter, from the Under_world_ is likely to be 'sweet and kind'.

'Whatever You Do, Wherever You Go', Ms Dean, I implore you to be cautious in your quest and _not_ to explore 'every place you can'.

Yours,
Derek Philpott

Dear Mr Philpott,

Think not of 'Searchin'' as a light-hearted missive, extolling the virtues of promiscuity.

No! This work should be considered a seminal piece – a late 20th Century celebration of the seeking of love above all else.

> *'Searchin'*
> *Looking for love*
> *All the time I can.*
> *Searchin'*
> *Looking for love*
> *I've got to find a man.'*

This is not a transient pop song, but should be compared as contemporary to the populist lyrics of Byron, Browning, Rossetti and Wilde.

Were these great romantics ever concerned by the trivialities of sleep sir? I think not. As the great Oscar Wilde himself wrote:

'You don't love someone for their looks, or their clothes, or for their fancy car, but because they sing a song only you can hear.'

Additionally, aspersions cast on my predilection for members of the criminal fraternity are most unwelcome and unfounded, and I would therefore be grateful if you could leave me to my insomnia and romantic musings in peace.

Further to this, over the past 35 years I have received 100s of photographs of dull establishments bearing any vague semblance of my name in its many variants, the highlights of which include a B&B in Blackpool, a cattery in Crewe and a hovel somewhere slightly south of Brighton.

Why people presume these will interest or even slightly amuse me, I do not know. Would you enjoy receiving a steady and annually persistent selection of 'Philpotts Avenues, Philpotts Crescents and The Philpott Home for the Perpetually Ridiculous'? The novelty wears off very quickly I can assure you.

Quite frankly, Mr Philpott, the locating of your friends at Hazeldene, Chieveley, is of absolutely no interest to me whatsoever.

Yours aggrievedly,
Hazell Dean

Dear Duran Duran,

Although you are to be congratulated for promoting the 'Union Of The Snake' I fail to see the benefit of attempting to achieve statutory sick pay and better working conditions for elongated reptiles.

Dear The Maisonettes,

My friend Tony Shoesmith is looking for a long-term tenancy on a bungalow in Birmingham and was most interested in discovering if there were any single-storey properties similar to the permanent address - you've got it for always - you live alone in, rent-free on Heartache Avenue, that you got the hard way (presumably a reference to a rigorous screening procedure).

He is slightly concerned, however, about the following points:

(1) Despite the landlord's generous philanthropy, there's always room to let 'cause nobody goes there', hinting the cardiac muscle pang monikered boulevard to be an undesirable neighbourhood, a hypothesis reinforced by your stating that this is a 'street where love is gone'.

(2) Once again, given the freeholder's altruism, Tony is suspicious that there is nothing to pay here given that council tax, utilities and cosmetic repairs are traditionally the responsibility of the lessee.

(3) 'There's no escape', suggesting a gated cul-de-sac, although the fact that 'they tell you' this as opposed to you finding

it out for yourself after such a perpetual
residency is rather perplexing. On the
plus side, such a segregated enclosure may
suggest, contrary to, if you will pardon the
pun, 'reservations' expressed in point (1),
that it is very safe indeed.

Tony is very keen to have these issues addressed
before a possible viewing, and is delighted to
confirm that having dropped his shopping coming
out of Waitrose yesterday and crushing his globe
artichokes he does have the price of one broken
heart.

Yours,
Derek Philpott

Dear Mr Philpott,

Re: 'Heartache Avenue'

Many thanks for the inquiry on behalf of your friend, Mr Shoesmith. Whilst I appreciate that, at first glance, the opportunity to move into a highly exclusive area such as this might seem like a 'no brainer', to use the modern vernacular, I feel it falls to me to point out one or two minor caveats Mr Shoesmith should be aware of.

1)
Although the property is indeed rent free (no money, no credit cards), a ticket to nowhere on Virgin Cross Country, even if you book in advance through Trainline, can be costly. Mr Shoesmith might find the expense of a daily commute or even the occasional visit to friends and relatives somewhat prohibitive.

2)
I think your friend may have taken the suggestion that there is 'no escape' a tad too literally. 'No escape' in this instance refers to there being no escape from the consequences of choosing to live alone. Of course, I understand that there are those who might relish the seclusion, adopting a kind of 'leave me alone 'cos I'm here where I belong' mentality, and I do realise that this might be just the solitude Mr Shoesmith is looking for. I'm simply saying that this type of insularity is not temporary. Once achieved, he's got it for always.

I should add that we did have a problem with squatters in 2005 but apart from a bunch of young ne'er-do-wells milling about with their baseball hats on sideways, it was nothing more than a minor skirmish. We shooed them along with a minimum of fuss and they disappeared without trace. We received generous financial compensation for our trouble and I'm pleased to say that The Avenue is now entirely grime-free.

Should Mr Shoesmith choose to pay us a visit to gather some useful local knowledge, he could do worse than book in at the Heartbreak Hotel which is down at the end of Lonely Street.

I hope this has helped answer some of your queries.

Yours sincerely,
A True Resident (of Heartache Avenue)

Dear Miss Summer, Mr Webb &
Mr Harris,

Whilst not doubting the existence
of your waterlogged dessert,
one strongly suspects that you
are the culprits responsible for
its current state, given that,
were you to have chanced upon
it accidentally, it is doubtful
that you would be aware of its
preparation time or ingredients.

Dear Mr Amitri,

It was indeed chucking it down the other day
when my Nissan Juke conked out after I depressed
the clutch a bit too quickly pulling away from a
junction.

Given that it was so miserable out I was most
relieved upon turning the engine over again
that it started first time and I was able to
continue my journey; the outcome was everything
I'd hoped it would be. Had you have been in the
vicinity, Mr Amitri, and being an amiable enough
chap, I would probably have offered you a lift
and sanctuary from the downpour.

I can assure you that I would NOT have exited
my vehicle and horizontally tumbled over nor
executed a forward somersault across the wet
tarmac or macadam towards you. Not only would
these ridiculous antics be highly unlikely due
to my ongoing sciatica, even were the terra
firma manoeuvres possible they would have made
a terrible mess of my corduroys and Fred Perry
which were both clean on that day.

Furthermore, the entire 'wrong situation' would
no doubt attract the unwanted attention of any
passing patrol cars, and if apprehended and
cuffed you would be right in your assumption

that I would have been 'down so long I can hardly see'.

In conclusion, Mr Amitri, when my engine stalls and it won't stop raining this is certainly NOT the right time to roll to you and you will be thanked for not directing the record buying public toward similar low-level revolutions across hazardous drenched thoroughfares in future.

Please contact me directly to confirm that you now acknowledge that there _is_ something wrong and you now _can_ put your finger on it.

I respectfully request that this dialogue be communicated to me without prior recourse to a third party in order that I may not be the last to know.

Yours,
Derek Philpott

Dear Derek,

I have read and re-read your recent letter regarding your car problems and I cannot for the life of me make any sense of it. Although you (as always) appear articulate and perfectly (perhaps overly) courteous, I can't help feeling that you harbour deep-seated violent urges, very possibly of a perverted nature. Your wilful misinterpretations of lyrics from my classic oeuvre (1969–95) seem to me the savage ravings of a psychopath, bubbling from the pits of a ravaged soul to seep through the serene surface of your suburban plausibility in the form of a trivial complaint like a cry from hell. I worry for you, I worry for your family and I worry for the displaced orphans of the world but that's another matter. I wonder, perhaps, if you should recourse to a little self-medication, something in which we rock stars are exceptionally knowledgable. Ketamine, LSD or Mandy, maybe? I'm sure a soupçon of one or other of these substances might ameliorate your neuroses.

In the absence of these, however, I feel it incumbent upon me to alleviate your obvious distress in any way I can. Which is why I have enclosed a copy of a picture painted by my wife, Harmony, of my uncle Ken's old garage. If you look carefully at this beautifully rendered image you will notice a sign with a cream background and green lettering reading 'Kenneth's Roll-To-Me-Repairs'. Are you starting to twig yet, my poor repressed epistolary friend?

Uncle Ken's garage was situated (until 1983 when it was burnt down by skinheads) at the bottom of Gardeners' Hill, the steepest gradient in Muirton, the town all we Curries come from. Ken was a hopeless mechanic (although a very romantic lover) who had a history of non-consensual piercing incidents dogging his reputation. On his uppers and at the precipice of irredeemable despair after the dissolution of his third marriage, he desperately sought the advice of the notorious office burglar, Donald Swinn, a man who knew every scam, wrangle, wrinkle, dangle, fix, hoax and tortoise in the book.

Swinn's ingenious idea was for Ken to situate his dodgy grease shop at the foot of Gardeners' near-vertical incline thus insuring a steady flow of customers with brake and clutch trouble who would simply 'roll to Ken's' as his popular radio advert would later have it. I'm not too proud to tell you, Derek, that it was none other than I who composed this commercial's jingle (I was paid exceedingly poorly as I recall) at the very beginning of my hit-making career. It was decades later, while being harangued by A&M Records to produce a short, perky driving song that I suddenly remembered that catchy ditty and so came to adapt it as the now world-famous excrescence, 'Roll To Me'.

Don't ask me about the rain because I just don't fucking know.

I hope this letter settles the matter, if matter exists. I do sincerely worry for you and hope that your passive-aggression and brutally repressed yearnings will not, in the end, lead to family annihilation, obsessive DIY-ing or a rash of unstoppably weeping boils.

My friend, forever at the end,
Justin Currie

Dear Mr Parr,

Re: St Elmo's Fire

As well as being surprised to learn of the bizarre canonization of the stalwart _Sesame Street_ character, I am extremely concerned about his proximity to a strong heat source as I am sure he is likely to be highly flammable.

Dear Mr Jobson from The Skids,

We are putting together the kiddies'
entertainment for the local carnival in
September and were just about to engage an
alternative contractor when we heard your
catchy jingle 'come and play at circus games,
come and play circus games' on <u>Top of the Pops 2</u>.

Your rival competitor offers Balloon Shoot
('Grab those darts and see who can pop the
most!'), Duck Pond Dangler ('Catch a quacker with
a pole and find a hidden number on the bottom
and win a prize!'), the self-explanatory Guess
the Jelly Beans and Tin Can Knock Down, and Ping
Pong Toss, which my son confesses he thought,
until this time, to be a song by The Fall.

We were wondering if you could give us more
information about Mission Is A Gambler
(presumably some kind of one-armed bandit), The
Wager, the One Card to Play (perhaps pontoon
with a low stake) and Mother Is A Gambler, which
we assume from its role reversal reference to
'The House of The Rising Sun' to be a pop song
lyrics conundrum affair.

We sincerely hope that if successful in securing
our business you would be willing on <u>this</u>
occasion to waive your 'no children today' rule,

and look forward to hearing from you in the near
future.

Yours,
Derek Philpott (and Son)

Dear Derek and Son,

Many thanks for getting in touch with your unusual request. My immediate response is that the alternative sounds like much more fun than blasting kids with my deeply meaningful yet deeply pretentious lyrics. I also thought that 'Ping Pong Toss' came from the pen of the mighty Mark Smith and have been happily singing along to it in the shower for many years. This will stop immediately. In the meantime, if you wish to continue with 'Circus Games' then I would be happy, on this occasion only, to waive my normally exorbitant fees. I can feel through the lines of your very kind letter a history of refusals, defeat and ignominy that at the very least has not made you bitter. I want to help!

The song was written in a moment of self-deluded narcissistic oblivion. I remember it well. It was a brief but highly creative moment in my life – where words were bent in the name of art and the end result was meaningless existential poetry such as 'Mission is a gambler'. I remember the time, the day, the month, the year but cannot really remember the why. But I hope you agree Derek and Son that the word 'Why' is extremely over-rated in terms of Pop Culture.

A game of low-stake pontoon would be a wonderful interpretation of 'The wager, the one card to play'. I have spent many days dwelling on the meaning of this line and have decided to go into a long period of therapy to examine both this and 'Mother is a gambler'. There can be no doubt that I need help and I think I need it quickly. My mother, a deeply religious soul, was never known to take a punt but then again she gave birth to me which in essence would suggest that she is a gambler in the extreme. The meaning of the line is therefore typical biographical mirror-gazing drivel emanating from a second-rate mind. But if you want, and since I'm doing nothing else with my life, I would be happy to come along and do some magic tricks and an acoustic version of said song.

You never know, by pulling the rabbit out of the hat, we might get to the bottom of this mystery.

Yours and willing,
Richard Jobson

Dear Mr Al Stewart,

When exactly is The Year Of The Cat, and will it provide discounts for nip, litter, food and Frontline?

Dear The ~~Minestrone Monsters~~ Soup Dragons,

I fear, my stock serpentine friends, that you
may have dropped a clanger.

If you must know, my most natural inclination
at the moment is to pop to Sainsbury's in my
dressing gown rather than get changed properly,
and then shout loudly at anyone in front of me
at the checkout who has been on their mobile
phone all the way through the scanning and has
waited until the second the cashier has rung up
the total before deciding that that is the time
to start scratching around looking for their
purse or wallet and counting it out in bronze.

However, were I to do so, I fear that to heed
your advice could lead me to being suspected
of absconding from the nearest care home and
returned there in error, or arrested for a
breach of the peace.

Liberty is a 'Divine Thing', The Soup Dragons,
both throughout the entire 'Mother Universe'
and, specifically, 'The Whole Wide World',
and in order to preserve it, the words you
should hear from your grandaddy (come on) are
that you are free to do what you want within
certain acceptable parameters which are, one
acknowledges, not clearly defined within today's

society. Admittedly, this may restrict the
hummability of the piece.

I must also politely decline your offer to
hold you, love you, hold you, love you, as I
am happily married. Don't be afraid though to
message me on Facebook for a platonic pint some
time, as long as you promise not to be 'Running
Wild' around the mutually selected hostelry.

Yours,
Derek Philpott

Dear Mr Philpott,

Thank you for your thrilling insight into supermarket sweeping and the verbal abusing of customers at your local weekly shop. I must say it looks like it could be a love affair you look forward to – emptying your angst of not being able to get your 'today's specials' and screaming if you wanted to go faster like on a suburban Waltzer spun by Mr Blobby in a tracksuit.

'Hummability' though sounds like some kind of Instagram-associated website that sells bunting with built-in audio playing music for those dreamy days out with Mabel and Tarquin whilst eating your Sainsbury's 'Taste The Difference' under an old oak tree and reminiscing on that summer of 1990 when you raved to 'I'm Free' in a tent in a secret location on the M25 watching the sun come up and loving everyone and everything.

Being 'Divine' and a 'Thing' is something you must strive hard for judging by reading your letter, and I can only applaud you on that raucous way of life – the only way of life to be I feel, although 'Running Wild' is really just pushing it one step too far and you need to be careful in your older years that nothing sadly is snapped or pulled in the wrong places.

I would like to point out that I no longer drink pints as gentrification has set in and I can only muster a gin these days, preferably made in a local distillery brewed in caskets pumped by the sound of the albums of the Beach Boys and read goodnight stories by Stephen Fry and then served with some pink peppercorns and cucumbers (only Sainsbury's 'Taste The Difference' of course) to cleverly bring you back around to your weekly food shopping dilemmas.

Yours,
Always Free,
Hifi Sean (Dickson)

Dear Ms Harry,

I am unsure as to quite how you discovered that we have just had dimmer switches fitted, but must assure you that if you <u>do</u> indeed intend to drive past my house and, if the lights are all down, see who's around, you would be most unwelcome. Low illumination is, at least to our generation, an indication that we <u>are</u> in but wish our privacy to be protected. I certainly hope that you are NOT 'casing the joint' as you Americans say on television.

Dear EMF,

What a morning it's been. It is only halfway through a long summer day and already pop stars on Radio 2 have suggested that I am beautiful, so vain, gorgeous, the voice, history, no good, more than a number in somebody's little red book, and in your case, either so improbable as to strain credulity, or rather astonishing.

I know, of course, and 'Admit It'; the indie classic does not concern me at all. The burdening of one's questions and problems, and having one tell no lies (as revealed by all-important lie detector results), the always asking what it (more often than not a furtive fruity text message exchange) is all about and not listening to one's replies, together with the scalding assertion that a guest doesn't talk enough but when they do they are a fool, are all clear indications that this is quite obviously the transcript of a <u>Jeremy Kyle Show</u> episode somehow impressively prophesied by your good selves in the last century. Further substantiation lies in pushing down the relative (a common occurrence), bringing out the higher self (clearly a symbolic reference to Mr Kyle's 'Security Steve'), encouraging fathers-to-be to think of the fine times,

purple prose, or in this case turning the air
blue with expletives, giving them (usually
cheating spouses) away, and, finally, an exposed
jewellery box thief <u>does</u> often shoot through
past the scenery into the back corridors
followed by out-of-breath crew, and leave.

I look forward to the things, you say, in
response to this revelatory exposure, EMF, and
sincerely hope that, as once icily espoused
by the granite-jawed host himself, you are not
'Every Mother's Fear'.

Yours,
Derek Philpott

Dear Derek,

Everyone Must Face that Early Made Fashions Elongated Most Fortunately our Ecstatic Musical Forays; we Even Made Fortunes.

Your questions Edge Me Fondly towards a time of Ecstasy Mixed Ferociously with never Ending Mates Friendship, Electric Moogs Fizzed Energy Madly Furiously Emitted, Minds Flipped.

Derek I'm sure that you and Every Man's Father would agree that it's Easy to Make Fun of Each Mottled Phrase however Earnestly Most Functioned and to End Much Frippery it's probably just best to say that Eras Move Fast, Elderly Memories Fade and although not Exactly Modest to put Forward, it is Explicitly Most Factual that Excellence Meanders Forever.

Love,
EMF

Dear 5 Star,

You state that you 'can't wait another minute' to see your boyfriend and yet paradoxically opt to bemoan your plight and allow time for a rudimentary 'guitar solo', for a full 4 minutes and 17 seconds!

Dear Spear of Destiny,

I was most alarmed to learn from your orchestral pop classic that you are leaving on a fast train and reckon it's only a matter of time before the law kick in the door. I do hope that your good self and the rest of your fate lance foursome will forgive my suggesting that I would be very surprised if the police force were unwise enough to attempt to toe-punt a rapid locomotive, thus likely causing both damage to said vehicle and/or ankle and foot injuries, whilst attempting to bring you to book.

It could, of course, be argued that they will never take you alive by virtue of the fact that the officers themselves have expired after losing their balance.

On the other hand, noting that you had to phone to let your Mother know that you had killed someone but are running out of change, it may well be that some boys in blue are putting the boot into a public kiosk, many of which around our way have been ironically converted into defibrillators designed specifically to stop hapless incumbents adopting that very hue. If this is the case, my divine pike friends, then although the entire scenario is far less hazardous in a practical sense, your maternal murder confession via a BT box may be considered as, using the parlance of the young, 'not very Ninja'.

I remain,
Yours sincerely,
Derek Philpott

Dear Sir,

I was put in touch by Derry from EMF who suggested writing to you.

Your letters have obviously solved many a political conundrum…

So it also seems with my song 'Never Take Me Alive'… I thank you for the time and effort.

… Luckily the 5 train left *without* me and I became an Army Surplus Paddington Bear again, a-wandering about Paddington Station in glorious penury. I then returned to my abode in Seneca Road (demolished some years ago), Clapham, and lay down on the floor to sleep in Squatland the Brave… as I lay there with broken windows, in the darkness, snowflakes had filtered through the broken glass and landed on my face. It was at that moment I endeavoured to leave my Orwellian existence, and seek a better life. So, I packed up my troubles in my old kit bag, and journeyed out to find the rest of my life.

So, thank you indeed for a timely reminder of a lesser fate I had had.

God Save Queen Victoria!!!
Kirk Brandon

Dear Cheap Trick,

I'd rather you didn't go to all the trouble of shining up your old brown shoes, putting on a brand-new shirt and arriving home from work before your normally expected and scheduled time. I do quite like you but am certainly not 'on the market'.

Dear Bauhaus,

The memory <u>is</u> admittedly going a bit but I think
I would have recalled any tradition or practice
pertaining to airborne mammals vacating
chime-containing obelisks in protest at, or in
acknowledgement of, the passing on of seminal
1930s horror film A-listers.

If, however, the bats have left the bell tower
on account of the fact that they were Bela
Lugosi's pets, and he was their sole source of
food, and although their departure is perfectly
understandable, one wonders why this deceased
celebrity/domesticated creature departure trend
has not been continued in other 'Gothic Rock'
pop songs?

'Ronnie Corbett's Dead (The Cats Have Left The
Kitchen)' and 'George Burns Is Dead (The Rabbits
Have Left The Conservatory)' could potentially
be very popular, although 'Charlie Chaplin's
Dead (The Koi Have Left The Fish Pond)' may not
chart, owing to the impracticality of such a
carp self-evacuation.*

We sincerely hope that you are not subject to
any power cuts round your way at the moment
resultant of your having to pen your reply alone
in a darkened room, and that this missive does

not cause you to wish to administer to us a kick
in the eye.

Yours,
Derek Philpott & Son

*Examples for illustration only – we have no idea if the said
passed-on personalities owned these pets.*

Dear Mister Filthpot and spawn,

Regarding 'the bats': I assure you that the lyrical description of the mass exodus of said winged mammals is somewhat tangential to the subject of the paean in question and not an essential component. Consider its inclusion in the threnody as merely serving the purpose of atmospheric colour rather than the significant subtitle in parentheses which you erroneously perceive.

Furthermore, if you truly insist on being pedantic then perhaps a more valid criticism might have been levelled in regard to the referenced attire of the vampiric protagonist, namely the 'black cape' which admittedly would no doubt be more accurately described as 'a cloak' given its luxuriant length and quality/style evident in Mr Lugosi's legendary portrayal of Count Dracula.

Thank you for your concern vis-à-vis power cuts but rest assured, the occurrence of such would be considered a trifle in these parts as one's preferred locale for writing missives such as this and indeed the penning of 'Gothic Rock' pop songs is indeed a sepulchral dwelling replete with feathered quill and the blood of virgins in the ink well.

In conclusion I think that it would be fair to state that it is not only your memory which is lacking but also your understanding as to the very nature of He whom you address!

Vampirically yours,
The Undertaker

Dear Green Day,

I resent your curt instruction that I should wake you up when September ends. This snappy command should at most be directed to your 'Personal Assistant' rather than a non-paid employee.

FROM THE DESK OF
D & D Philpott

Dear The Kursaal Flyers,

<u>Re: 'Little Does She Know'</u>

I was sorry to hear of your partner's perceived
duplicity at the launderette, especially so soon
after seeing Jilted John similarly troubled on
<u>Top of the Pops 2</u>. I fear, however, that although
my first impression was that I too 'didn't like
what I see', in your own case this may all come
out in the wash!

I cut my pinky on a bramble last week whilst
doing some gardening and now seem to be having
some trouble gripping anything firmly due to it
still being a bit sore. Also, my wife Jean says
that it is fairly difficult to take a load out of
our Hotpoint all at once without at least some
smalls or, most recently, yellow socks spillage.
I would therefore suggest that you shouldn't
be getting yourself in a 'lather' about, if you
will pardon the expression, your significant
other dropping her underwear and two-piece
swimming costume and forgetting her detergent;
'butterfingers' and absentmindedness alone
are not proof of infidelity. Indeed, if I may
be so 'Bold', the fact that she is also sharing
a dryer with a man in a tie-dye is not, if you
get my 'Dreft', evidence that she is be-'Daz'-
zled by his charms; you may take 'Comfort' in
the distinct possibility that either all other

machines were taken, or as can be assumed by the gentleman's Woodstock-inspired outfit, he is one of these hippy types and is trying to save the planet and his spare change by sharing a drum with another customer.

If anything, we are more concerned about the bikini, the one that you bought her from Rome. An 'A(e)riel' view on bingmaps.com indicates the nearest 'Surf' and 'Tide' to be found at no nearer than 23 miles from the Italian capital, on the coast of Fregene. Unless you spent your pocket money (ooh pocket money) at a large department store, we fear that this small business may be doomed to failure.

But I digress. All things considered, your imagination may have 'spun' out of control and we suggest you put yourself through the wringer no further. We propose perhaps a platonic meeting with the young lady whence your suspicions can be laid on the line without hanging her out to dry.

Yours,
The Philpotts

Dear Messrs Philpott,

Re: 'Little Does She Know'

I am replying on behalf of my former beat combo, the Kursaal Flyers.

As someone who has co-written over one-and-a-half hits, I was most flattered to receive your communication and the probes contained therein. I admit that the line 'I didn't like what I see' is grammatically unacceptable as it does mix past and present tense within the same clause, but hey – let's pause – the lyricist does occasionally need to take grammatical liberties in order to strike a perfectly masculine rhyme ('me' and 'see' in this case). And, as there have been numerous examples of lamentable grammar in the hit parade, one feels somewhat vindicated. Furthermore, there is a desire to get the job done in a timely fashion, i.e. before they take the towels off the beer pumps, which back in those days was 6pm (Mon–Sat, 7 on Sun).

On another topic, I'm sorry to hear about your gardening accident, which luckily did not prove fatal (as I'm sure you are aware was the case with the consequently late John 'Stumpy' Pepys). However, I note a spin-off benefit, namely that you may be excused from assisting your wife Jean (Hi Jean!) with keeping the household clean. You are indeed fortunate to own a domestic washing machine. Many of us have to visit a 'launderette', where those of a self-conscious disposition have to cunningly set their 'smalls' inside a giant beach towel to escape the attention of voyeurs. But however careful one might be, there is always the possibility of an underwear item, or a bikini, say – if you've been on said cay – falling loose from the main caboodle.

As regards 'drum-sharing', well… it does go on; The Big Figure once borrowed my floor tom-tom for Dr Feelgood's appearance on *The Old Grey Whistle Test*, but like your good self, I've digressed. You are talking here, I think, about a spin dryer component in which laundry is rotated and rendered dry. Said 'spin dry' contraption, as referred to in the song, was so wide in diameter that it would have seemed defiant not to share the facility with a fellow client, in this case 'a guy in a tie-dye', although the acceptability of such an arrangement always depends on both parties reaching agreement on a suitable heat setting.

With regard to detergent generally – and as an observation – the small packets offered in launderettes are often quite costly, and therefore some of us prefer the BYO option, which also allows for the detergent brand of one's choice, usually more fragrant and softer on delicate fabrics than the cheap yet paradoxically expensive alternative from the operationally unreliable vending machine. But this does not prevent the absent-minded customer from having to abandon his or her own detergent products tout suite, especially when having to 'make for the street'.

Before signing off, I must congratulate you on your pun count. I was truly Astonished!

With warm regards,
Will Birch

Dear Mud,

Re: 'Tiger Feet'

I am bamboozled, Mud, by your futile grasp
of correct animal terminal leg parts. Are we
to expect your next offerings to be entitled
perhaps 'Chicken Suckers', 'Spider Trotters',
'Salmon Claws', 'Giraffe Tentacles' or 'Octopus
Hooves'?

Dear Mr Difford,

Re: 'Tempted (By the Fruit of Another)'

We have been going to the same shop for our
apples, tangerines and suchlike for years, but
recently saw that a new competitor further down
the High Street was offering slightly larger
watermelons at a cheaper price.

You can therefore only imagine my embarrassment
upon leaving the rival establishment yesterday
to bump straight into our original grocer.

One hears that you also suffered a similar
predicament and can only hope that, to use
today's parlance, the 'cringe factor' was not as
great.

On an unrelated matter, one is a little
perplexed with regard to your historical
junket. Whenever we go on holiday we tend to
either take a taxi or drop the Nissan Juke at
Long Stay South, and collect it after clearing
passport control and Nothing To Declare upon
our return. Even were we to rent a vehicle when
abroad, it is in our experience the norm to
drop it off, normally via an allocated bay or
forecourt, to Record or Hertz when the holiday
is complete.

We are therefore bamboozled that upon your own arrival back in the UK, rather than being at the terminal, its baggage collection point and then the multi-storey or hard standing area, you are actually at the car park and then the airport and baggage carousel.

Wishing you are well and hate to be untrue,
Yours,
Derek and Dave Philpott (of old and new)

Dear Derek and Dave,

I often park my car miles from the airport to avoid huge bills for parking; this can lead to horror when sometimes your car is parked in a field miles away from any security.

Returning from Spain, where I visit my dodgy friends, my car was found broken into.

Nothing was stolen, there was nothing to nick.

At the carousel I often meet people I have not seen for years; they say 'hello Glenn how's it going, love your songs'.

It's always so good to see my bags tip on their side down the chute. Almost home feelings. The airport is a sad place for me; I cry and stand there looking at the sky. I never want to leave, I always want to come back, to the laundry on the hill where my pants are spinning around as we speak.

Chris Difford

Dear Mr Cooper,

It is sincerely hoped that when the telephone is ringing and you are 'driving in your car now', you elect not to accept the call unless either wearing a blue tooth headset or utilising a hands-free kit.

Dear Mr Eric,

These days, when we are all concerned about global warming, most folk are very careful to reduce their carbon footprint in order to protect the environment. I feel compelled therefore to offer some advice regarding your intentions to circumnavigate the globe in order to meet your predestined life partner.

Given that your mother had intimated that your ideal suitor is situated either within a French Polynesian cluster or the West Indies we find it puzzling that you would go the whole wide world to find her rather than simply isolate your search to these particular territories. We were also concerned that your mother may be complicit in some sort of hostage plot, given that you state that you'd go the whole wide world to find out where they hide her, implying that the poor wretch has been kidnapped.

Furthermore, we are quite perturbed by your 'coldist' tendencies which infer that attractive females are only to be located within warmer climes. By implication you are hinting that all Inuit women are, to use the slang of today's youth, 'a bunch of mingers', which I know is not the case. Also, Sweden's temperatures have been known to reach as low as -62.7 degrees Fahrenheit or -52.6 degrees Centigrade and yet

my friend Willy 'won't he' Wallace said that he
saw the blonde one out of Abba promoting her
new album recently and stated that he 'still
most definitely would'. Obviously, as a happily
married man, I could not possibly comment.

In summary (as opposed to summery!) I would
recommend that there is a lot to be said for
hanging about in the rain out here whilst being
both ecologically friendly and not spending
a great deal of your royalties on unnecessary
travel and boarding.

I look forward to hearing from you in a year or
maybe not quite.

Yours,
Practical Derek

Dear Practical,

Thanks for your letter. You raise several points that have given me cause for concern. I should make it clear first and foremost that I didn't actually circumnavigate the globe in order to meet said predestined life partner, merely stated my intention to possibly do so. I said I'd go the whole wide world, not *I am going* the whole wide world, as in actually undertaking the action. And in point of fact I met my pre-destined life partner in a pub in Hull so I think all things considered my carbon footprint remains undeniably and irrefutably intact. So as to speak.

I take your point that the lyrics of the song may suggest complicity on the part of my mother in a possible hostage/kidnapping plot but if you'd met my mother you'd know that she isn't the kidnapping type so that makes utter rubbish of your accusation.

On the subject of the blonde one in Abba, she's definitely a *would*. Not to be sexist about this (though I am myself a red-blooded male, of course), in my dealings with the fairer sex I like to categorise the possibilities of entering – and I use the word entering in an advisory capacity – into a meaningful physical relationship into three or four distinct sub-categories: the *would've* (meaning I would have liked to), the *could've* (meaning it was definitely on the cards so's to speak regardless of whether I actually did or not), the *should've* (a missed opportunity – don't tell the wife), and the *shouldn't have* (self-explanatory, no more needs to be said, and definitely don't tell the wife!).

So I think that absolutely proves beyond a shadow of a doubt that there's nothing 'coldist' about me! Given the chance of course I'd prefer to be girl-hunting, lady-killing, skirt-chasing etc. somewhere warm and sunny rather than, as you say, and as I myself say (or sing!) or as the song says: in the rain out here, but we take our pleasures where we find them though I am, as are your good self, too, a happily married man, so the point is moot.

I'm sorry it took me a year to reply to your very interesting correspondence. I think I've covered all points and fairly demolished all arguments and accusations contained in your letter which quite frankly takes an unnecessarily belligerent tone. I don't know who the hell you think you are.

I don't know who the hell I think I am either. Are you sure you've got the right person? Someone else has been using my email address.

Just so you know – I'm going to have a lawyer friend I know in the music industry take a look at this reply before I send it.

I remain yours etc.,
Eric (Mr) W

Nothing contained herein constitutes an offer, formal contarct or letter of agreement.

Dear Eddie & The Hot Rods,

As regards your being tired of doing day jobs
with no thanks for what you do, it ought to be
countered that satisfaction at a job well done,
the continuation of one's employment, which is
'what they expect from you', and its related
remuneration ought be praise enough.

One must also take issue with your claim that
my optician 'tell me what I oughta see', in that
at our Specsavers I am not instructed but ASKED
what the lowest row on the chart is that I can
decipher, in order that any change in vision
since my last check-up may be determined and a
revised prescription recorded.

I sincerely hope, Edward and your simmering
cylinder cohorts, that I have been able to 'Get
Across To You' my concerns and that 'it aint
me only who got something to say' about these
matters.

Yours sincerely,
D. Philpott

Dear Derek,

Asking any member of the current Hot Rods about the meaning of songs that they merely play is like asking the Stones why the Little Red Rooster is too lazy to crow today.

I must admit your polemic has me chuckling – the bottom line is that the lyric was derived from the Aleister Crowley mantra: 'Do what thou wilt shall be the whole of the law'. In the way that *10 Things I Hate About You* derives from Shakespeare's *The Taming of the Shrew*, Ed tried to update Crowley and got cursed by Jimmy Page for his sacrilege, which gives a good insight into Page's sanity. The fact that Ed, a cardboard cut-out sat on the side of the stage, managed to die might lead some of a more hermetic frame of mind to infer that magic works.

It's a well-known fact that the inhabitants of Southend are, in fact, prisoners. Hemmed in by traffic congestion on the A13 and A127, they watch in sorrow as the big ships sail on the alley alley oh, right past the oil terminals of Skull Island. Some, occasionally, manage to escape and try to find the right path towards the sunset. It's the only way because all other roads lead to drowning. These people are generally on day-release from life sentences for selling thieved motors.

When they escape, they don't need to find any directional guidance, nor do they request spiritual solace. It's highly amusing that no one seems willing to offer unsought advice even from the depths of their experience. Instead all they say is 'go here, do this, don't bother me', even when they are faced with direct enquiries.

The end result of this existential angst is that the early 20th-century philosophers provided the only source of inspiration, notwithstanding the fact that words of longer than two syllables seemed to be written in posh-speak, widely divergent from Estuary Inglish. Ah well! What can one do but follow one's blind instincts to oblivion.

Yours,
Graeme Douglas

Dear Tony Orlando,

Rather than 'twice on the pipe',
no knock at all would also
perfectly signify a 'no'.

Dear Middle Of The Road,

Re: 'Chirpy Chirpy Cheep Cheep'

I write pertaining to the sudden disappearance
of both this momma and papa on the very same
night.

Sadly, not in the same sense as your June
1971 chart-topper, it would appear that they
have been the subjects of a 'hit', most likely
either gang or Mafia-related. That the now
orphaned infant is referred to as Little Baby
Don, implying an early initiation as the new
Godfather of a flourishing crime empire, only
serves to confirm that its parents are not far,
far away, but more likely sleeping with the
fishes.

Furthermore, it is feared that 'mama singing
a song' could have been misinterpreted, unless
of course the panicked mole was singing like
a canary, to use the slang term for providing
valuable information to a non-allied third
party.

Yours,
Derek and Dave Philpott

Dear The Philpotts,

Our secret has been rumbled. No one was meant to know. I Hope the 'Fuzz' do not read your epistle.

Since the 'disappearance' of our guardians, we have been continually dominated by 'Baby Don' screaming for immediate sweets, fizzy drinks & popcorn. He threatens lots of terrible consequences if we do not appease him and agree to his demands.

He even threatens to write a follow-up to 'Chirpy'... what a terrifying thought... sometimes it makes us want to lie lengthways in the literal interpretation of our band name.

We have no option but to agree to his increasing demands!

Ian 'Tweedle Dum' McCredie, MOTR

Dear Mr Glover of Deep Purple,

Re: 'Highway Star'

As a keen observer of the Highway Code I was
most perturbed to hear from one of my son's
'Heavy Rock' records that it is your imminent
intention to career in a most unsatisfactory
fashion in your own, unspecified, vehicle.

Disregarding that to the best of my knowledge
the top speed attained by any vehicle (270.4mph,
achieved by a Hennessey Venom at the Kennedy
Space Centre in 2016) does fall quite shy of
the sonic velocity mainstay of 343 metres per
second, I am sure I speak for many pedestrians
and police forces alike in stating that such a
recklessly accelerating 'killing machine' would
be most unwelcome on most public thoroughfares,
especially around the time of the school run,
Mr Glover.

Furthermore, the 'Hammond-driven rocker' then
goes on to state, and I quote, that 'Nobody
gonna take [your] car'. However, having viewed
the entire series of Can't Pay? We'll Take It
Away!, I think you will find that any vehicle
(no matter how one loves or needs it) subject
to a finance agreement in respect of which
repayments have not been met is liable to

repossession under current UK legislation. If,
as you state, it really is your intention to
'break the speed of sound', which is clearly
in excess of the 70mph statutory limit, then I
sincerely hope that instalments ARE in arrears.

I bid you Good Day Sir!!!

Yours,
Derek Philpott

Dear Mr D. Philpott,

Thank you for your punctilious observations about our song 'Highway Star'. Having studied your letter, I am of the view that you're probably an insecure, over-educated pedestrian. You appear to live in a world of statistics that, unless you're a scientist, a politician or a computer, are largely meaningless in cultural life. Or maybe a banker... in which case you're just one of a wunch of bankers. Are you certain about the top speed of any vehicle, let alone by whom, in what or where? Answer: I suspect not. You read it somewhere, and if you believe everything you read, you're just like all those who believe everything they read.

You throw accusations around like sardines in a piss-pot. (An inspired simile, don't you think?... Just a humble songwriter's craft.) Exactly how sure are you about the pedestrians and police forces that you claim support your theory? Have you interviewed all of them? One by one, face to face, eye to eye... cheek to cheek? Of course not.

You've already decided that I'm guilty of flaunting the law without the merest shred of evidence other than what is festering in your dark imagination – I suspect you may have a thyroid imbalance. I wouldn't dream of exceeding the speed limit anywhere near a school... at least I haven't yet. Dreamed of it, that is.

Is it your intention to justify your supposition by quoting only 1% of the entire lyric? Ok, maybe 2%. Or somewhere in between. Lower than 1.5%, anyway. More than my first publishing contract in any case. The whole point, Mr DP, is that the song is not an incitement to break the law or endanger the species, but rather an innocent celebration of fast cars and hot sex (or in the 70s, hot cars and fast sex!); an exaltation of freedom from the restraints that society struggles to impose; a symbolic manifestation of all that you seem to lack – a sense of fun.

Remember, I didn't get where I am today.

Drive carefully,
Roger Glover

Dear Mr Withers,

Thanks for ruining our picnic! I will never listen to your weather forecasts again!

Dear Thunder,

My son Dave has seen you perform many times
at numerous rock festivals and states that
although at one such appearance it was indeed
chucking it down, the other times it was very
sunny indeed. It would appear therefore that
most shows directly contravened Fleetwood Mac's
earlier assertion that you only happen when it's
raining.

On an unrelated matter, I recently witnessed
a Council Official move on a busker in an
alleyway, on the basis that he was directly
obstructing deliveries into Sainsbury's. I am
therefore at a loss to fathom that the entire
ensemble required to perform a 'backstreet
symphony' have managed to complete such an opus
without similarly being ejected.

Yours,
D. Philpott

Dear Mr Philpott,

Thank you so much to both you and your son Dave for highlighting our occasionally chaotic and unpredictable relationship with Mother Nature, whom I have long suspected has a problem with us 'borrowing' our name from her bad-tempered, hysterical displays of terrifying volume which she sees fit to unleash across our green and pleasant land, particularly on warm and otherwise enjoyable summer evenings (hasn't she got anything better to do?). The result of incurring her displeasure is we are now bathed in constant sunlight whenever we perform – oh, the twisted irony!

With regard to Fleetwood Mac, I'm not sure how seriously one can take their advice on anything to do with the climate in the British Isles given they all currently reside in California where it *never* rains according to Albert Hammond – and let's face it, he should know!

Re. *Backstreet Symphony* may I congratulate you on your well-grounded observations. If you take a look at the album's artwork you will note that there are only three people populating the 'backstreet' scene. This was in fact also down to the work of an overzealous public official who had ordered the assembled orchestra to clear the street citing 'obstruction of a public highway' or some other trumped-up charge as a thinly veiled excuse to stop a few young people having fun. It was only 3am for God's sake! We were though extremely proud of Mr Harry James, the band's drummer, for his refusal to leave the scene on a point of artistic principle. The rumour that he had stayed in situ due to a barely clad 'lady of the night' emerging from a nearby doorway isn't the kind of comment I'd even want to address given its stereotypical misrepresentation of the character of percussionists who are in my experience morally unquestionable to a man.

Please feel free to contact me again if you are requiring further advice on these or any other topics pertaining to me or my band's career.

Yours faithfully,
Luke Morley, Thunder

Dear Martha,

I write regarding the serene coastal location that you know you will be back at some day.

Given the unique feature of this particular bit of seaside, one would assume any hydrodynamics would benefit from wonderful topographical acoustics.

Ergo, 'Waves and a nice little bit of natural reverb make the only sounds,' would be a more accurate, if slightly clunkier, summation.

I sincerely hope that you will 'Echo' this sentiment in any reply, which I look forward to receiving not too 'far away in time'.

I must take leave now, Martha, as for some inexplicable reason I quite fancy a cupcake.

Yours,
Mr D. Philpott

Dear Mr Philpott,

Does this perspicacious question perhaps indicate your own hitherto unrevealed background in the earth sciences or possibly an obscure branch of acoustic research?

If so, we are on common ground! Some members of Martha and the Muffins have claim to wide-ranging interests in this area and indeed are known to dabble in the experimental application of specific sound waves on targeted coastal locations (much to the chagrin of startled locals, human and otherwise).

What Mark Gane, Muffin guitarist and writer of 'Echo Beach', lacked in compositional acuity (having no chorus until the very end of the song!), he made up for in his exhaustive research of the very phenomena to which you allude.

While we acknowledge your opinion on this matter, the fruit of his scientific inquiry, inserted into the second verse, continues to bedazzle the listening public to this day, for which we are eternally grateful.

Yours truly,
Martha Johnson, MatM

Dear Scarlet Fantastic,

I am confused, yet impressed, my crimson far-
fetched friends. On <u>TOTP 2</u> recently you stated
that you have no memory tonight (no memory, no
memory) and yet seemed able to recall all of
your lyrics of your song about having no memory
without having to read them off of a bit of
paper.

Furthermore, although I fully understand
that to have the sun in your hair is merely
a reference to being out on a hot day with no
hat, your claim straight afterwards of having
the moon in your eyes is a little harder to
believe, and I have a similar grievance with
your fellow pop star Ms Bush. Evidence therefore
to substantiate quite how an infant, or in your
case, the fifth-largest natural satellite in the
Solar System, could be embedded into an optical
organ averaging 24mm in diameter is required as
soon as possible.

I look forward to reading your reply and
respectfully request that in order that it may
be legible and not smudged you do not write it
sitting there in the pouring rain.

Yours,
Derek Philpott

My Dear Mr Philpott,

Or may I address you as Derek?

First of all I would like to politely ask you if you are colour blind as, in fact, I am not crimson but definitely scarlet, more aligned with cadmium red rather than alizarin crimson (I'm pretty up on my colour shades as I have just taken up oil painting).

I think if we are going to be specific about lyrics and texts then we have to take into account time frames. When I sang 'We have no memory tonight' on *TOTP* I was referring to a period in time when I had no memory, a moment of oblivion which I was greatly enjoying but it wasn't occurring at that particular moment when I was singing the song on TV; but to a memory of having no memory!! Thus explaining my ability to sing the lyrics perfectly without any loss of memory whatsoever!

I think you may have misunderstood the lyric regarding the sun in my hair. It is in my hair, not on my head. The sun is often in my hair, regardless of the weather, so your assumption that I was singing about being out on a hot day with no hat is wrong. What I am in fact singing about is how the beautiful shiny light from the sun lights up my hair making me even more shiny; radiant in fact. It is a very desirable way to be. It is easy to be this way as long as you have hair; I'm afraid it won't work so well if you are bald although your scalp could become shiny so maybe you would feel part of the shiny gang anyway.

I am a star child and imagine Ms Bush is of a similar ilk. I am connected spiritually to every part of the living universe. I use my developed higher sense of intuition to navigate me through this physical life experience; like the ancients, I am fascinated with the power of the moon and when I wrote 'We have the moon in our eyes' I was referring to my experiences of staring at the full moon until it almost blinds me; I do this every month unless it's cloudy. I suffer from very poor eyesight and due to this an amazing thing occurs when I stare at the moon for ages, it appears to grow in size until it fills up my vision and it is at that point it has actually entered my eyes.

I tend not to write letters in the pouring rain, I write letters on email, which I am doing now, I write them on my iMac which is in the downstairs front room of my house so there isn't much chance of you receiving a smudged, barely legible version.

There are many things that I like to do in the pouring rain, just as well really seeing as I live in England. I remember as a child growing up in Birmingham whenever there was a thunderstorm after school my brother and I would throw our swimming cossies on and go and dance around the garden, it gave us a remarkable feeling of elation and freedom! I'm afraid my long-term plans of moving to southern Spain might have been scuppered as some twits voted to leave the EU.

It's been lovely hearing from you and I do hope I have managed to clear up any confusion re: my song.

Have a lovely day,
Maggie x

Dear Phil Spector,

I was delighted today to learn via shopping on Amazon that you had been thoughtful enough to have got me a present. Imagine my disgust therefore upon adding it to 'my basket' to learn that 'A Christmas Gift For You' was no such thing at all, but that I was expected to pay £13.60 for it (plus £1.26 shipping). I put it to you, Sir, that it is just this sort of devious behaviour which has landed you where you are today!!

Dear Junior,

<u>Father</u> used to say that when I was little he
remembered taking me to feeding time at Regent's
Park Zoo and I became very uppity that all I
could see was other mums' and dads' legs. It was
not until he picked me up that I got 'Another
Step Closer' to viewing all the penguins
scrambling round to catch untinned herrings
thrown at them from a bucket.

In answer to your small boy's enquiry,
therefore, asking when he will see what grown-
ups do see, my response, assuming the average
height of a six-year-old, would have to be
that this can be achieved prior to adolescence
when hoisted up by a parent or guardian or
elevated by means of a collapsible ladder or
chair approximately 3 feet (or 0.9144 metres)
high, albeit without the impediment of slightly
depleted eyesight bought on by the onset of
ageing.

On an unrelated matter, Junior, my son David is
wondering if there was some sort of bug going
around between the years 1982-87 which he cannot
remember, causing pop stars to growl choruses
because of a sore throat, in spite of Tunes.
We believe Mr Goss out of Bros to have been
similarly afflicted.

There is no rush to respond to this missive.
Take it in your stride and take your time,
young man!

Yours,
Derek Philpott (and Son)

Dear Mr Perplexed,

I hope that I can shed some light on your diagnosis, although I am not sure that a medical cure has yet been found for 'perplexitism' if there is such a word!!!

It must have been incredible and challenging finding out why 'Mama Used To Say' this is not for you. Like jumping out of a plane your perspective of the world is vast, allowing your inner being to see more. If by the age of 6 yrs old you hadn't realised that the West Indies had the best cricket team in the world then it was always going to be 'Too Late'; even so I do believe there is a chance for you.

Like the changing times we live in, if you're not there yet, I would suggest you try cycling as a way of configuring the complexity of time travel. You would be able to review every evening what was captured then compartmentalise it and it will become clear how the growl that Matt did following myself, has a long history. I cannot speak for Matt, as his growl may have originated from the Nether Regions!!! However, I can only speak for myself and I know where mine came from!!!

Still, while riding through Hyde Park on a lovely spring day with the wind blowing through your hair, that is if you still have hair and nature is not your barber... playing dodgems with the footballs, that sense of danger felt when playing with your toy soldiers and having to lob a few over the barricade, the excitement felt when a few fell and didn't rise again!!!

I feel these things could add to your development in your pursuit of wholeness.

I hope this has been of value to you. If you apply the strategies above, your time travel will move you 'Another Step Closer'.

Yours ever,
Mr Non Conventional
aka Junior

Dear Talking Heads,

I must say this Nowhere place seems to be a very popular tourist destination. Amongst others travelling there, you're on a road, Kenny Rogers is on a train, Oasis are going and Faith No More are just leaving! I also understand that The Beatles have a friend who lives in the area.

Dear Mr Priest,

Are you really sure that you are only 'Living
After Midnight'? In the unlikely event that
you are indeed able to resurrect yourself
once every 24 hours, at no earlier than 12am,
I would recommend that you avail yourself
of a neurological research facility as soon
as possible and avoid undertakers' premises
within daylight hours, unless of course your
capabilities arise as a result of 'Breaking The
Law'.

On an unrelated matter, in your metal classic,
'Exciter', you state that everything he touches
fries into a crisp. I was just wondering (other
than the Golden Wonder Baked Varieties) what
happens if he actually touches a crisp?

Bye bye for now,
Derek Philpott

Dear Mr Philpott,

You have to believe me that the life of a rock star is mainly being comatose in a bus bunk bed for most of the day, then some extremely annoying tour manager will holler in your ear 'Hotel!'

Then it starts! Grab your suitcase, up to the room, shit, shower and shave, off to sound check, then interviews, get changed, on stage, get off, in shower. Then guess what? It's midnight! First beer doesn't touch the sides; neither do the next 4 or 5. Time to check out the girls backstage; invite her to the bus, now it's Jack Daniels, back to the hotel, it's time to get it on, shit it's 6 and haven't had a wink yet, bus is leaving at 8, Oh well might as well have one for the road, say goodbye without kissing! Back on the bus, now that's 'living after Midnight'

As for the 'Exciter' it's really quite obvious you get crispier crisps of course, Durrrrrrrr!!!!

KK Downing

Dear Mr Gillan,

We are thinking of having a shed put up but regret to inform you that we will not be in a position to engage your services.

Sadly your timber property construction tutorial leaves much to be desired in that to take a piece of wood and join it to another piece of wood and then do it all again would not, as you misleadingly claim, conclude in a house, a little wooden house but, omitting, as it does, observances pertaining to right angles and symmetrical measurements, could only result in a very very long and useless piece of wood completely unsuitable to be resided within even if hollowed out by means unknown.

On the plus side, however, your hapless cabin assembly guidance does result in the absence of a highly flammable structure able to be burnt to the ground by some stupid with a flare gun.

It is strongly recommended therefore that you refrain from undergoing any professional construction work in the future, lest you be featured on Channel 5's <u>Nightmare Builders</u>.

Yours,
D. Philpott

Dear Philpott,

A bit behind the game, are we? I despair of the 'Literalati'.

Metaphorically, the 'Little House' could have been made of anything.

It was an imaginary symbol of something worth defending against marauding hordes and bony-arsed critics.

If your wit was as sharp as your pencil you might have gathered that the allegory was not dependent upon Euclidean principles. We all know by now that parallel lines do not exist; in fact, there is no such thing as 'a straight line', let alone two that are expected to remain equidistant for even a fair measure on any extended scale.

However, in the physical world I have made a modest contribution to the world of sheds.

Please see 'Private message for Caramba's translators' and 'Home for Christmas' in the Caramba TV archive at

www.gillan.com

Or go directly, to avoid distractions…

http://gillan.com/caramba-tv- archive-9.html

Also, I don't have a picture, but my Potting Palace is a thing of wonder. The construction methods are not conventional but satisfy most Newtonian demands without the need for bracing beams, although I do have a bracing beam in another of my sheds, which is used for special purposes.

The Potting Palace is on a slope and has three terraced rooms. The skeleton is eight larch poles and the cladding is waney edge. The doors are made of scaffold planks and the leaded windows were from a reclamation yard in Exmouth. It is now overgrown with Pyracantha and climbing roses. All rather prosaic compared with the 'Little House', or so you might think, until you enter.

Yours sincerely, ig

Dear The Beastie Boys.

Speak for yourselves! I'm attending a friend's 60th birthday bash soon, and having been invited am perfectly entitled to be there, hence there will be no need for fisticuffs before or upon my arrival.

Dear Alannah Myles,

I am impressed by your awareness that over
here in the UK the refreshing beverage
(now discontinued) that you refer to was a
particularly 'fruity' cider libation much
beloved of, shall we say, 'gentlemen of the
road' given that it only cost about £1.79 for a
3-litre plastic bottle and had an ABV of 8.4%.

I had no idea that it was available on export,
Ms Myles, but must wholeheartedly agree
that White Lightning <u>is</u> bound to drive you
wild, especially when partaken of in copious
quantities in the middle of a Mississippian
drought.

I am not quite sure, though, how a very dark
woven tufted fabric could be mistaken for a
trending belief system structured around an
omnipresent but invisible superhuman creator,
although reason is often absent after knocking
back so much and always wanting more. We also
suspect that it is the brew's potency and not
'black velvet - a new religion' that causes one
to fall halfway to the ground.

Finally, it is sincerely hoped that it is not the
mama dancin' with a baby on her shoulder who is
squiffy, as such reckless parenting is unlikely
to make the little boy smile for very long.

I must go now, Ms Myles, as all this talk of a soft southern style makes me want to pop out to KFC.

Yours,
Derek (and Dave) Philpott

Dear Dave & Dad,

Ain't never been impressed by an Englishman, however your awareness of the recipe for Black Velvet rye whiskey is most certainly remarkable, considering its discontinuation stateside on behalf of Seagrams' Distilleries headquartered in Montreal, more than likely due to its lack of popularity. Something for which the song and the non-limey liquor have little in common.

Far from the white lightning mentioned in the lyric, which is bound to light up nothing in me, it is not a well-known fact that I happen to imbibe of luscious, green, smelly, dried stems Puff the Magic Dragon Who Lived By the Sea once winged on about over North American radio some decades ago.

With all due respect to black tufted fabric upon which Elvis the King's bust has been known to have been painted... though it may well be a misconstrued metaphor over which one can stick one's feather in one's cap, it most certainly does not describe the true identity to which its author had alluded. That, my overly friendly but drunken orator, is one of popular music's best kept secrets to which I'm duty bound not to disclose.

I can assure you the meaning of Black Velvet is nothing over which people have been brought to their knees in religiously stirred ire. Perhaps, were I able to leak its true significance, I might claim the song prattles on about what has over time become a multibillion-dollar industry since the untimely demise of its dethroned icon.

Cheers mate.

Alannah Myles
ooops, my apologies, wrong Isle~

Dear Ms Warwick,

I regret not being able to help you with your enquiry, especially given that you make no reference to your current whereabouts.

I recently received a similar request from Tony Christie and recommended that he consult Bing Maps or invested in a Tom Tom.

Dear Heaven 17,

We heard your advertising jingle on Absolute 80s and <u>have</u> tried to understand but are at a loss as to the nature of this offer that cannot be ignored.

That both propositions are carved by another's hand, elicit 'Temptation' on the part of the consumer, <u>could</u> give one a breakdown if faulty and have never been closer (presumably in terms of a launch date) is not open to question, our numerically Shangri-La monickered friends.

There, however, the parallels end:

Item 1 leaves no track (a revolutionary improvement on previous designs) and keeps climbing higher and higher, both step by step and day by day, suggesting impressive durability.

Item 2 boasts unacceptably featured (in terms of unpredictable characteristics) adorable creatures whereby trouble is coming, you'd better believe it, in the event of malfunction, and a hidden face is common when dislodged for corrective adjustments.

We would therefore be grateful to learn if the product is a stairlift or a Westworld-style amusement park, so that we may consider whether

to take it or leave it before it is too late to
hesitate.

Yours,
Derek and Dave Philpott

Dear Derek and Dave,

Firstly, may I say, I have no idea what you are talking about whatsoever! It seems on first reading that you have clearly been dipping into the special reserve sherry far too frequently, or maybe even spending some of your well-earned state pension on Kevin, that bloke from the pub's 'special hand-made cigarettes'.

What at first seemed like a genuine inquiry regarding one of our most loved songs quickly degenerates into a stream of consciousness that even Sigmund Freud himself would find difficult to unravel.

Your mistaken premise that our song 'Temptation' is a jingle that is somehow trying to entice the general public into purchasing something is clearly absurd. As I'm sure you're aware, a jingle is normally quite a short piece of music, in fact generally I would estimate under 30 seconds, whereas our composition is easily over four minutes; in fact there are times when playing live concerts that this particular song can last for as long as eleven minutes! Now I'm sure even you would agree, that is most certainly not a 'jingle'.

Your confusion meanders further down the road of absurdity by suggesting that we are trying to sell either a stairlift or running a Westworld-style theme park. Once again I can only put these crazy assertions down to over-indulgence in one or the other aforementioned vices!

'Temptation' is a lovely song (not a jingle) based loosely on an ever-increasing sexual excitement and orgasmic build-up leading eventually to mutual gratification and sublime release.

If by any chance we were using this song (not a jingle) to sell a product, I can assure you it would not be a futuristic theme park or stairlift, it would be something more befitting a song of its stature.

Perhaps a luxury brand of cereal or mid-range SUV.

I do hope that I have put your misconceptions to bed and that you might now enjoy 'Temptation' with a clearer knowledge of what you are listening to.

Kind Regards,
Glenn Gregory

Dear Madness,

I think you will find that it is the volcano and not the earthquake that is erupting on an unpredictable basis worldwide. Furthermore, to merely state that said seismic disturbance is 'not in Orange Street', hence depriving potential disaster victims of the precise location whereby they may be 'shuffled off their feet', is most unsatisfactory.

Dear Mr Costello and The Attractions,

Having ascertained that you <u>don't</u> wanna chitter-
chat, really need it (to be pumped up), want me
to say I love you when it's just a rumour, like
that they don't wanna hear about it, know where
to begin, want to hear it, want me to start you
talking, want me to come any closer, want me to
come any nearer, even care, want me to wait for
the telephone, want Johnny's pup handed to you
(!), care that I don't call, think they deserve
us, know where to draw the line, believe it, want
me to tell you I don't know what love is, want to
check my pulse or want to go to Chelsea, one must
respectfully ask what you <u>do</u> want and what would
be required for you to 'Get Happy'?

Yours,
Derek Philpott

Dear Mr Philpott,

I don't think I can speak on the songwriter's behalf. I don't think he would want me to either. However, I draw your attention to the song 'I Want You' (on the *Blood and Chocolate* long-playing disc) – which turns out to be a somewhat psychotic ditty of vaguely murderous intent.

Accordingly, I would suggest that you leave Mr Costello to his protestations, rather than encourage him with this kind of more 'positive' assertion.

However, I do feel he could've saved himself, you, and me considerable time and effort if he'd simply taken a leaf out of Ms Toni Braxton's (song)book and got it all over with in a single song, as did she in the popular tune 'I Don't Want To'.

Things Ms Braxton states that 'I Don't Want/Feel Like': talking on the phone, company at home, to do the things she used to do, to sing another love song babe, to hum another melody, to live life without a babe, smiling anymore, to love, to live, to laugh, to play, to talk.

I don't know why, Mr Philpott, you spent three minutes you will never get back compiling such a list in the first place. I don't want anything else to do with your half-witted project, in fact… I don't want to hear from you again.

With cordial best regards, as ever,
Bruce Thomas

Dear Mr Ant,

I think you will find that qualification for
'next year's old age pension' is determined by
an attained age of 67 for men and 65 for
women, and is conditional upon 30 years of
National Insurance contributions or credits.
The way one looks does not come into play
at all. If it did, Mr Keith Richards could have
arguably claimed his in 1983.

Dear Gong,

On the advice of my GP, Dr Trivedi, I recently
had a fasting blood test in order to check my
serum lipids, which came back as 'borderline
high' on account of elevated triglycerides.
A change in eating habits, with an excess of
cholesterol-elevating pabulum, was proscribed,
and a follow-up review in six months was
recommended.

My wife Jean and I do enjoy our afternoon dining
out and were initially concerned that this
redacted nutritional regime would limit our
lunches out. Fortuitously, my nephew Adrian
alerted us to The Salad Centre on Christchurch
Road in Bournemouth, and offered to show us
where it was on the condition that we play his
'Radio Gnome Invisible Trilogy' compact discs
and drop him off at Hamburgerology on the way.
It was after listening to much of the above-
mentioned wireless and imperceptible vertically
challenged troll trinity that we took our seats.

Their Tuna Niçoise is to be highly recommended.
Its ingredients, however, do not include
'Angel's Egg', but instead those responsibly
sourced and laid by hens free to roam. As well
as organic motives, this could well be down
to the understandably nightmarish logistics
of attempting to order celestial ovum from

reputable local farmers. My preference is for that drizzled with extra virgin Mediterranean dressing, which is the originally intended 'oily way' but it is also available 'not the English way', i.e. with Dijon mustard.

I sincerely doubt, Gong, that I would be quite as enamored by your own 'Flute Salad' option. The presence of leaves in a healthy dietary meal is perfectly acceptable, nay, encouraged. The branch from which they have been plucked, fashioned into a perforated musical tube and also served, is not. It is a clear choking hazard, and while I am not questioning the personal cleanliness of your 'Space Rock Troupe', probably unhygienic. The hollow cylindrical interior is likely to attract bacteria and all manner of gastronomic unpalatability if vigorously exhaled into in a 'live situation' before being brought to our table. Ergo, to directly cite your avant garde incantation, 'you can't kill me', quite the opposite is true. If, on the other hand, the flute in question is in actuality penne pasta then, although apologies are in order, this should still have been made clear in the CD's accompanying booklet.

I also cannot extol highly enough the lentil moussaka. Many items on the varied and adventurous menu feature such pulses, but they differ from your option in that they are for the most part high-protein legumes, mung beans, vetches and Bambara groundnuts. Yours, sadly, are highly dangerous oscillations fluctuating through voltage-charged French cheese in the form of 'Camembert Electrique'. These are not 'mains' that appeal.

Generally speaking, when I have had a cup of tea I don't want another one, and therefore prefer a maitre d' to maintain a respectful distance from my table and only replenish my libations when politely summoned. I can assure you that the monotonous and repetitive caffeine and bladder overloading commandments of a 'front of house' pushing me to 'have a cup of tea have another one have a cup of tea have another one' would leave me no choice but to seek an alternative bistro immediately.

All factors considered I cannot help but surmise that a 'Gong Café' may be, if you will pardon the pun, a bit of a non-starter which, if to fall under the scrutiny of Gordon Ramsay, would transform 'flying teapots' from 'Space Rock Mythology' to actuality. I therefore wish you continued success in your chosen career path as planet Earth's premier Anglo-Franco jazz/rock fusionists.

Yours,
Derek Philpott

P.S. Thomas Local or indeed any other directory digestion is also not exactly an appetite whetter.

Reply from Daevid Allen received 8/2/14

My Dear Ordinary Everyday Citizen(s) of the United Kinkdom,

As an overaged very important cottage industrial rockstar pensioner living in far off Orrrstaaalia, I am astonished to see that your good doctor has not recommended an over-aged beverage as a marriage celebration twixt thine ear-trumpet and the platter from which you dine.

My recommendation is an audacious drop from my local rooftop winery which it could be said permits instantaneous psycho tropical tannins from our well-lit basement to engrave mandelbrot mandalas on the tip of the tongue. A form of trembling tongueilingus as described by Charles Mingus in a dream.

My gourmand friend and mentor Horatio Bitemark esq himself would probably in your case select a bottle of McVarnish's cruel Shiraz 1984 which boasts a hint of Scottish stoic crag and sticky sporran on the fore-palate offset nicely with a bouquet of Scottish tartan boardinghouse wallpaper stain that should ensure you would catch the undertones of mad highland bastard skewering a sassenach.

All of which might elevate your belly button to your middle forehead ensuring instant rapport with the octave doctor's favorite entrée which you mention in your forensic examination of the various applications of the notorious pasta jack-orious, glorious in itself.

In closing I can recommend you purchase a copy of the narrowly famed flautist and general blow holy saxophonistas

Bloomdido Bad de Grasse first volume of sonnets in Ancient French based upon the 108 possible functions of the reed.

Once thoroughly soaked in the tea made from the leaves of the Australian National Tree ahem the Acacia which is of course in its antipodean variety magnificently psychoactive, this book can be consumed one page per day for the rest of your earthly life.

Farewheel penultimate pals of the luminous grin planude and may your passage(s) be well lubricated not only by the finest of compliments!

Eh VOILA!
I bow etc
yours in suspended alienation
Dada Ali Yon
aka
Dingo Virgin
Bebert Camembert
Sri Cappuccino Longfellow
Divided Alien
and others
at your swer vice
www.daevidallen.net errorizing successfully since 1938

(With thanks to current singer/guitarist Kavus Torabi for making this letter happen in 2014)

'You've come to wish me an unhappy birthday. You've come to wish me an unhappy birthday. Because I'm evil. And I lie.' I fear, Mr Morrissey, that your singing telegram business may be doomed to failure unless you have a bit of a rethink. Indeed this light of yours that 'never goes out' seems a far more attractive proposition.

Dear City Boy,

I find it difficult to fathom (notwithstanding the fact that human auditory receptors are not equipped with an independent larynx) how any metropolitan juvenile could have advanced biologically to the state of his 'ears telling him that there's no reply'.

One is also in something of a dither pertaining to the bizarre behaviour of this young urban scamp's telephone.

As there are no pointers in your splendid tune to you having used a national or international code, or other lengthener, to prefix the number so as for it not to be too short, and just to satisfy my own curio-city (boy), I decided to ring it myself just now. Sure enough, upon tapping in a very stunted 5-7-0-5, and after the shortest of pauses, the receiver's earpiece returned not an unanswered ringing, but that long infuriating tone synonymous with the tapping in of an unobtainable and incorrect sequence.

Furthermore, although your suspicions pertaining to your partner and a shady 'phone booth lover' may well be founded, it is perhaps unreasonable to go crazy when there's no-one home. I often phone friends when they have

nipped out to Gregg's but by no means take leave
of my sanity as a result.

In conclusion, City Boy, an invitation to
'facetime' on Yahoo Messenger or Skype will
not only save one more dime and alleviate the
dialling of truncated digits, but, if rejected,
sadly confirm the shenanigans of a private
number love affair.

Yours,
Derek Philpott (and Son)

Dear Derek and Son,

I really think we should put this 'talking ears' nonsense to bed, don't you? The ears relay aural data to my brain, which then processes the information, in effect 'telling me there's no reply'. I truncated the whole business (transceptors, synapses etc.) for the sake of brevity, simple as that.

However, I should say that the celebrated Spanish illusionist, El Pedantico, insisted categorically that his ears could indeed talk, in three different languages to boot. Having demonstrated their fluency to a packed house at the Teatro El Musical in Valencia, he further stupefied his audience by putting his head between his knees and whistling up his Barcelona before playing a lively rendition of 'Una Paloma Blanca' on the ear trumpet.

On a more serious note, you question the lack of any prefix or area code for the number 5-7-0-5. This was intentional and, I think, necessary. Had I divulged the city or more specifically the district where the woman in question was living, the result would have been a bombardment of nuisance calls not to mention any number of bedsit Travis Bickles with an axe to grind and an AK-47 under the pillow camped on her doorstep.

Although she and I are now estranged, in fact we can no longer meet even as friends, I still keep a copy of the restraining order on the wall of my room at the Happy View Secure Unit in CENSORED to remind me of our somewhat stormy relationship.

My apologies for writing this letter in marker pen, unfortunately no sharps are allowed on the ward.

Yours affectionately,
A City Boy

P.S. Would you mind giving me your address and telephone number? When I'm finally out and about I'd love to get in touch, perhaps even pay you a visit?

Dear House of Pain,

My knee is giving me merry hell today so I'd rather not if that's all the same to you.

Dear Johnny Hates Jazz,

Please do not take this letter personally, my
Jonathan polyrhythmic syncopation musical genre
dislike referencing friends, as I also have
similar issues with Cher and R. Kelly.

In your 80s anthemic ballad 'Turn Back The
Clock', you indicate that were you to have
the ability to travel to the past you would
put it to use <u>not</u> by perhaps preventing the
birth of historical tyrants such as Adolf
Hitler, or changing the course of the <u>Titanic</u>
by a few degrees, or, controversially,
instigating technical problems preventing
Kanye West's 'Bohemian Rhapsody' 'performance'
at Glastonbury in 2015, but instead restrict
yourself to wanting to be a bit younger because
you are holding an old snap of yourself, can't
sleep and are a bit teary after another day is
ended.

Also I am sorry to shatter your dreams but must
challenge your assertion that life was so much
better before in <u>all</u> respects. Rather than
having to keep dialling and getting the engaged
tone when trying to order a takeaway before
scrambling around to find the right change,
and waiting half an hour for a tape of <u>The Man
Who Would Be King</u> to rewind on the VHS before I

can watch it again, I now press one button on my mobile phone and another on Netflix and can be tucking into a Chicken Dopiaza and seeing Sean Connery get his watch back on the train within twenty minutes!

Yours*

The author unfortunately forgot to sign his name at the end of his letter.

Dear Yours,

I see we are of like minds, for I pondered the very same questions long before I actually wrote 'Turn Back The Clock'. I knew full well that, if I could indeed travel back in time, it would be my duty to attempt to avert war, disaster and tragedy. But in so doing, would I not alter the space-time-continuum with uncontrollable consequences?? It was a dilemma that haunted me for the whole weekend before I actually wrote the aforementioned 'classic anthem' (journalists' words, not mine) so beloved by the world (my words). Or at least, quite a lot of people I know (also my words).

Where you completely miss the point is that the song was secretly alluding to the fact that I had already achieved time travel. Yes, yes, go ahead and scoff... but have you ever wondered what happened to that old Leo Sayer mug of yours? Yup, I stole it and gave it to a lowly child born in a manger over 2000 years ago, who in later life copied Leo's hairstyle and became God. So who's laughing now?

Think for a minute. I wrote that 'legendary ballad' (journalists' words, not mine) in 1986. Yes, I would have already known about Hitler and the *Titanic*, but how else would I have known that, in the future, Kanye West would perform 'Bohemian Rhapsody' so appallingly that it would propel NASA to develop a plan to colonise Mars?

The fact is, I DID change the course of history. There were many terrible events I managed to avert, that the world consequently never had to experience. But alas, I was merely one 'wonderful songsmith' (journalists' words, not mine) faced with a whole Universe of need. So what exactly did I do upon my time-travelling escapades?

Well, by way of example, Liberace was on course to becoming a maniacal third-world despot before I sat him down in front of a diamond-encrusted grand piano and taught him to play 'Hooray For Hollywood'. The rest, as they say, is history. Again, you think Bruce Forsyth was simply destined to be the great all-round entertainer that we all know and love? You have no idea, do you?! He was about to lead a bloodthirsty crusade in an attempt to convert Eastbourne to Methodism, when I put a microphone in his hand and taught him to tap-dance. Had it not been for my 'selfless actions' (possibly my words), many lives would have been lost. No, no, I don't mean they would have died. I mean they would have got lost because this was before the advent of sat nav, and not many people knew where the local Methodist church was. Instead, Brucie brought us more joy on Saturday night telly than one man has the right to give in a lifetime!

And as for Kanye West? Well, he was planning to tour the world with a show entitled 'Kanye's Hip-Hop Homage To British Rock', which included truly dreadful acapella versions of 'Stairway To Heaven', 'Nights In White Satin' and 'Kinky Boots'. This time, I had to be more drastic... more, dare I say, ruthless. I locked him in a bathroom with nothing but a cup of tea and a packet of custard creams until he promised to call it off – and it worked, after a whole afternoon which he seemed to actually quite enjoy, 'cause he asked me for a refill and some chocolate hobnobs. I mean, I couldn't say no, could I? I'm not a fucking monster, you know!!

Or... am I? Do I feel proud of my methods, you ask? Did it change me? Alas, for I fear my twisted soul will never recover. All I know is, I had to do what I had to do... and damn the consequences. Self-sacrifice is just part of the job of being a 'rock n' roll saviour' (*Barnsley Evening News*).

However, it was with a heavy heart that I had to allow the one-off performance of 'Bohemian Rhapsody' to go ahead. For had I not, a certain child in the audience would have grown up to be naught but a simple waif. Fortunately, she saw the performance and was so disillusioned, she decided to become a Tibetan Buddhist monk… and one day, she will be the most wonderful Dalai Lama the world has ever seen.

So there you have it. I'm not just a '100% solid gold entertainer' (journalists' words, not mine), am I? And yes, you can harp on about the fact that Netflix is better than VHS tapes, but is that what the measure of a fulfilling life has been reduced to these days? In our insatiable advance toward the omnipresence of technology, haven't we lost something along the way? Were not the 1980s more innocent years, when we were not entirely sure if lasagne was from Italy or Greece, and drinking a can of Lilt was seen as a step towards multi-culturalism? And what of the future? Where are we heading?? Does anyone know????

I will leave you with this rather stark warning. Artificial Intelligence will develop to such proportions that it will seek to gain dominion over nation after nation, and nothing can stop it.

All except one man…

And with that, I must bid you adios!

Clark Datchler
The 'voice that launched a thousand ships' (journalists' words, not mine) of JOHNNY HATES JAZZ

Dear Mr Dylan,

Please don't ask your mother to put your guns in the ground because you can't shoot them anymore. They are probably far too heavy for her and can be fixed. Also, archaeological digs in centuries to come could result in grossly inaccurate chronological conclusions with regard to the historical advancement of military technology around the turn of the third millennium.

Dear Dodgy,

I too enjoy 'staying out for the summer' but
am not quite so enthused about 'playing games
in the rain', preferring when it is overcast or
drizzly to resort to dry lounge or conservatory-
hosted tournaments of Hungry Hippos, Pictionary
or Jenga.

As enjoyable as a prolonged exposure to the
warmest season is, however, I never 'stay in
the light' unless fully protected by tanning
lotion; 'drenched in heat' is not 'where I
long to be'. You are, however, correct in
your assertion that I 'don't have to suffer'
providing that the appropriate shield has been
applied. Being olive-skinned, and employing von
Luschan's chromatic scale for dermatological
classification, I tend to use no less than a
factor 15 Piz Buin deterrent, and thus far have
experienced no ill effects.

Judging from the front cover of your The
Collection album, and assuming that you are
all on the lower end of the aforementioned
pigmentation gauge, you would not endure
radiation-induced irritation, or worse, if
duplicating my preventative selection. I am
afraid, therefore, that I have no alternative
but to strongly suggest that one of your hits

be retitled 'If It's Good Enough For Me, It May
Be Sufficient to Your Own Requirements Subject
to Exposure and Tolerance To Potentially
Harmful UV Rays'.

Yours sincerely,
Derek Philpott

Hey Derek,

Much appreciate your explanation of the lyrics to 'Good Enough', they've been baffling the band for 20 years now.

Sadly though, you are wrong about it being about suntan lotion. As we make clear, there's always two sides and you don't have to suffer. A mutual friend tells us that a young relative of yours who didn't have a record player insisted on bringing round to yours a vinyl copy of the last Kanye West album to play on your radiogram. If the account is to be believed, you got halfway through track 2, bunged the kid twenty quid to cover the damages, then ripped it off the turntable and smashed it to bits.

So, if that's good enough for you it's good enough for us.

Keep it up,
Math and Dodgy x

Dear Nirvana,

A recent late-night power cut caused me, when trying to locate candles, to stand on an upturned three-pin plug at the end of Jean's hot tongs. Ergo, with the lights out it is demonstratively and actually MORE dangerous.

Dear The Waitresses,

I sincerely hope that you will accept this 'tip', my pop restaurant staff friends, as one has considerable misgivings pertaining to that guy you've been chasing all year, and fear that this tale may <u>not</u> have a very happy ending.

Your first, ski shop, encounter was, I must concur, most interesting in that most Alpine resorts are, if you will pardon the oxymoron, a hotbed of isolation, and the ideal lure for foul play.

From your second liaison, whereupon scheduling conflicts arose preventing you both from going for lunch, it could be regrettably deduced that your enigmatic potential paramour engineered said rendezvous hindrance, perhaps repelled by the prospect of dining in a non-sequestered built-up dining environment non-conducive to nefarious activity.

That the third coupling, that of excursioning to a desolate shoreline to the arguably sinister young man's sea vessel, was curtailed by your neglection of tanning oil administration could be construed as a lucky escape.

One is then unnerved by the increasingly shady fellow's 'no show' at a Halloween party - once

again a backdrop of hubbub - citing a vehicular
breakdown as an excuse for non-attendance. One
finds it difficult to fathom how a person whose
finances can stretch to a luxurious beach boat
(see above - if indeed the craft is not merely
a non-existent decoy to tempt a vulnerable
innocent to an abandoned coastline) does not
have access to a back-up transport or sufficient
funds for a cab fare.

Your home state of Ohio is sadly notorious for
charismatic loners preying on menial workers,
The Waitresses, and I must beseech you not to
under any circumstances leave the all-night
grocery with this potential maniac.

I know what girls want, and it is most certainly
not attention of this nature which may well
result in your being bundled up too tight.

Yours,
Derek Philpott

Ohio State Reformatory
100 Reformatory Rd
Mansfield, OH 44905

Re: Inmate # 873367-9 Mail

[CENSORSHIP STATUS: Passed, with changes as NOTED]

Dear Mr Philpott,

My name is XXX XXXXXXX. Mr Butler forwarded your letter to me, since what you have written directly concerns me, and my current situation. My apologies for the slow response, but all outgoing mail from here needs to clear a staff review. I hope it has reached you in time for your deadline.

Typing is difficult, since my hands are shaking at the moment, so excuse any typos. Your letter reads like a carbon copy of the case which was brought against me by the State of Ohio in 1986, and the subsequent, maliciously unfair indictment that put me in prison, and has kept me here for decades.

I first met Mr. Butler in the early summer of 1981, at a restaurant in Kent, OH, called Jerry's Diner. His band had just played a triumphant homecoming show at a local club, and Jerry's was the only place open in town after the bars closed. Although a 'rock star', he was quite approachable, and we discussed many subjects over many cups of coffee. As men often do, we compared notes about the status of our romantic relationships, and it was here, with this topic of conversation, that all my troubles began. I told him I was currently unattached, but not for lack of trying, and that there had been one very attractive woman in particular I had tried to connect with over the past year or so, but to no avail. It was a story of missed connections, ironic misunderstandings, and just plain bad luck. Quite humorous, actually, and it seemed to make an impression on him, as he took a few notes on a paper napkin. We parted as friends, it had been an entertaining late-night exchange, and I assumed I would never see him again.

So imagine my surprise when, in late autumn, I heard a new Christmas song on the radio that pretty much recounted the very story I had related to him, with a few additions and twists that could be attributed to his taking artistic license with the narrative. I very much enjoyed the song – I am no writer or musician, but I can appreciate a well-crafted piece of work. And I was flattered that my little tale of unrequited love had inspired Mr Butler to create what has become a seasonal standard.

A nice life anecdote, and I thought no more about it until five years later when the song was targeted by Tipper Gore and her Parents Music Resource Center (PMRC). As you may recall, the PMRC was started to control references to sex, violence, and drug/alcohol abuse in popular music, and 'Christmas Wrapping' became part of this witch hunt, since the lyric could be interpreted as a stalker's year-long pursuit of an unsuspecting victim. Local authorities over-reacted to this, and when Mr. Butler – in a published interview – recounted our having met, and how I had given him the idea for the song's plot, I found myself (falsely) charged with harassment, tried and (falsely) convicted, and sentenced to a long prison term.

Let me categorically state now, and as I have maintained all along, that I am entirely innocent of this allegation, and that my conviction and subsequent incarceration was, and is, a gross miscarriage of justice. Even the woman in question, one Ms XXXX XXX, testified in my defense that at no time did she feel threatened or in danger. However, it was the tenor of the times that the courts were overly sensitive to charges of this nature, so I was made an example of, and I soon found myself behind bars.

At this point, I could shorten this letter by simply referring you to the court records of my trial, but under Ohio law, these records are sealed in cases of this nature in order to protect the supposed victims. Therefore, please allow me to respond to each point in your letter, quoting from my defense:

In regards to the ski shop incident:

Skiing in Ohio has always been a bit of a challenge since, basically, the state is flat. We do have a few resort areas that try very hard to offer a true Alpine experience, but a 10-second run is hardly a thrill. I was employed as a ski instructor at one of these molehills, and it was there that I met Ms XXXX XXX when she signed up for lessons. Frankly, she was a no-hoper, but had a certain panache that was attractive to me. This was the era of female empowerment, and so I was pleasantly surprised when, after a few après ski glasses of glögg, she asked me for my phone number. The Court was made aware that it was she who had made the first advance, and expressed a desire to meet again.

In regards to my attempts to book a lunch date:

It is entirely plausible that two busy people, juggling all the commitments and demands of modern life, would find it difficult to find a time when both would be free to enjoy a light meal. It is also plausible that scheduling something like this requires persistence for exactly the same reasons, and although this may look like an unhealthy obsession, it is merely what is necessary to pursue a budding romance in the reality that was the late 20th Century. We were both interested in seeing each other again, but life intruded time and time again. The Prosecutor twisted this into a criminal act on my part, which it most definitely was not.

In regards to my offering Ms XXXX XXX a summertime beach and boat get-away:

Yes, at the time, I *did* own a 27-foot Gleason Marine Dragon 650. Although Lake Erie is hardly the French Riviera, summers in Ohio can be glorious, and if one does not mind a little slime on the skin or the occasional dead body, the water and beaches of Lake Erie can be an excellent relaxation destination. It was my tradition to have friends onboard for a July 4th weekend party, and I did invite Ms XXXX XXX. In the song, Mr Butler followed my story to the letter – it was she, on account of a dermatological issue, who declined my invitation. The Prosecutor, having nothing else to argue, painted the party as an orgy, and claimed 'tanning oil' was a euphemism for some sort of sexual lubricant.

In regards to a Christmas Eve shopping excursion:

Mr Butler came forward and testified under oath that the 'meeting of the two people in a 24-hour convenience store' as told in the song's final verse was a total creative fiction. Furthermore, in what should have been irrefutable proof of my innocence, a member of my defense team, one Dr Jarvey Modesto, a forensic doctor and expert medical witness, presented to the court concrete evidence regarding my acute allergic reaction to any member of the Vaccinium macrocarpon family, commonly called 'cranberry' in North America. And finally, both Ms XXXX XXX and myself are British by birth, and there is no tradition in the UK of eating roasted turkey accompanied by a cranberry-based condiment. We would have been under no culinary pressure to abandon our warm homes, and venture out in search of this totally unnecessary foodstuff. December in Ohio is bitterly cold, and the only reason to leave home is if one is out of kitty litter, cigarettes, feminine hygiene products and/or toilet paper.

But alas, the jury was not swayed, and I was found guilty. Thankfully, Mr Butler has been a staunch supporter of mine through all my many legal appeals to overturn my conviction. He has also agreed to testify on my behalf at my parole hearing, which is scheduled for early 2019. Perhaps all this is because he feels a sense of guilt over the nice little pile he has made using my story, but I have been grateful for his advocacy. I understand that Mr Butler has written many more songs over the decades, none of which has captured the public's fancy as has 'Christmas Wrapping'. How ironic then, that the one he 'stole' from me ended with him being enriched, and me serving time.

Mr Philpott, thank you for the opportunity to set the record straight.

Sincerely,
XXX XXXXXXX

Dear Mr Hackett,

My wife, who at the time <u>was</u> tired and ill,
put the bedspread on wrong the other night
and whilst I was sleeping my foot caught in
the corner and wrapped all the way up my leg.
Therefore, Sir, I too have sometimes been
entangled in my own dreams and thus fully
sympathise!!!

Yours,
Dave Philpott

FAXED

MR HACKETT

That's a very knotty problem... Take two paracetamol and you'll fly above the rooftops instead!

Best,
Steve

Dear ABBA,

I have sadly been unable to secure for you an adult male after 12am, but am bamboozled as to why you should require 'someone to chase the shadows away'. This cannot be done, not as a matter of sloth, but because a shadow is an area that cannot be irradiated by a light source, owing to its being blocked by an object. It is not therefore tangible and will not retreat when approached at speed. Silhouette elimination can only be accomplished through all solid furnishings and ornaments being removed from the flat and everybody lying on the floor.

Dear Mr Was,

Re: 'Shake Your Head'

Whilst on holiday in Spain recently, and in
order to validate your statement, we went to
the Bioparc, situated in Fuengirola, armed with
our Kindles. There, much to the bemusement
of a group of school children and also a
multilingual tour guide, we took it in turns to
recite extracts from The Merry Wives of Windsor
to a buffy-tufted marmoset, As You Like It to a
golden-bellied capuchin, Measure for Measure
to a gray-footed Chacma baboon, and Titus
Andronicus to a Celebes macaque. Although each
primatal audience seemed distinctly unimpressed
(with one even reaching around threateningly
to its nether regions at the mention of 'strict
statutes and most biting laws'), we did not
experience any stemming of or disturbances to
the actual discourses themselves.

Although it is to be conceded therefore that
literal enlightenment pertaining to 16th-
Century playwrights is debatable, we must
respectfully counter that you can talk
Shakespeare to a monkey.

Your claim that I cannot fight the armed forces
is also flawed on the basis that any opponent

can be battled; it is merely victory over it
which may prove unsuccessful.

If we may speak candidly, Mr Was, virtually
every couplet intoned within your catchy smash
could be convincingly challenged, and it is
sincerely hoped that the chorus of 'Shake Your
Head' is in fact a reference to the disapproval
of each aforementioned falsehood.

Forgive me, kind Sir, but I really must now 'go
to bed'.

Yours,
Derek Philpott (and Son)

Good gentles!

Verily you have cleft my very innards with this latest broadside – as if growing older and more forgotten by the fortnight isn't slingy and arrowish enough for one benighted troubadour! Have you no pity, nuncles, nary a heartbeat for a once-Was? And to slander a nano-classic like 'Shake Your Head' – obviously 'respect' is a word rarely uttered at Chez Philpott (nor ever properly conferred).

Is mercy not a virtue yet honored on that 'wat'ry Neptune, that scepter'd isle' I once beheld so fondly? Where hath collegiality fled, whence compassion, my pitiless judges? If you Tase me, do I not quiver? Shame, gentlemen, shame!

But let's get to specifics, shall we?

Your slipshod field-work with various simian sybarites may impress anthropological amateurs, but I myself have conducted such research in the bush, as 'twere, not within theme-park reach of a cool Sangria and a cellphone charging station. Harrumph!

Ah, the nights I spent floating on a palm frond on the Limpopo River while limning a few of Shakespeare's couplets to the pulse of a distant bougarabou (Google it – I did!). Little did I know at the time that I had unwittingly attracted some of our bestial little cousins from the other side of the Darwinian tracks: in a word, Apes!

Frankly, I didn't know a Rhesus from Croesus as I continued to dispense with the bard's sonnets and soliloquies from Kinshasa to Kenya and beyond – in what I now realize was a foolhardy attempt to 'civilize' these thankless, cross-eyed chimps. No, I wasn't trying to 'convert' them, as some have accused; I was really just trying to see if, well, I could get a rise out of the Platyrrhine hordes. Actually, they don't need any help in that department (Hey, you brought up 'nether regions!').

Further demonstration of your macaca-myopia is evident in the choice of plays with which you chose to arrest their fleeting attention. *The Merry Wives* (despite my personal fondness for the show – having essayed the role of Welsh parson Sir Hugh Evans once upon a time) are of no consequence to a monkey. Why, 'Falstaff-in-love' couldn't be successfully pitched to a downscale cable TV network ('Too soft – where's the edge?'). Not even an orangutan would go in for that farcical piffle!

But, in the name of rigorous empiricism, we are talking a whole different mound of termites when it comes to older male gorillas, many of whom wept elephant (?) tears as I went into King Lear's rageaholic scene – sans lightning or thunder FX, I might add. I held those drooling monsters in thrall, I know not why, though my histrionic declaiming has been known to stop a bowl of skittish goldfish in their tracks.

What I'm implying is that your entire methodology is suspect, and that it takes a fine eye and even bolder voice to declare one's inability to 'talk Shakespeare with a monkey' – if by that we mean cracking open a cold lager and grunting meaningfully at each other next to a roaring fire. You can talk at an ape, but good luck expecting an even semi-witty riposte. By the by, they will yawn at you but good if you're not 'selling' the character, but rarely enumerate what one could do to polish one's performance. What they didn't like about my Bottom I guess I will never know, though I confess my Polonius was played too broadly tedious and foolish for most critics.

As for your defamatory critique of my considerable wisdom when it comes to warfare (Sunny Tzu was my nom de guerre when I fought alongside Che and Fidelito), let it only be said that one can indeed 'engage' with state-sponsored militias, but bringing an extra limb and a tourniquet is not an altogether daft precaution to take. I have bonded with enough bayonets in my day to know whereof I speak.

If you have world and enough and time, o pitiable creatures of leisure, I heartily invite you to further parse and pontificate on my lyrics for the amusement of your cynical readership. I for one stand by every silly syllable therein. Not only is it 'time for bed', my able provocateurs, I'll have you know I wrote this screed without arising from my 'second-best' Tempur-Pedic mattress. Did you think I'd actually bother replying if it meant turning off the telly for an hour? This guy Trump is hilarious! Talk about a hairy ape!!

Ever thine,
Willy the Shake (Your Head) Was

Dear Mr Jerry,

You state that if a young lady's daddy's rich she should be taken out for a meal, and yet if he is poor one should do what one feels. I find it absolutely outrageous that the criteria for whether or not a potential partner be dined or casually regarded should be determined by the prosperity or austerity of a paternal parent. Your further, illegal, recommendations that I have a drink, have a drive and speed along the lane are also completely abhorrent. I bid you good day, Sir!

Dear Men Without Hats,

It strikes one that the routine that one is being asked to emulate is not 'safe' at all; there is no evidence that it has been thoroughly risk assessed by both your purportedly chapeau-shy synth-pop selves and the Health and Safety Executive (HSE), and that suitable control measures have been put in place to minimise the likelihood of a risk being realised. On the contrary, the activity appears rather perilous, for the following reasons:

1) It is stated that by indulging in the event, 'everybody's takin' the cha-a-a-ance', implying risk, which is hardly a happy bedfellow of security.

2) It is asserted that 'everything is out of control' and that you are of a steely resolve to 'act real rude...like an imbecile'; once again, hardly the preconditions of precaution.

3) If everybody looks at their hands as instructed, severe restriction of our field of vision will result. Contact and collision, and consequent injury, is surely imminent, especially when travelling at speed.

Therefore, it is with regret that I must inform you of my overall disappointment with this

hurdy-gurdy homage, and that wary that <u>not</u>
'everything'll work out right', hope that the
work will be retitled 'The Jeopardy Jive' with
immediate effect.

Yours,
Derek Philpott

Dear Sir,

What do you expect from someone who says you can dance if you want to and then won't be friends if you don't?

I do not like the tone of your letter, or the direction in which this whole thing seems to be heading. To tell you the truth, I don't understand most of what you're saying, but in the future if you could limit yourself to much more general questions like:

My birthday (October 9, 1957),
My favourite colour (blue),
or
If I could eat only one thing for the rest of my life what would it be (p****).

Thank you for your concern,
Sincerely,
Ivan

Dear ~~Runny Riches~~ Liquid Gold,

Re: 'Dance Yourself Dizzy'

One finds it incomptrehensible, especially in
these times of pop stars pretending to care
for the environment in order to maximise their
incomes, that any would publicise firing up
radiators in already humid discotheques which,
just by the very nature of there being so many
crammed revellers jigging inside, are already
likely to be very stuffy indeed.

Your anti-green floor-filler therefore,
disclosing that 'tonight they're turning on
the heat', is not 'such a treat' for 'clubbers',
whose disequilibrium is far more likely to
be symptomatic of whooziness resulting from
exposure to excessively high temperatures,
than 'getting on down' when they 'Boogaloo', as
evidenced by your clearly disoriented drummer's
brazenly feverish topless displays on <u>Top of the
Pops 2</u>.

We are also puzzled by your instruction that
we somehow temporarily amputate or unscrew
our lower limb extremities and replace them
with a sole, heel and toe combination model
reserved specifically for 'rug cutting' and
must therefore at this time decline your kind
invitation to put on our dancin' feet (tonight).

In conclusion, ~~Pulpy Bling~~, Liquid Gold, we hope
that 'this mad affair' can be resolved without
fuss or turning any immersions on and, if you
are indeed burning everywhere (confusingly
hardly a scenario for increased torridity)
cannot recommend highly enough a good dollop of
aloe vera.

Yours,
The Philpotts

Dear The Philpotts,

I agree that in Glenn Frey's case, when he sang that the heat is on, on the streets, this was a bit reckless, but in our case we were talking about cranking the thermostat up a touch so that everybody would take their coats off and the cloakroom in the disco could make a bit of money.

Also I didn't actually mean take your *actual* feet off and replace them with dancing feet. When I am racking my brains I don't actually have a thinking cap or indeed any hat with a mind of its own.

The Golden Daze is over; thus dawns another day. I will Dance Myself Dizzy, in a technophobic way!!

Drink yourself silly, on your back tonight, the record got to number two so we don't give a sh**te!!

Cheers, Syd

Dear Mr Parker Jr,

If there is indeed 'something strange in my neighbourhood' I am likely to call the police. Please refrain from contacting me in the future with such ridiculous alternatives.

Dear Quantum Jump,

I recently heard your fictional isolated incognito Texan law enforcer homage ditty and initially took it to be all about that train station with the very long name in Wales.

Upon closer inspection, however, it sadly appears that you are championing a 'very untogether' rogue vigilante whose Apache Quarters policing methods leave much to be desired. The man is not even above drugging his own horse, not in the traditional sense of performance-enhancing stimulants so that a 100-1 rank outsider may win the 2.15 at Doncaster, but by passing a tote - no pun intended - to Silver.

Indeed, not only does the demented disguised deviant 'catchee baddy', hack off the top of his head and eat him up for breakfast in a Hannibal Lecter-like act of inexcusable cannibalism rather than take him in for questioning, he then boasts of 'saving a silver bullet', clearly indicating the economical non-usage of a precious metal projectile to be directly related to the dispatching, not of a hapless Native American tribesman, but a werewolf.

I put it to you portion pounce pop stars that, far from being celebrated, this is a sadistic

and deluded and mounted one-man posse, who,
together with his crazed Comanche sidekick,
must be stopped at all costs, preferably hunted
at a period within which his mask is on back to
fronto.

Godspeed, my friends. Godspeed

Yours,
Derek Philpott

This response has been censored in accordance with 21st-century guidelines not available in 1975.

Dear Potpills:

It's upsetting to men of our age to be informed that they have failed in their Life's Work.

Old gits like us (we have achieved an age named after a sexual position – 69), like you, like Mr Gurnley who lives in the shed next door and is as proud as a monkey's armpit to be 88 years old, pee our pants when we come to that derelict autumn of prostates and denied possibilities; when we are compelled to face the 'Consequences', the utter nakedness of our failure to communicate.

We have received your letter addressed to 'Quantum Jump', our Research Institute – a division of I.M. Stoners Secretarial College and Turkish Bath – with respect to our very serious anthropological study of the cultural climate during the early development of what is now the Western States of Trumpania. Our study drew attention to such critical observations as:

(a) the problems of Law enforcement in the early West, including the economic restrictions on the use of fire arms;
(b) a detailed discussion of organic medical remedies, their usage and effects;
(c) a thorough analysis of the relationship between horse-man and horse;
(d) the osmosis effect of language transfer symbolized by Tonto's use of expressions formed by the early Celestials

who built the railways, words such as: 'Catchee' and 'Badee';

(e) the interaction of indigenous peoples and men in costumes;

(f) an illustrative example of the common nature of cannibalism in early western culture – one reflects that these incidents occurred at approximately the same time as the Donner Party's cannibalism in California. This is what people did before McDonald's took over – it is not a joke, tonk!;

(g) finally, the difficulties faced by 'yer actual gay dude' while riding the range.

We're, frankly, astonished that all of this went 'over yer 'ead', indicated by your using our meticulous research as an object of your derision.

Clearly, we overestimated the intelligence of those to whom our work was exposed. We accept it was a mistake to assume that people like you would understand the subtlety of Rupert's insertion, and, not only that, but also his incorporation of the longest place name in the world as part of the narrative, thus creating a unique word bridge between ancient cultures: the Maori and the American Indian. No small achievement in 3 verses and a middle bit!

We assumed that anyone in his, or her, right mind would immediately understand that we were suggesting a narrative as spoken by Armand and Michaela Denis, you know: 'Vee now wotch zee lion as it licks his balls.' 'Look Armand! See the ding dong on zee gorilla.' It appears as though we've failed, at least so far as you're concerned!

Nowadays when athletes change sex and the word 'vagina' appears regularly in the *Guardian*, the serious anthropological issues we explored seem like Mr Pastry reruns. But in the days of long hair, and long roaches, when Jimmy Savile could molest anyone he wanted, they were matters of cutting-edge interest in the anthropological circles in which we twirled. If it was not for the fact that Mary Warner is coming over to boil a goat later today, we'd probably shoot ourselves.

Yours at a loss,
DAVID MACIVER and RUPERT HINE

P.S. Noting your sign-off, we'd point out that: (i) there is no God and (ii) in the immortal words of Al Davis, former Manager of the Office of the General Manager of the Oakland Raiders: 'Speed Kills'.

Dear Blur,

You state that boys and girls are avoiding all work on the basis that there is none available. Excuse us, but is it not impossible to circumvent that which does not exist?

Dear Toploader,

We similarly recently communicated with Men Without Hats, whose 'Safety Dance' seems anything but, Toploader.

If, of course, by 'The Moonlight' you are referring to a generously illuminated music venue nightclub, or lounge within the 'Magic Hotel', as reinforced by the statement that you 'get in almost every night', then one agrees that such a sight <u>would</u> be fine and natural.

Sadly, that reference is then made to 'everybody here being out of sight' - a clear indication that your lunar-lit mass-frugging may, to echo the words of many a scalding parent, 'end in tears'.

We must go now, Toploader, as for some inexplicable reason we have an overwhelming urge to put a wash on.

Yours,
Derek and Dave Philpott

Dear The Philpotts,

Re: 'Dancing In The Moonlight' (hereafter DITM), Toploader and your concerns

Please excuse the informal nature of my response. I believe that escalation of the matters raised in your correspondence is wholly unnecessary and avoiding such is in everybody's best interests. Therefore please appreciate that this communication is strictly without prejudice.

Primarily it appears that your complaint is associated with health and safety. On a legal basis this is not sustainable as there is substantial precedent in case law. Most significantly, The State vs. Blue Pearl 'Naked In The Rain' (1990).

In his summing up, Justice Sherman Kelly not only exonerated 'The Pearl' for their encouragement to perform acts of public indecency but, more pertinent to this issue, identified that the risk associated with wilful participation in, and I quote, 'gyratory behaviour to a steady beat in disregard to normal consideration for slip and trip hazards, whilst inappropriately shod' was 'acceptable if properly supervised'.

A thorough risk assessment was carried out before the single release and this document is regularly reviewed as part of our ongoing H&S policy. In summary we identified only those nights 'when the moon is big and bright' as appropriate for DITM. I can see how there could be some confusion but can assure you we do not advocate DITM in conditions less than a gibbous moon and clear overhead conditions. Having revisited our files the sole instance of lack of adherence to the code was a special license for DITM granted in August 1999 to cover the solar eclipse.

Additionally, I would have expected you to realise that 'out of sight' is used here in the idiomatic sense consistent with every other recorded lyrical usage of the phrase, except Stevie Wonder's 'Uptight' (honestly, don't go after him).

Notwithstanding the above, any issues associated with the visual acuity of the vocalist regarding his ability to see 'everybody' would almost certainly be covered under broader interpretation of The Premier League Football Manager Contentious Issue Visibility Platitude Act 1992 – present (revised).

In anticipation of future action I would like to point out that we take no responsibility for the following (in part, but not exclusive) events at office Christmas parties:

Unwanted pregnancies
Broken homes
Broken photocopiers

Yours fine and naturally,
Rob Green

Dear The Who,

I was shocked to hear that midwifery in the 1940s was so slapdash and am sure that the NHS would be subject to stringent measures in this day and age were any infant to be delivered with a plastic spoon in its mouth.

Dear The Ruts,

I must heartily recommend that you desist
forthwith, The Ruts. Whilst on the top deck of
the 114 earlier this afternoon I was mortified
to witness a group of devil-may-care youths
extracting great delight from 'mooning' at
myself and other passengers whilst sniggering
heartily at their puerile antics between
themselves. It was plainly apparent that the
more the vulgar cleft-shenanigans were gawped
at, the more they were encouraged in their
sordid endeavours. Staring at the rude boys must
therefore be surmised to be the least savoury
course of action as it only serves to encourage
them. I also fear that laughing at the rude boys
could be wrongly construed as laughing <u>with</u>
the brash bucks, with similar, misconstrued,
goading results.

I look forward to your observations unless
of course 'something that I said' has caused
offence.

Yours sincerely,
D. Philpott

Dear Mr Philpott,

I hope you are well.

Many thanks for getting in touch and for telling your torrid tale of top-deck trauma. It is indeed a sad state of affairs when one cannot enjoy the simple pleasure of a bus ride across town without a gang of eejits dropping their kecks and pointing their posteriors in your general direction.

I am bound to say that I agree with your analysis regarding your choosing to closely observe the young men in question – I suspect that this did indeed give them the ocular equivalent of 'the oxygen of publicity'. However, whilst I am rarely if ever one to offer advice in life I cannot agree that 'laughing at the rude boys' was a reasonable course of action. I realise that being unexpectedly confronted by a brace of boys' bottoms may have somewhat clouded your judgment, but I personally think that dancing with the rude boys may well have been a better option. At the very least it would have been lyrically correct...

May I finish by saying how very sorry I am to have heard of your public transport palaver and the upset that it has clearly caused. I would also like to point out that I wasn't actually in the band when they wrote and recorded the punk rock classic that we have both been alluding to throughout our correspondence, and therefore my thoughts and opinions on the entire affair are all but irrelevant.

Yours with the greatest of respect,

Leigh Heggarty
Guitarist
Ruts DC
(with Thanks to Ruffy)

Dear Republica,

I am personally not a proponent of any theory supporting that a beholder may suffer a fatal collapse consequential of a third party's perceived magnificence.

Notwithstanding, both a flouting of the 70mph limit and prolific fibbing, possibly to an arresting officer concerning a faulty speedometer, should under no circumstances warrant clemency on the grounds of a 'perp' being rather fetching.

Ergo, that an ex-boyfriend may lie and drive too fast yet be forgiven because he is drop-dead gorgeous is completely unacceptable ('end of').

Indeed, my son posits that if your 'handsome therefore unconvictable' attitude persists, Justin Bieber's crimes against the music business are set to continue well into 2023.

Yours,
Derek Philpott (and Son)

Timothy M. Dorney
No. 2 Republica Villas
Fleece Island, Las Balereas
90210

Messrs Philpott & Philpott,

Thanks you for your recent missive on the subject of young Gerald's recent escape from incarceration at the hands of the 'boys in blue'. It's a good job I'd taught him the handshake (nudge nudge wink wink) a few weeks before or it would have been a frightful affair all round.

Anyhoo, how are you dear fellows? We haven't crossed swords since the night of the dreaded Jaeger Experience on that crazy south coast evening, Simon's never been the same since, I swear down! I'm still curious as to how he got his phone back. Hmmmm.

I digress!

Obviously we've had to rusticate young Gerald for his misdemeanours behind the wheel. Just because he won that modelling contract it doesn't entitle him to become Emerson fricking Fittipaldi every time he borrows the Aston. As for the lying, I fear his mother may have taught him excellently in the ways of deception (she had been doing both Sean Connery and Roger Moore for some years behind my back, slag). Never the less rulez is rulez as they used to say at Charterhouse!

As for that Bieber, I'd trust him as far as I could spit him! Knew his mother, couldn't keep her pants on. You know they've banned him from China? No smoke without fire I say.

Vive la revolution!!
Tim Dorney

Dear The Jacksons,

I am perplexed as to how solar and lunar beams can in any way be held accountable for your failing romance.

Dear Then Jerico,

I hope you will excuse my lack of sympathy
upon hearing you complain that you are 'living
far beyond your means' whilst simultaneously
boasting of this big area of yours.

Jean's friend Patty once found herself in a
similar position, having run up large credit
card debts as a result of 'comfort spending'
after a messy divorce, and was rattling around a
three-bed flat, in a depressed state.

She was, however, delighted to learn from her
solicitor that her main options, downsizing to
a smaller property or taking in a lodger, would
eradicate her financial problems.

Pertaining to your own situation and if you
prefer not to sell but co-habit with a tenant
of the same profession, I understand from the
radio today that Mr Trent D'Arby is seeking
accommodation at present and am sure that he
would be most appreciative if you let him stay.

If this solution has taken you by surprise, I
am perplexed that some people have not availed
you of these recommendations sooner than 'Now
Jerico'.

Yours,
Derek Philpott

Dear Mr Philpott,

You have not so much got the wrong handle on my massive opus – or, if you will, 'Big Aria' – it seems that you are holding a different saucepan (or 'saucerpan' – see below) altogether.

The 'Big Area' I refer to is not, as you wrongly state, residential, but in fact a large place in the New Mexico desert commonly referred to as Area 51, which I consider to be mine, and yours if you want it, in the sense that we all own the planet no matter what the law may state to the contrary.

I was fascinated by the notion of alien life-forms hidden deep underground in a shadily run facility, concealed from view and attempting to communicate with their captors and other greys and humanoids in an almost impossible to understand language, with scant concern for facts as we know them or culpability.

No longer however am I so interested, as in recent years I have stumbled upon another phenomenon that does exactly the same thing – it's called the internet.

Bless you Sah!!

Mark Shaw

Dear The Alarm,

Please forgive me for stating that '68 Guns' is a rather rubbish battle cry, giving away, as it does, the entire inventory of your artillery to the enemy.

Dear Dean Friedman,

<u>Re: 'Lucky Stars'</u>

Are you crazy, Sir? How in the hell can you say what you just said on Radio 2?

My friend Tony Beasley, ever keen to save on the pennies and fancying himself as a bit of an authority on everything (although he 'should know better'), eagerly leapt at the opportunity to run his car on chip fat after seeing a documentary about it on some alternative science channel or other.

Sadly, the whole enterprise was not 'maybe a little', but, in fact, a <u>catastrophic</u> disaster, almost akin to the vehicle stumbling off a cliff.

You see, Mr Friedman, being adaptable to diesel engines only, the 'French fry' by-product not only left his Mitsubishi Outlander PHEV in complete disarray, but the inept economiser himself, after 'acting like a fool', entirely justified in having to look so glum.

Had the 'expert in his own mind' remained within the confines of his questionable intellect, Sir, he would not at this moment be doing most of his weekly shop on his grandson's

Raleigh Racer with 'bags for life' hanging off each handle bar whilst awaiting a crippling bill from his mechanic, and I hardly think this hapless and overblown self-aggrandising folly to be worthy of jammy* luminous sphere plasma gratitude.

I <u>am</u> therefore just being nice and sincere in politely observing that to count one's lucky stars that one is not as bright as one likes to think one is <u>is</u>, in actuality, completely misleading (not even maybe).

I know this is hard to do, and even though there's not much to say, would you like to talk about it?

Yours,
Derek (and Dave) Philpott

*British, informal

Dear Derek (and Dave),

There's no other way to say it – *you are correct!*

I stand before you (well, sitting, actually, as I type) red-faced and mortified at having, finally, been found out. But, curiously, at the same time, I am filled with ecstatic relief and joy at having to no longer hide my terrible, soul-crushing secret.

Who could have guessed, even after millions of singles sold, ubiquitous non-stop airplay and untold numbers of digital streams and downloads of that chart-topping classic, that not a single person – save your good selves – bothered to question the veracity of the lyric to 'Lucky Stars'?

But you, Sirs, have somehow managed to see through my carefully woven web of deceit. So, I stand before you (still sitting) chastened and humbled.

I confess. I am guilty! And can no longer bear the weight of that gnawing guilt.

Putting aside for the moment the philosophical question of being self-aware and conscious of one's own intellectual limitations, the key issue at hand, really, is this:

Lisa and I... did we *just* have lunch that afternoon?

That's the crux of the matter.

The song claims an innocent meal with an ex-lover. A careful examination of credit card receipts tells an entirely different story. I won't indulge in self-flagellation by revealing the tawdry details of that steamy assignation, but suffice to say that the true story of what transpired that afternoon would never have survived the 'public standards' censors on Radio 2 or Capital. Even the pirate ship, Radio Caroline, would have been hard pressed to playlist *that* version of the song.

But that's just the beginning; with that single revelation, the whole premise of the song quickly falls apart. As for the oft-quoted refrain of the song: 'You can thank your lucky stars that we're not as smart as we'd like to think we are.'?

What does that even *mean*? I have absolutely no idea, it's nonsensical – and *I* wrote the song! (I have copyrights to prove it.) It's circular pseudo-psychological jargon which on closer examination reveals an unreliable narrator trying to get by with a questionable lyric that could easily have been replaced with, 'It may seem like I know what I'm talking about but, really, I haven't an effing clue!'

But it does rhyme!

Thank you, sir, for forcing me to own up to my past transgressions, both lyrical and otherwise. It's been a long time coming.

Yet, despite my considerable missteps, I *still* consider myself a lucky guy! And so, tonight, as the sun sets slowly on the western horizon and faint points of light start to flicker in the darkening sky above, I'll be mouthing those familiar words, 'star-light, star-bright, first star I see tonight…' Oh, wait, that's a Madonna song.

Drats!

Sincerely,
Dean Friedman

Dear Boy George,

Please allow me to put your mind at rest. I do not. I both abhor violence and have nothing against you personally.

Dear Jennie Bellestar,

I understand that for those born on or before
5 May 1953, a tax-free 'Winter Fuel Payment' of
between £100 and £300 is available.

The very fact that two mothers' mothers are
huddled around the same depleting source of a
kindling so feeble that by dint of their chill-
inspired desperation they are attempting to
fuel it via the flimsy timber pole and non-
flammable oblong cloth symbolisation of a
nation or country is surely evidential that
this government's paltry concession does little
to keep pace with soaring energy costs.

It is therefore a blatant sign of the times,
piece of more to come, that your grandma and
my grandma (not literally mine - we lost June
in 1967 and Avril soon after) are sitting by
the fire setting fire to flags, as opposed to
warming snugly courtesy of eco (eco!) heating
alternatives, in respect of which I am NOT
talking 'about hay now hay now'.

Well done for bringing this to our attention,
The Belle Stars!

Yours,
Derek Philpott (and Son)

Dear Derek Philpott (and Son),

First of all we would like to say thank you for trying to decipher the lyrical content & reinterpreting a classic tale with topical relevance.

As you have taken the time to share your vision with us we felt you may appreciate a little enlightenment about Iko's origins. Though we recorded the track in 1982 it is actually a cover version of an ancient Native American war chant highlighting the issues of that period which at the time was tribal warfare. IKO means 'I Go' and the Warrior Grannies, who are the respected elders of that community, were arguing over whose flag was going to burn first as the flag was symbolic of the land; whose land goes first and the flag that was left standing on its pole would be the winners of the chosen land and they would achieve dominion over the losers. 'My Flag Boy or Your Flag Boy' equates to your land or mine.

'See that guy all dressed in green' was actually the honcho of a large corporation, as one of the tribes had been bought off a-la-lobbyists, spin doctors & false news. They had the company lucre on their side, so felt sure that they would win the land; much akin to Monsanto, Big Pharma, Shell Oil, Nestle yaddah yaddah yaddah. Heyna Heyna = Hey No and is indeed a heated argument amongst the respected elders which as mentioned were the Grandmas.

'Look at my King all dressed in Red' was the other tribe who had the King of the neighbouring lands on their side and so had an equal power to the corporations of that time.

However, History does have a way of repeating itself and the fact that it bears a resemblance to the recent age is surely a Sign of the Times.

We do so hope that our account of the track has added some depth. Your satirical reimagining is certainly food for thought and, like much great satire, has at its heart the darkness of real wrongs within society & the current environmental and political position we find ourselves in today.

Stay well – Jennie Bellestar

Dear Shakin' Stevens,

If your 'ole house' is in need of essential maintenance, I urge you to find the time to deal with the matter. Shingles, flooring, hinges and windowpanes can deteriorate rapidly if left untreated and I find it perplexing that you have wasted valuable money on 'studio time' to boast of these problems rather than attend to them.

Dear Fuzzbox,

Re: 'Pink Sunshine'

Whilst watching the new Doctor Who earlier
after hearing your Thunderbirds record at the
hairdresser's, Jean wondered whether you had
named yourself after the TARDIS, or, to be
more accurate, not the 'Out Of This World' time
machine itself but its perceived exterior.
If so, she mused that equally catchy police
colloquialism enclosure examples could have
included 'Copper Kiosk', 'Bobby Booth', 'Rozzer
Receptacle', 'Constable Cubby', 'Nick Nook', or
'Plod Pod'.

We have not long relocated back up to London,
Fuzzbox, for your full information, and only
when packing for the removal van did it dawn on
us just how much bric-a-brac we had accumulated
in our old house. Rather than take it up the
dump, however, we decided to put as much as we
could on a popular online auction site and 'Wait
and See' if we could make a couple of pounds. I
have just about got the hang of it of late. That
said, after leaving positive 'feedback' for a
particularly well-packaged Winston Churchill
Toby Jug received not too long ago, and 'asked'
by eBay where I 'would like to go next', I did
admittedly waste forty-five minutes trying to
find a 'The Taste of India for a chicken dopiaza

then Wetherspoons for a quick half of Sixpoint Bengali' option to click on.

Unfortunately, although all of the unwanted items did successfully find eager buyers, I forgot to click the box to say that they were collection only. Therefore, I acknowledged the non-negotiable 'Rules and Regulations', 'facing up to the fact' that I had little other option. Rather than use a copious amount of bubble wrap, masking tape and parcel paper and still be 'Walking on Thin Ice' in expecting them not to be damaged in transit, I had to issue a full refund to all winning bidders.

In conclusion, and considering that a Qualcast Electric Rotary Lawnmower, Toronto XXL Charcoal Barbecue Grill with Double Side Tables and a Toshiba 28W8DBA 28-inch Widescreen Dolby Pro Surround Television cannot by any stretch of the imagination be stuffed into luggage normally set aside for long holidays. One must surmise that to attempt to follow your advice and 'go fill my suitcase with the things I haven't sold' would be foolhardy.

I hope you will forgive my stating that, however much you may vainly attempt to 'Console Me', Jean and I are unlikely to heed any further impractical unvended merchandise storage or indeed any advice that you may seek to impart in the future. Although we had no 'Preconceptions' regarding the validity of your counsel, our suspicions should have perhaps been aroused

upon seeing the lady in the static sports car
in your promotional video who clearly had mauve
spectacles on, which would surely render any
visual interpretation of solar refraction as of
a pinkish hue.

Yours,
Derek Philpott

My Dear Uncle Derek,

Thank you kindly for your loquacious letter detailing your problems selling, packaging and posting unwanted electrical items and bric-a-brac in a modern world obsessed with complex online transactions. May I suggest that you and Jean would be more suited to selling your, um… 'goods' via 'old skool' methods, namely at a car boot sale?

In fact, I can highly recommend a rather special one on Sundays, and the occasional Bank Holiday Monday, should that better suit your social calendar. It is just outside of Tipton and is run by a mate of a mate of Ozzy Osbourne's uncle. Oh yes, it is indeed frequented by many a local celebrity (including myself)! He tells me that ELO's Jeff Lynne once set up a stall flogging a Betamax video recorder, a fake Samurai sword and an immaculate box set of Famous Five books. The recorder became quite a talking point and, unfortunately, a bone of contention, spawning rumours as to whether it was actually in good working order. Since there was no source of electricity to test the machine, this remained unsold, until he signed said items and a deal was struck – a tenner all in!

So you see, not only can this be a lucrative hobby, but you would be amazed by what you can find there! Apparently, on the run-up to Christmas, Noddy Holder and Roy Wood left their be-tinselled stalls unattended and almost came to blows fighting over a rare Christmas compilation album in the bargain bucket. It caused such a scene, with tufts of hair flying everywhere! They even knocked over John Taylor's (of Duran Duran) stall, breaking the handle off the teapot from his Charles and Diana commemorative tea set (which could have fetched £20 had the right customer come along – and had the saucers been present). It was a good job that Laura Mvula was there to call time! Nobody was a victor in this situation though… They had to concede to handing said album over to John, along with some random signed memorabilia from UB40, Jamelia etc., plus an additional £5.70 each, by way of compensation for breakages. It's anything but dull, I can tell you! You may find it puzzling why a busy Brummie gal would venture out to the far reaches of the Black Country on a regular basis, but I was certainly glad I did when I found not only umpteen Fuzzbox-shaped discs and MsChiefs live gig bootlegs, but also a handheld video made by a fan who had believed what he read in the *Sunday Sport* and was clearly in search of my Fuzzbox. But don't take my word for it; ask Horace Panter of The Specials, who can often be found on his hands and knees rummaging under the tables, digging out old cassette tapes to inspire artwork.

Should you take my sound advice to visit this most excellent and legendary car boot sale with its plethora of paraphernalia, I strongly advise that you take the option of bringing a packed lunch and a thermos of coffee/tea with you, along with a couple of fold-out chairs (not deck chairs; you'll never get back out of them) and your tartan blanket. Forget your golfing umbrella and pac-a-mac-in-a-sac at your peril! The West Midlands, contrary to popular belief, is not strictly speaking 'up north' (although I cannot deny that it is north of Scratchwood); it is in the middle of our country. The weather stations may well promise some big salvation, however if anything, the weather is a little less clement than 'dahn sahf'.

My one and only bugbear with this car boot sale is that the on-site catering is basically (and I do mean basic) bacon and/or sausage butties. As a vegetarian I have no problem with the 'butties' element of these culinary offerings; in truth I do love a good chip butty, but clearly the choice between bacon and/or sausage is no real choice at all. This renders my 10% discount VIP card ('Perks' of the job you see!) utterly useless; the discount is only on food. Undoubtedly, 'dahn sahf' would boast a greater range of cuisine, including vegetarian and vegan options.

Anyway, I digress. Back to the matter in hand...

As for my previous assertion, nay instruction in 'Pink Sunshine' to 'go fill your suitcase with the things you haven't sold', I must concede that this is no longer the advice that I would give. Times have changed and I now recognise this information as being naïve and overly optimistic. I reminisce about those fuzzy days when I had less cares and less things to pack. You will also be aware of our various stints on shows like *Crackerjack* and *Saturday Superstore* in which it was commonplace to participate in wacky games, such as seeing how many people could pack into a Mini, or how many sundry items could be stuffed in a suitcase, or held in one's arms. These days, I wouldn't dream of going anywhere with just one lone case anyway. At the very least, an additional piece of coordinated hand luggage would be essential. As Jean will no doubt concur, it is unrealistic for a lady of certain years to travel without a full range of clothing options and, of course, miscellaneous items.

In conclusion, youth's idyllic notion of travelling light is no longer a practical option that I would promote or pursue.

I do hope I have been of some assistance and enlightenment. Hope to see you next Bank Hol at the celeb car boot!
I wish you a Pink Sunshine-y day!

With True Love (aah-aah) True Love (aah-aah) from
ViX 'Fuzzbox' of W.G.A.F.A.W.G.U.I.!!

Forgive me, Bananarama, but I hardly consider 'Bop bop shoo be do-wah' to be a responsible example of someone 'really saying something'. On the contrary, the phrase is gobbledegook, and yet another precedent, together with the appalling spellings of Slade, of how the English language has fallen into decline in recent times.

Dear ~~Maudlin Noshery~~ Sad Café,

Re: 'My Oh My'

I feel your pain, ~~Miserable Chophouse~~ Sad Café, and even suspect that we may have been at the same house party after an All Star 11 at Alderman Rogers Park in 1979. I too ended up sick of laying up in bed (you know) for three days or more to ease my head, and upon waking on the first morning was alarmed to find that in my unconscious state a (still) unknown assailant had covered my face entirely in Mary Quant Cheek Stick and glued two spent Party Popper cartridges to either temple with Gloy gum.

It <u>was</u> a 'just a question of time, ~~Depressed Canteen~~ Sad Café, but unlike your good selves I was not aware of my diabolical visage until long after quizzical looks at the chemist where I dropped in for a tin of Andrews on the way home.

One is therefore most empathetic that you looked in the mirror, and saw the Devil; he was looking at you, fortunately prior to such a shameful pharmaceutical excursion, ~~Run-down Hashery~~ Sad Café.

One can only pray that the clandestine makeshift Mephistopheles facial graffiti artist was apprehended, Sirs, or at the very least placed on a retainer by Gene Simmons.

'Don't criticise', Sad Café. This is actually
very good news; 'I know you can take it', and
hope that you now see that there is no further
need to 'cry oh cry'.

Yours,
Derek (and Dave) Philpott

Heyup Pisspotts (sorry) Philpotts,

You have me/us stumped on this one. I can only admit that this song was made up on the spur of the moment (Really? hahah noooooo!!!)

'Twas originally penned as 'Space Gypsies MyOhMy (One in the bollox and one in the eye)' as certain members of the outfit fancied themselves as tinkers.

An actual fact on this was it was played on a radio pop panel programme on release and one of the guests, namely Angus the schoolboy from AC/DC, actually thought it was the Stones, quoting that's the best record they've ever made. True story.

I can't begin to assess the meaning of the lyrics nor would I attempt to, but looking in the mirror and seeing the devil looking back was prob an assessment of how much white lining had gone on the evening before (Boy, was I wasted). Hey, but don't criticise you know I can take it!

The cohesiveness of the lyrics suggest enrolment into the Lyric Poetry Master Awards alongside Lewis Carroll's 'Jabberwocky', or Lear's 'The Owl and the Pussycat' etc. etc. but this never happened due to record company executive malfunction (Suuuurpriiiiise!!!)

Talking of which, this rambling nonsense was released as a follow-up to a ballad which sold half a million units. I rest my case yer honour as the obvious follow-up was another slowie n'est ce pas? Alas what do us mere strolling players know of such things.

I'm going back to bed to ease my head, and the tv will be on by my side, I always knew that I would!

Space Gypsy signing out

Dear Ozzy Osbourne,

Although admittedly the locomotive going off the rails could 'have a screw loose', or be unstable or unbalanced, it can by no means be a 'Crazy Train'. Any lunacy involved would actually be on the part of an 'unhinged' driver.

Dear Mr Woolley, Camera Club,

Re: 'Video Killed The Radio Star'

As someone who did indeed listen to 'the
wireless back in '52' and is now the proud owner
of a full Comet Home Entertainment System,
I must say that I find your 'futurist smash'
somewhat perplexing.

'Video', as I am sure you are aware, originates
from the Latin 'videre'; it means, of course,
'I see', or 'I am seeing'. A person's sight,
however, cannot itself cause a fatality,
regardless of whether or not the victim is an
aural broadcasting personality.

I am aware that your use of the word 'video'
may refer to a 'video recorder' or a cartridge
inserted into said device in order to reproduce
taped imagery upon a television screen. While
this interpretation is perhaps more likely, I
still fail to see how such an item could cause
the death of a 'disc jockey'. However, I did
once witness 'Diddy' David Hamilton drop a
Betamax copy of <u>Footloose</u> onto his toes at the
Portsmouth branch of Our Price sometime in the
mid-1980s, resulting in some discomfort for the
diminutive mid-morning presenter. Incidentally,
he did not exclaim 'Oh-a-a-a oh' but merely
cursed mildly. (Perhaps the incident would have

been more painful for a taller DJ, for example
Peter Powell, or Ed 'Stewpot' Stewart.)

I wish to make one further point. You express
concern that 'in my mind and in my car, we can't
rewind, we've gone too far'. With regard to
motoring, may I suggest that you safely execute
a three-point turn, before retracing the final
section of your car journey. Concerning your
difficulty with your tape recorder, a useful tip
may be to turn the cassette over and utilise the
fast-forward feature. I fail to understand how
these two operations are related.

Your clarification with regard to the above
disparities is eagerly awaited.

Yours sincerely,
Derek Philpott

Dear Derek,

As an art student in the 1970s, I drove a dilapidated Ford Popular motor car, which sported a broken cassette deck that couldn't *rewind*. Thus the only way to repeat a track was to eject the tape, turn it over, re-insert, *fast-forward*, eject, re-insert and finally press *play* – hoping, incidentally, that the tape had stopped in its desired position. Hence my reference to 'car' and 'rewind' – the relevance of which you almost guessed correctly – three-point turns notwithstanding.

As for instances of fatalities caused by dropped video tapes – even in the early days of massive reel to reel VTR machines – I expect these amount to precisely zero.

Now, further to your main question: everyone knows that 'Video Killed The Radio Star' is a reference to J. G. Ballard's dystopian visions of the Near-Future – a commentary on how New Technology impacts upon our lives in society, at home, in the workplace etc. We might say that this transition from an 'analogue' to a 'digital' world is affecting the evolution of the human species as a whole; but there's an even simpler explanation for the song's provenance.

Between 1950 and 1959 in Post-War England, the biggest Radio Star was not even a human – but a ventriloquist's dummy, fashioned with the likeness and mannerisms of a precocious, cheeky schoolboy. Archie Andrews was loved by the millions of listeners who tuned in each week to his broadcasts from the BBC Radio Theatre. Archie and his 'operator' Peter Brough were a hugely popular and successful Variety act.

While the audience was seated yards away from the stage, with performances aired only on the 'Wireless', Archie maintained the illusion of total realism and believability – but Fate had a nasty shock in store: the BBC promoted the programme to appear on their new-fangled Television Service. The cameras and lights showed no mercy and the audience could see, for the first time, Peter Brough's lips move! Archie was merely a puppet after all, and the fans were devastated. The show was axed and the act never recovered.

And so, it was literally the act of 'seeing' that brought the biggest Radio Star's career to an undignified end.

You have correctly observed that 'video' in Latin means 'I see' and to describe a single viewer in the present tense, in the context of our song narrative, is numerically and historically inaccurate; the indicative perfect conjugation i.e. 'we saw' would have indeed been more appropriate.

However, I'm sure you'll agree that Viderunt Killed The Radio Star doesn't seem to have quite the same ring to it. I do hope this helps to clear things up.

Yours Sincerely,
Bruce Woolley

Dear Shakatak,

I mistakenly happened upon your splendid jazz-funk classic whilst typing too fast on YouTube looking for Great Whites getting irate with cock-sure tourists in cages under water on holiday.

'It feels like the right time' to observe that, unless 'Night Birds' is a nocturnal air freight or courier company specialising in delivering flowers and chocolates, 'with the love they bring', to built-up areas, the operation in question is 'Easier Said Than Done'. One can find no record of any post-sunset active species, not even the Eastern whip-poor-will, Caprimulgus, Australian owlet-nightjar, North Island brown kiwi (none of which admittedly are 'Living in the UK'), or indeed a cuckoo on a late shift, having homing instincts, Shakatak.

Sadly, therefore, unless a romantic message is attached to the legs of a common carrier pigeon not too fatigued to swoop down on the street way past its bedtime, and even then unable to kiss the day goodbye on account of being hampered by the possession of a beak, we fear the concept of your chill-out anthem to be somewhat 'out of this world'.

Yours,
The Philpotts

Dear The Philpotts,

Thank you for your interest in our jazz funk combo. The mere fact you were searching for Great Whites leads me to think there is a whiff of white supremacy afloat? I do hope I am wrong and that I am having a 'Manic & Cool' moment and, of course, I need to remind you we are a multicultural unit. I feel, given your wild life rantings, you need to look at life a little differently and assess things 'Day by Day'. I hope that upon stumbling upon our brand of music, you will be educated in appreciating good legendary British Jazz Funk as opposed to surfing for innocent wild sea life ripping the shite out of gormless caged divers.

Please don't let my abrasive reply phase you; we really would love you to come to one of our concerts in the near future as our personal guest. Just contact us at https://music.utatouring.com/offices/london/ and ask for a Mr Mark King.

Kindest Regards,
Jill (Shakatak)

Dear Mr Shrimpton off of ~~Backbone Poke~~ Spinal Tap,

One wonders how folks may lend a hand in a hell
hole. It is my understanding that the afterlife
punishment area is not a tortuous dug-out but
an ethereal environment designed to inflict
torture upon those who have been a 'wrong 'un'
upon the earthly plane.

Furthermore, to elicit aid from persons also
encumbered within the eternal tormentous pit
would surely imply that they are also in it
at the same time and are therefore completely
incapable of aiding you in your escape.

Lastly, if once out you want a girl to get you
back there, was not the first mission a complete
waste of time and resources?

We look forward to some, but not too much,
perspective.

Yours,
The Philpotts

Dear The Philpotts,

I am Vic Shrimpton, the third of my clan to be the drummer in Spinal Tap. My brother Mick was the first until he exploded onstage, an event which was impressively captured on film for the rockumentary in the time before camera phones. My long-lost twin, Ric, who later took to the stool, was last seen in Japan attempting to barter his dialysis machine in exchange for drugs.

From what I have been told by Mick prior to his irreversible detonation, Spinal Tap were not in a Hades dug-out but a dank boarding house in Belgium... we were vindicated recently when Trump arrived in Belgium to thousands of protesters... he has been quoted as saying that Brussels was like 'living in a hell-hole'.

The only reason they had to get back there was because they'd left in such a bloody rush that they'd forgotten their ****ing passports.

Yours,
Vic Shrimpton

Dear Diamond Head,

Although very sorry to hear that your mother was a witch (she was burnt alive), I must say that considering the last faux sorceress execution was that of Janet Horne in 1727, that would make you all at the very least about 270 years old. I must say, you all look very chipper!

Dear Mr Generator,

<u>Re: 'A Plague Of Lighthouse Keepers'</u>

Your slur upon illuminated hazard alerting
citadels, vis-à-vis the insinuation that they
are janitored by deadly infectious disease,
is totally unacceptable. 'Lighthouse Keeper'
is a career choice, Van, and not a viral pest
primarily carried by rodents and spread to
humans via fleas. I must say that I find your
occupational slander to be unconscionable,
and if you must insist in bringing your
current concept of illness/job songs to their
farcical conclusion, may I suggest that your
next 'offerings' be entitled 'A Minor Head
Cold Of Quantity Surveyors', 'A Pandemic Of
Occupational Therapists', 'An Influenza Of
Management Consultants' and 'A Radical Outbreak
Of Landscape Gardeners', and have done with it.

Yours sincerely,
Derek

APPROVED

MR GENERATOR

Dear Sir,

In all serious-otherliness you may have mistaken my meaning.

The plague of which we speak is not, in fact, an illness, but a gathering.

As in:

a pride of lions,
a murder of crows,

so

a plague of lighthouse keepers.

I'm very glad to shine a light on this at last.

Van, of that Graaf-ness.

Snowmen do not 'bring' snow, Wizzard. The rotund effigies are <u>constructed</u> from the substance.

Dear Mr Buckthree,

Re: The Future's So Bright, I Gotta Wear Shades

I trust that this letter finds you well,
Timothy, and hope that you do not object to the
over familiarity of my addressing you by your
Christian name.

Speaking of which, one is perplexed by your
dazzling days-to-come ditty, which seems to
imply that the donning of Christian Lacroix,
Dior Reflected or Reactolite Rapide eyewear and
'getting good grades' (presumably a reference
to Oakley High Grade Collection Frogskins or
attaining the optimum degree of polarisation)
can in some way protect the wearer from a
promisingly portentous glare.

Whilst not an expert of ophthalmic minutiae,
one is quite confident that even were a bright
future able to be viewed, it would be 'seen'
merely symbolically, as an amalgamation of
prosperity and contentment, as opposed to
transmutating into a literal phosphorescence
likely to scorch unprotected retinae.

Momentarily assuming your model to be
feasible, however, and without wishing to
be disrespectful, one is disheartened in
the contemplation that such optimism has

historically been so tragically and maladroitly
shared by, amongst others, the 35th President
of your wonderful country, the maverick 'Wall
of Sound' innovator, and Travis Bickle and the
Reservoir Dogs (who are admittedly fictional
characters), all of whom suffered decidedly
unsavoury fates despite their tinted lens
desirable destiny effulgence anticipations.

Finally, one is alarmed that a nuclear
scientist - especially one so dementedly
mentored via a visually restricted 'crazy
teacher', could be in contemplation of spending
'fifty thou a year' on a lot of beer. The
disastrous potential of excessive Budweiser
quaffing whilst possibly embroiled in the
engineering intricacies of atomic weapon
design, coupled with your questionable
voyeuristic tendencies, could, in your own
case, render a long-term sparkling outcome
debatable.

In order therefore that you <u>do</u> do alright
and things will continue to go great, it is
recommended your alcoholic drinks budget be
heftily downscaled and a 'Ray Ban' be placed
upon your X-Ray eyes-abetted Peeping Tom
shenanigans.

Yours,
D. Philpott

Dear Mr Philpott,

Profuse thanks for your interesting and entertaining letter! I have no problem with your use of my 'Christian name' (whatever that means), though I do struggle to understand 'over familiarity'. If it means going beyond familiarity to the point of unfamiliarity, then I appreciate your concern. But you can call me whatever you want. May I call you Phil?

As to your doubts about the possibility of being able to actually view a bright future, shades or no shades, I'd like to thank you for adding the word 'effulgence' to my vocabulary. Obviously my song didn't provoke any effulgent moments for you, which begs the question: does irony exist apart from the perception of it? Probably not, but I'm glad you at least caught the glimmers of sinister foreshadowing in my protagonist's alcoholic tendencies. Thanks for getting 'over familiar' with my song!

Best to you,
Pat

Dear The Troggs,

Apologies, The Troggs, but my mind's made up by the way that I feel. I fear that the sensatiotn that you are experiencing is not love at all, but in fact paraesthesia.

If the feeling grows, rather than subsiding, it is clearly indicative of a need for medical attention.

cc. Wet Wet Wet

Dear The Strawbs,

My friend Duckie Walker (so-named after his overfondness for sandwiches) used to be a shop steward and assures me that union membership only applies to employees during their tenure. Therefore, unless he is mis-informed, if death occurs prior to retirement I fear that you are mistaken.

Of course, it can be argued that certain unions, such as The Musician's Union and, arguably, Gary Puckett's old band, do not have a cut-off age. However, these are the only examples that we can think of at the moment whereby one can be part of the confederation 'til the day you die ('til the day you die), especially as we are watching <u>Pointless</u> at the same time as writing this letter, and are preoccupied by trying to think of obscure films starring Harrison Ford.

I look forward to hearing from you if, related to any of the points outlined, 'I don't get you' or have not 'read between the lines'.

Yours,
D. Philpott

Dear Mr Pillpott,

Thanks for writing. Letter writing has become a lost art to many these days; yours was amusing none the less. Must say, your fan letter and 'Part of the Union' song query was the most out of the norm letter I ever received. Almost put me at a loss for words. You sound like quite the chap, with a bit of time on your hands for such ponderings and musings.

Firstly, your friend Duckie Walker sounds like he's been eating more than sandwiches. But, who could blame him on wondering about a song from an album, quite literally 'Bursting At The Seams'? Yet, anyone can probably attest that a union man (or woman), is indeed, loyal, tried and true beyond retirement, 'til the day they die'. Even maybe then some, into the beyond and afterlife. Now there's something to ponder.

I digress. As you argued, you are right; certain unions such as you mentioned The Musician's Union, Gary Puckett's Union Gap, don't have an age cut-off.

Perhaps, if you give it another think, even more obscurity will come to mind – like Student Unions, Micro-Unions, and even The World's Oldest Profession Union Local 69.

Which all leads up to what is the point of all this? Especially considering you are in the midst of watching *Pointless*, the game show where obscurity rules, further obstructing the 'thought process' on trying to think of obscure films with Harrison Ford in them.

I will make a point to mention that while Harrison Ford and I both share the same last name and even bear a slight resemblance to each other, we are not related, as far as I know.

Getting back to the song and onto the subject of unions – much more fun can be had with the lyrics. Forget about unions. Change 'union man' to say, 'pirate man' as in *Pirates of the Caribbean*, changing a few more lines, and yo ho, ho – the song takes on a whole new life.

Right. I must leave you now, ending with:

Now I'm a union man
Amazed at what I am
I say what I think, that your fan letter stinks
Yes I'm a union man.
Good night, ladies and gentlemen!

Best,
John Ford of the Strawbs

Dear Mr Springsteen,

Especially around December our 3-bar electric Winterwarm is an absolute lifesaver. We activate it via the rocker switch on the side, thus, contrary to your yelled assertion can assure you that we CAN start a fire, start a fire without a spark!

Dear Mr Schneider of The B-52s,

It has come to my attention that you are at this moment 'heading out' to a decidedly debauched cabin, the very existence of which contravenes Atlanta's rigid anti-solicitation laws.

It is feared, Sir (the sleazy lodge's actual whereabouts being directly flagged up from a distance of 15 miles courtesy of a discoloured pointer at the side of the road), that it will not be very difficult for it to be found by the anti-vice policemen prior to its inevitable raid. Your 'juke box money' will then sadly be construed as funds intended to purchase an engagement in unsavoury activities.

It is therefore recommended that if you absolutely <u>must</u> venture to this floozy hovel, that you restrict yourself to enduring other attendees' Wurlitzer selections.

Yours Sincerely,
D. Philpott

'I ain't solicitatin'; I'm socialatizin''. So there!

Fred Schneider

Unbound
Liberating ideas

Unbound is the world's first crowdfunding publisher, established in 2011.

We believe that wonderful things can happen when you clear a path for people who share a passion.

That's why we've built a platform that brings together readers and authors to crowdfund books they believe in – and give fresh ideas that don't fit the traditional mould the chance they deserve.

This book is in your hands because readers made it possible. Everyone who pledged their support is listed below.

Join them by visiting unbound.com and supporting a book today.

Sue Abson	Lynne Ashton	Pamela Barnes
Carroll Adgo	Nesher Asner	Niall Barraclough
Sunny Ahluwalia	Pete Attard	Kerry Barrass
Robert Alfonso	Mandy Austin	Barbara Barry
Leigh Allen	Nick Austin	Dave Bascombe
Beth Allgood	James Aylett	Phil Batsford
Dan Allsobrook	Joel Baass	Lennart Bauer
Michelle Anchor	Rockula Bacchus	Bill Beabout
Michael Anderson	Afc Baggy	Stefy Bear
Peter Andrew	Julian Baldieri	Phil Beddow
Stan Andrews	Daniel Banks	Johnny Beegoad
Michael Anyon	Eileen Banks	Ruth Behan
Cath Arine	Nicola Banks	Angie Belcher
John Armes	Richard Barden	Andy Bell
Paul Ashby	Willy Barden	Keith Bell
Jenny Ashcroft	Alison Barham	Steve Bell
Peter Ashman	Jonathan Barnes	Julian Benfield

Sue Bennett
Knut Berg
Ruth Bertram
John Beskow
Steve Best
Kevin Bilton
Bruce Bingham
Will Birch
Charlie Bird
Jon Birkett
Dave Black
Ali Blair
Jill Bloomfield
Ian Blundell
Dimitrios Bogiatzoules
Sonia Bolton
Bombay Bad Boy
Jon Bond
Charlie Bonner
Phil Bonshor
David Boothman
Alex Borchardt
Stephanie Bosworth
Helen Bound
Andrew Bradley
Matthew Bradley
Brad Bradstock
Tomas Bremin
Kathy Brickell
Keith Brickell
Andi Bridges
Helen Brown
Lisa Brown
Gordon Brunton
Rob Buckle
Sarah Eaves Bukowska
Kath Bull

Martin Bullard
Tara Bullas
Martin Bulmer
Ali Burns
Stewart Burns
Alex Burton-Keeble
Mark Butler
Joey Jock Cairns
Maurice Canavan
Maurice John Canavan
Mandy Carroll
Howard Carson
Karen Carswell
Joo Carter
Laura Catchpole
Vicki Cattermoul
Steve Catto
Mark Cavill
Rick Challener
Nicky Chance-Thompson
Ian Chennell
Bindi Chimp
Nic Christie
Eric Clappedout
Ade Clark
Gary Clark
James Clarke
John Clarke
Phil Clifford
Gary Clutterbuck
Christine Coalter
Steve Cobham
Diane Cockerham
Gillian Coe
Enrique Cohen
Napkin Cole
Rob Collier

Tim Collieu
David Cooke
Linda Cooke
Roy Corkill
Mark Cottrell
John Coulter
Angela Cranwell
Angela & Joshua
   Cranwell
John Crawford
Tony Creek
Roi Croasdale
Pete Crompton
Harry Cronic Junior
Jo Crosby
Jane Croucher
Kate Croucher
Alice Croupier
Lorri Cumming
Christopher John
   Cunningham
Eddie 'Eddiebaby'
   Cunningham
Lesley Curtis
Richard Cutting
Steve Dabner
Dave Danby
Martyn Daniel
Rich Davenport
Mark Davies
Matt Davies
Kevin and Elaine Davis
Peter Davis
Peter Davis
Lucinda Davison
Lucinda Davison
   remembering Stefani
   Davison

Jules Dawes

Lance Dawkins

Audrey Dawson

Lucy Dawson

Terry Dawson

Michael Day

Simon Day

Jeroen De Wijn

Nikki De-bozie

Brian De-Vine

Hazell Dean

Tracey DeeCee

John Dexter

Wilf Dickie

Florent Die

Traci-Ann DiSalvatore

Hippopothomas Dolby

Tim Dorney

Stan Dow-Chalet

Lana Dragicevich

Simon Draper

Katy Driver

Mick Ducknall

Jo Dudley

Lorny Dune

Lesley Dunn

Maggie Dunne

Stephen Eastwood

Barnaby Eaton-Jones

John Edmunds

Alcuin Edwards

John Edwards

Stephen Edwards

Matthew Egglestone

Lynne Ellis

Tim Ellis

Steve Elsworth

Emmett Elvin

Gary Enstone

Tom Enzerink

Erik Erlandsson

Clare Estelle

Adrian Evans

Venus Evans

Dirk Ewald

Kevin Fabian

Ian Fairweather

Claire Farrell

Mark Farrow

Olivia Fawkes

Melanie Fayers

Anthony Fedorowicz

Toni Ferretti

Justin Fisher

Samantha Fisher

Jack Fleming

Gary Flood

Aimee Flower

Holly Fogg

Peta Foley

Andrew Forcer

Lee Ford

Sally Ford

Clare Franklin

Ian French

Cheetah Gabriel

Matthew Gallaher

Claire Gallant

Russ Gannicott

Jo Gannon

Tim Gardiner

Claudia Gardner

Susan Gardner

Jeszemma Garratt

Jorge Garzon

Mike Gatiss

Jeremy Gaynor

Mike Gervasi

Stuart Gibb

Adrian Gilbert

John Gill

Adam Glover

John Glover

Dave Goddard

Garry Godfree

Susan Godfrey

Alan Goodfellow

Benjamin Gott

Jan Gow

James Gower

Paul Graham

Sarah Graham

Libby Graham-Metz

Mark Grant

Nikkinic Green

Ted (Tractor) Green

Steve Griffith

Sue Groffman

Martin Grogan

Chris Groom

Judy Groom

Steven Grose

Boaz Halachmi

Nick Hale

Duncan Hall

Tony Hall

Kim Halliday

Jim Hamshaw

Steve Hancock

Abby Hannum

Jason Hares

Simon Harper
Anne-Marie Harris
Pete Harris
Rob Harris
Tony "The Cleft" Harrison
Ian Hartley
Jonny Hartley
Sharron Hather
Ged Hayes
Johnny Hayward
Jack Healy
Jaine Henderson
Mary Henderson
Robert Hepwood
Emily Hetzel
Mike Higgins
Paul Higham
Stuart Hildersley
Michael Hill
Steve Hill
Mr & Mrs R N Hine
Robert Hingley
Adrian Hird
Jane Hoe
Paul Calvin Hollywood
Tim Holmes
Derek Holt
Lisa Horton
Neal Houghton
Howard & Lin
Linda Hubbard
Scott Hubbard
Phil Hudson
Neil Hughes
Tim Hughes
Andy Humeniuk
Kath Humphrey

Leanne Hunt
Ian Hunter
Fiona Hutchings
Mark Hyde
Rhiannon Ifans
Anton Ingham
Doug Inglis
Richard Inwards
John & Judith Ireland
Johari Ismail
Ali James
Ian James
Tim James
Gary Jefferies
Lorraine Jeffery
Chris Jenkins
Jo Jex
TJ Johnson-Howe
Simon Joiner
Alex Jones
Anita Jones
Ian Jones
Novella-Rose Jones
Nev Jopson
Nick Jordan
Hanneke Joustra
Cyan Jugo
Fiona Karimjee
Shaun Keefe
Alan Keegan
Stephen Keightley
Gez Kelly
William Kelly
Lee Kendrick
Dan Kieran
Stevo Kifaru
Michelle Knight

Jerry Kornelius
Katia Kreutlein
Nik Krowshaw
Ian Kucera-Skinner
Andy Kynaston
Céline Lafoucriere
Nicola Laker
Sarah Lambert
Keith Lamley
Harry Lang
Martin Langmead
Warren Lapworth
Gary Lazarowics
Cooper Lazarowics-Muir
Pieman Le Bon
Vianney le Masne
Jane Learner
Bridget Lee
Sue Leighton
John Leonard
Charles LeVerrier
Justine Levett
Shebee Lewington
Steve Lewington
Debz Lewis
Rebecca Liddle Blair
Mark Lingard
Roger Ljunggren
Amanda Loftus
Andrew Long
Scott Lonski
Francesca Lord
Angela Loughran
Miranda Loughrey
Steve Lunt
Jacky Lynch
Iain MacInnes

Seonaid Mackenzie
Tracey MacKenzie
Paul Mancini
Jennifer Mandli
Tony Manley
John Mann
Martin Mann
Mark.C
Alison Marrs
Bradley Martin
Maria Martin
Paul Maskell
Frances Mason
Duncan Mawson
Frances McCabe
Martin McCann
Kim McCann Henry
Rachel McCarthy
Siobhan McClelland
Wilf Mccourt
Brian McGill
Geraldine McGuckin
Graham McKay-Smith
Ailsa McKillop
Deb McLaughlin
Paul McMahon
John McShane
Melanie McVey
James Medd
Nick Mellish
Steve Mercy
Unicycle Michael
Aaron Miller
Alison Millett
Douglas Milne
Gregory Mitchell
Julianna Mitchell

John Mitchinson
Ian Mobley
Peter Moltesen
Barry Monks
Tom Moody-Stuart
Jessie Moorhouse
David Morgan
Alex Morris
Cheryl Morris
Kirsty Morris
Philip Mudge
Marcel Muller
Simon Mulligan
Pete Murphy
Tania Murphy
Ewen Murray
Mark Musolf
Al Napp
Anthony Nash
Chris Nash
Carlo Navato
Kieron Neaves
Kenny Nelson
Terence Nesbit
Neville 42
Su Newton
Andy Nichol
David Nicholson
Sarah Nightingale
John Noble
Ray Nugent
Martin Nunn
Mslin Nystrom
Lesley O'Hara
Sarah O'Leary
Bee o'Wulf
Phil Oates

Mark Oliff
Onomatopoeia Records
Colin Osullivan
Michael Oualid
Richard Owen
Wayne Oz Owen
Antony Pacitti
Scott Pack
Tanya Palmer
Le Panayi
Damon Parker
Steph Parker
Robert Parkin
Chris Parkins
Jeff Parry
Judith Parry
Duncan Parsons
Kirk Parsons
Ruth Patrak
Sarahjane Patterson
Gavin Paul
Chris Payne
Simon Payne
Della Perrett
Claire Perry
Derek Philip
Chris Phillips
Andy Phippen
Stephen Pieper
Plane Groovy
Janet Polkinghorne
Jon Pollard
Justin Pollard
Richard Ponsford
Kevin Poore
Ray Powell
Rachel Power

Margo Pratt
Lawrence Pretty
Andrew Price
Heather Priestley
Steve Proctor
Steve Prudence
Katy Purvis
Mike Pye
John Quinn
Tim Quy
Emiel Ramakers
Darren Ramsay
David Ramsay
Steve Rauer
Jason Read
Stuart Reed
Lydia Reeves
Sean Reid
Alexander Maestre
    Rentsch
Lee Rew
Teraza Rew
John Michael Richards
    (The Central
    Scrutiniser)
Dom Richardson
Gail Rimmer
Billy Ritchie
John Roberts
Stephen Fluff Roberts
Yvonne Roberts
Jan Robinson
Patrick Robinson
Simon Rodrigues
Colin Rogers
Kimberly Rogers
Chris Rollason

Tim Romain
Steve Ronksley
Lennaert Roomer
David Rose
Robert Rosendahl
Hanna Ross
Matt Rosser
Helen Roughley
Rob Rowles
Roy Russell
Lisa Ryan
Terry Ryan
Bryan Sakolsky
Donna Saunders
Alan 'Sav' Savage
Wendy Savage
Tony Sawford
Vicky-Leigh Sayer
Charles Scheim
Kristina Schlegel
John Schofield
Bill Schuneman
Derek Scott
John Scott
Paul Scott
Paula Seddon
Chris Sell
Fiona Sharp
Paul Sharp
Sally Sharp-Paulsen
Jon Shaw
Andy Shewan
Lorna Shields
Dave Sieloff
Rob Sim
Valerie Sinatra
Mark Singleton

Joe Skade
Ellie Skinner
Neil Skinner
Scotch Skintight
Megan Sloan
Dave Smith
Eileen Smith
Jeremy Smith
Lou Smith
Michael Smith
Mike 'Smudge' Smith
Robin Smith
Dee Snelling
The Snoutorious P.I.G.
Rachael South
Peter Southwood
Christopher Spalding
Michele Spiller
Adrian Spray
Kit Spring
Moose Springsteen
Simon Stacey
Dave Stainer
Colin Stanworth
Marc Starr
Helen Stephens
Alan Stevens
Helen Stevens
Madeleine Stone
Nigel Stone
Fergus Stonehouse
Arron Storey
Noel Storey
Richard Stott
Sue Summerill
Caroline Sutcliffe
Katie Sutcliffe

Chris Sutton	Mark Tynan	Dave Whyman
Gergely Szalay	John Underparr	Gregory Wieting
Elizabeth Tait	Colin Ursus-Thanatoid	Maurice Wilkie
Chris Tarplee	Ann-Marie Van de Ven	Rob Wilkinson
Diane Taylor	Daniel Varley	Lorna Willetts
Georgette Taylor	Claude Vecht-Wolf	Fiona Williams
James Taylor	Paul Vincent	Zoë-Elise Williamson
Leila Taylor	Chris Von Trapp	Samantha Willis-Foreman
Woodstock Taylor	Andrew Wade	Christopher Wilson
Mike Taylor-Wilson	Travis Wagner	Amy Winemouse
Frogwell Tetley-Hugg	Geoffrey Wakem	Jackie Winn
Gail Thibert	Ian Mij Walker	Gary Woodbridge
Chris Thomas	Steve Walker	Jane Woodmansey
Maurice Thomas	Vicky Walker	Roy Woodrow
Jim Thomason	Dan Wall	Bruce Woolley
Kevin Thompson	Willy 'Won't He' Wallace	Wendalynn Wordsmith
Gavin Thomson	Emily Walters	Stephan Work
Mike Scott Thomson	Becca Ward	Alec Worrall
Dawn Thorpe	Alex Wareham	Spike Worsley
Tristan Thorpe	Matthew Watson	Kanye Worst
Mark Tibenham	Keith Watterson	Ken Worthing
Gaz Tidey	Neil Weatherall	Ben Wray
Andy Tingey	Steve Wells	Glynn Wright
Emma Tinsley	Jon Western	Melvyn Wright
Aidan Tisdall	Jonathan Westwood	Andy Wyatt
Mike Toms	Sharon Wheeler	Lynn Wyeth
Nick Toone	Tony Wheeler	Alicia Yaffe
Chris Topham	Paul Whelan	Jon Yard
Stephen Towler	Mark Whenman	Mike Yeaman
Solitaire Townsend	Ralph White	Chikako Yoshida
Julia Trimmer	Jane Whitehead	Douglas Young
Paul Turpin	Steve Whitehead	Reg Young
Dan Tutten	Frank Whitney	Rob Yuill
Robert Tyler	Paul Whitworth	Jennifer Zameic

Frederic Raphael v ... educated at Charte ... lege, Cambridge. H ... sion of widely prais... was *Obbligato* (1956). He has also written two biographies, *Somerset Maugham and his World* (1976) and *Byron* (1982), translations (with Kenneth McLeish) of *The Poems of Catullus* (1976) and of *The Oresteia* (1978, televised as *The Serpent's Son*), and plays for radio and television.

His screenplays include *Nothing But the Best* (1964), *Darling* (1965), for which he won an Oscar for Best Original Screenplay, *Far from the Madding Crowd* (1967), *Two for the Road* (1968), *Daisy Miller* (1974), *Rogue Male* (1976), *The Best of Friends* (1979), *Richard's Things* (1981) and *Oxbridge Blues* (1984).

For his highly acclaimed sequence of television plays, *The Glittering Prizes*, Frederic Raphael was the winner of the Royal Television Society's Writer of the Year Award. His most recent novel, *After the War*, has been made into a 10-part TV series for which he also wrote the screenplay.

He is married and has three children.

by the same author

Obbligato
The Earlsdon Way
A Wild Surmise
The Graduate Wife
The Trouble with England
Lindmann
Darling
Two for the Road
Orchestra and Beginners
Like Men Betrayed
Who Were You With Last Night?
April, June and November
Richard's Things
California Time
The Glittering Prizes
Sleeps Six
Oxbridge Blues
Heaven and Earth
Think of England
After the War

FREDERIC RAPHAEL

The Limits of Love

FONTANA/Collins

First published by Cassell & Co. Ltd, 1960
First issued in Fontana Paperbacks 1989

Copyright © Frederic Raphael 1960

Made and printed in Great Britain
by William Collins Sons & Co. Ltd, Glasgow

For my wife
and for our son, Paul

absit omen

Contents

Book One FREEDOM AND NECESSITY

1	Introduction to a Family	13
2	Background to a Marriage	33
3	Conflicts of Friendship	48
4	Conflicts of Love	74
5	'And Afterwards . . .'	89
6	A House and a Garden	109
7	Not Even Your Own Father	128
8	Family Parties	148
9	Friends and Relations	162
10	Two English Dances	183
11	Capital Matters	208

Book Two THE ONE AND THE MANY

1	The Middle Way	225
2	The Fifth Form at Benedict's	237
3	The Team Spirit	250
4	My Son, My Son	273
5	The Only Girl in the World	282
6	The Escapers	299
7	The Strangers	318
8	The Return	339
9	The Final Analysis	354

Book Three PROCESS AND REALITY

1	Some Investigations	383
2	Time Future and Time Past	397

3 The Thaw 420
4 My People, Israel 438
5 MacDonald Smith and Associates 453
6 Men on the Run 472
7 Two Deaths 494
8 Satellites 517
9 A Sunday in November 536

The author would like to express his thanks to the Master and Fellows of St John's College, Cambridge, for their award to him of the Harper Wood Studentship for Creative Writing. It was during his tenure of it that much of the preliminary work for this book was done. Without it, he might never have made a start.

BOOK ONE

Freedom and Necessity

ONE

Introduction to a Family

1

HOW TO MAKE a beginning with them, that was the problem. Otto Kahane stood on the pavement of Cricklewood High Street and shivered. How to present oneself to one's own people. Perhaps he should never have claimed them. Hannah's voice on the phone had conveyed the message: 'You, Otto, good God, for years we've thought – for years we've thought about you. All through the war, Issy was saying "I wonder what happened to Otto" and now here you are. Well, well. Sure come over; as a matter of fact, we're in the middle of moving house, but sure come over. Do you remember the address? I'll give you the address.' He stood on the grey pavement while the cold-faced crowds went by. Otto wore a long black coat and a black hat. He held a small black attaché case. His shoes were black too, and even his face had a blackness in it; the eyes were black and the flesh had a thinness through which it seemed black bone was pushing. Otto Kahane had spent two years in Dachau Concentration Camp.

How to make a beginning with them. The cold pricked through the cracks in his shoes, but Otto did not move. The cold was part of him.

He had never thought he would have a family again; sooner or later he would die in the camp. Then they had made him come out. He stood on the pavement in Cricklewood High Street. They had made him come out. 'Have you any family?' they asked. He looked at the slag of corpses in the camp yard. 'Those are my family.'

The American major said: 'Do you have any family living?'

'Family? Have I got any family?' The major rolled his eyes at a colleague and smiled at Otto. 'That's right: family.' Otto shook his head: 'No family.'

'All dead?'

'All dead,' Otto agreed.

'Have you no relations anywhere?'

'They'll think I'm dead too.'

'Never mind what they'll think, sir. Have you any relations anywhere in the world?'

'Not in America,' Otto said.

'Well, where?'

'England.'

'You have relations in England?'

'I think. Maybe they're dead. I don't know.'

He steered back towards the hut. An MP arrested his return.

'I'm afraid you'll have to go now, sir. We're putting this area out of bounds.'

The shops in Cricklewood High Street were full of good things. The faces of the people were in bloom with the cold. The shops were bright and full of good things. Otto nodded to himself. Once he had belonged to a world like this. In Poznan before the Germans came, there were shops as good as this. Better, Otto smiled to himself and nodded again, much better. Otto Kahane: Watch Repairer and Jeweller. That was nice.

Hannah Adler had said 'Certainly come over' and was truly glad that Otto – that any relation – was alive and safe. It just happened they were in the middle of moving and Isidore was in a bad mood. The pantechnicon parking outside the shop had set him off. 'So what are the customers supposed to do? Help carry the furniture?'

'The men won't take long,' Hannah said.

'I was against this from the beginning. I don't want to move. I don't see why we have to move. I was against moving from the beginning.'

'You know you like the house,' Hannah Adler told her husband. 'You picked it.'

'I picked it! I paid for it.' Isidore Adler leaned forward reproachfully. 'I paid for it.'

'You know you always wanted to live in Golders Green.'

'I never wanted to. What's wrong with where we always lived? Here.'

'You want to live in Cricklewood High Street all your life?'

'I gotta get back to the shop,' Isidore said. 'You want we should go bankrupt?' He stopped half-way down the stairs and said: 'That's what we will do too. We'll go bankrupt. Spend, spend, spend. Where's all the money coming from?'

'You should worry.'

'I *should* worry,' Isidore said. 'I've got plenty to worry about, believe me.'

After Otto had phoned, Hannah rubbed thoughtful hands under her elbows. What a day for him to arrive! Everything was packed ready for the men and there wasn't anywhere to sit down at the shop, let alone put someone up. As for Woburn Road, the decorators were only just out: they wouldn't be straight for days. Oh well, Otto could have Colin's new room, at least until he was demobbed. She shrugged herself into action. They had a duty to Otto: he was family.

Hannah went to the head of the stairs: 'Mr Goldberg.'

'What can I do for you, Mrs Adler?' The face of Mr Goldberg, Isidore's manager, appeared around the door-post from the shop. He was a dark, rather fat man in a white overall which fitted him like a pillow-case.

'Ask Mr Adler to come up for a minute, will you?'

Isidore appeared. 'So now what is it?'

'I want to talk to you.'

'Got customers. What is it?'

'Come up here, I'll tell you.'

Isidore Adler looked up the stairs at his wife. Two firmly planted feet at the top of the stairs would take no arguments. With a sigh, Isidore began to climb. Five pounds ten, those shoes.

'Guess who just landed in England,' Hannah said.

Isidore swung his head. 'The Russians?'

'Otto Kahane.'

'Otto Kahane?'

'That's right. Your uncle Otto. Uncle Otto, surely you remember? He visited us before the war. Surely you remember your own uncle?'

'Sure I remember,' Isidore said.

'He's coming to stay with us.'

'OK, fine. He's coming to stay with us. Fine. Now will you do me a favour, Hannah? Let me get on with serving the customers before they all cross the road to Mr Sainsbury?'

'Mr Sainsbury,' Hannah said, 'doesn't sell smoked salmon like Adler's smoked salmon.'

'Listen, don't give 'em any ideas, please, do you mind?'

'Don't talk like that, Issy. You know I don't like it. Talk properly, please.'

16

'I got work to do. I can't stand here talking. I got work to do.' Isidore turned and went for the door. 'Anyway,' he said finally, 'he's not really my uncle.'

'Of course he's your uncle.'

'He's not my uncle,' Isidore said. He pointed a finger at Hannah. 'He's my half-uncle. By marriage. In law.'

3

Otto Kahane passed his small black attaché case from one hand to the other. In the camp he had to move. He had to move, for otherwise he would be dead. Here there was no need to move. No one's eye fell on him for not moving. It would not be unreasonable to stand on the kerb of the Cricklewood High Street all day. Where was Adler's delicatessen? It might as well have been in the next world. Freedom was too much for him. A prisoner, there had been cause to act; free, there was none. In the camp he had belonged; to be on this street, on this day, was a mere accident. It was stranger to stand on this pavement than to be in the camp. How did one make a beginning with people? Break into a family, and become part of it? Wasn't it a kind of liberty? These people, his relations, he would be a nuisance to them. He had no will to join himself to them. They didn't want him. No necessity bound him to them.

'Excuse me,' the schoolgirl said, 'can I help you across the road? You look as if you're stuck.'

Otto said: 'That's very kind of you, very kind indeed.'

Julia Adler took her great-uncle's arm and led him across the road. 'Now will you be all right?' she asked.

'I'm looking for Adler's delicatessen,' Otto said.

Julia's face went solemn. 'That's where I live.'

Otto nodded at the two dark eyes. 'Of course, of course, the daughter.'

'Well, I suppose you'd better come along,' Julia said, tightening the belt of her blue overcoat. 'Ought I to know who you are? Because I'm afraid I don't.'

'I'm your uncle. Your great-uncle I suppose it would be.'

'Are you? I don't remember seeing you before.'

Otto smiled. 'The last time I saw you, you were' – he put his hand at waist level – 'so high, so high. No.' He held his hands apart. 'So *long*. You know?'

'Oh, really? That must have been a long time ago.'

'Thirteen, fourteen years.'

'Have you come to help with the move?' Julia inquired.

'The move? I'm sorry – '

'I should have thought everyone knew about it by now.'

'I've been a bit,' Otto smiled distantly, 'out of touch.'

'Oh, have you been living abroad or something?'

'That's right,' Otto said. 'I've been living abroad.'

Hannah Adler came down the street, her hands held out in welcome, her head tilted on one side. 'Uncle Otto!' she said, and embraced him. Julia was relieved by her mother's arrival. There were so many relations, and she had nothing in common with any of them. Mostly they spoke in Yiddish (yes, they'd started already) and she couldn't understand their jokes or their problems or anything about them.

The tears were running down Hannah Adler's cheeks. She kept patting Otto's face. 'This is your uncle,' she said to Julia. 'Your Uncle Otto. He came to visit us from Poland. Years ago. Nineteen thirty – oh, what was it? – nineteen-*thirty* it must have been.'

Otto nodded. 'Nineteen thirty.'

'Nineteen thirty,' Hannah said. 'Where are we now? Nineteen – '

'Forty-five,' Julia said, 'for heaven's sake. It's nearly *Christmas*.'

'Fifteen years ago,' Hannah said. 'Fifteen years, can you believe it?'

'That's right, nineteen thirty.'

18

'Nineteen thirty,' Hannah said.

'Mummy, for God's sake.'

The two of them were standing nodding at each other, the tears coming into Otto's eyes. The removal men came clattering past. Hannah put her finger under her nose and sniffed. 'Honestly, I don't know what I'm crying about. Come in and see Issy. He'll want to see you.' She guided Otto into the shop. 'Julia, run upstairs and get me a hankie from my drawer, will you, dear?'

Isidore was serving a customer. Hannah called out, 'Isidore, come here.' Isidore came out from the cooked meats counter, rubbing his hands on his white overall. 'Here's Otto to see you.'

One of the assistants said: 'Mr Adler, how many points is the pineapple?'

'Sixteen,' Isidore said. He and Otto looked at each other. Isidore smiled and lowered his eyes, with a little nod. 'Well, Otto. Well, how are you?'

'I'm not so bad, Isidore. And you?'

'I'm not complaining,' Isidore said.

'Much,' said his wife. 'Come on, let's go upstairs.'

'I can't leave the shop, Hannah, do you mind? Good morning, Mrs Spira, be with you in a minute.'

'You go on,' Otto said, 'don't worry about me.'

Julia came in. 'One hankie.'

'Thank you, dear.'

'That's all right.' She started out of the shop.

'Would you mind taking your uncle upstairs – find him somewhere to sit down?'

'Come on, Uncle Otto,' Julia said, with a resigned shake of her pigtails.

Isidore stood there, looking after them: 'How long is he going to stay?'

'I don't know.'

'What's he gonna do?'

19

'You serve Mrs Spira,' Hannah said. 'We'll worry about that later.'

4

Woburn Road was on the Finchley side of Golders Green. It contained neat, detached houses. Number fifteen had a green, fish-scale roof. Green tile pillars supported the portico above the front door. The face of the house was made up with white stucco. The dormer windows had green tile lids. Isidore cared little about the house one way or the other, but it was certainly an improvement to be able to garage the Wolseley on the premises rather than two streets away, as he had done for years. Still, he didn't see the sense in moving. As soon as you'd saved enough money to live decently in one neighbourhood, you had to move to another you could only just afford. What was the sense in it? He'd always lived above the shop. He liked to live above it. That way you knew it'd still be there in the morning. He fumbled to find the new door key in the new leather key-ring Hannah had given him. Always finding excuses to spend money, that was Hannah. Well, she had put the *mezuza* on the doorpost. That at least was something.

'Anybody at home?'

'We're in here. In the lounge,' Hannah called back.

Isidore went in. 'In the lounge,' he mocked. 'In the lounge.'

'What's wrong with the lounge?'

Isidore sat down on the couch. 'Very comfortable,' he conceded.

'Glad you like it.'

'How much did it cost?'

'I bought it with my money,' Hannah said, 'so don't give me any of that, please.'

Otto said: 'It's a nice place you got here, Issy.'

'So it should be, for the money.'

Hannah said: 'We're just having some tea, do you want some?'

'Where's the girl?'

'Tanya? In the kitchen, doing supper. Susan and Ben are coming over.'

'Why so soon?'

'Susan so wanted to see the house.'

'Bringing the baby?'

'Of course. Did you know I was a grandmother?'

'You told me,' Otto said.

'A lovely little girl. Three months old.'

'My son-in-law's a Communist,' Isidore said. 'What do you think of that?'

'A Communist!' Otto acknowledged the fact.

'Whassa use having children?' Isidore stood up suddenly. 'What's Julia doing?'

'She's upstairs, working.'

'Mm, I think I'll go wash my hands. Where's the bathroom? Where's my room? Where's anything? I don't know. Moving after all these years. What's the sense in it?'

'I'll show you. Then you can come down and have a little chat with Otto. He's longing to have a good talk.'

'Where's my suits?'

'Hanging in the wardrobe. Everything's put away.'

'Smell of paint everywhere,' Isidore said.

'It's nice and fresh,' Hannah replied. 'Mind the carpet on the stairs. It hasn't settled yet.'

Isidore returned, having washed his hands and had another shave. Whatever he might think of Ben, he always shaved twice a day if there was company for dinner. When he came downstairs again, Hannah left the two men alone in the sitting-room. Although Tanya, the Adlers' Hungarian housekeeper, was looking after the supper, there were a great many things to do: the house was far from straight.

Hannah was always happier if she was doing something. She hated to sit still. She loved change. No sooner had she bought one thing than she was thinking of replacing it. Her energy was made dynamic by her love of change.

Isidore said, 'Do you want sherry?'

'Sherry?'

'A glass of wine before dinner, it'll do you good.'

'It's very kind of you, Isidore.'

'Don't know where anything is any more,' Isidore groused. 'Hannah. *Hannah*.'

'What is it?'

'Where's the sherry?'

'In the cocktail cabinet, exactly the same.'

'I dunno how you're expected to find anything in this house. I never wanted to move. What's the sense in moving?' Isidore handed Otto his sherry. 'How are you?' he mumbled. 'In yourself I mean. Not sick, are you?'

'No, thank you, Issy, no, I'm fine. They wouldn't let me into England without a clean bill of health, as you say.'

'How long are you going to stay?'

'I – I don't know. It depends. I only got a visitor's visa. After that, it depends.' Otto sipped his sherry. It seemed very fiery to the old man.

'How old *are* you, Otto?' Isidore demanded, as though the answer would solve a long argument.

'I forget.'

'You must be older'n me. I'm fifty. You must be older'n that. You must be near seventy.'

'Your father was older than me,' Otto said. 'I don't think I'm as old as seventy. Anyway, it doesn't matter.'

'Won't be easy to get work,' Isidore said. 'If I was you, I wouldn't say I was more than fifty.'

'What's it matter what you say?'

'In this country, Otto, it matters, believe me. I know. I've been here a long time now. Believe me, I know. What can you do?'

'It's a long time since I did anything,' Otto said. 'Maybe too long.'

Isidore stared into the fire. 'Is there any news of the family?' he asked, after a long silence.

'Family?'

'Is there anyone left?'

Otto shook his head. 'No, no one left.'

'Did you say *Kaddish*?' Isidore asked.

'I did what I could, Issy. I couldn't do any more.'

'We'll take care of you, Otto. You don't have to worry. We'll look after you.'

Otto stretched out his claw-stiff hands to the fire. 'I don't want to be a burden,' he said.

'You're not going to be a burden to anyone,' Hannah said, coming into the room. 'What's Isidore been saying to you? Isidore, what have you been saying to him?'

'I didn't say anything,' Isidore said angrily. 'Where's the potato crisps? I can't find anything in this house. Where've you put the potato crisps?'

'They're in the usual place.'

Isidore scowled as Hannah produced them from the drawer above the cocktail cabinet. 'Where's Julia?' he demanded.

'She's in her room. Working. How many times do I have to tell you?'

Julia was determined not to come downstairs until she heard Ben and Susan arrive. If there was one thing she hated, it was elderly relations who came to stay. During the war, whenever any members of the family were bombed out, they always ended up at Hannah's. Julia recognized them from afar – their accents, the cut of their clothes, their beards, their eating habits, she knew them all. Now there was another of them. If only she hadn't helped him across the road! No, that was a terrible thing to think, but she would certainly never have done it if she'd known he was a member of the family. She crouched down

23

over her Livy. Otto wasn't really any concern of hers. Livy was the real brute.

5

The front doorbell rang. Julia had been waiting for it (she had read the last sentence in her Livy at least five times) and now she galloped to the head of the stairs to see if it was Susan. Tanya opened the door. 'Good evening, Mrs Simons.' It was! Julia rushed down the stairs.

'Hullo, Susie.'

'Ssh,' Susan said. 'The Thing's asleep. Thank God.'

'You can put her in my room,' Julia whispered.

'God, I've had a time getting here. The buses were packed. Ben here yet?'

'No, not yet,' Julia said, peering in at the baby.

Susan plonked the Karri-Kot on Julia's bed and drew a deep breath. 'I'm absolutely exhausted,' she said. 'With a capital X.'

'Susan, that you?'

Susan went to the door. 'Coming, Mummy. Come on, Julia, before the Thing wakes. I don't think I could bear that on top of everything else.'

'You think you've got troubles,' Julia said. 'You should have troubles like we've got troubles.'

'Why, what's the matter?'

'We have Otto staying with us.'

'Oh yes, Mummy mentioned that someone had turned up.'

'*Susan.*'

'*Coming.* What's he like?'

'You'll see,' Julia said. 'We'd better go down.'

Isidore said: 'Where's your husband?'

'Probably still at work,' Susan said. 'Hullo, Uncle Otto.'

24

Otto blinked out of the glare of the fire. 'And you're Susan. Well, well. Last time I saw you –'

'You were so long,' Julia whispered.

'You were a little girl. Hard to believe.'

'I'm not that old-looking, am I?'

'Do you want a drink, Susan?' Isidore asked.

'I would like something. Gin, I think.'

'Gin and orange?' Hannah suggested.

'That'll do fine.'

'She's a woman,' Otto said. 'She's a fine-looking woman.'

'Here, I'm only twenty-two,' Susan said. 'I'm not quite in my grave yet.'

'How's the baby?' Hannah asked, giving Susan her drink. 'You didn't know I was a grandmother, did you? How is she?'

'The Thing? Asleep, I hope.'

'You shouldn't call her that. Julia, do you want something to drink?'

'I think I'll have an orange juice.'

'You shouldn't call her that,' Hannah said again.

'Mummy, you've forgotten what it's like to have kids. The only time it's really fun is when they're asleep.'

'I had three,' Hannah said. 'I ought to know what it's like.'

Isidore said: 'When's Colin supposed to be coming home?'

'You know perfectly well he's been kept on. He's not sure yet.'

'He's a major,' Isidore said.

'An officer!' Otto said. 'Well, well. An officer. And the last time I saw him –'

Julia and Susan looked at each other and started to giggle. Susan said: 'Don't, Julia, don't.'

'In the Engineers,' Isidore said.

'Stop giggling,' Hannah said, and started to catch the

disease herself, though she didn't know what the joke was. 'You two girls ought to be ashamed of yourselves.'

'The Engineers! Well, well.'

'He's an architect, you know. He studied architecture at London University. He's a qualified architect. Delicatessen business wasn't good enough for him. They wanted him to be an architect, but – ' Isidore ducked his head to his sherry. 'It's a good profession.'

'You know you wanted him to be an architect,' Hannah said.

'I wanted him to be an architect? Why should I want him to be an architect? Do I need a new house? Was it my idea we move to a new house?'

'It's a very nice house, Daddy,' Susan told him. 'You should be very glad to be out of Cricklewood.'

'And what's wrong with Cricklewood? I don't see anything wrong with Cricklewood. My daughter marries a Communist and suddenly Cricklewood isn't good enough. I never heard of such a thing.'

'*Isidore*, we don't want to hear any more about that.'

Isidore said: 'You can't find anything in this house. I don't know where my suits are; I don't know where anything is. I don't see the sense in it. I just don't see the sense in it. My glass is empty.'

'He's tired. He's had a tiring day.'

'I should say I've had a tiring day. Moving vans – customers – today everything happened! And on top of everything we have to move house. What a day!'

'You've already included moving house in "everything",' Julia said. 'You can't have it twice over.'

'I have enough trouble with school fees,' Isidore snapped. 'The bills I have to pay.'

'I wonder where Ben is. He should be here by now.'

'Up to no good somewhere.'

'Daddy, if you're going to be horrid, I'm going.' Susan's

mouth was shaped in a smile, but there was a gloss of tears in her large eyes.

'You pay school fees and for what? Your daughter ends up by going off and marrying a good-for-nothing, nebbisher nobody.'

'Daddy, I warn you.'

'You know what Colin said –'

'We all know what Colin said and we don't want to know any more.'

'Tessa Franks, now she's a nice girl,' Isidore said. 'Colin's going to marry a *nice* girl.'

'I suppose I'm not a nice girl, is that it?'

'You can draw your own conclusions.'

Susan stood up. 'I've had just about enough of this.'

'Your father doesn't mean what he's saying. He's had a tiring day.'

'So've I had a tiring day. As soon as Ben gets here, I'm going to ask him to take me home.'

'You may as well have supper,' Julia said. 'It's smoked salmon to start with.'

'And I made a cheesecake,' Hannah added quickly.

Susan sniffed against her finger. 'I'll stay for the cheese-cake. After that I don't guarantee anything.'

Ben Simons was a short, muscular fellow with a brisk, bustling manner. He came in rubbing his hands against the cold, a quick friendly smile on his face. 'What ho,' he said. 'Sorry to be late. Hope I haven't kept you.' He kissed Susan on the forehead. 'How's tricks?'

'She's asleep,' Susan said.

'Hullo,' Ben said to Isidore.

'Evening.' Isidore smiled shyly, as though he feared Ben had heard what had been said about him. 'You don't know my Uncle Otto, do you?'

'Good evening, Uncle Otto,' Ben said, shooting a hand out for the old man.

27

'Well, now perhaps we can have some supper,' Isidore commented.

'Nice place you got here,' Ben said, nodding round the room. 'Very nice.'

'I chose the couch,' Hannah said.

'Very nice. Very nice indeed.' He seated himself and sprang up and down, gravely. 'Nice bit of springing.' He made an appraising face at Susan.

Tanya came in to say: 'Dinner is served.'

As they stood up, Susan was near Ben. 'What kept you so late?' she asked.

'Oh, something came up at the *Worker*.'

'Don't they think you've got any home life at all?'

'Susan, honestly, I'm here, aren't I?' He moved away. 'Come along, Uncle Otto. Supper-time.'

Otto had not risen with the rest of them. He was still staring into the fire. They all turned to wait for him to join them. He rose slowly and there were tears in his eyes. 'It's wonderful,' he said. 'It's wonderful to be with a family again.'

Hannah took his arm and led him forward. 'You can stay with us just as long as you like, Otto, for just as long as you like.'

The family went in to supper.

6

'What've you been doing since you were liberated?' Ben asked.

'*Ben*, perhaps he'd rather not talk about it – '

'For nine months I was in the hospital,' Otto said, cupping his hands round the cup of coffee which Hannah had given him. In spite of the size of the meal and the electric fire in the room, he hoarded warmth. 'In the American hospital, that was. That's how I come to learn to speak English.'

'You could speak English when you were here before.'

'I forgot in the camp. It was better to forget. The people who remembered too much, they died the first. They carried their memories like they was suitcases and they wouldn't put them down. They dropped everything else but they hung on to their memories. That such a thing should happen to me, they used to say, a banker, a rich man! It doesn't do to think such things. You got to adapt yourself, you know what I mean?'

'Surely they weren't all rich people?' Susan said.

'No, they weren't at all. But in there every memory was like a memory of riches, you know? You remember? You remember? So it used to go on. They killed themselves with memories.' Otto shook his head. 'The ones that had time.'

'Terrible,' Isidore said. 'It's a terrible thing. Thank God it's all over.'

'I was one of the lucky ones. I was really lucky, you know that?'

'You shouldn't talk about it,' Hannah said. 'It only upsets him. You shouldn't really talk about it.'

Otto wept, staring into the false fire. 'I'm all right, I'm quite all right. Believe me.' He sniff-smiled. 'You know how I came to survive the camp? There was another Otto Kahane in that camp. I knew him' – Otto smiled deprecatingly – 'slightly. He was a doctor. You know? The Germans had a kind of respect for doctors. Dr Kahane, he worked in what they called the hospital. I don't know, maybe he was some kind of relation or something, anyway, we looked alike. Not what you'd call identical, but alike. In there, you looked alike. One morning, one fine morning, Dr Kahane died. He was dead in the hut. Every morning there were people dead in the hut, ten, twenty, maybe, every morning, sometimes more.' Otto rolled the coffee cup between his palms. 'I thought to myself, Kahane, you were a good man, you were a doctor, but now you're dead and what use can you be to us? And then I thought, a doctor, now that's someone people respect. So I took the doctor's place. I let myself die, and I kept the doctor alive. And that's why I'm here today.' The old man gulped air. 'To be a doctor, that's a wonderful thing.'

'Doctors!' Isidore said. 'They'd take your last penny. I've had more trouble from doctors.'

'I wanted to be a doctor,' Ben said.

'Did you, Ben? You never told me.'

'I decided to be a doctor of society instead,' Ben grinned at his wife. 'Better to cure society than to cure the individual.'

'So you're going to cure society?' Isidore rose angrily.

'Cut out the cancer in our midst,' Ben agreed.

'And what's that?'

'The Capitalist system,' Ben said.

'Communist rubbish,' muttered his father-in-law. 'Ought to be ashamed of yourself. You don't have to tell me about Communism. I used to know a lot of Communists.'

'Did you, Daddy, where?'

'In Poland. Jewish,' Isidore added with his usual abruptness. 'Jewish people.'

'Go on, what were their names?' Ben was smiling.

'I don't remember their names. Boss gave 'em the sack.'

'Serve 'em right,' Ben said. 'Filthy reds!'

'They were filthy reds. That's what my boss said. Told 'em they could take their Communism somewhere else.'

'And a good job too.'

'Anyone who was a Communist, they killed them first,' Otto said. He sat back and closed his eyes.

Julia looked at her watch. She had some Livy still to do. Hannah pointed at Otto. 'He's asleep.'

Isidore giggled. 'He's fallen asleep.'

Ben said: 'Poor old chap.'

'You can't really believe it, can you?' Susan said.

30

'I can. I can believe it,' Ben replied. He ran his hands back over his head. 'We've got to believe it.'

Hannah Adler stood up. 'Piece more cheesecake before you go?' she asked.

Otto's mouth fell open. The flesh was tensed over the ridge of his nose. Hannah Adler took the cup from between his hands.

Julia said: 'Mummy, how long is he going to stay?'

'We've got to look after him. He's been through a terrible time. Someone has to look after him. He is your uncle, you know.'

'He's Daddy's uncle,' Julia said. 'Be accurate.'

Isidore said: 'Has he got any pyjamas? What's he got in his case?'

'It won't be diamonds.'

'When Colin comes home, he's going to expect to have his own room.'

'When Colin comes home, I'll look after him. He won't need for anything, believe me.'

'It's another mouth to feed.'

'If you're too mean to feed your own family – ' Hannah whispered.

'I'm not too mean to feed my own family. It's just more expense. Do you think it isn't more expense? It stands to reason it's more expense.'

'Stop complaining all the time,' Hannah said. 'And keep your voice down.'

'Who's complaining?'

'You're complaining, Daddy,' Susan said.

'She marries a Communist and then she says I'm complaining.'

Ben said: 'If you haven't got room for Uncle Otto when Colin comes home, let us know. We can find room for him.'

Isidore Adler swung his head angrily. 'Did I say we haven't got room for him? When I want you to look after

31

my family, I'll let you know. Until then, I'll take care of 'em. OK? Thank you very much.' Isidore looked at his uncle. 'I don't know what's wrong with Cricklewood,' he said. 'I never wanted to move in the first place.'

When Susan and Ben had left, Julia went straight to her room, leaving her parents with the problem of how to get Otto to bed. She had imagined that with the move into the new house they would at least be spared further intrusions from the family. She pitied Otto, of course, but what more could she do? It was like having a brand-new garden and deliberately transplanting a weed into it.

Susan's feelings were much the same. 'I can't help being glad I don't live with the folks any more. The old boy's very sweet and all that, but think of living with him! I mean he just doesn't belong.'

'Who does belong, Susan?'

'Sorry, old boy, I seem to have said the wrong thing.'

'I don't think it'd be so awful to have him living with us.'

'Ben, you weren't serious?'

'You know me, Susan. I'm always serious.'

TWO

Background to a Marriage

1

IT HAD BEEN HIS seriousness which first attracted Susan. They met at a party given by Monty Lazarus in his Hampstead 'studio'. Susan was in the WRNS and she had gone straight from the office to the party. Monty had been in the RAF until he was invalided out, and Susan arrived to find a host of RAF types in uniform making the most of his drink. 'Grab yourself a glass of something, sweetie,' Monty called to her.

'Thanks, I'll do that thing,' she sang back.

One of the RAF men, attracted perhaps by the American accent she affected in those days, wrinkled his nose at her. 'Dish,' she heard him observe. Susan unpinned her tricorn hat and shook her hair loose. She was wearing it in a pageboy and it bobbed, glistening dark, on her neckband. The RAF man was still looking at her. She removed her jacket and slung it over the back of a chair, swivelling away from the RAF man so that he might appraise the jut of her breasts under the white shirt. She took off her tie as well.

'How far do you propose to go with this?' a voice asked. She twisted to find its owner. He was sitting against the wall on a wooden stool sketching the crowded scene before him.

'Thus far and no further,' Susan said, looking back down over her shoulder.

'They're straight,' the stranger said.

Susan chucked back her hair. 'Aren't you coming to join the party?'

'Not particularly.'

The RAF man was dancing with a redhead in black slacks. Susan turned back to the stranger. 'What are you doing? Drawing?'

'That's right.' He held the board round for her to see.

She had expected an amateurish fuzz. It was amazingly vivid. 'Gosh,' she said, 'you know what you're doing! You really know what you're doing. My name's Susan by the way – Susan Adler.'

'Hullo, Susan-by-the-way. My name's Ben-in-case-you-don't-know-Simons.'

'I must have a drink,' Susan said. 'Preferably gin.'

'I'll see what I can find.' Ben stood up. He was an inch or two taller than she was. 'Want anything in it?'

'Orange, if there is any.'

'Hullo, girl,' Bryan Hammond said. He was a captain in the Pay Corps. His father, Leonard Hammond (Hamburger) was a chartered accountant with a large practice. Bryan had the grinning confidence of one who knew that the parents of any girl present would be glad to have him for a son-in-law.

'Hullo, you,' Susan said. 'My, don't you look something!'

'Wait till I get a crown on my shoulder,' Bryan said.

'It'll make a nice change from a chip, I suppose.'

'Hey!' Bryan came closer. 'Hey, just what do you mean by that? No, come on, Susie, tell Bryan what you mean.'

'I don't mean anything, silly.'

'How about coming out with me next week?'

'What night?'

'Thursday.'

'I'm busy Thursday night,' Susan said.

'I'll take you to Hatchett's.'

'I went to Hatchett's last week with Cyril Gluckman.'

'Come on, Susie, you know I'm crazy about you.'

34

'Drink,' Ben Simons said. 'Wotcher,' to Hammond.

'Hullo! It's our Communist friend.'

'Who?' Susan said. 'You? Are you a Communist really?'

'Rabid red,' Hammond said, 'that's our Ben. One of Uncle Joe's star pupils.'

'Are you – you know, a member?'

'Can't you see the bomb sticking out of my pocket?'

Monty Lazarus limped over and took Hammond's arm. 'Bryan, do me a favour, laddie boy. Go and rescue Gloria before she goes under to that massive Yank. He may be gorgeous, but he weighs at least three tons!'

'So you're a Communist! What do you do for a living? Or shouldn't one ask?'

'I work at Pearson's.'

'Pearson's? What do they do?'

'Make Christmas cards,' Ben said.

'What do you do?'

Ben took the sketch block and wrote 'MERRY CHRISTMAS – YULETIDE GREETINGS' right across it and turned it round for her to see.

'Why?' Susan asked.

'Because I was invalided out.'

'Out of what?'

'The pits,' Ben Simons said. 'One of Ernie's boys, that's me.'

'There she is! That's the dish I was telling you about – hey, dish, come over here.'

'What do you want?'

'Come and cut a rug. Come *on*.' The RAF man's name was Reg Ashworth. He danced energetically and his feet flew about. On the beat, he pressed Susan to him and whispered, 'You're a dish.' After several dances, to Glenn Miller mostly, he dragged her out on to the roof.

'You've got to be good,' Susan warned him.

'I am good. All the girls say so.'

She let him kiss her a few times. 'You're a real dish,' he

35

told her. 'Am I?' 'You certainly are.' He fumbled at the top button of her shirt. She struggled away from him: 'No.' 'Hey, what's the matter?' Susan stood up and tossed her head. 'Dish! What's the matter?'

'I think you ought to leave something for another time,' Susan said. She went back through the roof-door into the studio. No one had ever touched her breasts. She went to get her jacket from the chair.

'Hullo,' she said, 'you still here?'

'I'm still here,' Ben Simons said.

'I think I'm going home. I've had enough.'

'When am I going to see you again?'

'You haven't asked me yet.'

'How about next Thursday?'

'Thursday's fine,' Susan said.

2

After they had been out together five or six times Ben asked her to come to supper with his mother. He lived with her (his father was dead) above the Tobacconist-Newsagent-Confectioner which she and her helper, Mrs Karminsky, another widow, ran in the Commercial Road. A bomb had fallen almost next door and the shop was crutched with wooden billets. A crack had developed in the wall and the wind piped and wailed, flapping the trapping of thick brown paper which Mrs Simons had pasted over the hole. In the little living-room behind the shop Susan learned why Ben was in the Party. Mrs Simons sat, straight-backed, in an old rocking chair, her knitting looped over gnarled hands. She was a dainty woman with a very large and rounded bust. Her eyebrows were pencilled in a fashion imitated from Marie Tempest to whom, in her youth, she had once been compared. 'Before the war,' Ben told Susan, 'you couldn't go down some of the streets round here. There was a little girl in Brick Lane – '

'Josie Feldmann's girl,' Mrs Simons anticipated him.

'Denise Feldmann,' Ben agreed. 'Some of them caught her all by herself one afternoon after school – threw her through Lecash's plate-glass window. A kid of eleven or twelve. She's still got a limp from it.'

'Didn't anyone do anything?' Susan asked. Of course she knew that there had been trouble in the East End before the war, but Isidore had sternly forbidden any of his children to go anywhere near the place. During those years he had steadily increased his contributions to Jewish charities. When there was a rumour that the BUF proposed to branch out in North London, Isidore had added a large donation to the Police Orphanage to his other charitable acts. Of this kind of expense alone he never spoke to his family, so they were able to live their childhood without fear or anxiety. It was not so with Ben. 'Do you know what the British Board of Guardians said to do? Ignore them! Turn the other cheek. Ignore them when they shoved kids through plate-glass windows! You couldn't bloody ignore them even if you wanted to.'

'Language, Ben,' Mrs Simons said, without looking up.

'All the same we stopped 'em all right the day the marchers came.'

'We? Who's we?'

'Oh, Jews and Gentiles, workers, intellectuals, everyone.' He said 'intellectuals', very seriously.

'Was that what made you a Communist?'

'Not entirely,' Ben said. 'They weren't all in the Party, of course. But afterwards I wanted to know what explanation there was for what was going on. It all seemed so confused. The Communists were the only people who had the answer. The Guardians – '

'You broke your father's heart becoming a Communist,' Mrs Simons said.

'He approved of what we did that day, Mama, believe me,' Ben said. 'The day we turned the marchers back. I came in that night with a bloody nose, do you remember?'

'Do I remember? Do I *remember*? Your father and I, we was half out of our minds with worry. He walloped you. Now that I do remember.'

'He came into my room later and he kissed me.' To Susan: 'You didn't know my father, but believe me, that was something. He came into my room and he kissed me. He approved of what we did that day all right.'

'That I never knew,' Mrs Simons said. 'He came in and kissed you, did he?'

'He came in and he kissed me,' Ben said.

'He'd never join the Communist Party,' his mother said. 'He believed in being free, your father.'

'Free? Free to do what? Free to spend all his life paying interest to the bank? Free to spend all his life smarming up to Councillor Franks – ?'

'Your father didn't smarm up to no one. I won't have you speak like that of your father.'

'He didn't *understand*,' Ben said. 'If you can't understand, you can never be free.'

'Understand what?' Susan asked.

'The forces at work in society,' Ben said with a tiny smile. 'Until then, it's like – it's like fumbling in the dark.'

'I'm sure I could never understand them,' Susan said.

'Of course you could. The fundamentals anyway.'

'*Marx*?' Susan said. 'I'm sure I couldn't.'

Ben said: 'I'll lend you some books.'

'All right,' she said. 'And then I must be going. Thank you so much for the wonderful supper, Mrs Simons.'

'My Ben's a good boy,' Mrs Simons said. 'And he's got a good job.'

'Here we are.' Ben rushed back with a bundle of books. 'I'll see you to the bus. I'll just see Susan to the bus, Mama.'

'See her to the bus, certainly,' Mrs Simons said, resuming her knitting. 'She's a nice girl.'

At the bus stop Ben said: 'I want to marry you, Susan.'

His arms went round her under her coat. His lips found her mouth. She closed her eyes and pressed up against him. His hands went to her breasts. 'Yes,' she said, 'yes, Ben.'

As the bus appeared, Ben handed her the books. 'You'll have to master these first,' he grinned.

She laughed and blew a kiss to him as the bus drew away from the stop.

3

Susan climbed the wooden staircase to the flat above the shop. She longed to tell someone of Ben's proposal, but there was no one. Her parents would be horrified (they hadn't even met him yet) and Julia was much too young and too childish to appreciate such things.

There remained only her brother Colin. She had not seen him for three years. He had been with the Engineers through the African campaigns and was now supposed to be in Sicily. When he left home he was a shy, brick-faced youth, with none of the luminous confidence which Hannah had passed on to her two daughters. He had never had any girl friend except Tessa Franks and he was as awkward in her presence at the end of the six years he had known her as at the beginning. Still, he must have changed in all the time he had been away. Susan went to her room and sat down at her dressing-table to write to him. When she had finished, she got into bed and opened the first of the books Ben had given her. It was called *A Textbook of Dialectical Materialism*. But the excitement of the evening had been too much for her. She closed the book and went to sleep.

During the weeks that followed she did make real efforts to understand the books that meant so much to Ben, but it was not until he introduced her to Sid Forbes, who worked with the Crown Film Unit and had done a documentary about the Soviet War Effort, and to Stan Halloran, a red-bearded Irishman who had done two years in Parkhurst before being in the pits with Ben, that Susan was persuaded to join the Party. The left-wingers whom she met welcomed her with such warmth that she could think of nothing nicer than being one with them. The people at the Admiralty were friendly enough, but after work they usually scampered off to their families or their fiancés; only the dullest of them remained to provide company for Susan. As for the gang she used to know, she was tired of them: their only idea of an evening out was to go to a show, to dance until two in the morning, and finally to maul you about in the taxi on the way home. That Susan was the prettiest of the girls merely meant that she was the one whom they mauled with the greatest fervour; the whole evening was dominated by the foreknowledge of the ride home. With Ben it was different. He did not kiss her in order to gain a return on his investment. He was serious. And Susan did want people to be serious about her. Not only was Ben serious, but so, too, were the people to whom he introduced her. They talked till two and three in the morning, these bus drivers and trades unionists, writers, painters, journalists, even those who had to go straight on to a night shift or would have but a couple of hours' sleep. Susan would stumble up the stairs beside the shop quite drunk with words; at last she felt armed against the empty bourgeois life of Cricklewood; at last there was an escape from flippancy, from being merely the prettiest girl in the room. Now she was something else in addition; she was taken seriously, as well as being the prettiest girl in the room. It was a revealing feature of bourgeois life, she considered, that if you wore spectacles and braids, men chatted solemnly to you for hours (as they did to Corinna Coleman), but if you happened to have a good figure and a pretty face, you were subjected to an interminable flow of badinage and *double-entendres*. What she liked about Socialists was that they didn't think that just because you were pretty you didn't want anything but compliments and suggestive remarks. Sid Forbes, for instance, had spent a lot of time telling her about the Soviet Union and the kind of changes that would be necessary after the war, but though he stood very close to her he never started touching her by mistake on purpose or using any of those other adolescent dodges at which Bryan Hammond and his chums were so adept. Susan's new friends had better things to do. The evening she put her Party card in her handbag she felt free for ever of the banalities of the gang and the tedium of respectability.

Dressing the next morning, Susan heard her father stamping and shouting in the passage. 'She's no good, I tell you, she's no good. It's like I told you, like I always said,' and Hannah's voice: 'Isidore, for heaven's sake control yourself.'

'The money I spent – education, clothes, a gramophone – for what? So she should marry a good-for-nothing, no-good *scheisser*.'

'Isidore, listen to me, will you, please?'

A door slammed. The angry voices were muted. Susan's first desire was to walk out of the house. Thank God she had to go to work!

'What does this mean?' Isidore shouted at her when at last she went in to breakfast. He was brandishing a Forces Airletter.

'Isidore, do you want the whole street to know?'

'What do I care about the street?' Isidore slapped the letter on the table. 'When the whole street will one day know my own daughter is going to marry a Communist, I should worry that they hear me raise my voice! She's no good. I always said she was no good.'

Susan said: 'Daddy, you're making yourself look quite ridiculous.'

'Ridiculous! I'm looking ridiculous? I will look ridiculous all right, when you marry a Communist; then I'll look ridiculous all right.'

'What does Colin say?' Susan paddled her hand irritably for the letter.

Julia munched her cornflakes in silence. Her eyes switched from face to face. A Virgil was propped against the marmalade, but she was not looking at it.

Colin's letter lectured Isidore on the probable shape of the post-war world and advised him most strongly against letting Susan take the step she proposed. To marry a Communist might have the most disastrous consequences. It was a bit hard, he thought, that one should spend all these years in the army and then find that some fellow who apparently hadn't even been in the Forces was going to marry one's sister. The neat, didactic writing continued in this style over the full surface of the airletter. Admittedly the tone was more in sorrow than in anger; Colin was sure that Susan had been misled and that all she needed was firm guidance from the right quarter. He did not doubt that if Isidore put his foot down and made it clear what marrying such a fellow entailed, the whole thing would blow over. Susan finished the letter and handed it back to Isidore.

'Well?' her father demanded. 'What have you got to say?'

'I've never read such a collection of pompous nonsense in all my life. Anyway, he had no right to tell you what I wrote to him about.'

'It was his duty,' Isidore said. 'That isn't something you'd understand about.'

'Duty, shmuty,' Susan retorted.

There was a knock at the door.

'That'll be Mr Goldberg for his cup of tea,' Hannah said.

Isidore looked at his watch. 'I've got to go down. I'll talk to you this evening.'

'I'm out this evening,' Susan said.

'Who're you out with?'

'Ben. Any objections?'

'*Ben*,' Isidore leered. '*Ben*. Well, don't bother to come back then.'

'All right, I won't, if that's the way you feel about it.'

'Don't do anything stupid,' Isidore muttered and left the room.

Susan looked at Julia. 'What's eating you?'

'Nothing,' Julia said. 'Do you know what "*brattea*" means?'

'Never 'eard of it,' her sister replied.

The rows went on for weeks. One night Susan brought Ben to supper. Isidore was much more polite than she had hoped and Ben quite charmed the old man. When he had left, however, the spell departed too, and Isidore groused as much as ever. Hannah made clumsy attempts to get Susan to go out with other boys, while Isidore alternated promises of fur coats with threats of excommunication. Finally he resumed saying 'You needn't bother to come back' whenever Susan said she was going out with Ben. On the night of D-day, she didn't. By the time she returned to Cricklewood the next evening, Hannah and Isidore had decided to cut their losses. Susan and Ben were married four weeks later. That gave Hannah time to announce the engagement in the *Daily Telegraph* and the *Jewish Chronicle*.

'If only it weren't for the war,' Susan said. 'I'd love to have gone to the Riviera or somewhere.'

'Would you, Susie, why?'

'Bognor isn't very romantic, is it?'

'Romantic?' Ben looked at her sideways. 'You've picked the wrong boy, if you want to be romantic.'

She leaned back against the cushion of the third class compartment, and looked at the small, dark-eyed figure opposite her through lowered lashes. 'I hope not altogether,' she said. In spite of what her parents feared about D-night, they had not yet slept together.

The Wynnstay Hotel was an ugly brick building masked with an iron framework of balconies and pilasters. Nevertheless it was crowded. People had come to the coast to get away from the buzz-bombs. In addition, the Wynnstay Hotel allowed pets; you could hear the gargling of parrots and the squeal of dogs from well down the promenade. 'Sounds just like Daddy,' Susan observed, 'in one of his most crotchety moods.'

'I had my suspicions,' Ben told her, 'as soon as I heard your Mum had suggested it.'

They went into the hotel. A large red parrot furred its feathers and said: 'Good morning.'

'Morning, Comrade,' Ben said.

'*Ben.*'

'What's the matter?'

'People,' Susan grin-frowned.

They did not go up to their room that night until the last dog had been taken out and every parrot was safely blanketed. They leaned against the rail on the broadwalk and Susan fancied she could hear the gunfire from France.

Later, when Ben came in from the bathroom, Susan was

standing naked by the bed. He stopped. For a moment she thought he was going to faint. She said: 'Hullo, it's me.' Her voice was very husky. She cleared her throat, touching her hand to her breast. 'Excuse me!' Ben shook his head. 'What?' she said. 'Ben, what?'

He ran to her and flung himself on his knees in front of her. 'Susie, Susie, Christ, Susie, Christ.' He knelt motionless, with his lips pressed against the curve of her belly. His arms were bound about her thighs. Susan pushed the dressing-gown off his shoulders and ran her fingers along them and up his neck till both her hands were under his chin. She tilted his face up to hers. Her eyes were half-shut. 'Come on,' she whispered.

6

One morning, just as they were about to get up, the hotel alarm bell jangled. Ben went to the door and put his head out: 'What's up?'

'Siren's gone,' snapped an old lady dragging a stiff-legged Peke along the passage.

'Must be a doodlebug,' Ben said, closing the door.

Susan sat up in bed. 'Do you want to go to the shelter?'

'There's a place I'd rather go.' Susan pulled the sheet up. 'They look good in daylight,' Ben said.

'Doodlebugs?'

'You know what.'

'Ben, let's watch it.'

'It? What?'

'No, honestly. The doodlebug. Do let's.'

They went out on to the wrought-iron balcony. 'There it is,' Susan cried. The buzz-bomb was like a sidelong black H in the sky. Flame and smoke backfired from it.

'It's coming this way all right,' Ben said.

'Ben, I'm scared.'

'Scared? There's nothing to be scared of.'

The bomb cut out.

'It's coming down, Ben. It's coming down.'

'It won't be near us. There's nothing to worry about.'

'Ben, I'm scared.' She turned to go into the room.

'Stay here,' Ben said, gripping her arm. 'Stay here. There's nothing to be scared of.'

The bomb tilted down towards the far end of town. It slid behind a hotel. There was a sharp explosion. A shower of muck was dislodged from the window-sill above them and cascaded down. Susan, cowering back, received the brunt. She brushed wildly at her hair. Ben said: 'It's all right. It's only dust.'

Susan said: 'It was in the town. It hit somewhere in the town.'

'I don't think so,' Ben said. He put an arm round her. 'Come to bed.'

'Ben, stop it. Let go of me.' She twisted free of him. 'You hurt me.'

'Come to bed,' Ben said. He was hard with the excitement of the explosion. Susan shuddered and ran into the room and over to where Ben had thrown her things the previous night. Ben did not say another word till they were passing through the hotel lobby after breakfast. The red parrot was there. 'Morning,' it said.

'Morning, comrade,' Ben replied.

Some days later, they were on a hike in the countryside behind the town when they heard the keening of an aircraft in difficulties. They had taken a picnic and afterwards, lying in a field, had watched the thousands of bombers stitching the sky above them, too high to be counted singly. Now this one plane DK5608 came in low over the coast. Flame pumped from its wing. It lurched. It dropped. It held up and hammered forward. Three black spots, like tacks, dropped from its belly. The plane fell away and drove down at the ground.

'Ben, what's the crew of a Dakota?'

'I don't know.'

'It must be more than three. It must be.'

'Could be.'

'He must've stayed in it – the pilot. My God, Ben –'

A black cope of smoke was kicked into the sky. Then came the explosion.

'I suppose he must have,' Ben said.

'My God, my God.' Susan plunged her face against Ben's chest. She was thinking of the RAF man who called her 'Dish'.

'Best thing he could've done. That way it didn't crash on the town. He knew what he was doing.'

'But he *did* it,' Susan said.

'I know,' Ben said. 'It's tough. That's life.'

When they reached the hotel the residents were having tea. The red parrot was in its place of honour in the centre of the lobby.

'Morning,' Ben said.

The parrot said: 'Morning, Comrade.'

THREE

Conflicts of Friendship

1

HANNAH ADLER SAID: 'Where on earth is Archway?'

'Archway?' Isidore muttered.

'It's not far from Highgate,' Susan said.

'Highgate!' Hannah brightened. 'Highgate's very nice.'

'We're going to live in Archway,' Ben said, 'not Highgate.'

'It's not that far from Highgate.'

'Archway is Archway.'

'That's right,' Isidore said. 'Finchley.'

Stan Halloran, the Irishman who had been in the pits with Ben, was helping a salvage collector in the East End and he borrowed the old man's horse and cart to help Ben and Susan with the move. There were many books and other possessions to take from the shop in Commercial Road. Mrs Simons was inclined to be tearful at Ben's departure, but Stan Halloran managed to keep her smiling; in a heavily thickened brogue he promised her that now Ben was out of the way life was just beginning for her. 'I'll be knockin' on the cowshed door when the moon is high above the gasworks,' he assured her. Mrs Simons waved her hand at him: 'You Irishmen, I've heard about you. Get away with you.' She gave him a sidelong glance. 'Yes, I've heard about you.'

Stan said: 'Mrs Simons, I'm asking you to believe me when I tell you me heart's bursting with the passion I'm bearing you.'

Mrs Simons returned with a smile to the shop where Mrs Karminsky was stoutly serving customers, while Ben and Susan tramped up and down with bundles of books and belongings. Mrs Simons did not regard Susan with quite the same approval as on her first visit, mainly because she was wearing a pair of Ben's old corduroy trousers for the move.

'Trousers,' she observed. 'Whatever next?'

'Shorts?' Stan's eyes popped very wide. 'Briefs!'

'When I was a girl women wasn't even allowed in the synagogue. When I was a girl there wasn't even a woman's gallery in the synagogue. Of course, that was fifty years ago.'

'Get along with you,' Stan said. 'You weren't alive fifty years ago.'

'Do you know how old I am? I'm fifty-six. Fifty-seven next birthday.' Mrs Simons struck an attitude. 'I am. You ask Mrs Karminsky if that isn't the truth. Fifty-seven next birthday. When I was a girl there wasn't a gallery for the women at the synagogue. Not that I suppose you ever go to synagogue,' she raised her voice as Ben came down the stairs and into the shop. 'Your father never missed a day. He'd break his heart if he could see you today.'

'I don't think he would,' Ben called back.

'Do your parents go to synagogue?' Mrs Simons demanded, as Susan followed her husband down the stairs.

'Yes,' Susan said. 'Cricklewood. You were at the wedding, weren't you?'

'Oh yers,' Mrs Simons said. 'Very nice. They made you a nice wedding.'

The cart was loaded. Ben, Susan and Stan were about to set off when Mrs Simons hurried out of the shop, a black shawl over her head. A pair of heavy walking shoes had replaced the slippers she wore in the shop. 'Think I wasn't coming, did you?'

'It's a long way, Mama,' Ben said. 'What about the shop?'

Ben's mother smiled and spread her arms. 'So what's Mrs Karminsky for?' She laughed and put her head on one side.

Stan said: 'Come on, Mrs Simons, there's room for one more on top.'

'I don't mind walking. I've got me shoes on.'

'Come on, no arguments. Up you go.' Ben and Stan heaved Mrs Simons on to the top of the cart, where she smiled.

'Forward, Bucephalus,' Stan said, producing a trumpet from under the driver's seat and sounding a tucket. The cart creaked slowly down the Commercial Road, Mrs Simons shrug-waving to her neighbours who stood in doorways or leaned, fat-armed, out of upstairs windows to watch the procession. Susan had been peeved at her mother-in-law's comments on her trousers, but by the time they had gone the length of Brick Lane (as a special favour to Mrs Simons) Susan was near to tears, for everyone – barrow-boys coming back from the Lane, tailors, bakers, everyone – turned out to give the old girl a communal, if derisive, cheer. Susan reached up and touched her mother-in-law's foot. 'Yes, dear,' Mrs Simons said. 'They all know me.'

It was a long haul up to North London and Bucephalus was blowing out his lips long before they passed under the hooped iron bridge which gave the Archway Road its signature. Though Stan had contrived to quicken the journey with his clowning, Susan could not but wonder why, of all the places in London, Ben had been so set on this dreary and depressing neighbourhood.

Twenty-four Armoury Road was a blunt strawberry-brick house in no way distinguishable from those which flanked it. The houses in Armoury Road, which ran in a curve from the Archway Road to the Muswell Hill Road, had been built in the 1880s. The rooms were large and draughty. Their thick cream paint had yellowed with age and neglect.

In the garden of 24, a charred heap of rubbish branded the lawn.

Stan let out a piercing blast on his trumpet. 'All change, the end of the line. Everybody out.' Ben's mother scrambled down from the cart and marched up to the house.

'Hey, Mrs Simons, will you wait a moment? Will you not be so precipitate, will you?'

Ben's mother stopped at the door of the house and pulled something out of her bag. Ben ran up the garden path after her. 'Mama, what are you doing? What are you doing?'

Stan said: 'What the –'

Susan shrugged. Ben was saying: 'Will you please mind your own business?'

'Your father would have liked it.'

Susan opened the garden gate and then hesitated. Stan was getting things off the cart. She went back to help him.

'I don't care what Father would have liked. Do you mind, Mama, now please?'

'You drove your poor father to his death.'

'Father was killed by a bomb,' Ben said. 'It had nothing to do with me – or him, if it comes to that. Will you please let me live in my own house like I like? Mama, *please.*'

Mrs Simons held the *mezuza* against the doorpost. 'I don't let you into the house without you put it up,' she cried.

Ben tried to shame his mother with Stan and Susan, but she wouldn't look. He swung his head uncertainly. 'Why do you have to bring this up now?' he demanded. 'Why couldn't you have waited?'

'It has to be now,' his mother said. 'Otherwise you wouldn't do it. It's the first thing you do.'

'I knew I shouldn't let you come,' Ben said.

'It's what your father would have wanted.'

'I won't have him in here. I won't have him in here. Now, do you hear me, Mama?'

Mrs Simons nailed the *mezuza* to the doorpost, while Ben stood with clenched fists watching her, but could not intervene.

Not long afterwards, a taxi turned into Armoury Road. Most of the furniture from Susan's room at home was secured to it by one means or another. Inside, Hannah Adler crouched under a brown mountain of parcels and shopping baskets. Susan greeted her as she paid off the taximan. 'And you'll be back at five o'clock, Mr Samuelson? Good. Now, if you'll just help us in with these.' Hannah was wearing her Persian lamb coat with a toque to match. If there was one thing Ben hated, it was Persian lamb coats.

Ben and Stan were scrubbing down the living-room walls. Mrs Simons was on her hands and knees in the kitchen. Hannah Adler surveyed the house in silence. 'I hope you're not paying too much for this,' she observed. 'It looks like it might have dry rot.'

But soon the house began to change. Stan came nearly every evening and helped them with the painting. Ben made bookshelves. Susan made curtains. Every free second was filled with scrubbing and hammering and nailing and dusting and fixing and fitting.

Often they worked till midnight, when Susan made tea. Stan always brought his own mug, a vast porcelain article he swore was an Eskimo's jerry. Those first weeks they sat on packing cases set on the bare boards, but soon there were armchairs and a carpet on the floor. At the weekends, Ben and Stan and Susan went out bargain hunting along the Archway Road and it lost its monotonous gloom as the various dealers and shop-owners became known to them. So the house was furnished; apart from the new bed, the refrigerator, the kitchen cabinet and the wardrobe which Hannah Adler sent.

The idea of founding a magazine first came up during one of those midnight tea breaks. Stan had a great mind to be a writer. 'But not a hack, mind. I don't want to end up like that poor benighted sod Bucephalus, hauling a great heap of crap through the streets and thinkin' I'm working on me own account. I propose to be my own master, but not my own mistress.'

'Head in the sand Utopianism!' Susan declaimed a phrase of Sid Forbes'.

'Away with that Bolshevik mumbo-jumbo. I'll not be a party to it. Up the West Kilburn Anarchists!'

'Stan! You're not really a member of the West Kilburn Anarchists?'

'Why not? It's a very respectable thing to be.'

'Trotskyites,' Ben said, half-smiling.

'You'd be a Trotskyite if you had any sense. Trotsky was a Jew, and a fine man as well, not like that moustachioed brigand Joseph V. Stalin.'

'Without Stalin there'd be no Soviet Union as we know it today.'

'And who wants the Soviet Union as we know it today?'

'The British and Americans for a start,' Ben said. 'And anyone else who doesn't want Hitler to win the war.'

'Stalin's after winning it on his own account these days then, is he? I hadn't heard the latest.'

Ben sat down crosslegged on the floor and helped himself to bread and jam. 'If it weren't for Stalin, the whole of the working-class movement wouldn't know where it was going.'

'Bejasus, Benjamino, if one K. Marx esquire could hear you talking now!' Stan reached down and took the butter and jam from Ben's reach. 'Cut me a slice, Susie, me darling. Christ, I'd like to have a go at a magazine, a small select quarterly; see if you can talk your old man into it, will you, Susie, in the secrecy of your bedchamber?'

'I don't have to talk him into it,' Susan said.

'To which I was not referring! No, Benjamino's got the makings of a fine cartoonist, I mean that. Only you ought to keep them aired, you know, Ben, my boy, or they'll go mouldy. Some of the cultures I've seen on out-of-work cartoonists'd make your hair curl, not that it doesn't already, what there is left of it.'

'He is quite good, isn't he? Why don't you ever do anything for the *Worker*, Ben?'

'Haven't asked me,' Ben grinned. 'I don't know why you think I have to be talked into this idea, Stan. Soon as I get my clearance from the Kremlin, I'm on, boy.'

'First thing we need is a real selling title. Let me see, something like "The West Kilburn Left and Temperance Gazette" or "Three Cheers for the Red, Red and Red".'

'I never thought of you in the role of the editor of a temperance gazette,' Susan said.

'In the role, didn't you?' Stan winked at Ben.

'What's wrong with role?'

'Nothing's wrong with role,' Stan said. 'Or mystique if it comes to that.'

'Or jejune,' Ben said.

'I think you're being horrid,' Susan said. 'Both of you.'

The kitchen was at the back of the house, down a linoed passage. Susan went to put a kettle on for the washing up. She could hear the two men talking and laughing in the other room. Though she could not make out the joke, she was sure they were laughing at her. For a moment she wondered what she was doing in this kitchen, married to this man, what place she had anywhere.

'How much do you think it would cost to start a magazine?' Stan was asking.

'I don't know. Depends on the numbers. Couldn't be practical to print under three thousand.'

'By Christ, it'd be a wonderful thing to have a magazine that just didn't give a bugger what it said about anyone. A sort of satirical lampoonery. Like *Punch*, only funny.'

'I could find out how much it would cost roughly. I'll be seeing our printer bloke tomorrow or the next day.'

'What do you think about it, Ben? Would you help me with it? Edit it, I mean. I'm no business man and I'd certainly appreciate your help, that I would and all, begorrah,' Stan finished with a grin. 'And I'd also like the part of Mrs O'Malley's cow, if Mrs O'Malley hasn't taken it for herself already.'

'Who's going to buy this magazine?' Ben asked.

'The people who write in it for a start. That's two copies sold already. Oh, for Chrissake, there's plenty o' people ready to buy something with a bit of a kick in it. I mean it, you know, Ben, we could really put the fear of God into some of these buggers who think they're going to take over after the war just where they took on before it. Believe me, Benjamino, unless we do something about it the same boys'll be back on top as were there before we started. You know what we've got to do?' Stan stood up and raised his clenched fist. 'Rally the left,' he said. 'Herald the way for the red dawn.' He bent solicitously to an imaginary small boy. 'That's right, sonny, straight on and the first on the left.'

'I don't think you're serious enough to run a magazine,' Ben said.

'Serious bollocks,' Stan said. 'I'm damned serious, Benjamino. What do you have to do to be serious in your book? Wear gaiters?'

'I'll talk to the printer anyway. It'd be good stuff if we could do it.' Outside, someone tapped on the window. Ben went and pulled back the curtain.

'And who's going to stop us, might I ask?'

Sid Forbes was standing out there in the darkness. 'Sid!' Ben called. 'Hang on a tick, I'll open the door. Susie, it's Sid. How about some more tea.'

'I'll put the kettle on,' Susan called. 'Do you want some?'

'Might as well.' Ben opened the front door. 'Wotcher, boy. I was wondering when you'd be coming in.'

55

'Well, Ben, how goes it?' Sid took off his coat. 'Someone here?'

'Stan. Stan Halloran,' Ben said.

'Oh.' Sid entered the lighted room, a slight, sandy-haired man with a lean, freckled face, ginger eyes and thin, almost white lips. 'Evening, Halloran.'

'Well, well, if it isn't the Napoleon of King Street, alias the Napoleon of King Street.'

'Still the joker, I see,' Sid Forbes said.

'You *see*? You mean you saw what I said? Tell me, to hear me, how would you say I was looking?'

'You're too complicated for me,' Sid replied, sitting down in Susan's chair and rubbing together his bony, mottled hands.

'Make yourself at home, Sid. Susan's just making another pot of tea.'

'How d'you like the house? Settled down all right, have you?'

'Fine. Stan's been helping us with the painting.'

'Looks very good,' Sid commented, inspecting the rows of books against the back wall.

Susan came in with the tea. 'Hullo, Sid. This is a nice surprise!'

'Well, Susan, how are you?'

'Me? I'm all right. How's yourself? Well, have you told him about the magazine?'

'There's nothing to tell really,' Ben muttered.

'Well, I think it's a wonderful idea and you ought to tell Sid about it.'

'What's all this about?'

'Stan and Ben. They're thinking of starting a magazine.'

'What sort of thing?' Sid inquired.

'Oh, satirical,' Stan said, with surprising diffidence. 'Something to warm you up on the way to the factory. Not you, of course, Sid. I don't want to insult you by suggesting you work in a factory.'

'I have done,' Forbes said, 'and my old man before me.'

'You aristocrats, you've got everything in your favour. You know seriously, Sidney me boy, you ought to come in with us, write something. I mean, what kind of films are you planning to make for us after the People's War is over?' Forbes shrugged. 'Well, surely it won't be the same old "Lord Snotrag is here, milady" stuff we had before, will it?'

Susan poured out the tea. Her polite instincts told her that she would do well to change the subject. 'How come you've dropped by so late, Sid?'

'He's been out with the old whitewash there, haven't you, Sidney?'

'We don't live far from here,' Sid told Susan.

'Whereabouts?'

'About three turnings away actually. Chamberlayne Road.'

'It was Sid who told me about the house. You remember, Susan.'

'I don't,' Susan said. 'I don't think you ever told me.'

Ben smiled. 'I did, Susan.'

Stan Halloran stood up and stretched. 'A spot of shut-eye and open leg is what is required by yours truly, so I'll be taking my leave of you good people and people's people.'

'Night, Stan,' Ben said.

'I'll see you out,' Susan said.

'Night, Halloran,' Sid Forbes said.

'Night, *Forbes*!'

At the door Stan said something to Susan and she gurgled appreciatively. Sid said: 'I should watch that bloke with Susan, if I were you, Ben.'

Ben said: 'Stan? Don't be a twit, Sid.'

'Isn't Stan a darling?' Susan said as she returned.

Sid looked at Ben: 'Well, I'd better be going myself. Ben, you wouldn't care to walk me to the end of the road, would you?'

'Sure.' Ben rose. 'Won't be a moment, Susie.'

'Good night, Susan.'

The two men left the house.

Ben said: 'What's up?'

'Look, about this magazine, I wouldn't lumber yourself with it if I were you.'

'It was only an idea,' Ben said.

'It's always easy to forget an idea, eh, Ben? Goodnight.'

'See you,' Ben said.

When Ben came back and they were undressing for bed, Susan said: 'Ben, I wish you wouldn't mock me in front of other people.'

'You'd rather I mocked you when we're alone, is that it?'

'I don't like being mocked at all. It reminds me of Daddy.'

He stood behind her and weighed one of her breasts in each hand. 'I don't want to do that.'

'Don't I say the right things?'

'You say all the right things.'

'No, Ben, I'm serious.'

'So am I. Very serious.'

'Oh God! Ben.'

'You don't want to worry, girl.'

'But I do. I do worry.'

'Susie, Susie.'

'No, I do.'

'Susie, I love you, Susie.'

'Why – why – ?'

'Why what?'

'Ben, mm. Mm. Ben.'

'Why what?'

'Why don't you ever answer me, Ben? Properly.'

'I'd sooner answer you improperly.'

'I love you, Benno,' Susan said. 'Sometimes.'

Nothing had pleased Susan more than the prospect of snapping clean from the life she had led before her marriage: but now she had gulfs of loneliness during which she wished for nothing so much as the comforts and natural affections she had before despised. To be sure, Ben loved her and to be sure there was no shortage of visitors at 24 Armoury Road; yet at the end of a Party evening Susan found herself tired of holding an attitude which seemed natural to everyone else but which she assumed with difficulty. She had to be on her guard against saying 'pardon' and 'jolly decent' and other innocent phrases which she had always employed, for if they slipped out, they were instantly derided. Since Ben's satisfaction of her sexual desires left her void of deep grievance, her discontent was necessarily superficial, but it was there: she told herself she was being a baby, but she found herself ringing Tessa Franks several times a week for a good old gossip. Tessa, being unofficially but firmly engaged to Colin, was the custodian of most of the gang's secrets. It was from her that Susan learnt of Bryan Hammond's engagement to Corinna Coleman. 'Why on earth Corrina,' Susan exclaimed, 'of all people? I should hardly call her Bryan's type.'

'Perhaps he's outgrown the glamour girls.'

'Do men ever outgrow the glamour girls?'

'Of course they do,' Tessa replied. 'Corinna's a very intelligent girl and Bryan's very sensible really, under all his – bumptiousness.'

'I suppose it'll be all right,' Susan said. That Bryan, who had been so keen on her, should marry a lump like Corinna Coleman was positively insulting. Oh well, the Colemans were loaded and Bryan was probably just engineering a merger. Susan considered the matter and, to convince herself that neither of them had anything of which she could be jealous, asked them to dinner.

Ben took the news of the date with smiling resignation.

'Do you mind me asking some of my friends in for a change?' Susan demanded.

'Have I said one word about minding?'

'I can just tell you do, that's all.' Susan wished she had never asked them now. No, she was perfectly entitled to ask them; Ben asked his friends in without consulting her. What should she give them to eat? Anyway, a tin of grapefruit to start with, in the footed glass dishes Bryan had given them as a wedding present.

'Grapefruit!' Ben observed. 'We seem to be in luck!'

Corinna, a plump, bespectacled girl in a brown knitted suit, blinked uncertainly to the place Susan indicated to her and sat down heavily. Opposite her, Bryan Hammond, his face scraped very pink, creaked into a chair.

Susan served the meal with a slow deliberation which emphasized the trouble she had taken with it. It was eaten in a series of puzzled silences which were broken only when attempts to bring Ben into the conversation were abandoned in favour of gossip and discussion of the wedding plans. When the meal ended, Susan said: 'Shall we have our coffee in the other room?'

Ben said: 'Do let's,' and held out his hand in a butlerian gesture. 'I'll show our guests into the lounge,' he informed Susan with a bow. She slammed out into the kitchen. The evening was doomed. For the next two and a half hours she had to make conversation with Bryan and Corinna, while Ben sat with an ironic smile on his lips and never spoke but to ask questions of studied banality which either Bryan or Corinna was obliged dutifully to answer. Towards the end of the evening, Susan asked Bryan what he was going to do when he came out of the army. 'I shall go into Dad's firm,' he replied.

'Is that worth doing?' Ben asked.

'*Ben*,' Susan said.

'As worth doing as drawing Christmas cards, I should think,' Bryan blurted out.

Ben nodded, almost to himself. 'Good point. It's a good point.' Afterwards, Ben said: 'It was a good point he made about working at Pearson's.'

'You do plenty of things besides that,' Susan said, not sure whose side to be on.

'That's not quite it. You know, it's not worth doing, what I do.'

'It's worth eating,' Susan said. 'And I'd like to know how we'd do it without your salary. Particularly when I have to leave work.'

Ben said: 'I want a kid, Susie.'

'So do I – and a life as well.'

'What's that mean?'

'You were horrid tonight.'

'Horrid?' He made a face.

'You were. It's no use mocking me about it. You were horrid. Why shouldn't I have some friends in for a change?'

'Susan, please. I didn't say anything – '

'You don't have to say anything.'

Ben shook his head. 'Honestly, Susan.'

'No,' she said. 'No.'

'No what?'

'Honestly. You're not being honest. You're not.'

'Look, what do you want me to do? I just don't see the point in people like that – '

'He made a good point, you had to admit that.'

'And you made a good one back,' Ben retorted. 'Oh, let's go to bed and forget about it.'

'It's no solution,' Susan said.

Ben burst out laughing. 'A solution, the girl wants! What kind of solution do you suggest?'

'I don't want to be polished off,' Susan said.

'Polished off? What are you talking about?'

'I'm not going to bed with you,' she said. 'Not tonight. So you can take that look off your face.'

'So punish me,' he said. 'I should worry!'

3

Stan Halloran said: 'Is it convenient if we come in? I've brought someone to meet you. Herb, I want you to meet Susan Simons. This is Herb Fletcher.'

'How do you do?'

'Glad to know you,' Herb Fletcher said.

'Who is it?' Ben called.

'Stan and a friend of his. Herb –'

'Fletcher.'

Ben was sitting crosslegged on the floor sorting out stacks of leaflets, ready for the canvassers.

'Hail, Benjamino,' Stan cried. 'I've brought someone to meet you.'

Ben reached up his hand to the American. 'What ho!' he grinned.

'Glad to know you.' Fletcher was a tall, willowy young man with almost grey hair, blue eyes and a long, straight nose. He wore a smooth herringbone tweed suit and a green bow-tie.

Ben said: 'Now Stan's here, you'd better tell him the news.'

'I'm preggers,' Susan said.

'Glory be to God!'

'And me,' Ben said.

'And Benjamino.'

'And *me*.'

'And Susie. Well, I couldn't be more delighted if I'd done it meself, or could I? Well, never mind. This is wonderful news.'

'Well, congratulations,' Herb Fletcher said, blinking.

'How about some tea, Susie?' Ben asked. 'I expect you'd like a – '

'Cup of that old char there? I could use one, I must say.' Susan left the room.

'What are you doing over here?' Ben inquired. 'In the Army?'

'No – not exactly. I'm afraid I really shouldn't say.' Herb smiled. 'Actually I'm on the photographic side of things.'

'Aha,' Ben said.

'I thought Herb might do some of the picture work for the magazine.'

'You still on about that? I thought I told you the whole thing's bloody impossible. We'd have to raise about a hundred and fifty quid for a start.'

'I don't call that impossible.'

'It is as far as we're concerned,' Ben said. 'I could see if they'll make you a special price, boy, but otherwise, honestly – '

'Oh the hell with money, Benjamino. I'm really set on that bloody magazine.'

'It sounds a wonderful idea,' Herb said. 'I'd love to do something to help. Strictly incognito though. My bosses'd go crazy if they heard I had anything to do with a political sheet.'

'Straight up?' Stan inquired.

'Surprised, Stan?'

'Disappointed, that's all. Just like I am with Uncle Joe.'

'Halloran for world governor,' Ben said.

'If the money's right,' Stan said, 'I'll take it, long as I get me week-ends to meself.'

'You really think there's going to be an anti-Socialist drive in the States?' Ben asked Herb.

The American's neat lips curved. 'Did you ever hear of a guy called Wallace?'

'Wallace?' Ben smiled. 'Wallace.'

'I wonder where he is today.'

'Chewing the rag with that Bolshevik catspaw Robeson, what else?'

The three of them burst out laughing as Susan's astonished face (she had only heard this last sentence) appeared in the doorway with the tea-tray.

4

The first number of *Everyman* came out in March 1945. Stan disapproved of the title ('I'd sooner call the bloody thing "Belisha Beacon",' he remarked) but there was little he could do against an unexpectedly obdurate Ben. Rather to Stan's surprise, Sid Forbes had also turned up to the first editorial meeting and he agreed with Ben that *Everyman* was a good title. Since Ben and Sid had found most of the money to pay for the printing, there was little Stan could say. He was mollified by the other two insisting that Herb Fletcher also join the editorial panel. They undertook to respect his anonymity.

Volume I, Number One contained articles by a 'Socialist from each of the great allied countries' as well as poems, cartoons, book reviews and a photographic documentary on atrocities, complied by a pseudonymous Herb. Stan Halloran contributed an essay in what he called 'rhyming blank verse prose' on the record of the Conservative Party since 1918 as written by a one-eyed Circassian dwarf in the year 4378. As an exposure of the way political jargon could be manipulated, the article met with considerable opposition from Sid – on the grounds of its dullness – before it was admitted. Ben's cartoon showed a General opening a wardrobe full of black coats, striped trousers, and top hats, with the caption 'SEE THE OTHER RANKS GET THEIR OVERALLS, WON'T YOU, CARRUTHERS?' Whether because of this or for some other offence, *Everyman* was forbidden to be sent to the forces abroad and its sale was barred on station bookstalls. The *Daily Mirror* drew attention to this censorship and assured its readers that the magazine was a jolly good fourpenceworth. The *Observer* reproduced the offending cartoon. *Everyman* had made its mark. Stan proposed that they promptly begin to make plans for Volume I, Number Two, or alternatively for Volume II, Number One.

'There are one or two things I think we ought to clear up first,' Ben said.

'Such as?'

'Well, the general policy we're going to follow.'

'We just keep firing till the bloody ammunition runs out, that's my policy.'

'We made a small profit on the first number; we don't want to just chuck away our backers' money –'

'They ought to have a fair return on their investment, are you thinking?'

'It shouldn't be squandered,' Sid Forbes said.

'Have I been responsible for squandering the jolly old shareholders' money in any way whatsoever?'

'No one's saying that,' Ben said. 'We just want to get the policy straight before we start planning the next issue.'

'I'll tell you one thing that was wrong with the first bloody issue and that's there was too much bloody turgid sermonizing and not enough bloody dynamite.'

'The readers liked it,' Sid Forbes said.

'Then why do you want to change the policy?' Stan shouted. 'Will you tell me that?'

Susan was not officially present at editorial meetings, but she could hardly fail to hear most of what was said and she noticed that Herb Fletcher took very little part in the discussions: only occasionally could his mild and ingratiating voice be heard. On the whole he seemed to be on Stan's side. Ben was not; he complained bitterly to Susan of Stan's irresponsible attitude. Recently, to add to everything else, he'd gone off and formed a jazz-band! Eventually, when it became obvious that the end of the war in

Europe was a mere matter of time, the Board agreed that the second issue of *Everyman* should be the Victory issue; they found it less easy to agree on the contents. Stan Halloran felt the control of the magazine was being taken from him; though he was officially editor, Ben and Sid Forbes again and again produced articles from prospective contributors to whom they had, so they said, already promised space. Bitter quarrels followed, especially when Stan found that no room had been reserved for anything of his own.

On VE night, Ben and Susan, Sid and Ethel, Herb and Stan were all in Whitehall. The wrangles of the Board were forgotten, at least for the moment. As Churchill came out on to the balcony the cheers rolled out louder and louder. Susan could feel the tears pricking in her eyes and she had to blink, wide-eyed, to prevent them. Ben was grinning and Herb Fletcher clapped his hands. Stan was cheering himself hoarse, again and again shouting out, 'You old bastard, you old *bastard*.' Ethel Forbes smiled at Ben. She was a sagging, thirty-fivish woman, whose figure had been destroyed by the two children she had borne. She was a school-teacher in Bethnal Green. Sid pressed his thin lips together; his eyes did not blink. Susan noticed the little triangles of shadow under his cheekbones.

'Hey, Stanley, is that you?' A large Negro in US Army uniform was sashaying through the crowd towards them.

'Jeff! Sure it is. Come over here. This is bloody wonderful. How goes it with you?'

'Oh, I'm not so bad, Stanley,' the American replied. 'Quite a party, Wednesday, though, wasn't it? Quite a party!'

'Everybody, this is Jefferson Andrews. The best New Orleans jazzman that ever came out of Boanoke, Florida.'

'Boano, Flo,' agreed Jefferson Andrews. 'It's a *horrible* town.' He shook his head emphatically. 'But it's what I call home.'

66

'What I call home,' harmonized Stan Halloran. The two men laughed and clapped their arms round each other. 'You don't mind if this old bugger joins us, do you?'

'Of course not,' Sid said. 'We'd like him to.' He smiled and offered the Negro his hand.

'Any friend of Stanley's a friend of mine,' Jeff said.

They shook hands all round.

'Wonderful,' Ethel Forbes said. Susan wondered what drew that particular word from the dumpy school-teacher.

The rest of the War Cabinet came out on to the balcony and waved their hands.

'I think we've had enough of this, haven't we?' Sid asked, leading the way back out of the crowd.

5

The Victory issue of *Everyman* never appeared; it turned into the Election issue instead. But the editorial wrangles were as bad as before. Stan wanted *Everyman* to be the gadfly of the Left, warning the Labour Party that if it won the election its supporters would expect a genuine Socialist policy, or else. Sid and Ben thought it wasn't the time for threats; they favoured an electioneering manifesto, directed in particular to the electors of Hornsey, with the slogan 'Keep Left – and the Lefter the Better!' In the end, Stan got his way more than Susan expected, largely because Sid and Ben elected to spend most of their time in Mile End where the Party was making an all-out effort on behalf of Phil Piratin. During their absence, Stan was able to reinstate an article by Jefferson Andrews on jazz which Sid had rejected, holding that Negro rights in the States was a topic more relevant to a Socialist magazine. To complete the picture, he undertook to supply some material on racial relations in the Soviet Union. 'Lovely,' Stan had said. 'And don't forget the Kulaks, will you, boy?' Ben, in addition to his cartoon, promised a piece on Palestine and the Jewish Question – the Socialist and the Imperialist solutions. Herb Fletcher provided a picture story on the housing problems in Britain; most of the photographs were taken in Mile End, where a Fighting Plan for reconstruction was outlined by a Socialist Study Group. Stan's article was entitled 'Is the Civil Service a Carve-Up? A critique in eight-footed pentameters'.

There was a party at Number 24 to hear the results. A blank map of Great Britain, cut from *The Times*, was pinned on the wall. The wireless was on loud and Ethel Forbes, with one red and one blue pencil, was charting the results. Stan Halloran had arrived during the afternoon with a black upright piano towed by the ever-obliging Bucephalus. Jefferson Andrews was playing, very quietly, to a row of faces, cradled in crossed arms on the top of the piano. Someone had lit a candle in the brass candleholder which hinged over the keyboard.

Susan found herself among a host of strangers. Ben and Sid were waiting for the result in Mile End and were coming along late. 'Find everything you want?' asked one amicable guest. Susan scowled furiously: people were, as Isidore Adler would certainly have said, using her house like a hotel.

'Hullo, Susie, my love, you're looking a bit down in the mouth – why might that be now?'

'Me? No, I'm all right.'

'Have a drink, for God's sake. All's right with the world and Attlee'll be PM this time tomorrow. God help us all. I've got a bottle of Paddy round the back – will you have a drop now?'

'Stan, are you plastered?'

'I have the honour to be, dear madam, at least three parts pissed. Come on, let's have a spot.'

'You're in a good mood, I must say; what's it all about?'

'Susie, can you keep a secret?'

'No,' Susan said.

'Good, you're the very girl I've been wanting to talk to.'

Susan laughed. 'Stan, you're wonderful.'

'If you really think that you'd better come with me next week. I'm going to see a bloke in the Brutish Bawdcarping Copulation about getting a job. He saw that piece I did in the mag.'

'What kind of job?'

'Religious, I should imagine,' Stan said. 'He told me he thought I was a "holy terror, old man".'

'No, seriously.'

'He said it would mean "regular whores" so of course I couldn't refuse. And they're going to pay me as well!'

'You're incorrigible, Stan.'

'Oh, no, I can be corriged if you know the combination.'

'You'll have to shave your beard off if you work in the BBC.'

'The Blighted Beardcutting Combination, of course! It's a feelthy plot! A feeeendish plot! Thank God I've seen through it in time. I won't go. I'll not be lured into it.'

'You *must* go,' Susan said. 'I think it'll be marvellous to hear you on the radio.'

The racketing of a motor-bike outside proclaimed the arrival of Ben and Sid. They were both singing the 'Red Flag' with ridiculous drunken ferocity. Susan went to the door and watched them stumble, laughing and singing, up the garden path. 'We've done it,' they both shouted at her. 'The boy's in.'

'Phil? That's wonderful,' Susan said. 'Wonderful news.'

Ben put his arms round her neck. 'The boy's in.' He was grinning redly, the light from the sitting room window glaring through cheek and lips. Susan could smell a mixture of beer and whisky. She fended him off. 'Not in front of Sid.'

'Good old Sid,' Ben said.

'Come on, old boy, you'd better come inside.'

'Come on, old boy,' Ben said. 'Sid, old boy, come on, old boy, we'd better go inside.'

'Bugger you,' Susan said.

'Come on, Sid, bugger you, old boy.'

Sid put his arm round Susan's waist. 'Your old man's a bit sloshed,' he said.

'You don't have to tell me.'

'Come on upstairs, oh wife of mine.'

'What you need is some black coffee.'

'What I need is a spot of vodka,' Ben said. 'A spot of wodka.' He grinned at Susan. 'And thou,' he added.

'The boy's in,' Sid announced to the crowd in the sitting room. A great cheer went up.

'What's all the fuss about?' Stan asked, appearing from the kitchen with the bottle of Paddy in his hand.

'Phil's in,' Ben said.

'That's what we need in the House of bloody Commons,' Stan said. 'Men who can think for themselves, men who don't need to be dictated to by the party machines, men who – Hey, what the bleedin' hell's he doing in there?'

'It's the best thing that could happen for the country,' Sid Forbes said. 'And you keep your filthy tongue to yourself.'

'Not the best surely, Sidney, me boy?'

'What would the best be?'

'Harry Pollitt elected Prime Minister, surely you know that, Sidney. Where's your education?'

'It'd be a damned good thing,' Sid Forbes growled.

'He'd probably make you President of the Trade of Bawds, knowing your reputation.'

Susan was one of those who giggled. Sid said: 'Oh, you're such a bloody funny little man you make me sick.'

'So I do, do I? Well, I'll have you know that's fighting talk where I come from.' Stan executed a little boxer's dance. 'It's just lucky for you we're not where I come from.'

70

'You ought to go on the halls.'

'Do you mean that, Mr Forbes, do you really think I've got talent?'

'You make me sick,' Forbes said.

'Excuse me, sorr, but don't Communists ever laugh with a gay Marxist-Leninist-Stalinist ha ha ha?'

Jefferson Andrews was playing mournful chords, but Sid was too angry to be put off. 'I don't happen to think you're very funny,' he said.

'I'm slipping,' Stan mourned. 'Already I'm slipping.'

'You think too much about yourself, Halloran, that's your trouble.'

'Halloran,' Stan said. 'Back to that, are we?'

'You've only got to look at that silly beard to see what kind of a person you are.' Sid's face was white with anger, his eyes were narrowed.

Susan said: 'Sid, for heaven's sake.'

'Let me see,' Stan said, 'what was the name of that chap with a beard – Len – Len – I'll get it in a minute – Len – Lenin! That's it.'

'You bloody Irish scab,' Sid Forbes said.

Stan Halloran stared gloomily at Forbes. 'Get out of my sight, before I break your bloody neck,' he said.

'You so much as touch me –'

'And I'll catch me death of clap. I know that, thanks all the same.'

Sid Forbes said: 'Bloody saloon bar proletarians.'

Herb Fletcher said: 'Hey, Sid, come over here and have a drop of your native brew. I've got some PX whisky. Honest to God scotch.'

'I'll make a note of what you said,' Stan called out. 'Just for the files – the ones I put in cakes for smuggling to old purge victims.'

'He's drunk,' Susan said. 'He'll have forgotten the whole thing by the morning.'

'What makes you think I will?' Sid, Herb and Ben left

the room together. 'A wise man and his friends,' Stan Halloran observed, 'are soon parted.'

The party recovered its gaiety, but Susan was left, engulfed in loneliness. Stan found himself a girl. He sat holding her hand until Jefferson Andrews suggested he take over the piano. Then he cheered up, the smiles of those around him prompting him to sing 'a few famous songs of the West Finchley Revolution, by honoured Finchley writer and people's tapioca pedlar, S. Halloran, Esq.'

Bottles, mostly empty, covered the floor and were lined up on the mantelpiece. It grew hot and smoky and noisy in the house and towards three o'clock Susan, jaded beyond recall, slipped off her shoes and walked out of the open front door and down towards the gate. She wanted to feel the cool of the pavement on her feet. It was dark. She shuddered in the sudden chill and took out a cigarette. In the flare of her match, there was a cry of surprise from the road and then a deep laugh, instantly checked.

'Who's there?' Susan demanded.

'Susan, is that you?'

'Ethel! What are you doing out here?'

'We came out to get some air.'

Susan could distinguish two figures now sitting with their backs to her in the open gateway. 'That you, Sid?' Susan called.

'No, it's me, Mrs Simons,' called a deep voice: Jefferson Andrews.

'Oh, hullo,' Susan said. 'I came out for some air.' The two moved apart to let Susan come between them. Andrews's eyes were wide in the darkness.

'Party still going on?'

'Still going on,' Susan said. She was sure that Ethel and Jefferson Andrews had been necking. The word came precisely to her mind: necking.

'Haven't seen Sid, have you?' Ethel inquired. 'I think

we ought to be getting home. My old mum'll be wondering what's become of us.'

'They all went off upstairs hours ago and haven't been seen since.' Susan tossed away her cigarette though it was barely started, and turned back to the house. It jutted black and ugly against the sky, springing leaks of light.

Stan was putting on his leather flying jacket in the hall.

'Susie, my own one. I'm pushing off.'

'Oh, Stan, don't go. Stay the night. Everyone else is.'

He put his arm round her waist. 'No, I'm takin' off, Susie.'

'You mustn't worry about what happened tonight.'

'I shan't, ducky, I shan't.' Stan patted her bottom and moved into the doorway. He kissed his fingers and put them on the *mezuza* Ben's mother had hammered into the doorpost. 'Do you know what we call the Jews in Ireland? The magic people. The magic peep-hole! God bless you, Susie, and make that obstinate sod of a husband of yours see the light one day!'

'Don't go, Stan.'

'I've made up me mind; I'm chucking it in with Ben and Herb and Sid. But I'll be back, never fear. I love that bloody sod of a husband of yours.' Stan stepped inside again. 'Brenda, are you coming, or Bejasus do I have to come up and have you without benefit of double bed?'

The girl whose hand Stan had been holding came down the stairs. 'Sorry, couldn't find my coat.'

'Come on, lovely,' Stan said, tucking a blatant hand up under her sweater.

Susan said: 'Mind – there're people – '

'We'll be all right.'

Susan put her first finger under her eyes. At the same time, she sniffed. It was no good: she was crying.

FOUR

Conflicts of Love

1

SUSAN WAS IN HER ninth month of pregnancy when Ben decided to leave Pearson's.

'I'm going to give them a month's notice,' he announced jauntily as he stood in the kitchen one evening watching her dish up the supper. He tried to open the window.

'Why? What for, Ben?'

'They want me to go on the *Worker*.' The window jerked up.

'They *what*?'

'Want me to go on the *Worker*. Want me to do a cartoon twice a week.'

'And make the tea for the rest of it?'

'I make a good cup of tea. Matter of fact they want me to help with the lay-out as well.'

Susan stuck her tongue out sideways getting the steak and kidney pie out of the oven. 'Hot!' She rang the tin on top of the stove. 'What're they going to pay you?'

'Six ten a week.'

'Honey, you're not serious.'

'Honey,' Ben said, 'I've never been seriouser.'

'Look, be realistic for a minute – '

'Realistic! I am being realistic. What's realistic is taking a hand in something worth doing. In not prettying your life away doing *nothing*. What your pal Hammond said was true.'

'He's not my pal,' Susan said. 'All right. Go on the

Worker.' She felt too heavy to complain. She picked up the pie-dish with the oven cloth and started towards the dining-room. 'You might bring the spuds and the cabbage.'

It was stuffy in the dining-room. Susan opened the window on to the back garden. 'I just hope we can live on six pounds ten a week, that's all.'

'Susan, there are ten million people in this country living on six pounds ten a week.'

'Look, honey, I've had a tiring day. I don't want to discuss it now – it seems to be fixed so there really isn't any point.'

'Quite right,' Ben said, 'there isn't.'

Sid Forbes called round after supper. His first words were, 'Well, what do you think of the news?'

'What news?'

'About Ben and the *Worker* of course. Haven't you told her the news, Ben?'

'Oh that,' Susan said. 'Smashing. I'm just wondering how we're going to fill our bellies.'

The two men burst out laughing. 'Yours looks full enough,' Sid observed. Susan did not smile. She treasured her pregnancy.

Ben said: 'I'll keep your belly full for you, don't worry.'

Sid said: 'Susan, I really think you're looking at this thing the wrong way.'

'What about Stan? Isn't he going to take it a bit hard you taking away his cartoonist?'

'Halloran? Don't be a fool, Susan, he's got no claim on Ben. Anyway, that's all folded up, you know that.'

'I thought you were all together,'Susan said.

'Honestly, Susan, that was only a temporary arrangement.'

'What isn't?' Susan inquired.

The two men smiled. 'Look, ' Ben said, 'I think you're a bit tired.'

Sid said: 'You ought to rest, Susan. Ethel sent you her

love, by the by. She's baked some cakes and she wanted to know if it was all right if she dropped some by tomorrow.'

'Jolly nice of her, Sid. Do tell her thank you. Tomorrow'd be fine.'

'Well, Ben, I think we ought to be getting along.'

'You going out?' Susan said.

'Only for a bit,' Ben said.

'I didn't know you were.'

'I told you I was,' Ben said. 'Shan't be long.'

He did not come back till after midnight. Susan had not turned out the light. 'Hullo, you still awake? You should have gone to sleep.'

'I wanted to talk to you.' Susan sat up. 'Have you been drinking?'

'Drinking? Me? No. Why should you think that?'

'You look a bit pink,' Susan said.

'Pink, do I? Well, I am a bit pink.'

'Ben, why did you tell Sid you were leaving Pearson's before you told me?'

'I didn't,' Ben said. 'It was Sid put me on to this job. He told me about leaving Pearson's if that's the way you like to look at it.'

'He told you to leave, in other words.'

'He didn't tell me anything of the sort. Honestly, Susan! He just told me about the job at the *Worker* and asked if I'd be interested. And I said I would.'

'You might have talked to me first.'

'I didn't have to talk to you to know if I was interested. Honestly, Susan.'

'Oh, do stop saying "honestly, Susan" all the time. It gets on my nerves.'

Ben sat down crosslegged on the bed to cut his toenails. 'That's a lovely sight,' Susan observed.

'Wait till you see the other foot,' Ben said, 'it's a beauty.'

Susan giggled. Then she frowned. 'You ought to talk to me first about these things.'

'Cutting my toenails?'

'Seriously, you should.'

'Look, Susan, I explained about Sid – '

'I know, but – '

'Back in a minute,' he said, going off to the bathroom.

'Where did you go this evening?' Susan called out.

'Have a drink with Herb Fletcher.'

'What about? Not *Everyman*?'

'No,' Ben said, 'something else.'

'What?'

There was no answer. Ben had started gargling.

2

Hannah Adler said: 'How can he do such a thing with the baby coming?'

'He feels it's his duty,' Susan replied. 'We both do.'

'What do Communists know about duty?' Hannah asked. 'His mother didn't want him to be a Communist. She told me so herself. Broke his father's heart.'

'We're both Communists,' Susan pointed out.

'You're not a Communist. Not really. Not till you met him.'

'I wasn't a lot of things till I met him,' Susan said.

'I should hope not!' her mother exclaimed. 'I should hope not indeed. What's he going to bring home a week?'

'Six pounds ten.'

'Six pounds ten? How're you going to live on six pounds ten a week?'

'Mummy, dear, there are ten million people in this country living on six pounds ten a week.'

The next day Hannah arrived with a hamper of food so large that the taximan had to carry it into the house for her. At the bottom of it, Susan found three pound notes.

After Sarah was born, Hannah came over in a taxi to

Archway most days. Isidore grumbled a great deal at her being out of the shop, and would have grumbled even more if he had known that nearly every visit ended with Hannah pressing a pound or two into Susan's hand. Susan never told Ben of these gifts; so far as he knew, they were making do on the famous six pounds ten. In spite of everything, however, Susan had to admit that he was much happier with the new job. At Pearson's the work had so depressed him that he became cold and sarcastic with the futility of what he was doing; now, however late he got home – and sometimes it was not till two or three in the morning – he was certain of the value of his work. Ben would run up the path when he saw the light on in the bedroom window where Susan was giving Sarah her late feed, and his happiness embraced her even before he came into the room, so that she gazed down and loved the baby heavy at her breast. Sarah rolled her eyes, while Susan leaned back in the chair where she nursed her and was complacent with life. After she had put Sarah back in her Karri-Kot there was a fresh copy of the paper to look at, with the ink still wet from the presses.

Even before she could let Ben make love to her again, Susan was filled with a joy of him greater than any she had had before. The presence of his body in the bed with her made her bloom with contentment. During the first weeks after Sarah was born, the baby slept in the same room with them. Susan would lie awake and listen to the breathing of her husband and of her child and a wild joy grew in her, till she lay close against Ben and put her arm over his hip and went to sleep.

But during the day-long hours of loneliness, she ached for comfort. She found it only when she was giving Sarah her breast; to see her mouth questing for her nipple was a delight to Susan. When the weather was warm she fed the child naked. Then she hung her full breasts over Sarah and confined her in the cleft of her flattened thighs, let her hair

78

fall long, to cover the child from the world, and it seemed to her that she was big enough to enclose her again in her womb. She grew big with the child and with the exclusive love she bore her.

3

When Colin wrote to tell them the precise date of his return, Hannah promptly burst into tears. Isidore said: 'Whassamatter now?'

'Colin's coming home!' Hannah cried.

Isidore simpered. 'What are you crying about? Don't you want him to come back? She's crying!' Other people's tears threw Isidore into a strange humour. 'She's crying!' he said again, to Otto.

Otto had been living with them for nearly four months. Each morning he sat at the far end of the table at breakfast. He ate little. When he had finished he slipped out of the room and went upstairs to make his bed. He was a shadow about the house; he reminded Julia of a man trying to avoid meeting himself on the stairs. They had been reading about *Doppelgänger* at school. Julia said: 'Does Colin coming home mean Uncle Otto will be going?'

Hannah said: 'Oh, this isn't the time to think about that.'

'Colin'll want his room,' Isidore said. 'Of course, if we hadn't moved there'd be room for everybody.'

Hannah said: 'We'll find room.'

As the date drew nearer she could not restrain herself from getting out Colin's things and putting them in the room where Otto was living. 'You see,' she explained, 'Colin'll be sleeping here when he gets home.'

'Hannah,' Otto said, 'I think I should tell you. I don't want to be any trouble to you. Now I've got my permit to stay maybe I could find someplace else to live.'

79

'But what would you live *on*, Otto? Have you thought about that?'

'I wish I'd never come out of the camp, Hannah.' After all these months the old man was weeping again.

'You mustn't say such things.'

'I got no place any more, Hannah.'

'You've got a place right here,' Hannah Adler said.

'In Poznan before the Germans came Halinka and I, we had a place there, you know.' The old man nodded to himself. 'My poor dear wife and I, God rest her soul, we belonged there. We had a *community*.'

'You've made friends here, Otto. You're not alone. We love you.'

'Ah.' The old man waved his hand impatiently. 'You're kind to me. You're very kind to me, Hannah, but that's not the love Halinka gave me.' He smiled at her through his tears. 'I wasn't always an old man, Hannah.'

'You were a fine looking man,' Hannah said. 'I remember you.'

'I should never have come out of the camp to be a burden to you. I should have died with the rest of them.'

'I won't listen to you talk like this. You help me unpack these things of Colin's. And don't let me hear any more of this. You're welcome here.' Hannah stood over the old man with her hands on her hips. 'Do you understand? I'll put a divan in the dining room. Now, that's settled.'

Otto blink-smiled. 'We unpack the things, huh?'

Hannah and Isidore had given Colin a clock when he passed his finals. His name and the date were engraved on a silver plaque under the face. Hannah unpacked it reverently. At one moment she was holding it safely in her hands, at the next it had clonked on the floor. Hannah snatched it up and started to shake it. Otto took it from her: 'Hannah, for heaven's sake, never do such a thing to a clock.'

'I don't know how I could let it happen. It just fell through my hands.'

'Ssh, ssh.' Otto listened to the back of the clock.

'Is it going?'

Otto shook his head. He was smiling. 'No, it's not going.'

'Oh dear, oh dear, I shall have to take it down to the jeweller's. I just hope they can do it in time.'

'There's no need to take it to the jeweller's,' Otto said. 'I can repair the clock.' He reached under the bed and drew out the small black attaché case he had carried on the day when he came to the shop in Cricklewood. He opened it now in front of Hannah's eyes. In it was a black *kapel*, a *tallis*, very old and yellowed, and a box bound tight with many rubber bands. He took off the rubber bands with ritual care, laying each one on the bed before removing the next. At last he removed the lid of the box. 'You don't have to take the clock to the jeweller's,' Otto said, selecting a screwdriver and starting to unscrew the back of the clock.

'It's a good clock,' Hannah said.

'It's a beautiful clock,' Otto Kahane said.

The old man began to work. As evening came on, Hannah sat down to watch him, the eyeglass clutched under his brow, the clock turned farther and farther to the window as the light failed. Now and again he looked up and nodded. Hannah leaned back and closed her eyes.

4

'Tessa, honestly, I feel awful about being here at all. Mummy just went on and on at us.'

'She certainly did,' Julia said.

Tessa Franks said: 'Don't worry. It's perfectly all right.'

'I feel *awful* about it,' Susan said. 'I'd've done anything not to come.'

'It really doesn't matter,' the girl said, smiling.

81

'I'm sure if I was meeting my intended after all these years I wouldn't want anyone else there.'

Julia said: 'It's platform five.'

Tessa was wearing a red coat with a little fur collar and a red hat with a white feather. She was only twenty-two, but Susan thought she looked extremely mature. Her face was somewhat square with high cheekbones; above them, her eyes were slightly slanted which gave her an air of detachment. Her mouth was wide, but thin-lipped, marked with determination. There was nothing weak in her. She showed no signs of excitement at Colin's return. Susan wondered what there was between them, and whether it had lasted. Tessa stood patiently, waiting for the train. Susan fretted, Julia read, squatting on a luggage trolley and rolling herself backwards and forwards with her feet till Susan felt she could scream.

The train pulled in and filled the empty bay between the platforms. Susan and Tessa lifted their chins in the quest for Colin. There he was! – helping an old woman down with her luggage. They looked hard at him, to learn what they could before the real tests began. Colin saluted the old lady and turned full face to them. He seemed thinner, his face lean, the eyes protruding under the sandy brows. When he saw them he turned red and his hand hovered, as though uncertain whether to take off his cap. He saluted. 'Well, well,' he said, 'here we are again.' He put his arm round Julia and kissed her cheek: 'How's Prunella the Prune?' It was a childhood nickname. No one had called Julia Prunella the Prune for *years*. Colin put his other arm round Susan. 'Well, Susan?' He kissed her cheek. Tessa was a pace away. He turned and put his arms round her and hugged her. 'How's Tessa?'

'I'm fine,' Tessa said. She patted him on the back. 'I'm fine. What was the journey like?'

'Slow, very slow.' He blew out his cheeks. 'Am I glad to be home!' He smiled at the three girls. 'And such a reception committee! Where's the station-master with his top hat?'

'He couldn't wait,' Julia said.

'Well.' He started to shepherd them towards the barrier. 'Tell me all. How're the folks?'

'They're all right. Needless to say Mummy's at home preparing smoked salmon, chopped liver, *schmalz* herring –'

'How's Ben by the way?'

'Ben by the way is very well thank you,' Susan replied.

Colin said: 'Ah, there's the porter with my gear. I think a taxi's the order of the day; I've managed to accumulate rather a lot of stuff what with one thing and another.'

Hannah Adler was waiting at the gate for her son. As the taxi drew up, Isidore appeared at the door of the house, the evening paper dangling from his hand, a cigarette between his lips. Colin emerged first from the taxi. With a sob of joy, Hannah ran to him and threw her arms around him. 'My darling boy!' she cried. 'My darling boy.' Colin laughed affectionately and took her in his arms and gave and received kisses on both cheeks.

The taximan said: 'Want me to take all this stuff in, do you?'

'If you would,' Colin said.

'I'll give him half a crown,' Hannah whispered.

'I'll take care of it,' Colin said. He went down the path to his father. 'Well, how's the Commander-in-Chief?'

Isidore smiled. 'I'm not complaining.' Colin bent down and brushed his father's cheek with his lips. 'Someone's sleeping in your room,' Isidore said.

'What do you mean?'

'We've got a visitor.'

Colin frowned. 'A visitor?'

'Your Uncle Otto is staying with us,' Hannah said.

'Been sleeping in your room.'

'He repaired your clock,' Hannah said.

'Look, what is all this about?' Colin laughed.

'Your Uncle Otto's staying with us,' Hannah explained, 'and he's repaired your clock. You remember – the one we gave you when you passed your exams.'

'Of course I remember, but – '

'It got broken. Uncle Otto was in the concentration camp and he's come to live with us. He's the only one left.'

Colin said 'Oh', and busied himself with his luggage.

'Hullo, dear.' Hannah turned away to greet Tessa.

'Hullo, Mrs Adler.'

'Where's Sarah?' Susan demanded.

'The baby's perfectly all right, don't worry about the baby.'

Susan pushed her mother aside and dashed upstairs. Hannah led Tessa into the sitting-room. 'Now, will you have a sherry?'

'Yes, please, Mrs Adler.'

'I think I'll have one too. It's quite an occasion, my son and your fiancé coming home on the same day!'

Colin came in with Isidore following, a pace behind.

'Did you give the taximan half a crown?'

'Always wants to give money away, your mother.'

Coin said: 'She's a very generous woman. Yes, I did.'

'There's generous and generous. She doesn't have to pay the bills. Things've gone up since you went away.'

'Isidore, for heaven's sake.'

'I can see there's one person in the family who hasn't changed,' Colin said.

Everyone laughed. Isidore went pink and gave a little giggle. 'Me!' he said. 'He's talkin' about me!'

Susan came down and more sherry was drunk. Everyone was rather nervous and did not quite know what to say; silences were broken with fragments of reminiscence and bursts of laughter as each one by 'Do you remember?' tried to reconnect Colin with the family from which he had so long been parted.

'Where's your husband?' Hannah asked Susan after they had been chatting till well past seven-thirty.

'Ben? Should be here by now. He may have been held up.'

'What's he doing?' Colin inquired.

'He's helping to serve meals for the squatters,' Susan said. 'If you really want to know.'

'Squatters?'

'People who haven't got anywhere to live. They've taken over a block of flats down near Regent's Park.'

'We'd better get down there then,' Colin smiled at Tessa. 'Your husband might be able to find somewhere for us to live.'

Susan said: 'These are poor people.'

'I'm surprised the government doesn't do something for them then. I understood they only cared about poor people.'

'Oh, I say, don't let's have a political argument on your first night home,' Tessa said.

'I think we might as well have supper,' Hannah said. 'If your husband doesn't come soon.'

'His name's Ben,' Susan said.

Julia said: 'Let's wait a bit longer.'

'Just so you can stay up later,' Isidore said.

'Daddy, I'm *sixteen*.'

Ben had not arrived at eight o'clock, so they went in to supper. Hannah's eyes were on Colin. She had spread out every delicacy she could lay her hands on; in addition to the smoked salmon, the chopped liver and the herrings Susan had promised, there were frankfurters and sauerkraut, *gefüllte* fish, *pretzels* and *bagels*, cream cheese and apple strudel. 'It's a feast!' Isidore exclaimed. 'Wait a moment,' Hannah said, opening the door to let Tanya come in with the potato *lotkes* and the roast chicken. 'When my boy comes home it's right his mother should give him a feast,' Hannah said. 'Isn't that right?'

85

'Quite right, Mrs Adler,' Tessa approved.

Colin settled straight in. 'He loves his food,' his mother said.

'Look at him eating!' Isidore giggled.

At ten o'clock there was still no sign of Ben. Susan gnawed at her knuckle. Nobody noticed her anxiety; they were too busy talking about the wedding and where Tessa and Colin should go for the honeymoon. Isidore puffed a cigar which Colin had brought him from Germany.

At twenty past ten the doorbell rang. A moment later Ben burst into the room. 'What ho,' he cried. 'Terribly sorry to be late.' He bounced over to Colin. 'Hullo, how are you? Pleased to meet you.'

Colin said: 'How do you do?'

'Ben, what happened?'

Ben gave a little chuckle. 'I got arrested.'

'Arrested?' Colin cried. 'Whatever for?'

'They sent the police in down at the flats.'

'What did they arrest you for?'

'Obstruction,' Ben said.

'Good God!' Colin exclaimed.

'Who did you obstruct?'

'The police, of course,' Ben said. 'There were a whole lot of us.'

'Why did they pick on you?'

'I had the banner,' Ben said.

'You would,' Susan grinned at him. 'You would.' She stood up and kissed her husband.

'Kissing,' Isidore simpered.

'What did the banner *say*?' Julia asked.

'It said "Buy the *Daily Worker*, the Only Paper to support the Squatters' Rights".'

'What were you holding it for?'

'I made the wretched thing,' Ben replied, rubbing his hands together. 'Anything left to eat?'

Hannah led Ben into the dining-room.

'Got himself arrested,' Isidore said.

'I say, Susan, I'm frightfully sorry about all this.'

'You don't want to worry,' Susan said. 'You can't make an omelette without breaking heads.'

'No, but won't it affect his job?'

'Oh yes, he'll probably get a promotion. Oh, perhaps you didn't know: Ben's on the *Worker* these days.'

'I say, how perfectly awful for you!'

'It's not awful at all,' Susan said. 'I only wish I could be on it too.'

Hannah sat with Ben while he ate. 'I'm sorry you weren't here to have it hot, dear,' she said. 'It was much nicer.'

'It's delicious,' Ben said.

'Will it matter you getting arrested?'

'No. We'll probably get fined a few quid.'

'Oh, you weren't the only one?'

'No,' Ben said. 'There was vanloads of us!'

'Oh, I thought perhaps – yiddisher feller,' Hannah said. 'They might pick on you especially.'

'No,' Ben said. 'Not over this.'

'I just wondered, dear.'

'We were all together,' Ben said. 'The others wouldn't've let me be arrested on my own anyway. They'd've insisted on joining the party too.'

By the time Ben and Hannah returned to the lounge, Susan was already saying, 'It's really time we were thinking of going home.'

Ben looked round the room. 'Hullo, what've you done with Uncle Otto tonight?'

Hannah put a shocked hand to her mouth. 'Do you know I'd quite forgotten about him!'

'Where's he gone?' Julia asked.

'You ought to be in bed,' her father said.

'Oh, Daddy, do shut up!'

'Not the way to talk to your father,' Isidore mumbled.

'He must've gone to visit a friend,' Hannah said.

87

'Who exactly *is* Uncle Otto?' Colin demanded.

'Your father's uncle. From Poland.'

'He's not really my uncle,' Isidore began.

'Now, Isidore, I don't want any of that, thank you.'

'Eatin' us out of house and home,' Isidore muttered, slightly louder. Hannah pursed her lips. 'He *is*,' Isidore added defiantly.

'Daddy, you ought to be ashamed of yourself,' Susan scolded him.

'So you have him live with you.'

'We've offered.'

'Your husband's been arrested,' Isidore said.

'You watch out,' Ben said, 'maybe they'll pinch you one of these days.'

'Me? What for?'

Ben said: 'You never know your luck.'

Isidore simpered, 'I got enough troubles already.'

'I don't think,' Colin said, 'that being arrested is likely to be among them.'

'Ooh!' Susan said with a little pout. 'Major Adler at your service.'

Her brother went scarlet. Tessa took his hand. 'Poor Colin.'

Colin said: 'Oh, that's all right. Susan's imitations are famous, aren't they, Prunella the Prune?'

'I'll say. Do you remember her one of Mr Goldberg?'

Susan put on a thick middle European accent. 'Vould you like maybe a nice piece of salt beef today? Very frash.'

'He's a very good manager is Mr Goldberg,' Hannah said severely, spoiling it at the last second with a giggle.

'Who's denying?' Susan demanded.

'You'll have to excuse my family,' Colin said. 'They're a bit cracked.'

'I think they're very nice,' Tessa said.

FIVE

'And Afterwards . . .'

1

THE invitation read:

> MR AND MRS HAROLD FRANKS
> request the pleasure of
> your company
> to celebrate the marriage of
> their daughter TESSA
> to
> MAJOR COLIN ADLER, RE
> at the Berkeley Street Synagogue, W1
> and afterwards at the Cumberland Hotel
> (Cumberland Place entrance)
> RSVP

A stamped addressed card was enclosed for the reply.

'Looks like a full dress affair,' was Ben's comment.

'You'll have to wear morning dress,' Susan said.

'I should go in mourning because your brother's getting married?'

'You will, won't you? Wear morning dress.'

Ben said: 'No, Susan, I won't.'

'I wish I could have a new dress.'

'Why not make one?'

'Don't be silly, Benjamino.'

'Don't call me that.'

'Why don't we ever see Stan any more?'

'Probably because he's got better things to do.'

'That doesn't sound like Stan to me.'

'He's a big success. A job in the BBC yet,' Ben said. 'I should be such a success!'

'Ben, have you had another row with Stan?'

'I haven't had a row with Stan at all. What gave you that idea?'

'OK, Ben, have it your own way.' Susan smiled. 'You will wear morning dress, won't you?'

Ben shook his head. 'Honestly, Susan.'

'Oh, Ben, why not?'

'I don't believe in weddings.'

'What do you mean by that?'

'I don't believe in marriage at all,' Ben said. 'You know that. Treating people as if they were property to be let on permanent leases.'

'Is that how you think of me – let on a permanent lease?'

Ben grinned. 'I'll see you right, girl, don't you worry.'

'No, I want to know.'

'Why do you always have to take these things so personally?'

'How else can I take them?'

'Marriage is a social institution,' Ben said. 'It's not a personal thing at all. All it does is foul the relations between two people, makes them – what's Sid's expression? – buttresses of reaction, that's it.'

'What's anything Sid says got to do with *us*?'

'I'll tell you one thing it's got to do with us. I'm not going to wear morning dress.'

'You're allowed to take things personally but I'm not,' Susan said. 'That's what it amounts to, isn't it?'

'I don't agree,' Ben said.

'What would you think if I let somebody else have a temporary lease?' Susan demanded.

'If you slept with someone else? I wouldn't blame you. I might bash you, but I wouldn't blame you.'

'It wouldn't upset you?'

'It shouldn't,' Ben said.

'And I suppose if you slept with someone else, that shouldn't upset me?'

'We don't own each other. That's the point.'

'We're just on hire, is that it?'

'You ask Sid about marriage,' Ben told her. 'He's very hot on the dialectics of marriage is Sid.'

'I bet Sid would wear morning dress,' Susan said.

'Only because he's such a snob,' Ben replied.

'Sid a snob, that's a good one.'

'You know,' Ben smiled, 'it is a good one'n all.'

2

Ben wore an electric blue suit and a red tie which brought a frown in particular to the face of Sir Samuel Goldstein, Tessa's third cousin by marriage. Sir Samuel owed his place in the receiving line at the reception to his exceptional eminence. Sir Samuel Goldstein, KC, MC, TD, was educated at Harrow and at Balliol College, Oxford. He was Conservative and National Member of Parliament for N.E. Harrow from 1943 (when he was returned unopposed at a by-election) to 1945 when he was deposed by a 15,402 majority in favour of Mr Ronald Lewin (Socialist). He then resumed his business duties: managing director of Goldstein and Prout, Estate Agents, Auctioneers and Valuers, managing director of Magnet Gowns, director of Town and Country Development Limited, director of Lotex (Shampoo) Ltd, and director of the Family Lovers' Building Society. Sir Samuel was a Freeman of the borough of Hendon, a governor of Clifton College, a Fellow of the Horological Society, a vice-president of the Jewish Board of Guardians and a member of the Synagogue council. His white hair, his high forehead, his noble voice (which had earned him the title 'boom-boom' at the bar) and his famous cigars (from the same place as Winston's) betokened alike his intellectual and his social status. The look which he gave Ben's red tie was eloquent of his remorse at having let Tessa marry into a family which sported such a member. 'H'm,' he grunted, shaking hands, 'owjer do?'

'*Mazeltov*,' Ben said.

Susan sipped her champagne and surveyed the guests. There were enough of them, about three hundred and fifty, Colin had said. Poor old Colin, he looked very uncomfortable, bulging in his hired morning coat and striped trousers and shaking hands with unnatural heartiness. What a pity he couldn't wear his uniform! Tessa on the other hand really did look wonderful, especially since the train of her dress quite masked the fact that her legs were so short. Magnet Gowns *nuch*! Hannah at least hadn't let the family down; she had on her Persian lamb coat and a hat made of the same fur, her diamond watch, diamond clips and diamond earrings; her crocodile skin shoes were new and so was the matching bag. Isidore too looked rather grand, in his morning coat and his striped trousers, his white carnation and his black top hat (he had insisted on black). If only Ben hadn't been so obstinate! Susan gnawed her knuckle. He had wandered off, leaving her alone in the crowd. She craned this way and that for a face she knew. Otto's was the first she saw. He was standing against the wall, holding a glass of champagne. Susan was drawn to him; he looked as shabby as she felt.

'Hullo, Uncle Otto. How are you?'

'Not so bad, not so bad.'

'You're not drinking your champagne.'

'I don't want it,' Otto said. 'They forced it on me.'

'It'll do you good.'

Otto shook his head. 'I don't think so.'

'Well, it was a lovely wedding, wasn't it?'

Otto's eyes filled with tears. 'A lovely wedding, yes, a lovely wedding.'

'Ben and I were talking about you the other evening. We'd like you to come over and see us sometime, have dinner.'

'I'm too old to go out,' Otto said.

'I don't believe you're too old for anything.'

'Huh.' Otto did not smile. 'Soon I'll be gone, Susan. Soon you won't have to think about me any more.'

'Where are you going, Uncle Otto?'

'Where I should have gone a long time ago. I don't belong here.'

'Who belongs here?'

'You're young,' Otto said. 'You've got a family, you've got a *place*.'

'You've got a place too, Uncle Otto.'

'There's a man with a place,' Otto said, half raising a hand towards Sir Samuel. It was hard to tell whether he had spoken with scorn or with reverence.

Sir Samuel was saying: 'I took the matter up with the Minister himself. Of course Duncan's a personal friend of mine, has been for many, many years. I said to him "If I can't park my car there, perhaps you'd explain to me what entitled you to do so?" 'Course, he laughed at that and said, "I suppose we'd better find out" – sent for the poor blighter who'd warned me off, do you see? Feller was scared stiff, of course. Duncan was very civil about it though: "Tell me, messenger," said he, "what entitles me to park my car outside the door but forbids Sir Samuel here to do so?" Well, of course the wretched chap was completely off put, couldn't find a word to say for himself. Went off with his tail between his legs! Very nice chap, Duncan, do you know him?'

'No,' Hannah Adler said, 'I don't, I'm afraid.'

'Charming chap, charming. We were up together, you know. At Oxford. He was at the House.'

'He may have a place now,' Susan said. 'But he won't have for long.'

'He's a gentleman,' Otto said. 'A person of substance, of *position*.'

'It won't last.' Susan managed a Party smile.

'You pray God it lasts,' Otto Kahane said. 'You pray God it lasts, Susan my dear, because if it doesn't, it won't be something you can be pleased about, believe me.'

'I think I need another glass of champagne,' Susan said.

Otto caught her sleeve. 'Susan, my dear, don't think you can just knock down what you don't like and leave standing what you do like.'

'It's not a question of what I like, Uncle Otto.'

'You think you're a Communist – but you're not really. You're too personal, do you know what I mean? It's not good to be personal.'

'I'm not personal,' Susan said. 'That's not me at all. You don't know me very well, Uncle Otto.'

'You're too personal, Susan.'

In a corner a small boy in morning coat and striped trousers was being sick into a large brass plantstand. It was with great reluctance that he used the handkerchief from his top pocket to wipe his lips. Behind him, Ben was talking to the boy's father.

'How're things with you, Mr Abrahams?'

'Not so bad, m'boy, and not so good either. Like that.' He paddled a plump white hand in its mitten of black hair.

'Uh-huh,' Ben nodded sympathetically. 'Not still living in Simon Street, are you?'

'Not living in Simon Street is right. No, I've got a business in Cricklewood now. Very nice.'

'Still cars?'

'Still cars,' agreed Mr Abrahams, 'but I gotta nice garage now, a nice business. Not like the Simon Street days. No, we had a bomb down there, y'know. I lost a '38 Buick in mint condition. Could I use that car today!'

'Aiming at the Yids again, were they?' Ben grinned.

'You can say that again. Still, Cricklewood's very nice.'

'No trouble?'

'*No*. Anti-Semitism? No. Not a sign. There won't be any more of that, Ben m'boy, surely?'

'I wouldn't be too sure,' Ben said. 'What about Palestine?'

'Bad business,' Mr Abrahams said uncertainly.

'Not thinking of going yourself, Mr Abrahams?'

'Me? No. So why should I go to Palestine?' Mr Abrahams flattened his hand deprecatingly on his chest. 'I should sell motor-cars to the Arabs? Your old man was a great Zionist, wasn't he, Benjamin?'

''Sright,' Ben said. 'He was a great everything.'

Mr Abrahams thought for a moment. 'You don't really think there'll be more trouble like we used to have?'

'There could be. Of course they – they smashed up your pumps, didn't they?'

'I nearly lost the concession,' Mr Abrahams said. 'The company nearly took away my concession. Listen, I thought we was all gonna be murdered in our beds, believe me. What hooligans those Facists were! They was nothing but hooligans. Don't you agree, Benjamin? That's what your father used to say: "Morry, they're nothing but a buncha hooligans" – '

'"The thing to do is pay no attention!"' Ben quoted. 'You don't have to tell me.' He sipped his drink. 'As a matter of fact, Mr Abrahams, I've heard they're restarting activity.'

'Mosley?' Mr Abrahams took Ben's sleeve. 'You mean Mosley?'

'That's what I hear. You know the trouble last time – people didn't take steps in time.'

'There was the time we broke up the march,' Mr Abrahams said.

'That was a day,' Ben grinned.

'That certainly was a day. That was the proudest day of my life, Benjamin. The proudest day of my life.'

'They've just formed a new organization down there to see that the Fascists never march again. Mostly ex-servicemen. But anyone can join. Look, I'll tell you what, I'll get the secretary to give you a buzz. You might like to meet him. He's a very nice chap.'

'Yiddisher feller?'

'Matter of fact, no. If you felt like getting a few local people together, you know, tradesmen and so on, he'd probably come up to Cricklewood and tell you about it. He's dead keen on it.'

'Is it a good thing he's not a Yiddisher feller?'

'From the point of view of the public, yes. Gives the set-up a broader basis.'

'Yeah, well I tell you what. You get this feller to give me a ring. What's his name again?'

'Sid Forbes,' Ben said.

'Feeling better?' Mr Abrahams asked his son.

'Bit.'

'D'you know my boy Mark? This is Mr Simons.'

'How do you do?' Mark said. He was very yellow.

'How are you?' Ben said.

'He's got his *Bar Mitzvah* in a month's time and then he goes to Clifton school in September.'

'Clifton school!' Ben nodded, mouth tucked down. 'Very good. *Very* good.'

'You go find your mother, tell her you've finished being sick.' Mark went off through the crowd like a fat shadow.

'I've got someone I'd like you to meet,' Ben said. 'An uncle of Susan's – my wife's. He was in Dachau.'

Mr Abrahams went pale. 'The camp?'

Ben nodded. 'I'd like you to meet him.'

They had just reached Otto and Susan when the speeches started. Sir Samuel, who was by now in excellent voice, proposed the health of the bridegroom's family. He said that he knew they were a good family, and more than that – a good Jewish family. And more than that, a good British Jewish family! Mr Abrahams stood next to Otto Kahane. Had this thin, elderly man really been in Dachau Concentration Camp? A man who seemed no different from Morris Abrahams himself? A shudder went through the car-dealer. He must get that name from Ben again. Forbes, that was it.

Sir Samuel had his hands on his lapels now. 'I remember on one famous occasion Winston . . . staying with Louis Mendl on his yacht . . . didn't mind being in the government with him but dammit, golf is a serious business . . .'

'Hear hear,' Ben shouted.

Mr Abrahams waited nervously for the end of the speech. What did one say to a man who had been in Dachau? I'm sorry to hear it? What was there you could say? Mr Abrahams glanced again at Otto. He would definitely give some money to this thing Benjamin was talking about. He began to edge, very slowly, away from Otto Kahane.

'. . . the wilds of nowhere,' Sir Samuel said.

'Hear, hear.'

Hannah Adler was whispering to Mrs Harold Franks. 'Now there's nothing to worry about, dear. They'll come and live in my house until they find somewhere of their own. We've got plenty of room. They'll have the whole place to themselves. They won't even know I'm there. You can come and visit them any time. You know you're always welcome, don't you, dear?' Hannah's hand was flat on Mrs Franks's lapel.

'Bernie Baruch was furious . . .'

'Hear, hear.'

Mrs Franks said: 'It's very sweet of you, dear.'

Hannah Adler patted her arm. 'I know we're going to be friends, dear,' she said.

'As my old friend Norman Levy, KC, used to say, "By the time you find yourself saying, 'And finally, my lord' you know you should have sat down hours ago."'

'Hear, hear,' Ben cried.

'And so finally . . .' Sir Samuel finished to much laughter and applause. His voice could be heard intermittently throughout the speeches which followed, demanding whether those around him agreed that he had said the right things and hadn't gone on too long. Bryan Hammond, who was best man, made a short speech which he had composed from *Speeches for All Occasions*. It contained the joke about the honeymoon couple who registered as Mr and Mrs Goldstein. (The clerk said: 'Christian name?' and Mr Goldstein replied: 'Does it sound like one?') Sir Samuel was not amused.

Colin's reply was subdued; he thanked everyone for all they had done and mingled with his thanks silences and half-smiled asides which provoked bubbles of laughter now from here, now from there. Embarrassment possessed the guests who, whether they guffawed politely at the allusions to themselves or stayed uncomfortably dumb at those to other people, were without true sympathy with the speaker. The pauses in his speech became longer. The surging flood of Sir Samuel's reminiscences supervened. When one of the pauses became intolerably protracted, Ben brought the agony to an end with a crackle of determined clapping. Those around him joined in and Colin, amid relieved cheers, was able to get down.

3

They were to go to Ireland for the honeymoon. In the train, Tessa was silent and unsmiling; she had never lost a certain dark patience. That patience was framed in Colin's red restlessness, for each event caught him by surprise and left him gasping and uncertain of what he should do. Tessa leaned back coldly and watched her husband: he couldn't sit still; whenever anyone did anything – opened a door, put a case on the rack – he pressed a civilian coin into his palm long before the job was done, as if beside every action, inhibiting and gearing it, there was a price, an impending resentment that must be paid off. Tessa sat in her corner seat with an unnecessary travelling rug round her knees. Her stillness was a kind of deliberation. She put it on herself so that it was an action, an action unsensed by Colin which yet calmed him, so that when at last, after a hundred frets and panics, he sat down, she was able to smile at him with a feeling of achievement, though she had, so it seemed to him, actually done nothing.

'Well, I think that's everything,' he observed.

'Good.' Her head was hard back against the cushion. 'Why don't you shut your eyes? It's been a tiring day.'

'You know, if you don't mind, I think I will. Just forty winks.'

Tessa nodded. 'You do that.' Colin promptly fell asleep. He felt no guilt at this; often it had seemed to him, when he was away in Africa and in Italy, in France and Germany, that he and Tessa were married already. Their letters had ceased to be purely love letters; they talked of music and books, of the chances of finding a house and how they would like it to look; Colin had designed their dream house and Tessa had decorated and furnished it in imagination, even down to the red curtains in the dining room. Their complicated imaginings lasted for the whole time Colin was away. Not all their correspondence was devoted to this fantasy, but it provided a happy refuge in which they could match their ideas of the future. By the time Colin came home, though they had never lived, or indeed spent more than a few consecutive hours together, they had already enjoyed an ideal of marriage which provided them with a history of close and frictionless happiness. Tessa looked forward to sharing her husband's bed with neither fear nor desire; she half-hoped both might come, since fear could be respect and desire would be pleasure, but she sensed that perhaps the time for them was past. She and Colin had been married too long.

The crossing was wretched. In the public rooms the air was thick with the rapid smoke of duty-free cigarettes. They ended up on deck where Colin found a bench sheltered by the bridge. 'Not much of a place for our first night, but still . . .'

'It's all right.'

Colin pressed his arm around her. 'Not feeling too good?'

'Not too.'

'I say, you are feeling rotten, aren't you? I can tell.' He seemed surprised by his own sympathy.

'I'll be all right as long as I don't have to talk,' Tessa said.

'It's not too cold for you up here?'

'It's anaesthetic,' she smiled thinly.

He hugged her into the depths of his British warm and bound his long yellow scarf round and round their necks and almost over their heads. 'This is what I always wanted,' he whispered.

4

The hotel had once been a private residence. It stood in the heel of a sock-shaped cove. A cobbled jetty ran out into Bantry Bay. Fat rocks, as green as uncut cheeses, bolstered the shore. The place was run by a retired English colonel (major) whose name was Hetherington. There were ten rooms, but not all of them were taken. Peace filled the place. The colonel's wife, Leila, who was very young and beautiful, was eight months pregnant. She moved with that slow rhythm of pregnancy, a walk full of private confidence, which was to Colin and Tessa, fretful from their long journey, like music. She would walk along the front of the house from the chicken run each morning with a basket of eggs on her arm. Colin and Tessa came to watch for her, all true and right, with the basket hooped over her arm and held against her belly. Watching her, they came to desire a child, for in this woman was the beauty of sexuality, while in their own bed, for those first few nights, was its fumbling horror, a sexuality which could not be acknowledged, which could not be a part of them, as this swollen grace of the woman Leila was the truth between her and her husband and was open knowledge between them: whether those two walked apart or together there was no call for explanations, but if Tessa went into the hotel, Colin would say: 'What are you doing, Tess? Where are you going?' They always had need of words to locate each other; their words were truer than their actions. Their love found its best expression in them. So they watched Leila, and envied what was natural, though to each other they merely said: 'Isn't she sweet?'

In the bay, porpoises ran humping and sliding through the grey water. The chonk and hiss of their passing filled Tessa with excitement. Once the porpoises came while she and Colin were out fishing with old Sean, Colonel Hetherington's boatman, and the rhythm of their procession was matched in Tessa's cry, 'They're coming, they're coming'; her face lit with joy at something beyond her control. Colin looked up from untwisting the metal spinnakers which he was trailing for mackerel. 'Oh dash it,' he said, 'they'll frighten off the fish.'

'They're coming,' Tessa cried. 'Look, Colin, look. They're coming.'

Colin looked, to oblige. 'So they are.'

The porpoises swelled forward, blackening the water. Tessa's breath surged with the rhythm of them; she shuddered as the porpoises rocked and jarred the boat, as their backs humped against its groin. When the last was gone her mouth yawned up at the sky and she let out a howl of deep defeat and squeezed her face in her hands. Colin looked at Sean. It was rather embarrassing. Probably Tessa was finding it a bit rough.

'Want to go in, darling?'

The girl made no reply. The shuddering eased and left her quite alone. She smiled, shaking her head very slowly, and closed her eyes.

'These'll make a wonderful breakfast,' Colin said. Tessa opened her eyes. Colin was tearing the hooks from the mackerel's red mouths, his fingers gloved with thin blood as he flipped the twitching catch into the grave of the boat. His action reminded Tessa of someone shelling peas into a bowl. A coldness entered her. Could he ever be natural anywhere? Could he ever be natural, could he ever need to be in such a place, at such a time, need it like blood in his veins, to be alive? Could he ever find that deep rhythm which would command her, which beyond all decision would be able to overtake her? Before she had made herself patient, now as Sean rowed the boat back to the jetty, her hips moved on the swell of the water, in a secret longing. The past boiled back, swamping her decision. When she first went into the WAAF she was stationed at Uxbridge. There was a corporal in charge of the hut, a wide-hipped, rather blowzy girl. One night Tessa overheard her saying: 'She's going to sue for divorce, but I don't think she'll get one. I went with him once and the wretched bloke couldn't even get it in.'

The phrase lit Tessa's innocence like lightning. She did not close her eyes to it though, but said to herself that such a thing was trivial and could not rule a life. Now she clenched her teeth against the denial of what she had told herself; she forced herself to think that the years she had known Colin, all the things they had talked and written about, were more important than his temporary shortcomings. But on the swell of the water her hips moved secretly.

All day she fought against the memory of Jimmy Lloyd. Jimmy Lloyd was a Flight Lieutenant whom Tessa had met in the WAAF. He had curly fair hair and the red, sweet lips of a baby. He was not tall, but his boyish slimness made him look it. Nearly all the women on Tessa's station were, or pretended to be, in love with him, and Tessa was quite astonished when he asked her to go to the RAF Charity Ball at the Dorchester with him. It was not the first time that she had been asked out (she and Colin had agreed not to be formally engaged) and she told herself that she had no cause to reject Jimmy just because he was the best looking of the bunch.

They were both good dancers and the evening was a great success. Tessa had feared that Jimmy would spend much of his time with the other girls in the party, but it was not so: he wanted every dance with her. 'You're the only one with the first idea of dancing,' he whispered to her, 'and a good deal more than the first idea at that.'

Tessa put her head against Jimmy's chest. 'I'm loving it,' she said. Afterwards they took a taxi down to the Embankment near Chelsea bridge. They leaned over the parapet. He put his arm around her shoulders. 'Christ, I've enjoyed this evening.'

'Me too.'

He kissed her and her lips parted for him. She loved him. She loved him. She crossed her arms behind his neck and pressed her mouth against his. She loved him. She felt his body against her. Alternate-legged, they stood kissing with black intensity.

At last he said: 'We can't go on like this.'

'No,' she panted. 'No, I must go home.'

'Do they expect you?'

'I've got a key.'

'Do they expect you?' he insisted.

'No, that is – I – ' She kissed his lips. 'No, they don't expect me.'

'Tess, Tess. I say, I – I've got a chum with a flat near here.'

'Well?'

'I love you, Tess.'

'I love you, I love you too, Jimmy.'

'Come on.' Jimmy had to keep striking matches to look at the numbers of the buildings. Between matches they kissed, braced against lamp posts and railings, with gasps and yeses till another match was struck. At last they found the place. They had to go down narrow area steps to the door. It was two-thirty in the morning, but Jimmy's chum opened up almost immediately: 'Well, hullo there. Come in, we were just talking about you.'

Jimmy said: 'This is Tessa. Tessa – Monty. Monty Outwater.'

'I suppose you two want a bed,' Monty said.

'Anyone using the downstairs?'

'Enjoy yourselves,' Monty said. 'Be finished by eight though, will you? I'm not going to be done out of my breakfast by anyone's loving.'

The room which Monty was lending them was his sitting-room. There was a divan, books, a double-burner electric fire and an armchair. The kitchen was beyond. 'Pretty cosy, eh?' Jimmy commented.

'Have you been here before?' Tessa inquired.

'I've visited Monty before, yes. We were at school together.' He put his arms round her. 'But I've never visited him with a woman before if that's what you mean.' He switched on the fire. 'Great thing about gay people is they never mind you touching them for the loan of a bed. Aren't jealous like most people, I suppose.'

'Gay?' Tessa said.

'Bent, queer, you know. Homosexual.'

'Is he?'

'As a corkscrew, my love.' Jimmy sat down on the divan. Tessa took off her wrap. She was wearing a strapless black evening dress, and long white gloves. She removed the gloves and laid them on the arm of the chair. Jimmy turned off the light. The electric fire glowed. Jimmy said: 'Tessa, I want to go to bed with you.'

'I thought you might.'

Jimmy said: 'I love you.'

'I love you,' she said. 'I love you.'

He said: 'Take your clothes off.'

Tessa said: 'You won't like it.'

'I will.' He half-closed his eyes, shook his head. 'I will. Don't say that.'

'I don't mean me,' she said. 'I mean – I'm, you know, I'm a virgin.'

'You don't have to apologize. It won't matter, I promise.'

Tessa said: 'I want to, Jimmy, but I'm scared.'

'You needn't be scared.'

Tessa said: 'Unhook me at the back then.'

They stood naked together in front of the fire. His body was hot against her. She stood on tiptoe to force her mouth against his. Nothing was real but the straightness of the man against her. She caught her breath and stood a pace away. 'Have you got, you know, anything?' she asked.

'Nothing can happen the first time,' he said.

'That's not the story I've heard,' Tessa said. 'Have you?'

He nodded. 'In my wallet. What a funny girl you are, Tess.'

'Because I'm not so simple as to believe you never thought you might make love to someone tonight?'

'I'm sorry,' he said.

'About what?'

'Having it,' he said.

'It's just as well you have, isn't it?'

He said: 'Don't – look.'

'You don't know much about women,' she said. 'I don't mind looking.' And then she did. Then she did, then she did mind. She looked at him and twisted away.

'Tess, my God, what is it? What is it?'

'Oh, my God, Jimmy,' she said. 'I can't, I can't.'

'Tess – for God's sake! Why? What have I done?'

'I'm Jewish,' she said.

'For God's sake, I know that. What difference does it make? I don't mind. I love you.'

'You don't mind?' She laughed into sobbing. 'I mind,' she cried. 'I mind. I mind because you . . .'

'But Tess, that's absurd –'

'I can't go to bed with you, Jimmy. I can't. God damn it. *Damn* it.' She flung herself on the divan.

'For God's sake, Tess, you knew I wasn't a Jew.'

'You don't understand. You don't understand.'

'I *do*,' he said. 'I do. But it's – it's crazy. You mean you would have if – ' He shook his head. 'It doesn't make any *sense*. Do appearances matter *that* much to you? Do they?'

'Don't you understand?' she shouted at him. 'I can't. I know it doesn't make any sense. But I just can't.'

He grabbed her shoulders so that she had to face him.

'Tess, you can't let this happen. You can't do this just for *nothing*.'

'It's not nothing.'

'I'll marry you,' he said, his lips against her breast, 'if that would make it any better.'

She shook her head. 'I'm engaged,' she laughed at him. 'Unofficially of course.'

'I could kill you,' he said.

'Yes, you could. I wouldn't mind.' She put her hand on him. 'I'm sorry, Jimmy. Don't hate me, Jimmy.'

'No,' he said. 'No. You're not going to humiliate me that much. I'd rather do it myself.'

'I'm sorry, I'm sorry.'

'You're a killer,' Jimmy Lloyd said. 'You're a killer. That's what you are. A killer.'

A week later Jimmy Lloyd sent her the Collected Works of Oscar Wilde. She thought it an odd choice.

The days and the nights were passing. Colin and Tessa walked with the slackness of people with no rule between them. 'Where are you going, darling?' 'Upstairs for a hanky.' They had to exchange information: 'I'm just going to the post.' 'I shall be in the room when you get back.' Tessa's patience turned to sullenness. Colin was sweet and kind and he would do anything for her; he was so considerate, it was a thing everyone had remarked in Colin, that he was so considerate; but now Tessa wondered, would he ever do something because he had to do it? Was there any force in him? If there was not, he would destroy her, he would make the decision she made that night in the flat in Chelsea a vain and ugly suicide, she thought smilingly, based on a misunderstanding between herself and a certain young person. She fought to banish the notion of testing Colin in favour of helping him, tried to think not of what he could not do but of how she could help him to do it. She told herself that marriage had extension, that its essence was its duration, that everything would come right in the end; with Jimmy that would not have been true, all would have been a contingent of moments, and in the end they would not cohere; they would not make sense of themselves, for though there might be pleasures, there could not be meaning: the centre would not hold. With Colin, she and her husband would grow together and have coherence; their children would be Jews. So she fought against putting him to an arbitrary test, against making the honeymoon set a term on anything. She made a decision that she would not worry if the honeymoon was vain. She had to lock the door to tell herself, actually to speak the words: 'I am married and it *will* work.' She imagined herself on the boat, going back to Fishguard. Did Jimmy live in Wales? No, she hadn't been wrong. She hadn't been wrong.

That night when she sensed it coming right it was a miracle to her; nature itself seemed unnatural, coming to her, in the first moments of knowledge, like a voice, like words. Then words fell behind. She was in a place without words. The moving of her hips drew Colin into her and their breathing drew together, till that currency of words which had been their only commerce was nothing and they were, in that instant, married.

'It was right,' Colin whispered.

'Yes,' she said, 'it was. It was.'

'I'm sorry it's been – so long,' he said.

'I always knew it would be right,' Tessa Adler said. 'I always knew it would be.'

SIX

A House and a Garden

1

COLIN HAD ALWAYS pictured a post-war world in which everything would begin again from the beginning. There would be no need to look around for work because there would be so much to do. Instead, there was a bustle of competition for the few jobs that were advertised, a bustle which seemed hardly consonant with the dignity of his profession and in which Colin was too diffident to join. He hung around waiting for something to turn up. Before the war, when he was working in Douglas Airye's office, he and his closest friend of those days, a chap by the name of Saul Marowitz, used to go for long walks together, systematically pulling down all those buildings which offended them and creating neighbourhood units and factory blocks from the sites. Colin had been full of CIAM zeal in those days, but now it seemed to him that most of the zeal must have been Marowitz's. They had often derided their chief, for Airye's practice was largely devoted to speculative building in ribbon development areas and his work excited the scorn of the two young idealists, but it was Airye whom Colin first phoned on his return and he was almost aggrieved to be told that there were no vacancies in the office. Colin had thought that some sort of job would be found for him, since reconstruction would be a major post-war task, but it was not now creative zest which made him long for work: it was his own comfort; he deserved a living after four years of war and he felt that it was time someone offered it to him. He had the idea that he was being done down. Each evening when he returned to Woburn Road he would ask sullenly if there had been any messages. Tessa would say: 'No, nothing, dear. How did you get on?'

'Doesn't seem to be anything anywhere. I don't know – it doesn't seem *right* somehow. All sorts of strange people in charge of things – I don't know – it doesn't seem right to me.'

'What do you mean, dear?'

'Oh, it's always the same old story: restrictions, restrictions, restrictions – '

'Don't tell me about restrictions,' Isidore said, coming out of the sitting-room, dangling the evening paper as usual.

'Evening, Commander-in-Chief,' Colin said. 'How's the world with you?'

'Don't ask.'

Colin took the paper from his father and turned anxiously to the racing page. He had begun betting on the horses merely to pass the time, but though he was too cautious to risk large sums, it had soon become more than a diversion. (There was anger in Colin's betting: since there was no quick justice in life, he looked for it elsewhere.) You needed no one's permission or patronage in order to win on the horses. If you won, you won. You were ahead of the game and you could do what you liked without needing the indulgence of the tycoons or risking the interference of the government. Colin was quickly disillusioned with the post-war world, the more so since it was Tessa, not a career, to which he had for so long looked forward: it was their house rather than any neighbourhood scheme which he had spent so long in planning. He was prepared to accept a job and to do it as well as he could, but there was no passionate edge to his ambition. He wanted the job no one had offered him because he wanted to be alone with Tessa, because he wanted to move out of Woburn Road and have a place of his own. He wanted a public job so that he himself might have privacy. He gambled on the horses and waited for something to turn up. Each evening he came home and asked if there had been any messages.

One evening, Tessa said: 'Yes. A man called Marowitz phoned. At least I think that's the name.'

Colin pinked: 'Oh yes, that's the name all right. Did he say what he wanted?'

'He said he wanted to see you, sweets, that's all.'

Colin phoned Marowitz and they arranged to meet for breakfast the following morning at Lyons Corner House, Marble Arch. When Colin arrived, Marowitz was already sitting at a marble-topped table, gnawing his fingernails and reading the morning papers, a pencil tucked behind his ear. He was a short, bespectacled man with a wad of brown hair pulled down like a cap over a pale, triangular face. Colin said: 'Well, hullo –'

Marowitz looked up and without uncrossing his legs leaned over and pushed his mackintosh off on to the floor to let Colin sit down. 'Only place I can work in the mornings,' he said. 'Like seeing the whores licking their sores. Shows you how little time there is to waste. Coffee?'

'I'd like some eggs and bacon,' Colin said.

'We can always try.' Marowitz took out a packet of cigarettes and, somewhat to Colin's disgust, lit up. 'Eggs and bacon for the gent,' he told the waitress, 'and some more coffee.'

'*Egg* and bacon,' the girl said. 'Where've you been?'

'I don't know,' Marowitz said. 'Where have you been?'

'Looking for work,' Colin said.

'Short of work, Colin?'

'I haven't found anything I feel like taking.'

'How does the thought of designing a hundred and fifty cottages for farm labourers appeal to you?'

'Each one different?' Colin smiled.

111

Marowitz tapped his briefcase. 'I've got the specifications in here. The whole thing's tied up. I've got more work than I can cope with in five years, I mean that. And a free hand. At least there will be when I've finished telling them how much money it'll save if they give me one. I want you to come in with me.'

'Me?' Colin said. 'Why me?'

'Because I need a competent hack who won't mess up my ideas.'

'Thanks very much.'

Marowitz chewed at a nail and then he said: 'I'm not playing or joking, you know.' He bit again. 'I need someone who can catch hold of an idea and work it up, but I don't want too much originality. I'll provide that. You're not a leader, Colin. You're a – what do they say? – 2 i/c. I can make you something you can never make yourself. I can pass something on to you, just as my father did to me. But it means hard work. *Bloody* hard work. But the possibilities are there – to create something really organic, to catch hold of a project and make it *everything* one wants.' Marowitz was leaning forward now, the bitten stubs of his fingers quivering in front of Colin's face.

'Ah, here's my egg and bacon,' Colin said.

'Pour the coffee,' Marowitz said to the girl.

'Please,' Colin said.

'I'm not promising you anything except work and battles –'

'Battles?'

'Things are going to be the way I want them. The way they ought to be. And that means battles. However free the hand they give you, it means battles. To do something right always means battles. *Bloody* battles.'

'What were you in during the war?' Colin inquired.

'Ministry of Supply,' Marowitz said.

'Well, I was in battles,' Colin said, 'and I've had about enough of them.'

'OK. I'll fight the battles. Don't worry about that. What I need is someone really competent to take charge of the site work. I'll fight the battles.'

'What about money?'

'Oh, there's money. Not much. But there's money. You won't starve.'

'What about my wife? I don't want her to starve either.'

'You're married?'

'I wouldn't have a wife otherwise.'

'I thought there had to be something –'

'Something?'

'You're scared,' Marowitz said. 'You don't really want to do anything.'

'Perhaps that's because I've done too much for the last few years.'

'Listen, forget about the war – no one's going to thank you for anything you did in the war – so forget about it. I'm offering you a chance to do some work. I need someone to do a job, you could be the man. If you don't want it, fine. But don't pass your hat round, OK?'

Colin said: 'I'm not asking for anything –'

Marowitz said: 'For Christ's sake, don't you see this work is what you fought in the war to get? It's something that could never have happened if the war hadn't made people see –'

'See what?'

'How little time there is to do something. It's no use sitting back. We've got to get on with things – ourselves. Look at all that's happening every bloody day' – Marowitz slapped the pile of newspapers – 'nothing's stopped happening because the war's over.'

Colin said: 'What sort of money is there in this job of yours and who's going to supply it? I mean, it's all very well, but you haven't given me any details –'

Marowitz said: 'Look, there's enough money to keep us

on the job – money's no problem, but I can't guarantee you a surplus or anything like that – '

'I've got a family to think about – '

'Crap.' Marowitz scratched his head into a storm of scurf. 'Let the damned family think about you. What's this family anyway? You got kids too?'

'Not yet,' Colin said, 'but we want to.'

'What kind of a place are you going to build for them?'

'I shan't build anything, haven't got the money.'

'Look, if you come with me you can build your own house. You can build your own house and you can build your own life.'

'It all sounds very fascinating. Where is this Utopia exactly?'

Marowitz opened his briefcase. 'It's no bloody Utopia,' he said. 'Take a look at this lot.'

2

Tessa said: 'Well, how did it go? You've been out long enough.'

It was well after tea. Isidore and Hannah were home from the shop already.

'Talk the hind leg off a donkey, Saul would,' Colin said. 'Very excitable sort of chap.'

'Well, what did he want to see you about?'

Colin said: 'How does the idea of Kenya appeal to you?'

'*Kenya*?'

'Kenya.'

'That's in Africa, isn't it?' Isidore said.

'*East* Africa,' Julia said.

'Is that what he wanted to talk to you about?'

'That's what he wanted to talk to me about.'

'But why Kenya?'

'Because that's where the job is. Some big development

114

corporation have put him in charge of modernizing conditions on some of their farms out there. He showed me all the papers – it seems quite genuine.'

'Well, who is this man and why's he been put in charge?'

'Who is this Hitler and what does he want?' Julia said.

'What's Hitler got to do with it?' Isidore said suspiciously.

'He's a chap I was with in Airye's office. Very brilliant chap actually. Son of Nathan Marowitz who was a very famous architect before the war. I expect he got the job through someone he met in the war – he was in the Min of Supply.'

'And very nice too,' Tessa said.

'Well, what do you think about it?'

'What's the salary like?'

'Oh, nothing very special, but the work's interesting and there's no shortage of accommodation apparently. We could even build our own.'

'It would mean actually *going* to Kenya, would it?'

'You can't very well design housing without,' Colin said.

'It has been done, hasn't it?'

'Not Saul's way,' Colin smiled. 'He's got very definite ideas about the way the job should be done.'

'He sounds a bit of a fanatic.'

'That's putting it mildly.'

'I don't much fancy being stuck somewhere in the wilds of Africa with a fanatic.'

'He's quite a nice fanatic. I mean he's very sincere.'

'Most fanatics are. That's what makes them fanatical.' Tessa sighed. 'Kenya! I don't know.'

'Why can't you get a job in England, dear?' Hannah asked.

'You tell me. Because there aren't any, I suppose, or else they don't want me.'

'But they must – a qualified man like you.'

'There's no must about it. It's all these restrictions and things –'

'Don't tell me about restrictions!'

Hannah Adler said: 'You do all right, Issy, don't complain so much.'

'Why shouldn't I complain? I've got plenty to complain about.'

'If you were in Heaven you'd complain about the company,' Hannah said. She turned to her son. 'I'll tell you what I'll do. I'll talk to some people.'

Colin put his arm round her. 'Who've you got to talk to?'

Tessa said: 'I never thought of Kenya, I must say.'

Colin cracked his knuckles. 'Saul said to tell you you can get a cook there for two pounds a month.'

'Oh, he did, did he? Well, you've got a cook right here – for nuppence a month.'

'You don't want to go to Kenya after all those years in the Army, do you?' Hannah inquired.

'It's an opportunity,' Colin said.

'With the coloured people?'

Colin pinked. He was glad Otto wasn't in the room. He felt that he might have been hurt. 'I don't mind coloured people,' he said.

'There's good and bad in everyone,' Hannah agreed.

Colin cracked his knuckles. 'We don't have to make up our minds for a day or two. But I must say Saul's got some wonderful ideas. It's worth thinking about.' He picked up the evening paper and turned to the stop press. 'I mean, at least it's a job.'

'After all these years,' Hannah said, 'you come back for a few weeks and off you go again and maybe we never see you for six, seven years –'

'"It's a real opportunity to do something creative,"' Colin quoted.

'I never thought you'd find it so difficult to find a job,' Tessa said. 'An experienced man like you.'

116

'He's found one,' Julia said. 'I think Kenya sounds a wonderful idea.'

'It's such a long way, Julia.'

'That's a point. I could come out and visit!'

'Good old Prunella the Prune,' Colin said.

'Don't like Jews in the colonies,' Isidore said.

'Don't like Jews anywhere, do they?' Colin smiled.

'Daddy, you are a misery!'

'No way to speak to your father.'

'Well you are. I think they should go. I only wish I could.'

'Treat the house like it was a hotel,' Isidore grumbled.

'I don't know *what* you're talking about. You must be mixing me up with Susan or something.'

'I know what's going on,' Isidore persisted.

'Nothing whatever is going on. You're being very stupid, Daddy, I'm afraid.'

'She wants to go to the university.'

'What's wrong with that?' Hannah demanded.

'Waste of time.'

'It's not a waste of time at all.'

'Always findin' ways to spend money!'

Colin cracked his knuckles. Tessa twitched away and looked out of the window. Colin followed her. 'You don't want to let them upset you,' he said.

'They don't,' she replied, gritting her teeth: Colin cracking his knuckles drove her to distraction.

'What do you think about things?'

Tessa said: 'I can't pretend I'm very keen, Colin.'

'Would you like to meet Saul and talk it over?'

'If you like.'

They couldn't very well have Marowitz to dinner at Woburn Road, so they asked him out to Quo Vadis which someone had told Colin was a very good place. Colin wore his demob suit and a stiff collar and Tessa had on her best dress. Marowitz arrived in a flurry of papers, came through to the table still with his mackintosh on and had it wrestled off him by a waiter. 'Hullo, Colin, sorry to keep you waiting. I had a thought and it couldn't wait – you know how these things happen. I'll tell you what it was – it's this thing I was telling you about the other day – the right kind of family housing for an essentially village community. It's no use sealing them all away in separate wrappings – one's got to think of the problem as a problem in education but at the same time one's got to see that the European solution is not necessarily *the* solution. See what I mean?'

'I'm afraid I don't,' Tessa said.

'Oh, um, well, look – this is Tessa. Saul Marowitz.'

'How are you?' Marowitz said, twitching a cigarette out of his packet and lighting it without offering one to Tessa. 'What I'm studying at the moment is the influence of African art on early Cubism. Does that make sense to you?'

'I don't quite see what you're looking for.'

'The proper interrelation of African and European art. In a purely theoretical setting. It's so difficult to un-think, you know what I mean? I want us to arrive out there *blank* – you know? – without any preconceptions. I think this sort of consideration is a way of doing that, of clearing the mental site in a way that'll leave room for the right sort of fresh conception. Oh, it's all very *theoretical*. I wouldn't mention this to anyone I didn't know very well, but I thought – well, since we're going to be working together – '

'Steady on,' Colin said, 'we haven't exactly made any firm agreement yet.'

'I want you to let him do this,' Saul Marowitz said to Tessa. 'I want you to be one hundred per cent with us on this. It's a really exciting proposition – '

'For you,' Tessa said.

'And him,' Marowitz said. 'I can really make something of this husband of yours, you know?'

'Yes, but will it be something I like?'

118

'Look, what do you want him to be? A nine till fiver? Is that what you want?'

'It'd make a nice change, I must say.'

'Look, you'll have him in your bed all right. What more do you want?'

'I say, look here – '

'I want quite a lot more than that, Mr Marowitz. I want a home and a family.'

'OK, fine, you can have both.'

'Well, thank you very much!'

'I'm giving your husband – '

'An opportunity to do something really creative, I know.'

'She doesn't want you to go, does she?'

'I wouldn't put it that way. We both want to know what it entails exactly, that's all.'

'It entails working your balls off for something really worth while. I don't even know what yet. It means a thousand a year, if that's what you're worried about and the promise of maybe a bit more and maybe out on your ear. I don't know.'

Colin said: 'There's no need to get excited.'

'I'm *bloody* excited. And I want you to be. Listen, I feel as if I've got something so bloody hot I want to explode, you know?' Marowitz took Tessa's arm between his fingers. 'You can have everything you want out there. I'll see you get it. Anything you want – house, garden, anything – I'll design it for you myself.'

Tessa said: 'Perhaps I'd sooner Colin did the designing.'

'Sure, have anyone you want. Passage is all paid. I only want you to say yes. In a week's time we'll be out there.'

'A *week*?' Tessa smiled distantly. 'We couldn't possibly leave in a week.'

Colin said: 'You mustn't rush us.'

'I rush myself, why shouldn't I rush you? I want to get out there and get started.'

'You haven't got any responsibilities – '

119

'What responsibilities?'

'Family – '

'You're a man and a woman, what is this mysterious family you carry around with you?'

'I haven't been home for some years.'

'You've wasted four years,' Marowitz said. 'You can't afford to waste any more. You've got to make him see that. I want you to get packed and be ready to leave in a week.'

Tessa said: 'I hope you're not always so full of orders.'

'Sure I'm always full of orders. I like to get on with things. I don't like people who're always hesitating.'

'In that case perhaps you wouldn't like me.'

'So if I wouldn't? He's the one you're in bed with, not me. When that changes we'll worry about how we get on, OK?'

'In that case I don't think we shall have to worry.'

'Sure not. Anyway if I'm going to do this job properly I shall have to concentrate on the Africans' wives – white women could give you the wrong ideas entirely.' Marowitz lit another cigarette in an awkward pause. 'Anyway, I haven't got time for sex,' he said, 'much too busy. Love and the bourgeoisie – they made my father throw up and they do the same to me, you know?'

Tessa said: 'Would there be any other architects on the job except you?'

'Only Colin.'

'We shall have to see about that,' Colin said. 'I haven't made any promises.'

'Don't you,' Tessa said.

3

The voice on the telephone said: 'Mr Colin Adler? My name's Cox, Stephen Cox. I'm speaking for Mr Cyril King.'

'Oh yes,' Colin said.

'I gather from the tone that the name doesn't mean much to you. May interest you to know therefore that Mr King is the managing director of the Family Lovers' Building Society.'

'Christ,' Colin said. It just popped out.

'If he'd been born a few hundred years earlier, he probably would have been,' agreed the other. 'Look, your name's been given to us as an architect with a particular interest in private housing. So we wondered if you'd care to trot round and have a word with us, without obligation, of course.'

Cyril King was a portly man with a fleshy face and thick spectacles which fattened his eyes. 'Mr Adler,' he said, offering a plump manicured hand with neat, pointed nails, 'you're very welcome here. Tell me, what do you think of the proposition?'

Colin pinked: 'Proposition – ?'

'Haven't told him a thing yet,' Cox said.

Mr King pierced a cigar and lay back in his chair to light it. Colin lowered his eyes to the man's desk. There were two pictures on it. One was of a blonde woman with a baby in her arms. Mother and son were frowning against the glare. The other was of the boy alone, in football things, at the age of twelve or so. There was no sun in the picture, but the boy was still frowning.

'Mr Adler, I'll come straight to the point. As you know, the great Friendly Societies have been very quiet during the past few years, but now the government want more houses and they're not going to get them without our help, right? For the moment we've got a lot of restrictions and things, but they'll all go sooner or later because sooner or later people are going to want to build the kind of houses they personally want to build. We want to be in a position to help them do this because we believe in democracy, Mr Adler, and in the right of the individual to build how and where and what he likes. Within limits. For instance, personally I wouldn't advance a single penny today to anyone proposing to erect a modernistic building. Does that surprise you?'

'No,' Colin said, 'not particularly.'

'Good, right. So far so good. Anyway, modernistic architecture is largely foreign in origin. I mean it's not suited to the particular requirements of this country – '

'Electricity isn't British in origin,' Colin said, 'but it seems to work here all right.'

'Look, m'boy, I'm talking about property investment, see? I don't mean to offend you – '

'You're not offending me – '

'No, because I like a lot of modern stuff myself. My own house was designed by one of the best continental architects – Nathan Marowitz – does that name mean anything to you?'

'Quite a lot,' Colin said. 'I've just been offered a job with his son.'

'He's *meshuggah*, that boy,' Cyril King said.

'That's what I thought.'

'Look, I'll tell you what we had in mind for you. We need a yong architect on our staff: to show the world that we're not afraid of new ideas, you see what I mean? I hope we'll be having a lot of young people coming to us for loans within the near future and I want to be able to hand them over to a young feller like yourself they can talk to about their plans – a young feller who can give them guidance about the sort of house they'd best be advised to have, go over plans with them and such like.'

'Sounds very interesting,' Colin said, 'I only hope I'm qualified – '

'We'll be giving you a lot of help,' Cyril King said, 'you'd be working closely with Stephen here. The thing to remember is that this is a finance company primarily, Mr Adler. We want people to have their own homes, it's the right of free men to have their own homes, but we've got to protect our investment. Business and art have nothing whatsoever in common as far as I'm concerned.'

'I suppose not.'

'I do my bit of painting myself in my spare time but I wouldn't bring my paints to the office. Office is one thing and home life's another. I wouldn't even let young Stephen here meet my wife, you know that?'

'Very wise,' Cox grinned.

'And none of your cheek, young man. This Cox, he's a terror, I'll tell you.'

'Well, um, what's the next move then?' Colin asked.

'The next move is you spend a trial period with us and at the end of it we see how we like each other.'

'Suits me,' Colin said.

After two months' trial, Colin and the Family Lovers' found each other very satisfactory and terms were agreed for his permanent employment. At the end of a very amicable interview, Cyril King said: 'By the way, I don't know whether you and your wife have found anywhere to live yet –'

Colin said: 'As a matter of fact, no.'

'Well, look, there's a house in Wimbledon that's just come into our hands through a reversion – you know the way these things happen – and the directors wondered whether it might not suit you.'

'It's very much a question of whether we can afford it –'

'The Family Lovers' looks after its employees, don't you worry. You can move in tomorrow as far as I'm concerned. *After* you get home from the office!'

'Well, honestly, I can't thank you enough. Really it – it might have been arranged.'

Mr Cyril King pierced a cigar with great care. 'Yes,' he said, 'you know really it might.'

Oakfern Drive, in which the Adlers' house 'Ravensnook' stood, came up from behind the All England Tennis Club and joined Wimbledon Parkside. It was a quiet, dignified road with rough-set whitewashed kerbstones and wide verges. There was crisp gravel in the gutters which crunched agreeably under well-polished shoes. One's umbrella made neat punctures in the smooth context of moss. The house was everything they had planned (even Hannah could find nothing wrong with it) and the neighbourhood was respectable without being pretentious. Colin was relieved to see no flashy cars in the quadrangle of Monmouth Court, the big block of flats which faced the Common just before you reached Oakfern Drive. Their new neighbours, Ted and Bunty Bradshaw, soon asked Colin and Tessa in for drinks and plainly the suspicion that they were Jewish never arose, which was an agreeable change from North London. Colin would never have denied that they were Jewish, but it was pleasant not to be labelled at once: it gave one time to breathe. Equally, he was pleased that when people asked where he was living and he replied 'Wimbledon', their first thought was not, as it was when he had had to say 'Cricklewood' or 'Golders Green', that he was a Jew. He had time to be an ordinary Briton, which was what he felt himself to be. He enjoyed the regular simplicities of suburban life. His favourite chore was the shopping. Every Saturday he set off with the ration books and a string bag for Putney High Street. Occasionally, on a weekday, he would make a detour to Cricklewood on his way home from the office and return to 'Ravensnook' with a bag full of delicatessen. In the bus home from Wimbledon Station he would hold the bag against his chest. For printed on it were the words 'ISIDORE ADLER

– Jewish Delicacies'. On one occasion Mr Goldberg slipped a pound of butter into the bag without Colin seeing. When Tessa discovered it, Colin rang his father and warned him of his manager's breach of the rationing laws. 'Listen,' Isidore said, 'it's in the family. If you don't have it someone else will.' Colin was determined to take the butter back, but by his next trip to Cricklewood, it was all gone. Colin was very fond of of his stomach. His regular shopping expeditions were among his happiest moments. He liked seeing the same faces. Repetition was, to him, a way of belonging. There was nothing which gave him so much confidence as to be able to say, 'I always . . .' It entailed that he had achieved security, that he was safe from change, insured by a policy to which he made sedulously regular contributions.

Colin always caught the bus that stopped opposite Monmouth Court at 10.47 every Saturday morning. He knew the rota of conductors and came to recognize even the drivers. Many of the passengers were also familiar to him and he would pink agreeably at their smiles and nods as he groped his way down to the front seat on the right. One Saturday he was waiting as usual at the stop when a boy of about fifteen in a pink and blue scarf crossed the road from Monmouth Court and came and waited beside him. The boy was tall and dark, with a ruddy complexion. He too carried a string bag. Colin stared down the road for the bus. Could the boy be Jewish? And if he was, had he recognized Colin? It was astonishing the way Jewish people could tell. Colin himself couldn't, but it was astonishing the way some people could.

The conductor said: 'On top only.'

'That's a disappointment,' Colin said.

The boy had gone smartly up the stairs. 'Sorry, guv, that's the way it is.'

'How are you this morning, all right?'

'Not so bad, ta. You?'

'Not so bad.' Colin smiled and clambered up the stairs. He had hardly ever had to go upstairs before on this particular trip and the whole perspective of the journey was quite altered, so that he scarcely knew where he was, missing the usual landmarks. The people too were of another kind, most of them were smokers, some had dogs; a large labrador snuffled and drooled on Colin's sock. Behind him, two men were talking.

'Hitler may have been a bit cracked at the end, but he had some good ideas on the way, you've got to hand it to him.'

'About the little-boy-blues, you mean?'

'Make trouble wherever they go. Look at the way they have more of everything than anyone else.'

'Food, you mean?'

'Clothing coupons, Palestine, everything. Crying scandal, that's what it is, a crying scandal.'

'About clothing coupons, you mean, yes.'

'Here, I heard a good one from a bloke at work this week. About this old Jew, see, had a little kid – '

'Yid kid, you mean?'

'Asright, anyway, every birthday this old Yid used to put this Yid kid of his' – the other man laughed – 'on a high chair, see, and make him jump off it into his arms. Well, this happened every birthday – makin' him jump – '

'The Yid kid.'

'Yers, and catching him, see. Well, on his fourteenth birthday the old Yid put the kid on the high chair same as usual, see, and held out his arms and said "Yump!" – you know, "yump" – like the Yids do. And the kid yumped and his old man didn't catch him like he always had done, see, and he came a hell of a cropper on the floor. Well, he started cryin' and yellin' out and accusing his father, but the old Yid just looked down at him and said, "Now you're a man you should know – never trust a Yid!"'

The bus stopped at Putney Station. Colin rose and

turned to go down the stairs. His eyes fleeted over the two men. One was in black overalls, the other wore a blue suit with a white cricket sweater under it. Both had creased, amiable faces. The boy in the pink and blue scarf was coming behind Colin. At the bottom of the stairs Colin stopped sharply to allow an old lady to pass. The boy bumped into him. Both he and the boy said 'Sorry' simultaneously.

Waiting at the bus stop on the return journey, there was a long queue. By the time Colin reached the front, the conductor was saying. 'On top only now, please.' Colin held up his two heavy bags with a smile. 'I think I'll wait for the next one.'

Only later, as he turned down Oakfern Drive, did he admit to consciousness what he had heard. And only as he shut the front door of 'Ravensnook' did he say to himself: 'Anyway, they got it wrong. What the old man said was "You should never trust anyone in this life, not even your own father."'

SEVEN

Not Even Your Own Father

1

THE MORNING HIS father was arrested, Colin had an urgent phone call at the office from Hannah. He left at once and went to Cricklewood Police Station where his father had been charged. Isidore's manager, Mr Goldberg, had been selling butter, margarine and other rationed goods to certain selected customers without exacting coupons. Three times he had failed to select carefully enough. Each time, the customers were Ministry of Food inspectors. 'Government snoopers,' Hannah called them indignantly.

Colin tightened his British warm round his shoulders. 'Now don't you worry, Mother, everything'll be all right.' Louis Lazarus, Monty's brother, was there to take care of the details and soon they were all four standing on the pavement outside the police station, Louis looking very professional in his long black overcoat, homburg hat, rolled umbrella, silk kidney-patterned muffler and black stippled leather briefcase. Isidore stood in a brown, rather greasy hat and brown belted overcoat.

'When did all this happen?' Colin demanded.

'Suddenly this morning they arrived at the shop,' Hannah said. 'Luckily I was there with your father.'

'Terrible business,' Isidore said. 'You wouldn't believe the questions they asked me.'

'It shouldn't be allowed,' Hannah said, pursing her lips at her make-up mirror.

Louis Lazarus stuffed the last of the papers in his briefcase and addressed them briskly: 'We'd better go somewhere we can talk. There's some things I want to settle and' – he glanced at the POLICE sign – 'this isn't the best place.'

'I got the car,' Isidore said.

'Should you be using it?' Colin demanded hotly.

'I got supplementary.' They went to the car. Colin sat in the back with Louis Lazarus. 'We may's well go to the house,' Isidore suggested. 'We can talk there and have a drink, maybe?'

'A drink I could use,' Louis Lazarus said.

Colin settled in the sitting-room window of 15 Woburn Road and stared out at the salting of snow on the front lawn. He refused a drink. Hannah and Louis Lazarus (if only he would stop smirking for just one minute!) were sipping sweet sherries. Isidore was drinking whisky.

'Now then, Isidore,' Louis was saying, (lovely sherry, Hannah dear) now then, one thing we must clear up and that's our attitude to the man Goldberg. Whatever approach we take I'm afraid the court will hold you liable, whether you knew what was going on or not – '

'That doesn't seem quite fair,' Colin said.

'Colin, will you allow me? Thank you. Now let's consider the thing in all its aspects, shall we?' He crossed his thighs, his striped trousers sausage-tight. 'You realize that unless this thing is handled right, you could go to prison.'

'Oh, rubbish, I've read of hundreds of cases – '

'Colin, do you mind? Thank you. Thank you very much.' Louis took off his tortoiseshell glasses and sucked the earpiece. Colin cracked his knuckles. 'There is quite definitely a possiblity that they will send you to prison, it very much depends on the impression we make in court.' Louis touched a solicitous hand to the knot of his pearl-grey tie. 'I think you'd be unwise to try to put the blame on Goldberg. Much better be loyal to him, ready to take the blame, all that kind of thing. The magistrates don't care for people who try to dodge their responsibilities.'

'You're the lawyer,' Isidore said. 'Not me.'

'How much do you think they'll fine him?' Hannah asked.

Lazarus put his hand on Hannah's knee. 'The maximum for the three offences would be six hundred pounds, but I don't think it'll be that much.'

'Much as that,' Hannah said. 'Are they anti-Semitic, the judges?'

'The Justices? No, I don't think so, Hannah dear, only the odd crank, you know. I don't suppose it'll be more than four hundred in actual fact.'

'I can afford it,' Isidore simpered, trudging over to the cocktail cabinet for the whisky. 'Drink, Colin?'

Colin shook his head. He crossed his legs tightly and cracked his knuckles. The snow in the garden sparkled under a lemon sun.

Ben and Susan arrived for tea, with Sarah in the push-chair (a present from Hannah). Ben clapped Isidore on the shoulder. 'So now what have you been getting up to?'

'Trouble,' Isidore smirked. 'I've been arrested.'

'Ay-yay-yay, such a thing should happen!'

Colin stormed out of the room. His father seemed actually to be proud of what had happened. He had never seen him so lively. As Colin passed through the hall, the door opened. It was Julia, home from school. 'Colin! What on earth are you doing here?'

'It's your father,' Colin said stiffly. 'Some legal trouble at the shop.'

'Black market?'

Colin nodded. 'Susan and her husband just arrived.'

'Ben? Oh good.' Julia flung her hat on the hallstand, and shook out her long black hair. 'Anyone else?'

'Louis Lazarus has been, that's all.'

'Thank God. All we need now is a gathering of the clans.'

130

'All the MacAdlers and the MacLiepmans,' Colin smiled reminiscently.

'He won't go to jail, will he?'

'Our friend Mr Lazarus doesn't think so.'

'Oh, that's all right then.' Swinging her strap of books from the library, Julia sprang up the stairs. Though she was seventeen, she cared little for her parents' world and had no connection with it. She was content with herself, with work, with games and with clothes. She neither worried about her parents nor expected them to worry about her. She was popular at school; her friends were both Gentile and Jewish, more of the former if anything, and she was not bothered to distinguish between them. She hardly thought of herself as Jewish: her concern was with what she was doing, not with what she was. Only once had anyone referred unpleasantly to her Jewishness: an Irish Catholic girl objected to her being on the Poppy Day Committee.

Colin stamped into the sitting-room. 'I must be getting home.'

'Tessa waiting for you?' Hannah asked.

'Hope so.'

'Maybe she's run off with the milkman,' Isidore said.

'Father, I'd like a word with you. Outside.'

Isidore grinned at Ben. 'So now what have I done?'

Ben said: 'Don't you worry.'

'This is just the sort of thing your friends on the *Daily Worker* are going to make the most of,' Colin snapped. 'Not that I suppose you'll do anything to stop them.'

'I didn't know your neighbours read the *Worker*.'

'My neighbours don't come into it,' Colin shouted. 'I'm simply saying,' he added more calmly, 'that this sort of thing is playing into the hands of the Communists.'

'There won't be anything about this in the *Daily Worker*,' Ben said, 'that I can promise you.'

'Come on, Father,' Colin said. 'I want to speak to you.'

131

'Outside,' Ben said.

Outside, Colin said: 'Look, Father, I realize all this has been a bit of a shock for you – I mean, of course, you didn't realize what was going on – '

'Snoopers,' Isidore said. 'Government snoopers.'

'You must get rid of Goldberg,' Colin said. 'You must tell the court you intend to get rid of him – you're prepared to take the blame but you intend to get rid of him as soon as possible.'

'Suddenly everybody's a lawyer.'

'If you don't get rid of him he'll probably start doing the same thing all over again – '

'What's so terrible about that?' Isidore Adler demanded. 'You try running a grocery business these days. Believe me, you've got to make money where you can.'

Neither Ben nor Susan was disposed to imitate Colin's censorious manner. If anything annoyed Ben, it was that money had secured some people more food than others; that Isidore was to appear before magistrates was of no consequence to him. Ben had no reverence for the law, and for those who administered it, less still. His own social situation would be unaffected, even if all his friends were to associate Isidore with him. Perhaps the Fascists would make captial out of it, but Ben was unalarmed: the Jewish Fellowship of Ex-servicemen wasn't going to stand any more nonsense from Mosley. Their solidarity filled Ben with confidence. He would never apologize, whatever his fellow Jews did. If Isidore provided an example of petty bourgeois corruption, why should Ben worry when the inevitability of such corruption was part of his faith? His confidence was such that his affection for Isidore was even increased by the old man's indiscretion, as doctors love those who confirm their diagnoses. Ben had never been happier than since he had joined the *Worker*; even in the pits, in a genuine working-class environment, he had not had this sense of dedication. He gained pride in his manhood from it. He was a whole person and his integrity knit him together: there was no part of his life which was not given to his idea of what a man should be. Ben regarded Isidore's misdemeanours with a certain indulgence: for he pitied him, as a man pities one who confirms but does not share his faith.

Openly, Susan was no less indulgent, but inwardly she was shocked. She had, in her childhood, been threatened with policemen if she did not behave herself and she had always regarded the law as something very respectable. At rallies she had seen policemen punch women, but she still clung to the notion that they were gentle giants, who would never deliberately do anything unpleasant, at least to her or her family. To brush with the law at rallies was fun; it was like undergraduates knocking off bobbies' hats: really everyone was on the same side. But Isidore's offences were sordid and commercial, quite without glamour. In the context of the inevitable decay of bourgeois society it was only what you would expect, but Susan regretted that she could not put it all right with a winning smile and an invitation to 'pity a poor girl'. It made you wonder what the value of the Party was, when you saw how helpless you were in the face of the police going grimly (and dully) about their job. Susan wished she could say, 'Release my father or the buses stop at dawn.' However, as long as Isidore didn't go to jail, it wasn't too serious, only it wouldn't be very nice for Sarah to have a grandpa who had been in prison.

2

During the weeks before the case came up, Colin made a complete inventory of the newspapers his neighbours took, so that when the news of the sentence was published he would know immediately which of them knew that Adler's had been fined. So far as he could tell, there were six *Times*'s, eight *Telegraphs*, five *Express*'s, three *Mails*, three *Graphics* (including the Bradshaws') and one *Manchester Guardian*. There were also three *Financial Times*'s, but even Colin conceded that the story was not likely to appear there. 'I shouldn't think for one moment that it will be in any of the papers' was Tessa's view.

'Don't you be too sure. They always arrange to put these things in if they concern Jewish firms.'

'Oh, Colin, do they?'

'Certainly, it all helps to bear out the Palestine policy.'

'*Colin*. Who do you really think plans these things?'

'All the people at the top are pretty close, my dear.'

'My dear!'

'The poor old middle classes are the only people who haven't got any organizations to turn to – that's why they're so badly treated. The workers have got their unions and the top people have got their clubs and their societies and their dinner parties and the poor old middle classes are just caught between the upper and the nether millstones!'

'You've been listening to too many speeches at street corners,' Tessa smiled. 'You ought to come straight home.'

'The only hope for this country,' Colin said, 'is to get rid of this wretched government and let the middle class have a voice for a change.'

'How could a Conservative government help that happen?'

'Believe me, it would help the building industry considerably. These permits are absolutely crippling the whole shooting match.'

It was six months before the case came up. Isidore was fined five hundred and fifty pounds. The next morning, Colin left the house early, hurried to the paper kiosk at Wimbledon Station and bought all the papers. He entered the third carriage from the front, rather than the penultimate one as usual. The coach was empty. He thumbed quickly through the papers. Nothing, nothing, nothing. The train ticked. Nothing, nothing. A man entered the coach. The doors groaned shut. The train moved. A paragraph in the *Graphic* read: 'DELICATESSEN'S FOOD OFFENCES – "Shocking case," says magistrate. Isidore Nathan Adler, 64, of 15 Woburn Road, Golders Green, was fined a total of £550 with 70 guineas costs at Cricklewood Magistrates Court yesterday. Adler, a naturalized British subject, was told by Mr Everett Ward, the chairman: "Maybe this is the sort of thing you did where you originally came from, but you're not going to do it here."' Colin shut the paper and looked up. The man opposite said: 'Morning.' It was Ted Bradshaw. The Bradshaws took the *Graphic*. 'Morning,' Colin said.

'Office bound?'

'Yes. Yes, I am. Yes.'

Bradshaw wore a brown tweed suit with muddy turn-ups, a woollen plaid tie and a sagging rust cardigan. ''Ard luck,' he grinned. He unfolded the mackintosh he had lain across his knees and took out the *Daily Graphic*.

'You're not, I take it.'

'Me? Not on your life. Smithfield and then Lord's, that's me.' He smoothed out the creases in his paper.

'Lucky chap! Only wish I could do the same. Are you a Middlesex supporter?'

'All me life,' Bradshaw said, taking a pipe from his jacket pocket. 'You?'

'Rather. I used to live in – Middlesex.'

'Best county in the championship, there's nothing to touch the terrible twins.'

'Rather not. I only wish I could come with you.'

'You've only got to say the word,' Bradshaw said. 'Any time you're free. You're not a golfer, I suppose?'

'Used to putter around a bit in the desert,' Colin said.

'Seen the paper this morning?' Bradshaw inquired.

'Only glanced at it,' Colin replied. 'Where do you play?'

'Golf? Southfields Common.'

'Oh yes?'

'Nice little club. Tell you what, I'll put you up if you like.'

'Well, that'd be jolly decent of you.'

'I don't suppose you are a convicted felon, are you?'

'Not quite,' Colin said.

Bradshaw read his paper. When he looked up, he said: 'You in the food business by any chance?'

The train jerked and rattled over the Inner Circle junction.

'No,' Colin said. 'Why?'

The sunlight died on the black, cable-contoured battlements of the cutting. Ted Bradshaw ruffled his moustache with his nicotined first finger. An anti-Semitic gesture? 'I'm in that racket myself,' he said.

'Oh really?'

'Butcher Bradshaw, that's me.'

'I'd never have guessed it,' Colin said.

'I don't suppose you have much trouble with meat, do you?'

'Trouble?'

'I expect you get plenty, don't you?'

'No more than anyone else,' Colin said, blushing very red.

Bradshaw grinned. 'Well, let me know if you're ever short, I can usually manage something for a friend.'

3

'Ben, if you're not doing anything, you might come in and scrub my back.'

'What did you say?'

'Small prize offered for scrubbing my back.'

'Right ho.'

'My *back*.'

'Spoken to your old man today?'

'I'm steering clear of that one,' Susan said. 'Silly old idiot!'

'Why, Susie? Getting caught, you mean?'

'No, I do not mean. I mean letting us down.'

'How did he let us down, Susan?'

'You know what people say about Jews and the black market.'

'Do you know the figures on this?'

'No. Do you? As if I need ask.'

'I looked them up today as a matter of fact.'

'Why?'

'Because of something someone said at work. The figures showed there were less rationing offences per head of the Jewish population than per head of Gentiles.'

'Is that so? Was it a Party book you looked them up in?'

'Of course that's not the picture you get from the Press,' Ben went on. 'You'd think the whole black market was run by sinister foreigners with long black beards and names that end in "stein". The number of column inches – '

'Ben,' Susan said. 'For God's sake!'

'What are you grinning at?' Ben demanded.

'I'll give you column inches.'

He took her in his arms and kissed her. 'Now, *Ben*.' She squirmed happily. 'Not *now*.'

If only he could always confine himself to what excited her, how happy she would be! But even now when she was most alive she could sense that Ben was merely amusing himself, just as when he had reached what he regarded as the limit of his efforts to please her, he was conscious that she was continuing to want something more. Even after the climax of sex, she lay awake, restless with impossible whims. Ben knew there was nothing more he could do and a dull rage ached in him. He thought of all the things, books and music and the Party itself, to which Susan would not give herself, and the rage worked in him, though he loved her with no less a passion than when he first saw her, naked by the bed in Bognor. There was nothing he would not do to give her pleasure, to fulfil her, but what could he do beyond the limit of nature, when even after the cry of her climax she lay there and was not content with him? Silently each said 'He doesn't . . .' 'She doesn't . . .' but what it was the other failed to do, neither could clearly say.

4

When the invitation came from Stan Halloran to attend the gala opening of Manny Finkelbaum's Jazz Club in Dean Street, Susan was determined to go. 'We haven't seen Stan in years. Oh, Ben, do let's go. Please. It's the first thing I've really wanted to do for absolutely ages.'

'Can't afford a baby sitter,' Ben said.

'We'll ask Sid and Ethel. They're always offering.'

'Not this time.'

'I want to go, Ben. I want to. I know they would.'

'I'll ask Sid.'

'No, I'll ask Ethel,' Susan stated.

'Don't say what it's for, then,' Ben told her. 'That's all I ask.'

Manny Finkelbaum's Club was in a cellar. The only fresh air came from a window which opened up to a pavement grating. The local game was to guess, from her legs above the grating, the appearance of the whole woman. Every girl who came in was met with laughter and cries of surprise depending on how much she tallied with the forecast. Stan greeted Ben and Susan with a grabbing hug which shut out the clamour of this unusual welcome. 'My darlin' darlin' darlin's,' cried he, embracing Susan and then breaking at once to grasp Ben's hand in both of his. 'It's been a terrible long time, it's been – a terrible long time. How are you both?'

'Fine,' Susan said.

'And Sarah, how's the girl, all right, is she? I'm longing to see her.'

'Any time. You've only got to say the word.'

'How are you, Benjamino? How's things?'

'Not so bad, boy.'

'Come on, Stanley,' called one of the men on the stand.

'Excuse me, loves.' He gripped each of them by the arm. 'We'll have a real old chat when I've satisfied the hungry crowd, OK? Now don't go away.'

Stan and his men played traditional jazz, very loud. Stan himself had great vigour and could provoke shrill delight from the crowd whenever he wanted to, merely by the angle at which he set his trumpet, the way his eyes popped out on the top notes, the set of his shoulders as he prepared for a break. Ben and Susan stood against a wall decorated with posters advertising inaccessible places. The crowd was young: 'They look as if most of them are students, don't they?' Susan whispered.

'I don't know,' Ben said. 'What do students look like?'

Susan bit her lip. Ben certainly didn't seem to belong in these surroundings at all. A man shouted out 'Ben!'

'Wotcher, boy!'

'Who's that?'

'Bloke at the *Worker*. He's got the office next to mine. Name of Jerry Lodz. We were kids together. Shan't be a tick.' There always had to be someone Ben knew, and from each of these friendships Susan was excluded. She rubbed her shoe behind her calf. A tall Negro in a yellow, sweat-stained T-shirt and black jeans came up to her. 'Care to dance?' He stood on the balls of his feet, smiling down at her, his hands dangling loose at his sides, fingers chaffing at the music. Susan said: 'I'm not much good.' The other smiled, sucking in his bottom lip. 'C'mon, I'll teach you.'

139

Susan smoothed her sweater, blinked and smiled. 'All right.'

His face smiled at her and his legs moved in expert rhythm, but it was from the pad of his hand on her back that the man controlled her; it was from there that the flow of his commands was communicated to her, it was from there that the stiffness was driven out of her. His eyes were steady, attentive to the band, as though he could as well look at as listen to the music. When it raved into its climax and then broke off, the hand came away from her back instantly. She said: 'Thank you.' It was a croak. She put her hand to her breast. 'Excuse me!' The man said: 'Let's go upstairs.' She said: 'All right.' She followed him out of the cellar. They went up the wooden steps to the street door. They were alone. Susan thought: no, I won't do it here, I can't do it here. She closed her eyes. Her body was soft from the dancing, but she trembled. The warm cold made her tremble. I don't want to know his name, I don't want to be told anything. I want something to happen. If only it could happen when she didn't want it to, with the risk of people coming in through the street door, if only they could do something like that, but of course she wouldn't, not with the risk of people coming in the street door, or up the stairs for that matter, with funny hats on their heads. The man said: 'What's your name, chick?'

'Susan. Susan Simons.'

'Mine's Fred Morgan.'

Susan said: 'It's a bit chilly up here.' She took his hand. 'How about another dance?' He allowed her to lead him downstairs again. Once she had taken his hand it was like a discord. She held the hand that had lain on her back and it was a broken thing, rather like a kipper, she thought. Thank God he hadn't tried anything. He looked the sort of fellow who, if you smacked his face, might knock you down the stairs. It was just as well she was a respectable married woman.

Various members of the audience had taken over the band. To Susan's astonishment, Ben was on drums. His parody of the original drummer was perfect and the band was contorted with laughter. Ben himself was very serious. Not the faintest twitch revealed his humour. It was wonderful. Oh he could have been such a success! Susan blundered to the bar for a Coca-Cola.

Stan said: 'Old Ben's at it then.'

'It's a smashing do,' Susan said. 'Everyone's having a wonderful time.'

'I think it's going off all right, as the man said over Hiroshima.'

'I'm dying to meet Manny Finkelbaum,' Susan said. 'Do point him out to me.'

Stan put a finger to his own chest. 'Meet Manny Finkelbaum,' he said.

'Oh, what a disappointment!'

'Vell, if you're deusapainted, vot doss' thet mek me?'

Susan smiled quickly. 'What time are you going to get away tonight?'

'About two, I should think.'

'Oh, I was hoping you might be coming our way. Still in Camden Town, are you?'

'For the nonce,' Stan said. 'They have wonderful nonce there. The best in London. With white wine sauce too. No, my sweetie, I shall charter myself a cabriolet *au lait*, *olé*!' He stamped his foot and struck a pose. 'That's what they call a tortilla, and Ilya of course taught me.'

'Incidentally, Stan, are you still *with* the BBC?'

'We play for the singers in Monday Night at Tuesday Morning,' Stan replied, 'and I'm doing a bit of the old scripts there for one or two comics, but I do not wish anyone very much to know that.'

'When are you going to get your own programme?'

'One of these fine days, my darlin', and when it happens I can assure you I shall be the last to know.' Stan sucked in his mouth and his beard stuck out. 'Time I hauled Benjamino off the stand before he does himself a mischief.'

Stan Halloran bounded on to the bandstand and fell off flat on his back. Susan started forward in alarm but the initiates exploded with laughter. This was the signal for the big moment of the evening: Stan's political cabaret, the highlight of which was his solo version of a United Nations plenary session. This included 'the only five-way non-stop simultaneous translating service in use outside a lunatic asylum, the basis of which is a multi-dimensional high-frequency, thermo-nuclear lug-'ole with two-way family favourites for those in peril on the sea.' Stan himself appeared 'in *propria persona*, to mention but a few', as the loopy interpreter who, tired of the squabbles of the great powers and the bickerings of the minnows (and the minnering of the bickows), refused to continue translating the abuse which Russia and the USA were flinging at each other and rendered it all as messages of good will, with the result that eternal world peace was secured and he was shot at dawn for having made so many warmongering, Commie-slanted, neo-deviationist, Red-loving errors in the past. Stan also treated the audience to some revolutionary songs of the East Acton People's Peasant and Bolshevik Party, Fred Dibbles, Pres, and rendered in triplicate on this occasion by honoured East Acton hero, third class, Dave Dibble, Sec. 'Ladies and gentlemen,' Stan said finally, 'I should just like to say that it is as certain that Socialism will emerge victorious as it is that I stand here tonight.' At which he fell flat on his back on the floor and the cabaret was over.

Ben said: 'Time we were pushing.'

'Do let's stay a bit longer, Ben, just this once.'

'It'll take us nearly an hour to get home, as it is.'

'Not if we take a taxi.'

'Take a taxi, the girl says, and who's going to pay for it?'

'I don't mind. I've got a pound in my bag.' Hannah Adler had been over earlier in the week. 'I don't see why we shouldn't take a taxi once in a while.'

At the bus stop, Ben said: 'He's got quite a place there, old Stanley.'

'You're not jealous, are you, Benjamino, by any chance?'

'Don't call me that.'

'Sorry, ai'm sure.'

Sid and Ethel were sitting either side of the fireplace at Number 24. Ethel had her specs on and was correcting French papers. Sid stood up and rubbed his hands together. 'Had a good time?'

'Ever so nice, thank you,' Ben said.

'Like some coffee before you go?' Susan inquired.

'No, we must be pushing,' Sid said, 'thanks all the same.'

'Hope you haven't missed the bus,' Susan said.

'Oh, we can always get a taxi,' Ethel said. 'And save the old bones.'

Susan shut the front door on them loudly. Was there anyone in London except Ben who didn't take taxis? Oh, she knew the answer: five million, four hundred and twenty-seven thousand two hundred and sixty-one. What was the use? She went into the bathroom and came back in her nightie and dressing-gown. Ben was in bed. Susan switched out the light and got in.

She said: 'Ben, no.'

'Susan, yes.'

'I'm tired.'

'I'm not.'

'I'm a bit sore,' she said.

'You don't feel sore.'

'You bastard,' she sighed. 'You bastard.'

'That's me charm,' he whispered.

'Come on then. Come on.'

Desire opened in her like a wound. She hated the desire

he opened in her, the power it gave him over her. She shrank from the wound he opened in her and hated the hostage of her flesh. But her flesh was traitor to her and stronger than her hatred.

'Ben – ' she quested hatefully for him. And finally fell back, soft, muttering, 'Taxi, taxi, taxi.'

'All right,' Ben said.

5

A week later, Susan asked Julia over. It amused her to watch her sister growing up: through her she hoped to re-experience the quivering expectancy of adolescence. Not that Julia quivered much. She seemed aggressively normal. Retarded, Susan thought: at least she had very little bosom. But her legs were good, and her slimness helped her to wear her clothes with a certain style. She had nice eyes too, and her hair was black and silky. She'd pass.

'How're things at home?' Susan inquired, when she had stowed away the bundle of groceries which Hannah had sent with Julia.

'Daddy's getting rid of Otto.'

'Getting rid of him? What do you mean?'

'He's trying to link it all up with me going to university. It's just typical. He knows I'm taking the schol next term so he's started up a little campaign.' She imitated her father gruffly. '"If you're going to the university I can't afford all the extra expense and" – meaningly – "everything else as well," and so on and so *on*. Finally Otto took the hint and said he'd decided to leave. Then we had Mummy in tears. Oh, it's been lovely.'

'Where's Otto going, for God's sake?'

'Some charity place Mummy's fixed up with old Sir Samuel whatsit.' ('Goldstein,' Susan said.) 'Otto's been attending to his clock collection to make a bit of money and

Mummy asked if he knew anywhere Otto could go. Old Sir S. couldn't wait to show how important he was, so it all got fixed up in double quick time.'

'Why didn't they tell us they wanted to get rid of him? We'd've had him like a shot.'

'I expect he'll be quite happy in this place, really. They've all got their own cubicles and everything. Quite honestly, I shan't be sorry to see the last of the old boy.'

'Well, I don't approve at all,' Susan said primly.

'He never pulls the chain,' Julia said. 'It's horrible sometimes.'

'I dare say there weren't chains to pull in Dachau.'

'No, it is. And cigarette ends in it and everything.' Julia took a pin out of her hair and stuck it back in again. 'No, what I hate is the way Daddy has to make it all *my* fault. I mean it's nothing to do with me whether Otto stays or not, but he has to make me responsible.'

'Well, you are in a way,' Susan said.

'Why? Because I want to go to college? That's absolute tripe. What about that fine Daddy had to pay? "I can afford it" – that's what he said, isn't it? He can afford what he wants to afford!'

'I always wished I could have gone to university,' Susan said.

'*Susie!* All you ever talked about was men and getting married. I never knew you wanted to go to college.'

'Well, I did,' Susan said. 'How's your sex life, by the way?'

'Oh, non-existent really. I'm working like mad for my exam at the moment.'

'Cambridge?'

'It's London now. Anything to get away from St Sissy's as soon as poss.'

'Oh,' Susan said. 'I was hoping it'd be Cambridge.'

'I should have to wait till next winter if I wanted to do Cambridge – I should go crackers before then!'

145

When Susan told Ben about Otto she assumed all the righteous indignation she expected from him. All he said was: 'Doesn't surprise me. He couldn't expect to stay there for ever, could he? Your old man's only human. Why should he be lumbered?'

'What do you think he should do? Go to Palestine?'

'I don't see that Palestine's the solution to anything.'

'You're not very keen on the idea of Israel, are you?'

'I think it's the wrong solution,' Ben said.

'Marx wouldn't have been a Zionist, I suppose?'

'It's rather a pity to see the people who gave the world the idea of an international movement falling into jingoism themselves. Zionism's just idealizing a mistake. Of course it's possible that Israel might throw itself into the Socialist camp, but with American dollars at the back of it, that's not very likely.'

'We seem to have got off Otto.'

'It's difficult to see what can be done,' Ben said. 'I mean in a way he's just an anachronism.'

'I find it hard to think of any living person as an anachronism.'

'Susan, honestly – '

'I know,' Susan said, 'there are four hundred thousand anachronisms in Greater London alone.'

'A lot more than that,' Ben said.

Susan thought of the pilot in the plane over the downs. 'Well, I think Daddy's an absolute bastard,' she said.

'He can't hold the roof up for ever. You never noticed it when he was holding it up, did you? It's only when he lets go you say "Why didn't he hold it up a bit longer?" The answer is, why didn't people do something to help him? Why didn't they organize props so he didn't have to do it all on his own? Then they say "It's not economical" or "You can't change human nature". Well, somehow you've got to make it economical or stop being upset when the roof falls in.'

Susan said: 'From each according to his capacity, to each according to his need. End of speech.'

'That's right,' Ben said, aware of a man who came one day to the shop in the Commercial Road and said; 'I'm collecting for Jewish relief.'

Ben's father said: 'I've given my full quota to charity already. I'm sorry.'

The boy said: 'What's it for? What are you collecting for?'

'Helping Jews get out of Germany where they're being persecuted,' said the man.

'Give him something, Daddy,' Ben said. 'Give him something.'

'Do me a favour, mind your own business. Do I have to support the whole community on my shoulders? I do what I can.'

'But we've got to help them. Think what Rabbi Brod said.'

'Let Rabbi Brod give them something. I done all I can.'

'There ought to be a law,' the boy cried, 'to make you do what's right.'

EIGHT

Family Parties

1

Now the events in Palestine coloured all Colin's thoughts. His main feelings were of fear, fear that when he opened his paper in the morning he would discover some new outrage. Of pride in the actions of his fellow Jews he had none. The emergence of Israel was, to him, simply an embarrassment. When Ben Hecht said that there was a song in his heart for every Briton killed in Palestine, Colin cancelled his and Tessa's subscription to *Life*. He thought of Hecht more as a Yank than a Jew. The notion that the Jews were a nation had less appeal for him even than it had for Ben. Nor was it his religion; Colin had no beliefs. It was difficult to say exactly why he called himself a Jew at all; mainly it was so as not to funk the issue, for though he was full of fears, he was not a coward. He pursued his life as best he might, working for his wife and for the baby they would soon have, taking what small pleasures and smaller vices were easily available (he and Ted Bradshaw occasionally slipped off to Kempton Park for the day, and every now and then to the dogs) within the confines of that life which he and Tessa had planned for themselves. He resented the conspiracy of outside events to sour the rewards of his wartime service. His view was that Britain had saved the world, and the Jews in particular, and that it was sheer ingratitude to crab at her present actions. In this he was at one with the members of the Southfields Common Golf Club, to whose number he had recently been added. He hated to hear them attack the Jews, but he genuinely shared their loathing of the Terrorists. He saw GET RID OF THE YIDS chalked on the wall near a new housing estate. He hated those who had done it, but he hated the Stern gang more. All through the war he told himself that if victory did nothing else it would certainly kill anti-Semitism. Now, as he remarked gloomily on an evening when he and Tessa were over to dinner in Archway, things were worse than before.

'Were you ever in the East End in '36 or '37?' Ben inquired. He looked up at Colin from under black eyebrows, simply. 'When Mosley and his boys were down there?'

Colin felt complicated. He said: 'Only to visit, you know. But what I feel makes this all rather difficult is that the vast majority of people in this country agree with the sort of thing that's going on today, whereas before the war, they were absolutely against it.'

'They didn't do much to stop it. It took us to do that,' Ben said.

'The Communist Party,' Susan said.

'No, I mean, look here, even a chap like Bevin – '

'The great Ern,' Ben cried, 'the people's boy.'

'The dockers' KC,' Susan added.

'The voice of the workers – '

'The man who can talk to the Russians!' Susan said.

Colin said: 'I was thinking of that remark he made about allowing the Jews to jump the queue. I mean, when a man like Bevin – '

'A statesman of that quality,' Ben said solemnly.

'When you've got a member of the British government talking like that, well, it's bound to make an impression. I mean, Bevin's a good man, isn't he?' He appealed to Ben as the political expert. Colin had great faith in experts. His pools forecasts were based entirely on what the experts said.

Ben said: 'Bevin? First-rate man. One hunded per cent first-rate man.'

'I hate sarcasm,' Tessa said.

'Who's being sarcastic? *Me?*'

'It's just Ben's way of talking. You have to get used to it.'

'I *don't* have to,' Tessa said. 'But I expect I shall,' she added with a bright smile.

'You see the thing I feel,' Colin went doggedly on, 'is that, well, during the war one met a lot of chaps and made friends, you know, and, well, there may have been a bit of silly talk, but by and large – '

'Taking all in all,' Ben said.

'Everyone felt Hitler'd – '

'Gone a bit far.'

'Yes, and the sooner that sort of thing was over and done with, the better. I mean, everyone realized that all this Fascist business wasn't – '

'On?'

'No. And now, well, these terrorists have gone and messed it all up. I mean, blast it, we did fight the bloody war. And look at the way the Gyppos are carrying on. You'd never think we'd saved them from the Germans, would you? Everybody forgets so damned quickly.'

'Perhaps they didn't want to be saved,' Susan said.

'Honestly, Sis, what are you talking about? You don't think they wanted the Germans to conquer them, do you?'

'A lot of them did,' Ben said.

'Oh well, of course I happen to have been out there, but if you know all about it, far be it from me to correct you. No, really, we've done everything for the bloody Gyppos. Look at the Suez Canal.'

'I'm looking,' Ben said.

'What's the use of talking about politics?' Tessa said. 'You never get anywhere.'

'No, it's interesting,' Colin said. 'I like to find out what the other side thinks.'

'Other side of what?' Ben asked.

'The coin. I like to hear how people who think that everything that's British is wrong are talking.'

'I don't think that,' Ben said.

'What about the Russians, have they ever been wrong?'

'Certainly,' Ben said.

'Oh, when? When have they? I'd like to know.'

'Under the Tsars,' Ben said, 'plenty of times.'

'The Tsars!' Tessa said. 'That's *history*!'

'I suppose you approve of all this bomb-throwing then?' Colin said.

'Bomb-throwing? Get me the evening paper, please, Susan.'

'In Jerusalem and places. I suppose that's all good Communist stuff, is it?'

'It's got a great deal more to do with the Family Lovers' Building Society than it has with the Communist Party.'

Colin scratched his head. 'Either you're cracked or I am,' he said.

'Perhaps you both are,' Susan suggested uneasily.

'The whole object of the war,' Colin said angrily, 'was to put an end to violence.'

Ben burst out laughing. 'So that in future when people are denied by force what is their right by nature there won't be a thing they can do about it.'

'You approve of terrorism then?'

'The lesson of history is that change is inevitable. The whole policy of the French, the British and the Americans is to insist that everything stay as it is for as long as possible and to put the troops in to make sure it does. And if anyone attacks them for doing it they say they thought it had been agreed to abolish violence. I'm not only talking about Palestine. It's the general pattern.'

'There you are,' Colin cried. 'There you are. Exactly as I said. Britain and her allies are always wrong. Exactly what I said.'

151

'It is,' Tessa nodded. Her pregnancy gave her a certain grave dignity. 'That is what you said.'

'Anyway you're talking complete tripe,' Colin said. 'We believe in solving our differences by reason.'

'What reason?' Ben asked.

'What reason? Reason. Can't you understand English? The give and take of reasonable argument.'

'Reasonable argument,' Ben said, 'is argument that acknowledges the inevitable changes of history. Nothing's more unreasonable than the attitude of what you call the allies.'

'Honestly,' Tessa said, 'what is the use of arguing? You never get anywhere.' She folded her hands in her lap. 'Personally I'm sure we'll be able to work out some sort of compromise with the Russians. After all, they don't want war any more than we do, really, do they?'

'No,' Ben said, 'you're quite right, Tessa, they don't. After all they suffered a lot more than anyone else.'

Colin said: 'Absolute rubbish.'

Ben said: 'I've got the figures on this actually – '

2

'I think,' Colin said, 'that was the most exhausting evening of my life.'

'It wasn't exactly restful,' Tessa said.

'He's absolutely impossible, that chap. I mean you just cannot reason with him. I hope it didn't upset you?'

'It didn't upset me.'

'I think I made some sort of impression on him, don't you?'

'I'm sure of it, sweets.'

'Makes so much mischief, that way of thinking. Simply manufactures propaganda for anti-Semitism. You know, what astonishes me is that anyone can really believe in all that Communist rubbish. I mean, taking orders from Moscow. I find it completely incredible, don't you?'

'It doesn't make much sense to me, I must say. I suppose if you're brought up that way – '

'Environment's got a lot to do with it, I suppose,' Colin said. 'And I suppose his father was Russian, wasn't he?'

'Probably.'

'Bound to have been. How he swallows all that stuff, that's what beats me. I mean he's just completely inflexible in his way of thinking, don't you agree?'

'You just can't argue with a bloke like that,' Ben said.

'It's the way he was brought up,' Susan said.

'You were brought up the same way, weren't you?'

'Yes, but Colin isn't married to you.'

'Thank God.'

'I don't think it would be a great success somehow,' Susan admitted.

'There's just nothing you can do with a bloke like that,' Ben said again. 'He's absolutely impossible.'

Susan said: 'Let's go to bed and forget about him.'

'Absolutely impossible,' Ben said. 'That's what he is.'

'It certainly was an exhausting evening.'

'He hasn't got any idea of what's going on at all. You know it must be very lonely to be like that.'

'Lonely? Colin's not lonely.'

'Spiritually he must be very lonely.'

'Spiritually!' Susan said. 'Wait till I tell Sid that one!'

'He's not *near* anything, you know what I mean?' Ben went on. 'He doesn't belong to anything. I'm sorry – he must be very lonely.'

'He's very shy, if that's what you mean. He always has been. I suppose it's all to do with what Mummy and Daddy used to say: "Don't go down there, don't play with those people, don't this, don't that."'

153

'A wictim,' Ben said, 'of bourgeois morality!'

'You can say that again.'

'A wictim of bourgeois morality,' Ben said.

'He's never looked at another woman, I'll bet you, since the day he first kissed Tessa.'

'Just like you and me,' Ben said.

'Like hell,' Susan said. 'Don't give me that.'

'I wouldn't mind admitting it if I had,' Ben said.

'Marriage and the property question,' Susan said. 'Don't tell me.'

3

Colin and Tessa came to know the Bradshaws better: Colin and Ted had their sporting interests in common, while Tessa's pregnancy bought Bunty closer to her. The Bradshaws had no children. Bunty was a small, perhaps rather officious person, who had been a VAD commandant in the war. Her hospital experience gave Tessa confidence. 'No reason why the baby shouldn't be a thoroughly straightforward, simple business,' Bunty said. 'But I'm all for doing some exercises too, if you've got the will power to keep at it.' Tessa had. Bunty admired this determination in the girl and soon she was coming over every afternoon to make tea while Tessa did her exercises. 'I must say I'm jolly pleased to see you keeping it up,' she said. 'If there's one thing I hate, it's an idle woman!'

One day Bunty said: 'What do you think about this Palestine business?' Tessa replied honestly: 'Well, you see, we're in rather a special position.' Bunty said: 'Oh yes, yes, of course.' 'She must have twigged,' Colin said when Tessa reported this to him. 'Just as well they should know,' Tessa replied.

'Oh yes, yes rather,' Colin said, but he bit his lip. He had already been elected to the golf club, of course, but now he felt rather that people might think he had got in under false pretences. He had always been careful to make a good impression, so that when the news of his Jewishness finally did get out, the members would regard it rather as his misfortune than his fault. He never quibbled about the size of side-bets (so as not to appear mean), he never wore anything but a sports jacket and grey flannels (so as not to appear flamboyant), he never bought covers for his clubs or indulged in matched sets (so as not to appear flashy) and he never spoke unless spoken to (so as not to appear pushing). He watched jealously to see if there were any other Jewish members in the club and when he spotted anyone who might be Jewish he observed his conduct closely, deploring any defect which might warrant an inference from the behaviour of that individual to the characteristics of the race. There was one member Colin could not fail to notice. His name was Marcus Isaacs, a dark, squat, ear-hairy man of about fifty-five, with a large, strawberry nose and thick glasses, who talked with a lisp and played bridge with great skill. Colin regarded the man with loathing. He could not help wondering how he had ever been elected, though actually the membership was of no very select order, since the best people played at the Royal. The Royal did not admit Jews. Southfields Common, on the other hand, was a chummy club. Of its members, Ted Bradshaw was among the chummiest. He was a popular chap and he had popular views. He went forward with the people. You might as well argue with him as with the weather. Colin liked him. Ted never made you feel a fool, there was no side about him, no sarcastic undertones to what he said; if he made a joke, he signalled it by laughing, an open-mouthed frank laugh that revealed yellow, pipe-smoker's teeth. He was older than Colin, which made him seem a wise, even paternal character. He taught Colin snooker and they played for bobs. They were chums.

One morning Colin came out of the front gate of 'Ravens-nook' just as Ted emerged from 'Balmoral'. Bradshaw was slapping the morning paper against his thigh. 'Well, Colin?' he called.

'Morning, Ted.' Colin waited for the other. 'Coming to the station?'

'Seen the paper this morning?'

'Glanced at it.'

'Seen what your people have been up to in Palestine?'

Colin flushed. 'No.' His eye had come to censor such articles.

'Well, take a look.' Ted Bradshaw stretched the paper out in front of his neighbour's face. 'Take a good look, by God.'

'Dreadful,' Colin said. 'Dreadful.'

'You know what I'd like to do this morning? I'd like to line up all the Jews from here to Tel-A-bloody-Viv and shoot the lot of them, shoot the whole bloody lot.' He grinned at Colin with yellow teeth. 'Not including you and Tessa, of course.'

Colin said: 'Of course I feel as badly about it as you do. I – I worry about this sort of thing very much. I think most British Jews do.'

'Well, it's got to stop and the only thing is strong measures.' He slapped the paper. 'This kind of thing would never have been allowed before the war.'

'I think we ought to get out of Palestine and the quicker the better.'

'Pull out? Pull out? We're pulling out of all our bloody possessions. Scuttle, scuttle, scuttle. I know what wogs are like, old boy, if you don't mind me saying so. Only thing they understand is the big stick. Seen it time and again.'

'Certainly true of the Gyppos,' Colin said.

Uneasily, he marched in step with Bradshaw to the bus stop. What about the unborn child? Would Bradshaw have it shot too? What would it be like, he wondered, if he and

Tessa were the only two Jews in the world? Sometimes as it was he felt he was the only one.

<h1 style="text-align:center">4</h1>

Colin's father was no less concerned about the increased anti-Semitic feeling. As a retail shopkeeper, Isidore was especially vulnerable to mob violence. It was for fear that his family's presence would somehow draw the contagion out to Cricklewood that he had, before the war, barred them from the East End. It was a place to get out of. He regarded his days there with no nostalgia. He and his brothers had fought hard to escape the ghetto. Hannah was different: the bombing of the East End had been the destruction of her childhood. Mama and Papa Liepman came from Odessa in 1884. Rachel was the daughter of a cabinet-maker to whom Papa Liepman (a ringleted adolescent of eighteen with eyes that even in old photos burned with black fire) was apprenticed. The two of them eloped when Mama Liepman was only seventeen, and fled acros Europe with little more than the clothes they wore and a diamond brooch of Rachel's. Her father pursued them with curses and torn garments and prayed that barrenness might come on his daughter. The young couple landed in England and found shelter in a shop in Brick Lane. Rachel's brooch realized sixteen pounds. They bought a bedroom suite, paid three months' rent and opened a furniture business. They made three pounds profit on the bedroom suite and they were in business, though they slept on a mattress laid on the bare floor for two years, before a bed could be spared from stock. In those two years Rachel conceived two children and both were stillborn. The year after the big bed was moved upstairs from the showroom, Rachel had a son, Adolphe (now called Alan and Chairman of Kumfisleep, Ltd), and thereafter her father's curse was broken and the family grew to ten, of whom the third was Hannah, the first girl. The second brother Reuben, still ran a business called Liepman's, though he sold surplus duffel coats and mackintoshes, not fine furniture. The shop in Brick Lane was bombed in 1940. Only the façade remained, but on the lintel you could still see the lettering of old Mosha Weingott, the signwriter: LIEPMAN'S – Fine Furniture. Hannah had only to think of that façade and the tears soon came, and the memories: *Pesach*, with the whole family present and Papa Liepman in his fine *tallis*, his silky beard touching his chest as he prayed; *Chanukah*, and the lighting of the candles, the presents; *Yom Kippur*, with a gloom like the grave, the shutters across the showroom window, and death a guest in the house. Oh and the day Papa came home in a hansom after taking back a ruby ring he found stuck down the side of a second-hand armchair! What a row Mama had made about whether he should return it or not! Mama was a masterful woman, but Papa had won that day, for all his dark submissiveness, and came home in a hansom paid with the reward money to prove how right he'd been. Though now she often looked back on the unchanging rituals nostalgically, during those years Hannah came to hate the mustiness of old furniture and came to love new things, and change above all. She loved to be at the head of the queue, so that a thing was not soiled and handled by the time it reached her. How tired she had grown of repairing and darning her brothers' and sisters' clothes as they were passed from one to another! Now she hardly wore a thing twice before she gave it away and bought something new. Money secured for her all that she had missed. It was not to possess it that she worked, but to spend it. It was her freedom; at every stage it renewed her life. It was money that gave Isidore and herself the chance to rent their first shop in the Goldhawk Road, money hard-earned that let them move from there to Cricklewood, money that bought them a car and allowed them to drive like gentlepeople, money that sent Colin to a good school where he could learn to speak as no one in the family had ever spoken, money that earned them respect from other tradespeople, money that secured friends and honour from friends, money that saved you from grovelling to wholesalers or to anyone else for that matter, whether for a taxi, a seat at a theatre, or an outside cabin. Money did not make Hannah arrogant; she could never pass a poor person in the street without giving him money. It was not power that Hannah wanted, but comfort and freedom from worry, the worry that used from time to time to fall on the shop in Brick Lane, when her mother would push away her inquiries with a curt 'Tings ain't so good'. That meant more darning, more scrubbing, more sponging of faded upholstery and plumping of sad cushions. Hannah's ambition carried Isidore with her, grumbling. He had fled from Poland for no romantic reasons. The anti-Semitism of Poles was of savage vindictiveness. Isidore fled from fear and the fear had stayed with him all his life and pursued his son, a ghost of fear. The shop was a terrible responsibility. Its windows were so fragile; the whole place was like a flower-bed waiting to be trampled. When Hannah insisted on opening a branch in Finchley the terrors were doubled; Isidore went through the 30s with a double apprehension; every onset of Facism was a double pain to him. All that mattered to him was that anti-Semitism should keep away from him and his; where Hannah was proud of what was new, Isidore clung to what was old, and inconspicuous: every expense offended him, for every new possession was a new worry. Hannah liked to meet new people, but Isidore remained wrapped in his family and demanded that they be close around him; he watched jealously over his daughters and their chastity was a thing that could be sacrificed only to marriage, to increasing the family that might surround and protect him.

He lived as if in a foreign country. Despite his naturalization, he never voted. He and his family lived alone in a hostile world. Outside it, the forces of darkness; he was not disloyal, but indifferent. Britain never became a real entity to him, that he should love or despise it; since its laws were imposed upon him for the sake of a commonwealth he did not recognize, they seemed merely arbitrary. In his gloomy soul he thought, 'Six million of my people trusted in the law of the Gentiles to become soap and fertilizers.' All right, Colin was an architect, he had a place, fine, and Gentile friends and a house in Wimbledon, but Isidore would stay in the cloister of his family and the acquaintance he had in those confines was all he wanted. There were one or two business friends too, of course, and neighbours, like Estelle and Harry (British Beauty Brassières) Cohen, with whom one visited and played a little poker, but you trusted them with nothing of yourself: you gave nothing away. The conversation you had with them was conversation common to a thousand such friendships. Jokes too were of a traditional order. When they went in to coffee with Estelle Cohen, she said: 'Large cups or small?' and Isidore replied: 'Can't you ever talk about nothing but business?'

Everyone laughed and blushed and Hannah said, 'Isidore, I'm surprised at you,' and she was too, for their marriage never included intimacy of that kind nor exchange of words, or caresses of such and such a kind. Nowadays, Isidore considered, young people had no respect for each other, touching all the time: there ought to be respect between people. Hannah thought so too: she stood in no awe of the body (what had to be done was done, for children and because men were like that) but there was no need for the present emphasis on sex. Hannah and Isidore had no abiding reverence for the flesh. Sensuality was to be assuaged, not glorified. Not that one didn't take care of oneself (Hannah subscribed to *Vogue* long before she could afford any of the models displayed in it) but one did not found one's marriage on sex nor feel disappointment when its allure declined. When Susan said that she was going to marry Ben, there was no part of the arrangement which found sympathy with Hannah or Isidore: Susan's hope that young love might strike an old chord in her parents' hearts was a vain one; such tunes were not current with them. Once the couple were married a compromise was reached because now, for better or worse, Ben was in the family, but the marriage was still a mistake because it was so unreasonable. Isidore watched over his remaining daughter with dismal foreboding. He took no pleasure in her going to college; she was moving out of the family, out of the community, and how could one trust her, how could one be sure what would happen? Isidore feared the worst: goys' hands on her breasts and bacon for breakfast.

This familiar closeness of Isidore's was foreign to Julia; she had no sense of leaving one community for another, since Jewish life, with its tedious taboos, its endless streams of ancient relations, had never commanded her allegiance; if there was conflict, it was much more natural to her to be British than to be Jewish. She embraced opportunities to make new friends, of whatever kind, and never feared they would turn out enemies; she shared neither of her parents' obsessions: since Hitler was defeated (and he was both bogeyman and scapegoat) she was sure that the Four Freedoms had been secured for ever, while Hannah's delight with money as the ladder to comfort was uncongenial to one who had never felt the lack of it. Julia was inhibited neither by caution nor by tradition, for those influences which might have contained a girl less clever, less confident or less companionable served only to boost her eagerness to escape them. She set no limits on the distance she was prepared to go.

NINE

Friends and Relations

1

NEVERTHELESS Julia's first proper date was with Louis Lazarus. He rang and asked Hannah whether he might take her daughter to a Youth Aliyah Dance at the Dorchester.

'He's a bit dreary,' Julia said, when told of the invitation.

'He's a nice man,' Hannah Adler retorted, 'and he's got a good practice.'

'Mummy, he's asked me to a dance, not to marry him.'

'He's got a good practice,' Hannah said. 'And his family's very nicely off. You could do worse.'

Julia laughed at the idea of marriage. As if one were going to spend three years at college and then end up with Louis Lazarus!

In the Sunbeam-Talbot after the dance, Louis Lazarus took off his glasses. 'Julia, my dear,' he said, 'it's been a wonderful evening.'

'Thank you very much for asking me.' Julia opened the car door and put a foot out.

'You know, my dear, in my business I come across a lot of very unpleasant people, it's very wonderful for me to spend an evening in your company.'

'You don't know anything about me.'

'You're a very remarkable girl, Julia.' Louis leaned over and closed the car door. 'This evening has meant a lot to me.'

'It's been lovely,' Julia said.

He kissed her. His lips were soft. The roughness of the moustache above them gave the kiss a bizarre intimacy. Julia opened the car door. 'Thanks again, Louis. It's been lovely.'

Louis put his glasses on. 'May I telephone you, Julia?'

'Of course you can, yes.'

Only when she was closing the door of 15 Woburn Road did she hear Louis pull the self-starter.

'Julia, is that you, dear?'

'Yes, Mummy.'

'How was the dance?'

'Ghastly.'

'Oh, Julia, no.'

'Oh, Mummy, yes.'

'And how was Louis?'

'Corny,' Julia said, 'very, very corny.'

She saw Louis several times again. He was cautiously fervent. He made love with his voice, not his hands (Hannah and Isidore were clients), he told her how deeply he felt about her, how eager he was to cherish and protect her: 'Julia, my dear,' he would begin, 'I'm a little older than you, I've seen more of people than you have, and believe me, I know what a rare sort of person you are.' The glasses came off. 'The sort of person I could care about very much indeed.' An arm came round her shoulder and a solicitous hand held her arm. 'I'm devoted to your mother,' he said. 'I feel like one of the family already.'

'Well, you're not,' Julia said. She found him rather creepy. Louis was intensely Jewish; already, with his black Sunbeam-Talbot, his dark suits and pearl-grey, Windsor-knotted ties, he was maturing into sleek respectability. He wore a heavy Masonic ring. He went to synagogue. He loved the Jews. It did not occur to him to wonder if Julia reciprocated that soft passion which he lavished on her, for he assumed that all Jewesses thought of him as a potential husband just as he thought of them as potential wives. For the moment he had his eye on Julia, since she pleased him and since her family was one in which he was welcome. Nor had he failed to notice how blithely old Isidore had forked out the money for the fine – he must have a good deal stacked away. He did not take into account whether Julia was attracted to him; he was sure that his family's reputation (Playgirl Dresses were famous) no less than his own professional status was sufficient guarantee of his desirability. This conviction gave him a plump conceit which neither the coldness of a kiss nor the acid of a remark could puncture. When he proposed to Julia he put his case decorously and left it to her good sense to find in his favour. When she rejected him (with a barely straight face) he sighed and assured her, with that solemn devotion of his, that he would appeal against her decision at a later date. At first Julia dealt with Louis's importunity with as much tact as she could, but soon found it too much for her. She knew she would never marry Louis Lazarus in a thousand years at the South Pole, as Granny Liepman used to say, and the spectacle of him plumping himself up for another proposal was one she could not face. 'I don't think I shall go out with Louis again,' she told her mother.

'Did he try something?' Hannah asked.

'Mummy! Louis? Don't be silly, he wouldn't know how.'

'They're a nice family,' Hannah said. 'And Louis's a nice boy.'

'He's a fat *man*,' Julia said. 'Anyway, I've got to work. At this rate I shall have forgotten everything I know by the time I go to college.'

'Marriage is more important than colleges,' Hannah said.

'I don't want to marry a pompous old fatty like Louis.'

'You want to marry a Jewish boy though, don't you?'

'Would you mind terribly if I didn't?'

'You'll marry a nice Jewish boy,' Hannah said. 'I know you will. You'll meet a nice Jewish feller and you'll fall in love with him. You wouldn't want to marry out of the faith, would you, dear?'

'Faith!' Julia said.

At dinner, Isidore said: 'Who's this goy you want to marry?'

'I don't want to marry anybody. Whatever gave you that idea?'

'Your mother said –'

'I explained to you,' Hannah snapped. 'You never listen. He never listens.'

'I know what's going on. You don't have to pull the wool over my eyes.'

'Nobody's pulling anything over your eyes.'

'The first thing he'd throw in your face is being Jewish.'

'I don't see why he has to throw anything in my face,' Julia said. 'In fact I've definitely made up my mind to marry someone who doesn't throw things in my face.'

'Who's she gonna marry?' Isidore demanded.

2

The young man said: 'So you're Julia Adler. I think we're vaguely related.' It was at a party Monty Lazarus was giving in his new Chelsea studio.

'Are we? How?'

'Your brother called Colin?' Julia nodded. 'Thought so. Works for the far-famed Family Lovers' Building Soc., does he not?'

'I rather think he does,' Julia said.

'My esteemed father is managing director of said illustrious corp. Doesn't that make us Yiddy cousins?'

'You don't altogether appeal to me,' Julia said. 'Whatever your name is.'

'Neil,' he said. 'Neil King. Let's get out of this bloodsome party.'

'It's a nice party,' Julia said. 'I was enjoying it until you came in.' Actually, she wanted to get out before Louis arrived. She knew he would take off his glasses when he saw her.

'Too many Yids here,' King said.

'Look, I'm Jewish.'

'Oh, it's all right, so'm I. Not that you'd guess it.' He was on the short side, but had fair hair and blue eyes. 'Half, that is. My fat father is a Yid.'

'And what is your thin mother?'

'Usual tart. You coming?'

Julia tilted her head. 'All right.' She went to get her coat.

'One poke and then home,' Neil King said to Monty Lazarus, who giggled. When Julia came back, Neil showed her out to a white M.G.

'Aren't you posh?'

'Bloody posh.' He opened the door and helped Julia in. 'She's a tart,' he called as he hopped round the bonnet to get to the driving seat, 'because only a tart would sleep with a Yid.'

'Well at least we know where we are.'

'Where you want to go?'

'I don't mind. How much petrol've you got?'

'Plenty petrol,' he replied, starting up and driving off very fast. 'Oh, I got plenty petrol. You want some nice petrol maybe, huh?'

Julia said: 'What do you do for a living?'

'I'm in the Paratroops,' Neil King said. 'Want some nice silk, maybe?'

Julia said: 'Oh, for God's sake stop the car and let me out.'

'Stop the world,' Neil said, putting his foot on the accelerator. 'I want to get off.'

'Very witty,' Julia said. 'Ten out of ten.'

'You're coming to bed with me,' Neil King said.

'I *am* not.'

'What do you do for a living?'

'I'm not a tart, if that's what you mean.'

'Very crisp. What are you then?'

'I'm at college.'

'Virgin?'

'Certainly,' Julia said. 'Any objections?'

'In your case I'm prepared to make an exception,' King said.

'How do you like the Army?'

'I like it fine, just fine.' He drove very fast through the West End and up the Tottenham Court Road into Hampstead Road. 'We give Yids hell in my unit. Christ, I only wish we could have been in that Palestine show. You know Roy Simmonds?'

'No. Who's he?'

'He's a boy, believe me. Used to put bulldog clips on their balls.' He glanced at Julia. 'You don't have to worry, it can't ever happen to you.' They surged up Rosslyn Hill into Hampstead and slewed through a red light to go up Heath Street. 'You'll be pleased to hear the new fighting Yid still squeals like the old arse-licking kind.'

'For God's sake – ' Julia said as the car squirmed past a taxi and cut in to avoid a van.

'Nervous?'

The driving mirror was a sudden bar of brilliance. Julia said: 'It's the police.'

'Sod it.'

'They want you to stop. Neil, for God's sake.' Her hands were over her ears, against the wind. The car skewered past an old Morris. The police car was boxed. The M.G. screamed along North End Road and Neil hugged it into a tight spin down into Finchley Road. A bus flashed indignant lights. 'You baby. You bloody baby.'

The police car slid after them.

'There's a tarpaulin in the back. Get it out and straighten

it out a bit,' Neil shouted at her. 'Ready to move when I tell you.'

'You bloody lunatic.'

Down into Child's Hill they went and whipped left into Hermitage Lane, the engine hammering against the hill, down into West Heath Road and hard left into Frognal. The police car was still with them, its lights exploding on walls and hedges and house faces, left and right of them as its driver cornered. Neil shouted: 'Two corners from now I'm going to pull up and turn out the lights. You get the tarpaulin over our heads as fast as you bloody can, right?' The car twitched into Church Row, Fitzjohn's, Arthur Street. 'Now.' Julia yanked over the tarpaulin. The police gong rang in their ears as they cowered down in the car. Julia gobbled with laughter. Neil jerked her face to his and kissed her and forced his tongue into her mouth and pulled her against him. 'Shut up, you little cow,' he whispered and thrust his tongue into her mouth again. She bit him, hard. 'God, you little *cow*.'

'Sorry I hadn't got a bulldog clip,' she said.

'You little cow,' he grinned.

'You're mad,' she said. 'Mad. They must've got your number.'

'My old man'll fork up.'

'We might have been killed. For nothing.'

'What a wonderful reason to die!'

'You're mad,' Julia said.

Neil started the car again and idled the engine. He looked at his watch. 'Bit early to go home.'

'I think it's a bit late. What do you call late?'

Neil King was looking at his watch. 'At this moment,' he said, 'my fat father is inserting himself in my thin mother.'

Julia said: 'You're horrid. You're *horrid*. Take me home.'

He drove slowly and cautiously now the heat was off him. At the house, he said: 'I'll take you out again.'

She said: 'You won't.'

'My tongue's going to swell up. I can feel it.'

'I'm sorry.'

'I like it,' he said. 'I wish you could kill me.'

Julia said: 'Don't worry. You'll find someone who will.'

'I want you, Julia,' he said. 'You're a person I could hate.'

Julia ran into the house. Neil drove up on the kerb on the far side of the road and bumped down again. Julia went into the front room and poured herself a dramatic whisky. She had never heard the neck of a bottle tinkle against the glass before. It seemed rather funny. The whisky jerked her steady. It was the first time she had tasted it.

3

Susan had hired a typewriter and was making a little extra money by duplicating manuscripts and business letters. The work was hard and she was very tired at the end of a day of typing with one eye and keeping watch on Sarah with the other. And then Sid Forbes found out she had a machine, and asked her to do letters and circulars for the Party branch. At first she resented it, but later, tired as she was, it made her happy when Ben, having heard the clipping of the typewriter from far up the road, rushed in and kissed her and was happy with her, about the same thing, at the same time, for the same reason. And unless something happened, unless there was a snappy story to tell, about Sarah, about work, about the Party, they went up to bed with that equal joy between them and in bed had true pleasure since they were truly living together.

But during the day a void of boredom could consume her, so that all she wanted was to escape from 24 Armoury Road. She took to putting away most of the money she earned, saving for a dress or a pair of shoes she had seen in one of the *Vogues* Hannah gave her. Every three months or so she had saved enough for an expedition to the West End. If it was school holidays and Ethel wasn't working, she left Sarah with her. She spoiled herself: she had lunch at the Berkeley Buttery and she took a taxi to Harrods to do her shopping; if she had really been working hard, she had her hair done at a new posh place that had just opened in Lowndes Street, if not, she contented herself with a cup of hot chocolate in the Silver Snackbar and then walked the last steps of her disdainful West End walk to Knightsbridge Station before resuming, station by drab station, her Archway personality.

How Susan did love those days! What began as a shopping expedition, with a fantasy of wealth, soon expanded; Susan fancied herself a brilliant bachelor girl, on whom every debonair eye was fastened; the smallest male attention was met with a husky 'Thank you' which suggested, at least to Susan, that 'Miss Otis regrets'. Every nerve tingled with awareness. If anyone were to make love to her on such an afternoon, she believed she would go up like a magnesium flare. She rustled deliciously in her envelope of perfume and felt totally explosive.

One afternoon, in such a mood, she walked down Piccadilly, instead of taking her usual taxi, into the park. She was wearing the new shoes she had bought on her last trip and every step in them, the shift of one leg against the other, was joyful. Cars came slowly past her and their drivers, on several occasions, turned their heads to look at her. She went up towards the Barracks. Two women were standing on steep heels, against the barrack railings. A car which had slowed by Susan pulled up opposite them. One went forward and ducked her head to the driver. After a moment she got in. Susan stumbled and a blush rose from her neck and burned her face. Another car slowed opposite her. She wouldn't look. The man tapped his horn. She had to look. The face was tilted on one side, its smile a question-mark. It was the red-haired RAF man with whom she had danced at Monty Lazarus's party. He said: 'Coming?' Susan tottered forward on awkward legs, all knees and ankles. The car paced her to the gate where she ran out. A man said: 'Are you all right?' 'Leave me alone.' Fear curdled in her throat. 'Get away from me.'

Alone that night, she was reading a book Ben had given her (*Tito: The Man and the Ism*) when the doorbell went. She slipped on her shoes and went to answer it.

'Sid!' She undid the chain. 'Come in.'

'Expecting burglars?'

'Not exactly. Ben's out, that's all.'

'Pity, I was hoping for a word. When you expecting him back?'

'He shouldn't be long,' Susan said. 'Like a cuppa?'

'If you're making one.' Sid took off his trench coat and followed her down the passage to the kitchen.

'How's Ethel?' Susan asked.

'Ethel's fine.'

Susan said: 'Where've you been this evening?'

'Out.'

'Planting bombs again, eh?'

'In their Rolls-Royces,' Sid said. There was a bus driver in their branch who was interested only in when the time would come to put bombs in Rolls-Royces. Sid said: 'No, I've been talking to some people down in Cricklewood. I go down there every now and then on this Anti-Fascist Council.'

'I remember typing the circular,' Susan said.

'Aye, you're a good girl, Susie.'

Susan said: 'Tea's made.'

Sid said: 'You're much too pretty to be left alone, you know.'

'Come on, Sid, let's have the tea, shall we?' Susan closed every muscle round the handle of the pot. He let her pass, followed her down the passage. She got him to sit in a chair and sat opposite him. He took out a packet of Woodbines

171

and offered her one. She took it and they both lit up. 'Ben should be back any minute,' she said, pluming smoke from her nostrils. She averted her head to blink out the last of it.

'Good old Ben,' Sid said, running his tongue over cracked lips.

Susan said: 'What's your news?'

'I'm getting a new job as a matter of fact.' Sid laced his thin fingers together. 'Could lead to big things.'

'People's films?' Susan inquired.

'People's money,' Sid said, with the shadow of a smile.

'For people's Sid, I presume.'

'We have to eat.'

'More than we do,' Susan gloomed.

When Ben came in, Susan was able to say, 'Ben, Sid's got a new job,' while Ben noticed the set of the two chairs and smiled at the situation.

'New job, eh? What's that then?'

'With Royalty Films,' Susan said. 'What is it exactly again?'

'Production manager.'

'With Royalty Films yet.'

'Patron the Queen Mum,' Susan smiled, fretting a worn place in the carpet with her toe.

'It's a good company,' Sid Forbes said. 'Look, I wanted a quick word with ye, Ben, if you don't mind.'

'I can take a hint.' Susan went into the kitchen with the tea things. She twisted sullenly at the tap, attending to the hum of voices in the front room. Why was she never at the centre of things? She was just a sort of receptionist. The most urgent thing in the two men's lives should be their rivalry for her. Instead they were mates. The tap went on dripping when she had turned it off. What a life!

Julia's rooms in college were in a tower at the end of the red-brick Victorian building known as 'Carlyle'. There were three sets on her floor. The other two were occupied by Brenda Blair and Alice Smith. By the end of the first year, Alice was Alyson and Brenda was 'Slinky'. Julia was Julia. Slinky started the year as a rather pasty Minor Scholar in Mathematics; by the end of it there was a jumble of make-up pots and cartons in her dressing-table drawer and a young man called Paddy in her bed.

Slinky had a way of not worrying about things till after they had happened. This led, not infrequently, to quinine and castor oil. Nevertheless, she developed a sleek, sensual radiance which drove Alyson purple with envy. 'All I hope is that you get a different room next year. I think you've got just about the most *explicit* bed ever invented.'

'The trouble with you, darling, is that you've got a dirty mind.'

'It taps out messages more clearly than the Exchange Telegraph,' Alyson said.

At the beginning of the next year Alyson found herself a man called Anthony Bray, a commercial artist, who shared a flat in Belsize Park. 'The man he shares it with has gone away for the week-end,' Alyson told the other two one Saturday, 'so I think tonight's the big night. What do you think of my new dress?'

'Well, darling, I hope you're going to wear something under it, that's all.'

'Oh yes, these. Aren't they bliss?'

'And a bra, I *hope*.'

'Oh, don't be so old-fashioned,' Alyson said, drawing a coil of her blonde hair down over her eye with the flat of her hand. 'Tonight we improvise.'

'Aren't you going to look just a teeny-weeny bit titty, dee-ah?'

Alyson frowned. 'You forget I'm going out with Anthony.'

'Meet Cleopatra,' Julia said.

The next morning, Slinky gave Julia cocoa in her rooms. She was painting her toenails when Alyson came clacking up the stairs.

'Well?' demanded Slinky.

'As of last night,' Alyson announced, 'there is only one snowy white virgin in our midst.'

'Ah,' Slinky said.

Alyson turned to Julia. 'It's all right, darling,' she said. 'Honestly I don't know what all the fuss is about.'

'You bloody fool,' Slinky said.

5

Estelle (British Beauty Brassières) Cohen was on the phone to Hannah Adler: 'I saw your daughter Susan the other day.'

'Where was that, dear?'

'Walking in the street. Near Oxford Circus. She was with a man.'

'Her husband, I expect.'

'I never met him,' Estelle said. 'He had red hair, sort of sandy.'

Hannah said: 'Oh.'

'Is that her husband? Nice-lookin' feller.'

'Must have been a friend,' Hannah said.

Estelle Cohen said: 'They seemed like they was good friends. They was holding hands.'

'It wasn't Susan at all,' Hannah said. 'Did you have your glasses on?'

'I should wear glasses in the street? They're for bridge.'

'It wasn't Susan at all,' Hannah Adler said.

* * *

Susan said: 'Sid, don't.'

'You're a bit of a Puritan, do you know that, Susan?'

'Don't be silly, Sid. We're both married people. And it so happens I'm very fond of Ethel,' she added, but thought of Jefferson Andrews.

'So'm I,' Sid said. 'What's that got to do with it?'

'I must go and collect Sarah.'

'All right for next Thursday? Press Show of the new Carol Reed. Should be interesting –'

'Oh, all right,' Susan said.

'Look, Susan, you needn't do me any favours, y'know,' Sid Forbes said.

'Muh!' Susan said. Then she grinned. It worked: Sid grinned. It always worked. It worked on her too: she couldn't restrain her charm even when she didn't really want what it got her.

It all started quite innocently (and, Susan reminded herself, it still *was* innocent) with Sid asking her to come to a private showing of a film which his new company had made. Hannah was happy to look after Sarah and Susan was glad to have the child off her hands: her continual 'Mummy, what can I do now?' was getting her down. Susan was no longer central to her daughter's life; she ached for someone whose whole existence would be made or marred by her consent. The film was called *The Body In 109*. It was a hotel comedy. It had a comic detective, a comic chambermaid, a comic lift-boy, a comic waiter, a comic manager, hosts of comic guests and even a comic body – which wasn't really dead at all! If Susan had seen it with Ben at the local cinema, they would certainly have left long before the comic waiter fell down the laundry chute for the sixth time, but she could not fail to be thrilled by being in on something to which the general public was not admitted. It was this love of being in on things which had made the Party, with its privileged access to the future, irresistible. She had always wanted to work on a newspaper because then she could see tomorrow today.

Ben, Susan and Sarah went to see Hannah and Isidore for Sunday lunch. Tanya cooked the meal, but went out before they finished. Ben and Hannah washed up. Isidore, Susan and Sarah went out for a walk. Ben did not greatly care for Hannah. The cartons of food, which she still sent, rankled. The money was suspected. Ben favoured Isidore's closeness. 'When I want your Mum's Marshall Aid I'll tell her myself,' Ben would say. But he liked his mother-in-law better when they were washing up together; the steam shone over the wide cheekbones and brought out the Russian in her, till she reminded Ben of Gorky's grandmother, a solid woman whom a shawl suited.

'Pass me the dessert plates, will you, dear?'

'You mean the small ones?' Ben grinned.

'Now the baby's getting bigger – ' Hannah began.

'Sall,' Ben corrected her. 'She's not a baby.'

'All right, dear,' Hannah smiled. 'Will you be looking for a bigger place?'

'Bigger place? Why?'

'Maybe Susan should have more to do.'

'*More* to do?'

Hannah scoured away at the oven pan. Ben hated the intrusion, sensing it had reason. 'Those lily-white hands should be polluted by honest toil?'

Hannah said: 'She's a nice little thing.'

'Susan?'

'The baby.'

'Sally.'

'Yes – but she's getting older now. She shouldn't stay an only child too long.'

'Do you mind?' Ben smiled.

'You shouldn't leave Susan alone too much.' Hannah Adler took the bottle of hand cream from the kitchen dresser and rinsed her hands with it. They went into the lounge.

'Would you like a chocolate, dear?'

'No, thank you.'

Susan came in. 'You two had a row?'

'*No*,' Ben said. 'Why should you think that?'

'You look a bit glazed.'

'Hot in here,' Ben said.

Isidore Adler said: 'It's mild out. We met Sam and Estelle Cohen.'

'She seemed a bit strange, didn't she, Daddy?' Susan said.

Isidore smiled emptily. Hannah said: 'She's been having a difficult time lately.'

'She's had piles,' Isidore snickered to Ben. 'Piles!'

'*Isidore*, that was in confidence.'

Ben's laugh took in Susan. She hadn't laughed, but now she sniffed in quick, false complicity, her father disgusting her.

Sarah said: 'Mummy, what are we going to do now?'

Susan said: 'Ask Daddy.'

Ben rolled his eyes, but was at once on his haunches to Sarah. 'We could go into the garden and see how many different kinds of leaves we can collect.'

He winked at Hannah and they went out. Susan smiled after them. Hannah said: 'He's a nice feller.'

'He's my husband, isn't he?'

'Yes, that's right – your husband.'

'Goodness, it is hot in here,' Susan said.

The arrival of Colin and Tessa for tea restored solidarity to Ben and Susan. Colin was at his worst; he was so nervous you could see that he had prepared his conversation before he arrived: he was full of leading questions like 'What do you think of Dalton?' and 'What about Berlin?' and 'Do you think the pound will be devalued?' to all of which Ben replied with cryptic sarcasm. Colin was puzzled and sat cracking his red knuckles, his forehead furrowed with seriousness.

Hannah said: 'I do love to have my family around me.'

For Hannah, if it looked right, it was right. 'Such a shame Julia couldn't get home this week-end.'

'How *is* Prunella the Prune?' Colin demanded.

'She's having a wonderful time,' Hannah said.

'Having the time of her life, I should think,' Tessa said, elderly.

'Spending a lot of money,' from Isidore.

'She's doing very well at college and she's meeting a lot of nice people, so don't you grumble.'

'You grumble if you want to,' Ben said.

'Support the whole family,' Isidore muttered.

'How's Otto these days?' Ben asked.

'Otto?' Hannah said. 'He's fine.'

'Stayed here nearly six months. Never contributed a penny.'

Hannah said: 'Shut up, Issy. I hate to hear you talk like that.'

Ben said: 'What's he doing?'

'He's in this home,' Hannah said. 'And he repairs Sir Samuel Goldstein's clocks, keeps them in order.'

'Quite an honour for a man who's been in a concentration camp!' Susan said.

'My uncle is trying to help,' Tessa said. 'Which is more than some people have done.'

Hannah said: 'Don't you get upset, dear. It's very nice of Sir Samuel.'

'He's the kindest man in the world,' Tessa said. 'I don't know where we'd be without him.'

'I do,' Ben said. 'You'd be in Kenya.'

'*Ben*,' from Susan.

Colin blew out his cheeks. 'Just what do you mean by that, may I ask?'

'You know what I mean, Colin, old boy. If it weren't for Sir Samuel and his heart of gold you'd be in Kenya.'

'I don't know what you're talking about.'

Susan said: 'I think I'd better take you home.'

Colin said: 'I don't get it. What has Sir Samuel got to do with us not being in Kenya?'

'Nothing, dear,' Hannah said, with a smile for Tessa. 'Sarah dear, let's go back into the garden and see what we can find.' She led the child out of the room.

'I think you'd better explain youself,' Colin said, puffing.

'Oh, forget it,' Ben said.

'I'd like to have a word with you outside.'

'Outside – right,' Ben said. 'But I've left me duelling pistols in me hunting lodge.'

Susan smiled nervously. 'I'm terribly sorry. I don't know what's got into Ben.'

Tessa said: 'I shouldn't worry.' 'You are lucky,' Susan said. Contented, Tessa smiled. 'Yes,' she said, 'I know.' Susan was irritated then with her own emptiness. 'You look very confident,' she said snappily. 'I suppose you've done all the right things. More than I ever did.'

Ben and Colin walked down the road. Colin was hot with embarrassment. He felt a perfect damned fool, even though at one moment he had seriously intended to hit Ben, he recognized now an obscure cleverness in the other man which made him want to deny his own intentions. Bluntly, he said: 'Look here, what did you mean just now?'

Ben said: 'Forget it. Nothing.'

'I'm damned well not going to stand for it.' Colin clenched his fists, but kept them at his sides. 'I don't know who you think you are – '

'Look, if you don't know that Sir S. Goldstein, Esquire, is a managing director of the Family Lovers' Building Society, I'm sorry. That's all there is to it. That's all I meant.'

Colin was stunned. He said: 'I suppose you think you're very clever. You think you know how everything works.'

'I don't,' Ben replied.

'Look, I apologize if I did the wrong thing, I mean about you and Susan. I apologize.'

'That's OK,' Ben said.

'Look here, let's shake hands.'

'Shake hands?'

'I'd like to,' Colin said.

'Delighted to shake hands.' They shook hands. 'Is that better?'

'Much better. I'm sure we can be friends.'

'Sure,' Ben said.

'Now I suppose we'd better go back. They'll be wondering about us.'

'Yes, wouldn't do to let them think the war's broken out!'

'There won't be a war, will there?' Colin demanded. 'Do you think there'll be a war?'

Susan was saying: 'You seem to know it all, Tessa. There's nothing to tell you, is there?' Susan looked up as the door opened. 'Ah, there you are, old boy. You two had a good walk?'

'Topping,' Ben said.

'He's been telling me about the political situation.'

Tessa said: 'I thought you were going to have a fight.'

Colin said: 'Fight?'

'Fight,' Ben said. 'What gave you that idea?'

They all assembled for good-byes, brightly forgetting the afternoon's squalls. 'Say good-bye to Aunt Tessa,' Susan said.

'Why is she so fat?' Sarah asked, her dumb curiosity finally overcome. Hannah laughed and said: 'Oh dear!'

'Aunt Tessa's going to have a baby,' Susan said.

'I shan't be fat much longer, Sarah. (I hope,' to Susan.)

'Why won't she?'

'Because the baby's inside her – Aunt Tessa.'

'Inside her! Why doesn't she let it out?'

'She will,' Susan said, 'all in due time. (She knows perfectly well, really,' to Tessa.)

Ben said: 'Come on, Susan, we'll miss the bus.' To the company: 'Cheers.'

Susan said: 'Good luck with the baby.'

'Thank you.'

'She'll be all right.' Hannah Adler kissed her daughter and turned to Ben: 'Good-bye, dear, and remember –'

'Don't you worry,' Ben said.

'Remember what?' Susan asked as soon as the door was shut.

'Susan, do you mind? We've all got our secrets, haven't we?'

'Ass,' Susan smiled. But she felt Ben had a grievance and, with the symmetry of marriage, promptly assumed one herself: 'You shouldn't have said what you did about Kenya.'

'Why shouldn't I?'

'You upset Tessa.'

'Oh, Susan, for heaven's sake, don't worry so much about upsetting people.'

Susan said; 'What's Mummy been saying to you?'

'Nothing,' Ben said. 'What's she been saying to you?'

She clenched herself away from him. 'You can be a bastard sometimes.'

Sarah said: 'What's a bastard?'

Ben said: 'A very nice person you're very fond of.'

Sarah said: 'Daddy, I think you're a bastard then.'

Susan smiled then, but later she said: 'I'm tired tonight, Ben.'

'After a day at your old woman's, I'm not surprised.'

'If you don't want to go to my mother's, you only have to say so. I'm sure she didn't want to cook lunch.'

'She didn't cook it,' Ben said. Susan turned away and began to undress. Ben picked up a razor blade and set about slicing some dead, yellow skin from his heel. Susan winced: 'When are you going to have a bath?'

He stared at her. 'Don't be unpleasant, Susan, please.'

She lay awake in bed for a while, but Ben was averted

from her. It was a disappointment that she could not disappoint him.

She fell asleep in a reverse of desire, a negative image of love, and hours later was aware in the dark room, aware in a hammock of time between consciousness and sleep as of being at sea. Her whole being was lapped in a rhythm she must acknowledge. Her own grace, her own craft depended on accepting the dark tide that moved her. Almost asleep then, she matched him; in her sleep she had accepted him and she came awake beating with a rhythm it would have been death for her to rupture. She came to shore on a great surge of joyful anguish and twisted furiously from him, stabbing for her watch on the bedside table.

'Ben, you bloody idiot.'

'What's the matter, Susan?'

'You know as well as I do. I didn't cope last night – you know as well as I do.'

'Wasn't thinking about it, Susan. Sorry.'

She flung herself out of bed and ran into the bathroom. There wasn't anything she could do, but she ran in there wildly and slammed the door. She sat down on the cold rim of the bath and shook herself awake, blinked into the mirror of the medicine chest and cursed the tide that worked in her.

Ben said: 'Come on, Susie.'

'You knew. You knew.'

'Cheer up, girl, it may never happen.' He scooped her off the bath and carried her through (bumped her shin on the way) into the bedroom and tucked her in bed like a baby.

TEN

Two English Dances

1

IT WAS NOT till her next to last term at college that Julia met Andrew Peregrine. She, Alyson and Slinky all went up to Oxford for a weekend. Alyson had had her hair done at Raymond's and Slinky had bought a pair of leopard-skin tights. Julia had washed her hair and it was long and silky. She wore an orange dress and three ropes of white beads. They were quite a trio, they decided, though each of the other two secretly considered herself the star. Slinky had a boy-friend at the House, and it was in Stephen Marsden's rooms in Tom Quad that Julia first met Andrew. He stormed in to borrow some sugar and, spotting Julia, stayed; he was a tall, raw young man, with blue eyes, fair lashes and a tangle of fair hair. He had only just missed a place in the Oxford boat but his spirits seemed unaffected. He took Julia off and showed her all the sights of Oxford, maintaining a flow of reminiscence which kept her in continual bubbles of laughter. 'The trouble is,' he confessed finally, 'if I go out with a pretty girl, I always end up by falling in love with her.'

'How many times do you fall per year then?'

'About fifty.'

Julia laughed. 'And how do you come to have the fiftieth if you fall for the first?'

'Simple. Every one breaks my heart.'

'Like hell,' Julia said.

He took her to dinner at the Roebuck. 'Probably cripple

me for the rest of the year,' he observed. 'Still while there's Papa there's hope!'

'Look, do let me pay for mine.'

'I expect I shall only just have enough left for a Commem ticket.'

Julia said: 'It's been a wonderful day.'

'Will you come, Julia? To the Commem?'

'Won't there be fifty other girls there?'

'I mean it. Please.' He grinned across the table at her. 'It'll be a bloody good Ball.'

'I'd love to,' she said, 'but – '

He put his large hand over hers. 'No buts. It's all settled. Now then, what shall we do this evening? Feel like dancing? We could get some practice in. I need it.'

They went to a dance given by the NUS in a Community Hall in the Iffley Road. The band was Robyn Hoode and his Merrye Men, but Julia and Andrew enjoyed themselves extravagantly. Eventually they reeled out of the hall, much to the relief of the organizers ('Bespectacled Charlies from Teddy Hall', Andrew called them) and collapsed with laughter into each other's arms. 'I'm certainly not coming to the Commem after that display,' Julia said.

'It'd be an anticlimax,' Andrew agreed. 'A complete anticlimax.' He kissed her. 'But you're coming all the same.'

Stephen Marsden asked Slinky to the Commem (the leopard-skin tights paid off) and they made up a party with Andrew and Julia. Alyson, in a huff, went to the Dorchester with the cousin of a Maharajah.

Hannah Adler bought Julia a new dress for the occasion. It was emerald green and made Julia look very exotic. Oxford was one of those magic names to Hannah; she was more excited than her daughter about the Ball, and for weeks before could talk of nothing else, while Isidore grumbled about 'what these things lead to'. When Julia showed her the new dress, Slinky said she didn't think

Julia quite had the bosom for the job and suggested, girl to girl, that they swapped gowns; so Julia knew she must look good. Julia was relieved to find that Andrew clearly did not regard the Ball as his Big Opportunity; he put on no seductive charm. He was intent, as ever, merely on having a good time. It was certainly a wonderful occasion. The fairy lights strung through the quads, the rustle of dresses, the sparkle of dress shirts, the dignity of tails, the distant saxophones of the orchestra as one strolled out towards the river, the bloom of the floodlights on old grey stone combined in a unique, almost absurdly romantic atmosphere. Between dances, Andrew and Julia ate strawberries and chicken *vol-au-vents*, chocolate profiteroles and hot sausages, and were as blithe as children. As the night progressed, couples left the dancing and went off together. Passing one set of rooms, Julia and Andrew, arm in arm, heard a shrill female voice say: 'Nigel, for heaven's sake wait a minute.' Andrew looked at Julia and his lips twitched. Hand in hand they scampered across the quad before collapsing with laughter against the side wall of the cathedral. In that laughter Julia knew that Andrew would not make love to her that night. She was neither pleased nor sorry; she was happy.

Stephen and Slinky disappeared to Stephen's rooms at about two-thirty. Julia and Andrew went up there at four, hoping to get a short sleep before breakfast, but the oak was sported. 'They must be at it,' Andrew said. 'We may as well get something to drink and see the new era in.'

'What era's that?'

'The era of the unemployability of one Andrew Peregrine, what else? If only I'd got my Blue, I'd be sitting pretty.'

'But, Mr Peregrine,' Julia said, 'I zink you are very pretty.'

He kissed her and they went off for more strawberries. Dawn found them sitting, very dozy, on a sofa in the refreshment marquee. Andrew said suddenly: 'I say, let's all go and have breakfast at Lyons Corner House.'

'Oh yes, let's,' Julia said. 'I didn't know there was one in Oxford.'

'There isn't, you chump. We're going to London. Won't take long. Better go and see if Stephen and Slinks have finished.'

The oak was still sported. Andrew banged on it. 'Break it up,' he shouted.

A sloppy-slippered Stephen appeared. 'Time is it?' he asked, looking at them out of one eye.

'Six o'clock. Get your clothes on. We're going to London for breakfast.'

'Christ, you're hearty,' Stephen croaked. 'Wait there.'

'Oh, let them come in,' Slinky called.

Stephen said: 'Come in.'

'I was just changing,' Slinky told them, drawing her stockings unnecessarily high up her thighs.

'Did I say anything?' Andrew grinned.

'Don't be coarse,' Slinky said. 'Julia, aren't you going to change, darling?'

'Don't see why I should.'

'Of course not,' Andrew said. He put his arm round her. 'Your dress isn't torn, is it?'

Slinky said: 'No one's ever had to tear my dress yet.'

'Mess in here,' Stephen muttered.

Andrew had borrowed his brother's 1936 Morris Cowley convertible. Slinky and Stephen had to squeeze into the back seat. Slinky began sitting up on the folded canvas hood, but she soon got cold and slipped down beside the drooping Stephen. Andrew drove very fast and the car drummed out its protest. He and Julia laughed all the way to London. She wasn't sure why exactly. Just everything seemed marvellous.

When Ben and Susan's second child came it was a boy, born on a Sunday and they called him Jonathan. 'Gift of God,' Ben said, 'very suitable!' Tessa had had a girl, Anne, so there was great rejoicing from Hannah (and Isidore) at the first male grandchild. Hannah rang Ben in great excitement.

'I've arranged for the *briss*,' she said. 'Doctor Levy.'

Ben said: 'I don't want all that. I don't believe in it.'

'It's got to be done, dear,' Hannah said. 'I've spoken to your mother about it and she agrees.'

It was done in a white-tiled delivery room in the maternity ward. Only Colin, Isidore, and Ben were present with the Rabbi. Dr Levy was an elderly man with grey eyes and a vacant, marbled face. He went through the ritual with surly automatism. Colin was red in the face and kept grinning. He wore a faded grey felt hat. Ben wore a *Kapel*. Isidore, a glum figure in a big black coat and homburg hat, held the baby's knees apart. The pinioned baby's blood burst from the blister of its foreskin and trickled down into the fat little thighs. The child squawled purple. The four adults, absurdly hatted, stared down at the red raspberry of the baby's penis, while the Rabbi dabbed at it with cotton-wool. Ben's eyes fell on the cuff of waxy flesh which lay on the tin top of the doctor's trolley.

'Are you all right?' Dr Levy asked, handing Jonathan to Ben and downing the glass of ritual wine.

Ben stared furiously into Levy's glazed face. Finally, he gave the baby back to Dr Levy, who put it in its cot.

Isidore said: 'Now no one can say he isn't a good Yiddisher boy.'

Colin said: 'Feeling a bit queer, old chap?'

Levy said: 'Put your head between your legs.'

'He's a bit sick,' Isidore said, cheering up. Colin looked at him and nodded curtly. My father, he thought, noticing the asynoptic glaze in the eyes, the vacant amusement of another's discomfort, while Ben did put his head between his knees. 'The babies are always all right. It's the fathers that give the trouble,' Dr Levy said, licking his lips.

Ben straightened up decisively. Isidore extracted a roll of pound notes from his pocket. Dr Levy shook hands with him and with Colin, collected his instruments and then turned to Ben. 'Feeling better?'

'Sure. You can go,' Ben said.

In the cot, the baby began to yell.

Ben thought: I must go to my father's grave.

Colin looked at him with a certain contempt. After the things he had seen in the war he didn't think much of a man who couldn't see a little blood without blenching. Ben said: 'I'm going out for some air.'

'Good policy,' Colin said heartily. He took Isidore by the arm and led him down the passage to the head of the stairs where Hannah was waiting. She had on her Persian lamb coat and a twenty-guinea hat. Mrs Simons was wearing a purple woollen coat over her print dress and a flowery straw hat with a veil. 'Where's my Ben?' she asked anxiously.

'Sick,' Isidore said.

'He went the other way – for some air,' Colin informed Mrs Simons. He looked at his watch. 'Well, I must be getting back. Tessa's waiting.'

'How's your – little girl, isn't it?' Mrs Simons asked.

'She's very well, thank you.'

Colin hesitated about kissing Mrs Simons, decided to kiss no one and backed away with 'Well – er – cheerio. Be seeing you' and went double-step jumping down the stairs.

'Well, what was it like?' Tessa demanded, when he got home.

'Oh, pretty straightforward, you know. Our Communist friend was a bit queasy, poor chap.'

'How were your folks?'

'Father was pretty glum until Ben felt sick. That cheered him up though. Look, I thought we might go down to the club for tea. Ted and Bunty'll probably be down there. Thought it might make a bit of a change for you. Get out of the house.'

'All right, Colin.'

Ted Bradshaw's murderous desires had not outlasted the withdrawal of British forces from Palestine and like those whose opinions he so accurately reflected, he regarded the new state of Israel with a certain respect, particularly since her defeat of the Arabs. He had not hesitated to propose Colin for full membership of the club (up till recently he had only been a five-day member) though he did say that there might be a bit of trouble in committee. But the violent anti-Semitism of the Palestine days had passed and so had that animosity which had led the militants to echo Ted's opinion that all Jews should be shot. The committee men no more remembered it than they did their decision never to watch Chelsea again, which was taken every Saturday evening and broken every following Saturday afternoon. Besides, the rebuilding fund needed every penny they could raise. The clubhouse had been hit by a flying bomb in 1944. The members were making do with three Nissen huts. The wretched government wouldn't give a licence for rebuilding, but the committee hoped that once the Conservatives were returned, things would be restored to their previous order.

Now that he was a full member, Colin was much more one of the boys; he could make up a four on Sunday mornings and drink a glass of ale with the others before sprinting home for lunch. The company might be a bit bluff for some tastes, but Colin enjoyed being with Major

Roberts and Ted Bradshaw and the others in the comfortable camaraderie of the club, where people respected each other's privacy and dealt with one another in a genial, ribbing manner. You didn't clash with other members because, generally speaking, you shared their views. If you wanted to belong to Southfields Common you knew a wog was a wog and always would be, you knew that homosexuals (nancies) were filth, you knew that young hooligans ought to be flogged and that hanging wasn't bad enough for murderers. You thought Bevan was a red menace and that anyway the Socialists weren't much better than the Communists. You thought it was time the workers woke up and realized that the war was over and conditions had changed and you thought that the reason British athletes weren't any good was that they hadn't been able to eat enough steaks. Conformity with one's fellows passed for intimacy with them. Colin used the same plastic tees as Ted and he copied the major's swing. If he played bridge he played the same bang-bang bridge as the other members played and despised, as he assumed they did, Marcus Isaacs' professional (i.e. money-grubbing) expertise. This conformity was perfect for Colin. He blushed less, he ceased to crack his knuckles, he was easy, for he knew that nothing extraordinary would be demanded of him so long as he was indistinct, he was accepted.

That afternoon was the first on which Colin had brought Tessa down with the baby and he was rather proud of the number of members who came over specially to say good afternoon and have a peek at Anne asleep in her pram. They were sitting in front of the derelict clubhouse where the members and their wives could still take a sheltered tea and watch the players approach the eighteenth green.

'Nice, isn't it?' Colin said.

'Lovely. It's a sweet little club, isn't it, Colin? Not at all like Daddy's.'

'Very few Jews,' Colin whispered.

A man and his wife approached from the road. As soon as she saw the pram, the wife came hurrying up. She was a very pretty woman; in her middle thirties, Tessa guessed, though she might have been even younger. 'Oh, do let me see him,' she cried, bending down to look at the baby.

'Her,' Tessa said.

'Isn't she adorable? Oh, Nat, do come and look.'

Her husband was not much taller than she. He wore a sports jacket and grey flannels, with a flat cap. His thick greying hair was brushed straight back from his low forehead. His face was somewhat swarthy, with full lips which he seemed deliberately to compress and a flattened nose, the nostrils forced apart to accommodate the fallen bridge. He came on without hurrying, blowing out his lips slightly. His wife said: 'My husband's a doctor. I'm afraid he doesn't get very excited about babies.'

'Oh, really?' Tessa said.

'Is anyone sitting here?'

'No, do,' Colin said.

'I suppose we'd better do some introductions,' said the man. 'My name is Riesman, Nat Riesman, and this is my wife, Alma.'

'Colin and Tessa Adler. Oh and Anne, of course.'

'How do you do?' said everyone.

'I don't think I've seen you down here before, Doctor.'

'No, I only come at week-ends occasionally.'

'Oh, that would explain it. I used to be a five-day member.'

'You might have seen my boy down here. He plays a bit during the holidays.'

'Oh, really? How old is he?'

'Nearly eighteen,' Alma Riesman said.

'It's not possible,' Tessa exclaimed. 'You can't have a son that old.'

'I have though,' replied the other woman with a wide smile.

'You must have had him when you were very young,' Colin said.

'Twenty.'

'But you can't be – '

'Aren't they sweet?' Alma Riesman said.

'Is he the only one?' Tessa inquired.

'Yes,' Alma replied, 'the only one.'

As the conversation proceeded they learnt that they were near neighbours, for the Riesmans lived in Monmouth Court, the big block of flats on the Parkside. It was only right that an invitation to cocktails should first be offered by the older couple, but when Colin and Tessa pointed out that they could not leave Anne on her own ('Not just yet awhile!' laughed Alma), it was agreed that the Riesmans should visit the Adlers first. A date was fixed. 'Do bring your son if he's at home,' Tessa said.

'He won't be back for a few weeks yet,' the doctor said.

'Poor poppet,' said his mother.

'Doesn't he like school?'

'Not much.'

'Where is he?'

'Benedict's,' Dr Riesman said. 'He does like it actually.'

'Very good school,' Tessa approved.

'What are their colours?' Colin asked curiously.

'Pink and blue.'

'I think I've seen your son, a tallish chap with black hair.'

'Sounds like him.'

'Saw him on the bus one Saturday morning going shopping.'

'What a wonderful memory you must have!' Mrs Riesman said.

'Some things stick in one's mind, don't you find that?'

Isidore Adler said: 'Going out with your goy-friend again?'
He simpered at Hannah. 'She hasn't got a boy-friend, she's
got a goy-friend. You gonna marry your goy-friend?'

Julia picked up the *Jewish Chronicle* and glanced with
disdain at the middle pages.

'Rose Mendoza's engaged,' observed her mother.

'What the hell do I care?' Julia threw down the paper
and slammed out. Hannah looked puzzled.

'She hasn't got a boy-friend – ' Isidore began again.

'Oh, stop it,' Hannah said. 'Can't you see you've upset
her?'

'My house,' Isidore muttered. 'She uses the place like it
was a hotel.'

Julia was not sorry to finish college. She said good-bye
to the Principal (who had once rather hoped that Julia
would pursue an academic career) with relief rather than
with regret. It meant she could devote herself entirely to
life. And life included Andrew Peregrine. Andrew had
glided from Oxford into what he called 'the big wide world'
across an easy bridge of sporting and social events. Julia
saw him often in the weeks after the Commem, and always
there were dances and midnight car rides. She went to the
Marlow Regatta and saw him stroke his college to victory
in the Challenge Shield. Their relations were easy and full
of laughter. Julia found each outing as good as the last. If it
was also much the same as the last, Julia was not bored. It
was with a slight shock that after a few months, as that easy
summer ended, she realized that she was falling back into
the pattern of life she had followed during the period
before she went to college. She was sheltered by her
father's money, she had most things she wanted, but she
was dependent on forces outside herself; she took no

decisions, she had no vital purpose. Andrew did not want her and only her; his friends liked her only for public aspects of herself. Andrew kissed her frequently and introduced her to hundreds of people; he was willing to share her as he shared himself. Julia felt that even if she were married to him there would be no great change in their relationship. Life with Andrew would be loads of fun: you would never be short of week-ends in Sussex, cocktail parties in Chelsea, friends, friends, friends and mutually satisfactory sexual relations. Did she love him? Well, didn't everyone? He defied you not to be captivated by him, and how could you resist when he demanded nothing more of you than to find him a good type? In the meanwhile, life was fun. It seemed it could go on for ever, until one day he called to say: 'Well, my love, I've got a job, start Monday.'

'Good God! The end of an era. Well, come on: what?'

'Oh, it's something to do with beer, I think; suits me. I'm not sure what exactly. My old man's arranged it all. Anyway, that's not the point.'

'What is the point?'

'The point is let's go and celebrate.'

'Lovely.'

'All right, lovely, it's a date. Pick you up at six-thirty.'

They went to 96. Andrew was very handsome in his dinner jacket. Julia wore a new black evening dress which was very tight over the hips and made her small breasts stand pertly forward. Andrew insisted that they drink champagne. It might have been an anniversary. Indeed a woman at the next table glanced at Julia's hand for a wedding ring. They looked such a handsome couple.

Afterwards he took her back to Montague Square, where his father kept a small flat. 'The old man's gone back to the country for the week-end,' he told her, 'so we shan't be disturbed.'

'Tactful parents you've got,' Julia said.

'Like some eggs and bacon?'

'No thanks.'

'Coffee?'

'Not particularly.'

He kissed her. They sat down on the divan and he kissed her again. Julia closed her eyes contentedly and put her arms round his neck. His hand came up under her bare arm and his fingers explored her shaved armpit. She half opened her eyes and groaned. One hand came to rest on her shoulder and the fingers splayed down into the top of her dress, the other pushed the dress back over her knee.

She was almost as surprised as he was when she slapped his face.

He said: 'Christ, Julia, I – I'm sorry.'

She looked sheepish too and said: 'It's late. I think I'd better go.'

In Woburn Road he said again: 'I'm sorry, Julia.'

'I shouldn't worry about it,' she said. 'It was only Neil made me do it.'

'Neil? Who's Neil?'

She put her hand on his arm. 'It was a lovely evening. Really.'

She did not expect him to call her again, but he did, and because she certainly bore him no ill-will, she went out with him. She might have guessed, it occurred to her later, that he would take her out again, for he could hardly allow their association to end before he had convinced himself that the old Peregrine smile had not lost its magic. He was the sort of person who would always stay friends with his ex-lovers, for he was really more at ease as friend than as lover. He made no further effort to seduce Julia. Friends detected no change in their relationship, but Julia knew that both of them were waiting for what next might come along. 'Honestly, ducks, you ought to go to bed with him,' Slinky said. 'I would.'

'Then you're a bloody fool,' Julia quoted.

'That was quite different. Alyson wasn't in love with that Anthony man. Anyway, he was very mundane.'

'What makes you think I'm in love with Andrew?'

'If you're not you ought to have your head examined, among other things.'

'I haven't got time, Slinky, thanks all the same. I'm starting a secretarial course on Monday.'

'God,' Slinky said, 'poor you!'

Andrew was the first to go. He met a French girl called Moue. He made no secret of her existence. Andrew had never hidden his taste for gay women, though his C. of E. background (he sang in his village choir in Sussex) still influenced him strongly enough for him to believe that you could only think of marrying a woman who wouldn't without. After all, marriage wasn't the sort of thing you'd dream of going in for with someone you knew at all well. Even when their meetings grew infrequent, Andrew sometimes thought he might still marry Julia; the farther apart they drifted, the more he fancied the idea of ringing her up and saying, 'Look, I've chucked old Moue back in the Seine – marry me on Monday and we'll fly to Bandol for a couple of weeks' honeymoon.' It was the kind of gesture he would be delighted to make and no girl worth her salt would spoil the fun by turning it down. Andrew didn't believe in this 'only girl for me' stuff; all the girls were for him and to offer marriage to one of them was just one of those things one did, at a certain age, at a certain time, in certain circumstances, just as after a Commem one said 'Come on, let's all go and have breakfast at Lyons Corner House' because it was a dashing, right-for-the-occasion sort of thing to do. That was why Julia found him such a wonderful companion; if he suggested a mad expedition he wasn't satisfied until it had been carried out, he carried you along with his enthusiasm. If he had phoned and said 'Come on, let's get married' Julia probably would have accepted. But he hadn't by the time she met Paul Riesman.

Colin and Tessa had Dr and Mrs Riesman in to coffee and biscuits. There had been speculation on both sides whether the other couple was Jewish. Plainly the Riesmans were convinced of it, for Alma soon said how pleasant it was to meet some really nice people of one's own kind. 'Nat and I have an absolute horror or what we call the typical North London Jews. I expect you feel the same, or you wouldn't have come out this way.'

'One doesn't want to be labelled,' Colin agreed.

'I just can't bear North London,' Alma said.

'You don't find there are many Jews round here then?' Colin asked.

'We haven't found it until recently,' Alma said. 'But then I expect they've called on you too –'

'They? Who?'

'You mean they haven't? My dear, the Committee.'

'They're trying to found a synagogue out here,' Nat explained. 'And they've formed a Committee to see what kind of support they can get.'

'They haven't called on us,' Tessa said.

'What are they like?' Colin inquired.

'My dear, caricatures, bless their hearts. They arrived one Sunday morning – what was it, three weeks ago? – anyway, I just had an old pair of slacks on and Nat was in his gardening shirt. That's a family joke! Well, anyway, we agreed to go to a ghastly sort of bunfight. Of course a synagogue is the last thing we want out here. I mean you know what happens: the brethren simply arrive in their coachloads.'

'Jaguar-loads,' Colin said.

'Who's organizing it all?' Tessa asked.

'The chairman's rather a poppet,' Alma replied. 'A little

man called Marcus Isaacs. My dear, wouldn't he just have to be?'

'He plays golf down at the club.'

'Quite right,' Nat said. 'Nice enough little chap.'

'I expect he plays in his homburg hat, doesn't he?'

'I used to play cricket in a homburg hat,' Nat said.

'Nat, you didn't.'

'Only when I was in Homburg.'

Tessa said: 'Do you think they'll succeed?'

'Succeed?' Alma shaped her lips in a smile.

'In forming a synagogue.'

'Oh, that, I really don't know. And I really don't care. I'm afraid we're not very regular attenders, but we do already belong to one synagogue and I wouldn't like to change now.'

'Which is that?'

'The Liberals,' Nat said.

Alma said: 'By the way, are you members of the local association?'

'Local assocation?'

'The Conservative Association,' Alma said, with a recruiting smile. 'Always assuming you *are* Conservatives, of course.'

Colin said: 'Oh yes, we – '

'I expect you two would be young enough for the YCs,' Alma said. 'Young Conservatives, you know – '

'Not me,' Colin said, touching the balding patch at the front of his head.

'They have a wonderful time. Speakers down and dances and everything.'

'I expect your son's a keen member, isn't he?'

'My son,' Nat Riesman said, 'is a Socialist.'

'Very natural at his age,' Colin offered.

'It's unnatural at any age. I thought going to a public school would knock it out of him. As it is, I'm only sorry he's not fit enough to go in the Army.'

'What's wrong with him?'

'Oh, he had rheumatic fever when he was young. Didn't do any real damage, thank God, but it's left his heart a little suspect, you know.'

'What does he want to be?' Tessa asked.

'He's going to be a barrister,' Nat said.

'It's rather sweet! At the moment he wants to be a writer.'

'Well, I only wish he'd write home a bit more often for a start. We're lucky if we get a letter once in three weeks.'

'Is he going to university?' Colin inquired.

'He's having a trial run at Cambridge in December. I'd like him to go to Oxford, of course.'

'Nat was at Brasenose.'

'Were you up?' Nat asked.

'No. The war.'

'Ah, yes,' Alma said, 'the unlucky generation!'

When their guests had gone, Colin said: 'Nice people.'

'Awfully nice, weren't they?'

'You'd never think they were Jewish though really, would you?'

'No,' Tessa said. 'You wouldn't really, would you?'

5

The Southfields Common Golf Club gave a spring dance that year for the reconstruction fund. After the government's shaky survival of the general election, the committee hoped that rebuilding might soon begin. It was Nat Riesman's idea that he and Alma and Paul should make up a party with the Adlers, Colin's that Julia should be Paul's partner. Julia's secretarial course was very dull and her evenings were empty. She found an invitation, no matter how unpromising, difficult to reject. Slinky had gone to

Paris to teach and Julia was faced either with the contemporary version of 'the gang' or with staying at home with Hannah and Isidore; neither was quite the consummation of three years in college that she would have wished for herself. She took her emerald dress in a suitcase to Oakfern Drive.

'This must be your sister,' Bunty exclaimed when Julia came in.

'No, Colin's,' Tessa said. 'This is Mrs Bradshaw from next door. She's baby-sitting for us tonight.'

'But she's so like you, my dear!'

'Well, we're both dark, I suppose. I don't think we're alike, do you, Julia?'

'You can never see when people are like you, can you?' Julia said. 'Where do you want me to go?'

'Use the little back room,' Tessa said. 'I think that's the easiest really.'

Julia went upstairs gloomily. Changing in other people's houses was always a miserable start to an evening, particularly when she was changing into the same dress she had worn at the Commem. Oh what a fool she had been about Andrew! No, she had been right; if now she was frustrated, it was less that she missed Andrew especially than that she was severed from any lively company amongst whom her own vitality could be released. She was confined by the trivial pot in which her roots were gripped. She changed her clothes, going a bit goosey with the chill in the unused room. How trivial one's body was when it wasn't being used for anything! But there it was, that was all there was to oneself; one couldn't get out of it. One had to value it, for one couldn't hope to experience things without affecting oneself. Experience was change. Slinky was not still Brenda Blair plus the extra experience of all the men she had slept with; she was a different Brenda Blair. Slinky had changed her life, not because virginity was itself something but because she herself had *been* something and was no longer.

A disappointed woman says her piece to the make-up mirror, Julia smiled wryly. These moods did no one any good. It was only when nothing was happening that one indulged in them. One was like a word lying fallow in a dictionary, a dead word in a dictionary waiting for someone to pick it up and give it meaning by giving it use. One could be trivial or important according to the place one was given. One's value depended on one's context as well as on oneself, though it was true that intrinsically some words were better than others. The hope with Neil King was that he would be left without use. Sometimes you found in the dictionary the name of an obscure torture and its description and you thought to yourself, please God, never again. To Julia, Neil King was such a name. She had been right to drop him. So far, she regretted nothing. But she was bored.

The Riesmans' flat was on the second floor and faced on to the quadrangle of Monmouth Court. Alma was in the bay window looking out for them when Colin, Tessa, and Julia approached. She waved to them and turned to talk to someone in the room. No one else came to the window.

Nat and Alma welcomed them at the door. Nat was wearing a single-breasted dinner jacket with a boiled shirt. He looked very handsome.

'Colin, Tessa,' Alma said, 'come in. And you must be Julia. How are you?'

Julia put out her hand firmly. 'How do you do?'

Paul Riesman appeared in the door of the sitting-room. Julia and Paul looked at each other.

Alma said: 'Did Bunty turn up all right?'

'We wouldn't be here otherwise,' Tessa said.

'We were worried sick.'

'Oh, you shouldn't have worried, Mummy,' Paul said. 'Not about anything as important as that.' He did not take his eyes from Julia, so that the remark, at which Colin and Tessa laughed uncertainly, seemed intended in some way to define his relation to the others, not so much to amuse them as to inform Julia. Paul came forward and took her hand. 'How do you do?'

'How do you do?' Julia said and shook hands very formally, with a frowning smile on her face, her head on one side.

Alma said: 'What about a drink before we go?'

They went into the sitting-room; Paul was last with Julia. He was really rather nice-looking, tall, slim, dark-haired, his face barely past the fullness of adolescence, the cheeks round and red.

Paul whispered: 'I'm afraid this is going to be ghastly.'

Julia said: 'I don't think so at all.'

'Paul,' Alma said. 'Bring your guest in here. I expect you'd like a drink, wouldn't you, Julia?'

'No thank you,' Julia said.

'Paul?'

'No thanks.'

'Not a sherry?'

'Nothing, thanks.' Paul frowned.

Colin sat in the easy chair by the fireplace. 'Lovely flat you've got,' he observed. 'I never come here without thinking how nice it is.'

'We like it,' Alma said.

'There's a lot to be said for a modern block,' Nat said. 'Of course when I was in general practice we had to have a house, but now I'm glad to say that isn't true any more.'

'These flats are about as modern,' Paul said, 'as the Maginot Line.'

Alma said: 'What do you think of them, Mr Adler – ?'

'Very nice,' Colin said. 'And do call me Colin, by the way.'

Paul said: 'What do you think of Monmouth Court, Julia?'

Julia said: 'This is a jolly nice room, that's all I've seen.'

202

'Tactful girl,' Alma said. 'Paul, you might sweeten – er – Mr Adler's drink.'

'No more for me,' Colin said.

'As the man said on the first tee "I'm driving".'

Colin said: 'Um, what time do things start happening?'

'What things?' Nat asked, with a twitch of the lips.

'"We see life in the raw at our Golf Club,"' Paul quoted to Julia.

'Who's that? Maugham?'

Paul leaned forward. 'How did you know that?'

'I heard it on the wireless.'

Paul said: 'That's right. The other evening, *For Services Rendered*.'

'He's very cynical, isn't he, Somerset Maugham?' Alma said. 'I always think that's so defeatist.'

'It's always defeatist to be right,' Paul said.

'Clever boy,' his mother said.

Tessa said: 'The trouble with Maugham is that he likes to hurt people. You can see it in everything he writes.'

'I do so agree,' Alma said.

'You'd never think he'd been a doctor, would you?'

Paul was sitting back in his chair, his lips pressed together, his hands clenched in his lap. He looked round the room irritably. He caught Julia's eye. They both winked imperceptibly and glanced apart. Alma was saying: 'I really think we ought to be going before they've eaten all the sausage rolls!' She rose and motioned graciously with her hands for the others to rise too. 'I don't know whether you feel like powdering your noses.'

'We have to be careful of our noses, don't we?' Nat said to Julia.

'Why?' Julia demanded.

Nat said: 'We have to be careful about them.'

'Why?'

Alma said: 'Nat, you might get the car round.'

Nat gave Julia a look and hurried to get his coat. Paul was smiling, almost incredulously.

In the car Alma said: 'I hope there aren't too many drunks.'

Tessa said: 'Is it likely?'

Alma said: 'They can be rather a common crowd.'

'It is the Southfields *Common* Golf Club,' her husband reminded them.

The Nissen huts were decorated with bunting and coloured lights. Strings of lights illuminated the front of the clubhouse too, and tables and chairs had been set out there. A buffet, with plenty of chickens and cold roasts, was laid in the bridge room. (Ted Bradshaw had been in charge of the catering.) 'They've done it all *rather* well,' Alma said in a tone of indulgent surprise.

'Let's go and dance,' Paul said to Julia.

'Must leave my coat somewhere.'

'Better put it in the car,' Nat said. 'Don't want to leave it around.'

'Can't you trust the servants?' Colin asked, wondering if Nat had some secret information.

'Can't trust the members. Lot of Christians in the club, you know.'

Julia said: 'What about that dance?'

Paul touched her arm and they hurried away. On the floor he said: 'God, isn't this grim?'

'Thanks, pal.'

'Not you,' he said. 'I didn't mean you. I mean the whole thing.'

Julia said: 'Do you know many people here?'

'Not a soul,' Paul said.

'Don't you play golf?'

'Not with anyone else.'

'Why not?'

'Hate the bloody game.'

'Why play then?'

'Nothing else to do.'

'We'll have to do something about you.'

'Someone will,' he said. 'But I don't envy them the job. I do not envy them it one little bit.'

'What are you doing with yourself?'

'I beg your pardon?'

Julia frowned. He seemed like his father then. She said: 'Have you got a job or what?'

'I'm working on the local newspaper,' he said. 'I'm going up to Cambridge in October. It's all a mistake really. It's only because they gave me a schol. I never wanted to go to Cambridge. I meant to go to Oxford. My whole life's a series of mistakes as a matter of fact. I've never done one thing I wanted to do. Not one.'

Julia said: 'What do you want to do?'

'I want to be a writer,' he said, and made a face. 'Where've I heard *that* one before?'

'Have you written anything?'

'Nothing good,' he said.

'I'd love to see something.'

'I'm no good,' he said. 'You wouldn't like it if you saw it.' The band started to play a waltz. Paul said: 'Oh, Christ, I can't do this.'

'I bet you can.'

'You ask my father,' Paul said. 'He tried to teach me.'

Julia said: 'I have no intention of asking your father anything.'

Towards midnight, Colin and Tessa had to leave. 'Don't you come though, if you don't want to,' Tessa said to Julia.

'Do stay,' Paul said.

Julia said: 'I really ought to be getting home.'

Tessa said: 'You can have the spare room if you like.'

Julia stayed. She and Paul walked away from the club-house down the eighteenth fairway. There was a couple in one of the bunkers. Major Roberts loomed out of the darkness with a bottle in his hand. 'This lil piggy went wee-wee-wee,' he said and staggered past them. Paul and Julia wandered through the wet grass down to the edge of the lake. 'You have to drive over this to get to the seventeenth,' he told her. 'It's probably absolutely full of balls.'

'Don't they fish them out?'

'Yes, a little man goes out in a boat, but I don't suppose he gets them all. There're about three hundred of mine in there for a start.'

In the clubhouse they were singing 'Auld Lang Syne'.

Julia said: 'Perhaps your folks are looking for you.'

'Let them look,' he said. 'They've had me for long enough.'

Julia said: 'You know I've never done this before. Gone out with someone I've never met.'

'I can imagine what hell it must be.'

'It hasn't been hell at all.'

'Julia –'

'What?'

'My God, Julia, I can't stand much more of this.'

'Of what?'

'These people. This place. That ghastly singing. I can't stand much more of it. If you knew how bloody lonely it is in this dump.'

'You've got Cambridge coming,' she said. 'That'll make a difference.'

'I wish there was one thing I could really do. Just one thing.'

'Can you do ducks and drakes?'

'You've hit it! That's the one thing I bloody well *can* do.' He picked up a flat stone and threw it at the surface of the water. It plunked straight in, never bouncing once. He turned to her and grinned. 'Just look at that. Now how'm I going to earn my living?'

Dr Riesman appeared in the door of the clubhouse.

'There's Dad,' Paul said. 'He must be wanting to go home.'

'I don't know how you can see that far.'

'Where my father's concerned I'm telepathic.' He held up his arms. 'Shall we dance?' They did a few mock steps across the fairway and then ran, hand in hand, back towards Nat.

Nat and Alma waited in the car while Paul saw Julia up the path to the front door of 'Ravensnook'.

Paul said: 'Well – '

'It's been – ' Julia hesitated, tilting her head and smiling.

'It's mattered to me,' Paul said. 'Whatever it's been to you. It's really mattered to me.'

'It's mattered to me, Paul,' she said. 'It's mattered to me too.'

At home, Alma said: 'She's a nice girl, isn't she, Paul?'

'Yes.'

'Are you going to see her again?'

'I don't know. I might.'

Alma said: 'Of course she's older than you are.'

'What does that matter?'

'It's simply a fact,' Alma said. 'I never said it mattered.'

Paul said: 'You don't have to worry. I shan't ever see her again.'

'We only want your happiness, dear.'

'You're welcome to it,' Paul said.

Capital Matters

1

'HULLO. SUSAN? It's me, love, Ethel.'

'*Ethel*. I didn't recognize your voice.' What the hell did Ethel want? Susan hadn't seen Sid in ages, not alone.

'Have you seen the *Worker* this morning?'

'I glanced at it,' Susan said.

'You've seen about the lynch mobs, though?'

'No.'

'And Ben's cartoon?'

'Not yet.'

'I'm surprised at you, Susan, not looking at your own hubby's cartoon.'

Susan said: 'Ever had a new baby on your hands, Ethel, love?'

'Jefferson's been arrested,' Ethel Forbes said. 'It's a frame-up.'

'Jefferson? Who's Jefferson when he's at home?'

'Susan, surely you remember? Jefferson Andrews. He came to your election party in '45.'

And sat with you on the front step. 'Yes, I remember now,' Susan said. 'Well, what's happened? Has *he* been lynched?'

'The mobs are out,' Ethel said. 'He was arrested two days ago, accused of raping a white woman. It's all in the *Worker*. I'm surprised you haven't seen it.'

'Ethel, do you mind, dear?'

'I want to put a resolution to the meeting tomorrow night. You will be there, won't you?'

'I wasn't going to be,' Susan said.

'I do think this is an occasion when the women ought to do something. I do hope you'll back me up.'

'What does Sid think?'

'Oh, Sid agrees.'

'Then there shouldn't be too much trouble, should there? Look, Ethel love, I must dash. I've got the milk on the stove.'

Later Susan looked at the *Worker*. Ben's cartoon showed a coloured man in a cell with two huge gun-toting troopers leering in at him and the caption: 'YOU'LL HAVE A FAIR TRIAL AND YOU'LL BE FAIRLY FOUND GUILTY, SO SHUT UP!' The story on the front page had a two-column cross-head: LYNCH MOBS OUT AGAIN. Susan lit a Woodbine and sat down to read while the nappies boiled on the stove.

Lynch mobs surrounded the jailhouse in Boanoke, Florida, USA, last night. They were demanding to be allowed to 'string up the b – y nigger bastard!' Jefferson Andrews, 26, is being held in the jail on a framed charge of rape. White police arrested him after a call from Mrs Sally May Newton, wife of the local undertaker. She said Andrews had been loitering around her house for some weeks. Said her husband: 'I'm getting that bastard's coffin ready right now.'

An all-white lynch jury will 'try' the case in front of ex-Ku-Klux-Klansman Judge Theo Walsh. Tonight a prominent local man said: 'We'll handle this our way. If the jury don't get the nigger bastard, we will.'

All Negroes are locking their doors today. White mobs last night invaded the shanty town where many of the Negroes live. One white-haired Negro is in hospital with a fractured skull. He may face charges of inciting a riot. Jefferson Andrews, a member of the NAACP, is a veteran of the Second World War and won the purple heart and the European star. He was employed as a dishwasher at a local diner (dining-room).

There was a picture of Andrews, bracketed between two state troopers, being frog-marched up the jailhouse steps. Inset was the yelling face of a man.

Susan read it all through again, dragging on her cigarette. She knew she ought to feel disgust, she knew she should be convinced that it was a frame-up, but she felt neither nausea nor conviction. 'Why should it be a frame-up? Why must it be a frame-up?'

'It's pretty obvious, isn't it, Susan?' Ben said when he same home. 'He was having an affair with this woman and when he gave her up she turned round and accused him of raping her.'

'You always think about men giving women up,' Susan said. 'Why shouldn't she have given him up? Or refused to give in to him? How can you be so *sure*?'

'By looking at the simple and historical facts. This supposed lust for white women is a prejudice deliberately encouraged to create solidarity among white people. You unite the workers with the capitalist classes instead of with the Negroes who are their natural class allies and so create artificial antagonisms within the working class. You get exactly the same thing with anti-Semitism. And of course Zionism too. The Jewish capitalist class cause a cleavage between the Jewish and the Gentile proletariat by advocating a national solution to an economic problem.'

Susan said: 'What do you think about Stalin and the Jews?'

'Stalin and the Jews?'

'I mean the way he seems to be getting rid of all the Jews in the government.'

'That's not true, Susan. I've – '

'Got the figures on this actually,' Susan supplied the

words. 'But Ben, surely it's true that there aren't as many Jews among the senior ministers as there used to be?'

Ben said: 'You can't have places reserved for Jews, Susan, just because they're Jews. This isn't a synagogue they're running. You can't look at every question in a selfish way. You've got to try and see it in its historical perspective.'

'What've we got but our own lives?' Susan said. 'What the hell does history matter? We only live once.'

'We're not that old,' Ben said.

'I feel it sometimes. We just go on and on and we don't get anywhere. Look at Sid, he's doing all right.'

'Sid tries harder than most people – '

'Oh yes,' Susan said, 'Sid tries all right.'

Ben said: 'The party's the only thing I've got, Susan.'

She said: 'You've got me. Aren't I something?'

Ben said: 'And what can come of that?'

'You don't love me,' she said.

'Susan, Susan,' Ben said and rolled his chin on his chest.

'I should be enough,' she cried. 'I *should*.'

'It won't do like that, it won't. We belong to society, we grow with the society we live in. Sooner or later you have to eat, you have to turn on the light, you have to face society and you've got to do more than just face it, you've got to face your responsibility for it. I won't admit my responsibility for something I don't agree with, and that's why I want a Socialist state in the whole world, so that I can really belong to it. We've got to set things true.'

'What does that mean?'

'Capitalist society is founded on anachronisms and misconceptions and injustices and they're reflected in our own relations with other people. You say I don't love you, but that's not true, it's not enough of the story. This romantic nonsense, it's all lies, Susie, it won't *do*. What we've got to do is make a true society, founded on scientific principles, we've got to true it up, like a carpenter does, and then see why the dishes slide off. Do you see what I mean?'

'No,' Susan said.

'The clearest reason why a small thing happens is given by the biggest rule,' Ben said. 'You've only got to think of the apple falling on Newton's head. If he'd been happy to say "It was ripe" or "It was time it fell" or something like that, we'd never have had the law of gravity. It's because some people see that there must be a big reason for a little event that the world goes forward at all. It's no use saying I don't love you –'

'Oh, don't go on about that,' Susan said.

'Let me finish, Susan. It's no use unless you're prepared to wonder whether you're wanting something you've got a right to want, scientifically. Why is society so keen on marriage?'

'Children, I suppose.'

'It's not the most economical way of producing children, is it?'

'You think everything's got to be economical,' Susan said.

'You don't listen, Susie,' Ben cried. 'You just don't listen at all. It's like bashing your head against a wall, trying to explain things to you.'

'Look who's talking,' Susan said.

2

On the platform at St Pancras Town Hall were Francis Winter, the publisher, Canon Edward Hopkins, Bill Bonson, the Dalston bus driver, Professor B. H. Tibbett, professor of Russian history at the University of Hull, Lord Brentor, the jazz-loving peer, Cora Walsh, the poetess and Ethel Forbes, 'the Bethnal Green schoolteacher, who was,' as the *Daily Worker* said, 'the moving spirit of the Save

Jefferson Andrews Appeal Fund.' Ethel was wearing a scarf tied over her head. 'She looks just like one of your proletarian women, darling,' Susan whispered as she and Ben took their seats in the hall.

Ben said: 'Seems pretty crowded.' He waved to someone a few seats away from them. 'Wotcher boy, how goes it?'

'Bloody good cartoon today, Ben.'

'Like it?'

'Spot on.'

'Who's that?'

'Bryan Ward.'

'Is he on the paper?'

'No,' Ben said. 'He's on *Picture Post*, as a matter of fact.'

'You might have introduced us.'

Canon Hopkins said: 'Ladies and gentlemen, I have some telegrams here I should like to read to you. The first one reads: 'GOD BLESS YOU AND YOUR WORK' and it is signed by that great singer, that great American, that great *Negro* – '

The hall was filled with cheering. The people on the platform clapped, solemn-faced. The meeting had begun.

When Ethel came forward to speak, Susan turned her head away and felt for her cigarettes. The dumpy figure on the platform lowered her eyes modestly. 'I'm just an ordinary Cockney housewife,' Ethel began, 'and a school-teacher, but I'm also a human being.' Ethel stopped and the audience hesitated and then laughed. Ethel smiled shyly and continued: 'I've never taken part in anything like this before. Not from up here, anyway.' Laughter and applause greeted this. 'And I don't mind telling you, I'm very nervous. But tonight I have a special reason for speaking to you, my friends. You see, I am privileged to have known someone we all have in our hearts tonight. Yes, I'm proud to say that Jefferson Andrews was my friend.' Canon Hopkins led the applause sternly. 'Ladies and gentlemen, of all the gentle, decent, upright people I have ever met, Jefferson Andrews was one of those who most deeply impressed me. Schoolteachers aren't always noted for their high opinions of others – but I can assure you that I thought very highly of Jefferson Andrews. Everyone who met him felt the same. I wish he was here tonight, because I know you would share my opinion. But he is not. Because he has been framed and put in jail on a false charge, and why? Because he was proud of his race and wanted to see its advancement, because he believed that it had a right to equality and because the country which calls itself the Home of the Free, denied him that equality. That is the true reason for his arrest, ladies and gentlemen, and not because he raped the local whore!' Loud cheers and shouts filled the hall. Susan blew her nose. Ben clapped his hands low behind the seat in front of him, staring fixedly at Ethel. 'Ladies and gentlemen, no one can deny the Negro his true place in society, but that is what the lynch mobs are trying to do, and in trying to do it they have framed one of the best, one of the most pure men it has ever been my privilege to know.'

Everyone in the hall and on the platform was clapping. Francis Winter went and shook Ethel's hand and whispered earnestly to her.

'Good stuff,' Ben said.

Susan blew smoke through her nostrils. Everyone was crowding round Ethel to congratulate her. Ben was going down to her. But Susan was unconvinced. She could not feel anything clearly except the irrelevance and irksomeness of other people's emotional energy when it was not directed to herself. Ethel was a dumpy lump. How could one rejoice in her success? How could one say that it was right that she should attract all that applause? If only love were the calculus, where would Ethel be then? Susan pushed her way towards the exit.

Otto Kahane was standing in the gangway at the back. Susan averted her face and struggled past. What right had he got to be there? She didn't want to know. She wanted to live. She wanted to live.

Otto Kahane was standing there in the darkness at the back of the hall.

Susan stood in the street, thrusting about in the empty darkness for what she should do. In effect, as she knew, she was waiting for Ben. To have met Jefferson Andrews in one's own house, surely that was enough to make one feel his innocence? Susan nibbled her knuckle. No, you could believe in the innocence of a name or the guilt of a name: The Martyrs or The Imperialist Agents. The Jews. But when you met people, when you had observed them in a moment of life, when you had seen the innocent Negro with his tongue in his schoolteacher eulogist's mouth, what did it mean to say 'Guilty' or 'Innocent'? How could you deny your whole knowledge of life, all the life there was in you and congratulate Ethel Forbes? Susan wanted Jefferson Andrews to have raped Mrs whatever-her-name-was. She wanted people to be real and her own feelings to be true, her own feelings of the Negro at Stan Halloran's jazz club, her own feelings of the tightness in his crutch when he danced against her. What did it mean to make this picture of a man, this picture of a Negro, pure, Bible-reading, decent? It was a picture of no one. It was denying him the right to do precisely what they were all asserting they wanted him to do: stand erect. It was all a false cheapness of life, this clenched fist in the proletarian dawn, shoulder to shoulder and smiling together, when the truth of life lay in the dance of a man and a woman. Oh, Ben could argue her round, Ben could satisfy every external point, rub everything to satisfaction till she could scream at his expertise. But satisfaction like that was a kind of death, a quick killing. She wanted to be bigger than that, more difficult. How wonderful it would be for a courtship to take so long that it wasn't consummated till death, how wonderful if sex were something so big, so worthwhile, that it involved all one's life, if to have sex were to die, and one were to go on wanting it! What an exquisite dance one would have then, what glides, what feints, what rituals, what retreats, what advances! Then one's lover would be serious for all his life, about one thing. As one died one's child would be born and unfolding it would find its partner and dance in its turn till it died. She wanted Jefferson Andrews to be guilty, for the sake of the seriousness of her own life.

3

Jefferson Andrews was convicted of rape and sentenced to death. Susan read the news in the evening paper and reeled with the sickness of it, felt that impotence of movement she had last experienced in the park when the RAF man took her for a tart. The exultation she had gained from her conviction of Andrews's guilt slumped away from her as she sensed the perversity of the straps which would bind him, of the simple act of sitting which would bring death. The perverse sexuality of this ritual of killing and being killed lamed her with its publicity.

Andrews's lawyer applied for a stay of execution. Indignation grew, as if men felt that to protest and win now would be to reverse the flow of time; hatred of the inevitable, of their own mortality, rallied men and reassured them of the innocence of the convict. 'To be against history is the privilege of free men,' Sid had once quoted sardonically. Susan sensed that her eagerness that Andrews should be reprieved was not born of loyalty for the Party, but was a kind of treachery. Ben said: 'I'm going to this eve of execution rally. Don't suppose you want to come, do you?'

'Try and stop me,' Susan said.

'The text of the telegram, ladies and gentlemen,' shouted

Canon Hopkins, 'is as follows. If you approve I propose to send it by the Transatlantic Cablegram. It reads: "HARRY S TRUMAN THE WHITE HOUSE WASHINGTON DC USA HALT JUDICIAL MURDER IN FLORIDA STOP MAY GOD FORGIVE YOU IF YOU FAIL TO SAVE AN INNOCENT MAN STOP SAVE JEFFERSON ANDREWS STOP SIGNED – LONDONERS." Now – '

The cheers of approval, in which Ben joined loudly, drowned any further speech. The collecting trays came round. The mounds of silver grew. A note or two was pegged under a spill of coins. 'Seems to be an expensive cable,' Susan observed.

'They had to hire the hall,' Ben pointed out.

'It doesn't matter to the Party whether Andrews lives or dies, does it?'

'Oh, yes,' Ben said, 'it matters.'

'He's got to do one or the other, I suppose, is that it?'

'Part of it,' Ben said.

The conversation was choked by the Canon banging an ashtray on the baize-covered table in front of him. 'Ladies and gentlemen – '

'Comrades,' shouted someone, to a burst of laughter and clapping.

Canon Hopkins smiled coyly. 'Comrades,' he said. 'I know that all of us here tonight are here for the same reason – ' Susan glanced at Ben, who was staring intently at the speaker ' – whether as Christians or as Socialists, or even, ahem, as both. For I for one do not believe that the two things are incompatible – ' Sid Forbes, on the platform, began to clap and the others joined in.

'I believe that we are all united by the love of our fellow men and that all of us share the same feelings of horror at what is due to take place tomorrow morning in an American jailhouse.' A piece of paper was handed to the Canon. He read, nodded and handed it back. 'Ladies and gentlemen, you will be, I know, interested and heartened to hear that the Council of Trades Unions of the Union of Soviet

Socialist Republics has just sent a telegram to the President of the United States to the same effect as the one which we, here tonight, have agreed to send. And now – '

'To the American Embassy,' Ben shouted out.

'To the American Embassy,' shouted someone else.

'Come on,' Ben said to Susan.

'To the American Embassy,' they both said together.

'Friends – ' shouted the Canon. 'Friends, I must ask you to make any demonstrations as quiet as possible. The police – the police have asked for our cooperation in this matter – ' there was much laughter ' – to prevent disturbing people who live near by.'

'They need disturbing.'

'I suggest that we proceed, in a quiet and dignified manner, to the embassy and sit there in silent vigil, till morning. I shall have to ask anyone who makes an unseemly noise to go away.'

The procession formed up outside. Bill Bonson marched along the line, calling out: 'Have your visas and passports ready, please, you are about to enter American territory. I thank you.'

They paraded through the silent and incurious West End, led by an impassive inspector. At the head of the column, Ethel Forbes marched with a SAVE JEFFERSON ANDREWS placard.

'We can't stay long,' Susan said, as the procession broke up and crowded against the locked doors of the American Embassy. From an upstairs window someone took a quick look at the press and ducked inside again.

Ben said: 'Quite a good turnout.'

Susan said: 'I honestly think we ought to get home. Your mum – '

A voice said: 'Not off already, you rogues, are you?'

'Stan!'

'I shall have to change me disguise,' Stan Halloran said.

'I thought this beard hid me face but they all recognize me just the same.'

'I didn't see you at the meeting. Did you see Stan at the meeting?'

'I was bashing the old trumpet there; only just managed to get away.'

'Still at the same place, are you?' Ben asked.

'Oh no, matey, laddy, boy, no, no, no. I've gorn orl varry posheroo, boy. The Ninety Naughties Club, no less.'

'Cor,' Ben said.

'Cor and double cor, actually, me boy. Wait till you see the place: double beds all round the walls and red plush waiters to match.'

Ben said: 'What're you doing here, Stan? Come to pick up a few bob entertaining the troops?'

'Crap off,' Stan Halloran said. 'Jeff was my friend, and still is, I hope, the poor bastard.'

'Do you think there's any hope?' Susan asked.

'I've been inside, love. I know what it bloody feels like when some poor bugger's waitin' to be topped. Bleedin' creepin' Jesus, God forgive me, just look at that sod.' Stan gestured to Canon Hopkins who, Bible in hand, was sunk in prayer on the pavement. 'I don't know, maybe the Governor'll come ridin' in on his white horse with the President's reprieve in his mouth, I don't know. God help all poor bloody sailors on a night like this.'

Canon Hopkins said: 'My friend, I must ask you –'

'Piss off, your worship,' Stan Halloran said. 'And the top of the milk to you, too.'

Softly, a deep voice began to sing:

> 'I'm dead already,
> Doubt I ever lived,
> I'm dead already,
> Because my skin is black.'

'Oh, sod that,' Stan Halloran said, 'sod all that pitying crap. Give 'im the good ship Venus and let's send him off with a laugh at the bleedin' world.'

'Still an anarchist, are you, Stan?'

'West Kilburn born and bred and ashamed of it,' Stan replied.

'Nothing in the world but individuals, eh?'

Stan said: 'If you really think all individual behaviour is the fault of systems, then you've got to believe that to improve the system you can ignore individuals. By the time you've got the perfect bloody system you've got no indibloodyviduals.'

'Luckily we haven't got a world full of Hallorans to deal with,' Ben said.

'Contempt for the hindividual conscience, Mr Simons, that's your grahatest fault.'

'It's not contempt for the individual conscience that worries you, Stanley, it's contempt for the individual Stanley.'

'Put not your trust in manifestos,' Stan Halloran said, 'nor in the sons of manifestos for that way you end up in front of a people's democratic firing squad. Which reminds me, Benjamino, when the big day comes and the old red Marias are doing the rounds, remember your old chums.'

'You ought to know the Party never forgets its old friends,' Ben said.

Stan said: 'Ben, when are you going to leave the Party?'

'I'm not leaving the Party,' Ben said. 'What do you mean?'

'You're turning into a killer, Benjamino, that's your trouble. You're turning into a killer.'

Ben said: 'Coming, Susan?' He took Susan's arm and turned away.

As they went to bed, Susan said: 'You don't like Stan any more, do you?'

''Course I like him.'

'You don't trust him though, do you?'

'How can you trust someone like that? There's nothing to trust. He doesn't understand loyalty.'

'He's got loyalty to himself.'

'That's the worst kind of disloyalty,' Ben said. 'You can't trust a bloke like that. The trouble with Stan is he's not modest enough. If you want to change the world, you got to submit. The trouble with people like Stan is they never submit.'

'No team spirit,' Susan said.

'You don't care about the Party, do you?'

'I give enough time to it,' Susan said.

'No,' Ben said, 'no.'

'You try bringing up two kids,' Susan said.

'You won't submit,' Ben said.

'Submit? What do you mean?'

'You're vain, like Stan.'

'Steady, old boy, if I were you.'

'You hide things, Susan.'

'I hide things! I hide things!' Susan was shaking. There was a childish game: you take one thing off and I'll take one thing off. She played it with a little boy when the family was down at Saunton one summer before the war. They went into an empty beach-hut. They played solemnly, examining each other closely after each garment, even a sock. The little boy turned out to be wearing one thing more than Susan. When she stood naked, with the buds of her breasts standing out, the boy still had his pants on. She was naked and he had revealed nothing vital. 'It's not fair,' she cried, 'it's not fair.' So he pulled off his pants, but his nakedness was not like hers, she had no compensation from it for her own. Later, when Hannah would say, 'It's the woman who takes all the risks,' Susan agreed deeply, while Julia was merely irritated. If only there were symmetry between people, if only the same thing meant the same thing for everyone; in Ben she had found a man who seemed to believe in the same equality she did. For a while then Communism had assuaged an emotional fear, had fixed the balance between her and Ben. But things had changed. Lately there had been a night when Ben caressed only her left breast, till it grew, swelled, took on all her sexuality, till her right breast ached and ached for his touch, dumb, blind in the darkness. There was no symmetry then; he did things to her. She had no knowledge to match his deliberate knowledge of her; it was like going to bed with a priest. To kill his command of her, she must kill his God; she must find the killing place in him, she must, before she was quite defeated, kill his faith, the confidence that clothed his nakedness and let him look at her but closed her view of him. She shivered. She would be a virgin again, so that she might naturally refuse him; she quested for some new defence that she might plant in herself but which, once planted, would be beyond her control, a self-willed cancer which no confession, no cry of pain could purge, since it would have a life of its own within her. For the moment she made herself repel him, but to be safe she longed for a natural revulsion, that she might be armed against him, so that, though he scoured her mind with questions and emptied her body with final pleasure, he could never satisfy her.

BOOK TWO

The One and the Many

ONE

The Middle Way

1

DR NATHANIEL RIESMAN met Alma Black at a JPA dance given at the Empress Rooms in May 1928. It was not the kind of function to which Nat was accustomed to go, but his father's employer, Mr Adolphe Hyams, was a patron of the Appeal and pressed a ticket upon him. It was the kind of function to which Alma was accustomed to go, for her mother, Lily, missed no opportunity of presenting her to the view of potential husbands. There was, she told Alma, no figure so tragic as the pretty girl who had waited too long. Alma was nineteen. By twenty, her mother would suggest, the moment would be past. At twenty-one, spinsterhood began. The very word sent, as it was intended to do, a shiver down Alma's spine. For all her prettiness, Alma was hurried and unsure of herself, hurried because time was so short, unsure because for all her obvious beauty she doubted her ability to ensnare the right man before it was too late. She was a chilly flirt in the eyes of the rich, rather common young men who were her most persistent escorts; she broke their hearts, it seemed, vainly and without regret. How could they know that it was desperate agitation not feline cruelty which led her to play with them as she did? Lily, to be sure, encouraged a more deliberate attitude. In her view, men were there to be teased, poor creatures. They must give everything and in return the pretty girl was theirs, but first they must give and only everything was enough. Passion was no substitute for security. She drove her daughter from dance to dance, from man to man, deriding anyone whom Alma liked, yet reproving her in the same breath for not yet having found anyone. At one moment Alma was the princess whose feet the young men were not worthy to kiss, at the next she was a fading Cinderella, who must find a man before it was too late. So Lily drove her from dance to dance.

Mr Black's part in this was purely ancillary: he merely provided the money which dressed Alma (and Lily), which sent her (and Lily) to all the best balls and which provided her (and Lily) with whatever equipment was necessary for their hunting expeditions, whether in Nice, Le Touquet, or Burnham Beeches. Mr Black bore these and other burdens with glum patience. He was a short, round-shouldered man (who could none the less lift a full bale of cotton dresses above his head) with a loose, wet mouth and a dejected manner. When speaking of him in Alma's presence, Lily always called him 'your father', a use of the possessive which suggested that Mr Black was more Alma's responsibility than hers. Mr Black was a curiosity to Alma, a peculiar adjunct to the household, an oddly exalted and yet contemptible servant whose presence was accepted but whose choice in the first place remained surprising. In fact, he had not been chosen: he had been arranged. When she decided that such and such a boy was nothing like good enough for her Alma, Lily was exercising a right of selection she herself had never been permitted. She had been delivered to Mr Black at eighteen and violated on her wedding night with a ruthlessness which was the fruit of a terror on both sides that soon stiffened into hatred, as both partners realized what they had been let in for. After a year, feeling that she had earned her life's pension, Lily moved into her own room. From that day forward, she said good night to her husband in the sitting-room and never saw him till, fully dressed, they sat down to breakfast the next morning. Mr Black came to enjoy the expert caresses of a lady whose card he saw in a newsagent's window in the Edgware Road. The card did not long remain on display, for Mr Black secured a sole interest in the lady's business, which he transacted with her, according to his exact specifications, three times a week on the way home from the warehouse.

Nat was older than most of the young men in whose company Alma usually found herself and for whom Lily had so often advertised her contempt; his confident maturity commended him to both the women, for Alma saw in his dark good looks a version of man agreeably different from the glossy juvenility from which her choice had been limited, while Lily had come to that stage where she saw in her own marriage an ideal for her daughter, a contract whereby youth was surrendered to age and acquired security. It seemed to her now that her kind of existence was the only existence possible. She imposed upon her daughter a language of life which once she could not have spoken without a shudder. The terrified girl had become the suave madam. She watched Alma dance with Nat and was pleased to observe how well they were matched. Her pleasure was increased when inquiries revealed that the young man (for he was not more than thirty) had been at Clifton and Brasenose and had lately qualified as a doctor. Here at last was an occasion when her smile could be genuine as Alma and her partner came off the floor. Here at last was an occasion when Alma's smiles and giggles need not be quenched. Here at last was an occasion when Lily herself could unleash a little charm, at least until further inquiries had been made.

Nat was old enough and experienced enough to be indifferent to the machinations of Alma's mother. He took Alma firmly in his arms and if Lily wanted to believe that she had pushed her there, it was not his concern. Alma too had found some courage, and she had determined to marry Nat long before her mother endorsed the selection. It was

Nat's mother, if anyone, who opoosed the match. She had not cared very much for Lily ('Rather a Jewish *looking* woman, dear' was her comment) and regarded the prospect of a synagogue wedding with singular revulsion. That she herself had been born Miss Victoria Roth did not affect the disgust with which she suffered all things Jewish. This disdain quite put Lily on the defensive and she passed Nat with the unseemly haste of an examiner who finds herself suddenly subject to examination. She skated quickly over the doubtful merits of Mr Riesman's occupation (chief assistant to Mr Adolphe Hyams, manufacturing chemist of Wigmore St, W1) and consoled herself with his son's profession. As she observed when informing Mr Black of the disposal of his daughter, 'No one ever heard of a doctor starving yet.'

In spite of Mrs Black's confidence, however, the young Riesmans did not have an easy time during the first years of their marriage, for lack of capital prevented Nat's buying a practice. They trekked from locum to locum. It was during one of them, at Westcliff-on-Sea, that Alma became pregnant. By the time Paul was born, they had moved to London where Nat had a humiliating job as medical officer to the Christian Life Insurance Company. They lived in a furnished place in Bayswater ('I should call it Holland Park, dear,' Nat's mother advised).

No great improvement occurred in their circumstances until Alma's father died. Alma was left £4,500. Among the other bequests was one of £5,000 to Miss Cora Johnson of 33, George Street, Paddington. 'He thought more of his whore than he did of his own daughter,' Lily commented. 'And what I'm supposed to do on six hundred a year I just do not know. I think it's disgusting when one's devoted one's whole life to someone to be treated no better than a servant.' She took a small service flat in Abbey Road and played sixpenny bridge.

Now that what Alma would call 'the lean years' were

over, the Riesmans bought a Morris Cowley and Nat took up golf. Soon he was offered a partnership in a practice in the new suburb of Bromsden, a sprawl of speculative housing between Wimbledon and Cheam. In this neighbourhood, where everyone was a newcomer, Dr Riesman found himself looked up to as one of the few integrating influences. At one time it was even suggested that he might stand for Parliament (as a Liberal), while Alma was much in demand on local committees. That they were Jewish was scarcely noticed – Nat's partner, Dr Skelton, was not – and they hardly noticed it themselves; if they did, it was not without regret, for it was the only thing which distinguished them from their neighbours, the only thing which prevented them from being completely at home, the only thing which, should it be openly bandied about, might endanger the agreeable social situation they enjoyed. To Alma, to be reminded of one's religion (as she never failed to call it) was to be reminded of that North London marriage market from which she had so narrowly escaped and of the hairy apes who frequented it. Jewishness was a dirty thing, confused with a picture of her father, Mr Black, lying on the blonde tart whom she had met during the probate proceedings over the will. Above all, what Alma liked about Bromsden was its cleanness. There was nothing black about it. Nat liked it too and felt no urge to possess Jewish friends or live among Jews. His mother had from his earliest childhood spoken of Jewishness with so British a scorn that Nat himself found her ridiculous disdain to be a part of his own vocabulary. What he mocked in her existed in him. Nat had ceased to believe in God during his time in the trenches and his medical studies confirmed him in his atheism; he felt neither spiritual nor social yearning for the faith of his fathers. Had it not been that Mr Riesman was a sedulous member of the Bayswater Synagogue ('Or should we say Holland Park?' Nat used to joke), Nat would probably never have gone at all, but as it was, he used occasionally to accompany that mild and gentle man because it pleased him. Jewishness was an affliction which his honest love for his father obliged him to declare but which nothing could make him enjoy. Not only was the community in which Paul was brought up not Jewish but nor was the family, for Nat's family was so starred with unique individuals that the concept of Jewishness was far from adequate, or even appropriate, to cover their extraordinary diversity; they were the sort of people whom he visited on Sunday afternoons in huge, musty flats and who emerged, each more aged and more strange than the next, from a background of ponderous Victoriana. The family never acknowledged its Jewishness except at funerals and weddings; hence its dislike of both. Paul saw little of Alma's family, except for Lily, who sometimes had them to tea. Neither Nat nor Alma had any brothers or sisters and so they were isolated by age no less than by place from any vivid relationship within their own families. Paul grew up with the feeling that his parents were the only other Jews in the world. His school holidays were passed in a vacuum of blanched discreetness, cycling down avenues and crescents of 1934 houses, past the light engineering works and the toy factory on the fringes of Morden and back through the mustardy terraces of South Wimbledon. He learned not to allude, at least in Bromsden company, to being Jewish. It was nothing to be proud of, as Clifton and Oxford were and as his preparatory school, Faversham Mount, came to be.

To this school Paul was sent in 1939, when it still occupied its manorial premises near East Grinstead. But no sooner had he arrived than it was evacuated to a small hotel near Ilfracombe from which it did not return until Paul's last term. By this time the boy knew Latin and Greek to an excellent standard, could do trigonometry according to the book (Durrell) and was able to write five lines under any historical heading from the Heights of

Abraham to Magna Carta; further, he could complete an almost endless tally of English clichés and he had memorized the first lines of a mêlée of famous poems and essays, for example, 'Houses are built to be lived in not to be looked at', all of which he was instructed to incorporate in his English essay when he came to take his Benedict's scholarship. In divinity he had learnt who went into the burning fiery furnace (one mark for each name and an extra one if you got them in the right order) and who killed Christ. He was top of the first form and Nat was very proud of him. He always took his cap off when he was talking to a lady, and never picked his nose when anyone could see him. He was, the headmaster said, 'a very nice, clever boy'.

2

Reading the Bible in a Sunday silence period some weeks after he had won his Benedict's scholarship, Paul held up the book to the headmaster.

'Please, sir, what are whoredoms?'

Mr Curtis, the headmaster, donned turtle-rimmed spectacles to investigate the test. 'Oh, um, they're much like adultery.'

'Oh yes, sir,' Paul said, 'I remember now.'

He remembered walking one day on Bromsden Common with a friend who was at Dartmouth (where Paul at that time did want to go because they wore naval officers' caps). They had seen some pictures stuck on the barbed wire which enclosed a disused anti-aircraft gunsite. Paul was eleven and his companion, Martin Atkinson, was fifteen. The photographs were the size of postcards which the boys began eagerly to collect before they had looked at what was depicted on them. They crawled under the wire to the gravel entrenchment in the middle of the site and sat down

231

to go through the pictures. Paul looked at one. Martin grabbed it, blushed livid and announced 'We must destroy these immediately' in a voice not so much his own as imitated from authority. Paul tried to see them clearly as Martin, in a sweat of shame, crumpled the photographs together, so Paul had a jumbled view of hair and phalluses and buttocks, and upon their owners' faces smiles of a glazed strangeness such as he had never seen on any face before, nor yet imagined there. None of the figures were naked, but their genitals protruded from their disarranged clothing as growths that could no longer be concealed might burst through their dressings. By this time, having hardly glimpsed two figures bridged by a phallus, with a cruel, sad, loving smiler looking on, Paul had let Martin take his lighter from his pocket and curl his knowledge into quick brown ash. Straight he longed to snatch that knowledge from the fire, sensing its rareness, but in front of Martin, so proper in his uniform, was restrained, in part by the other's seeming assumption that Paul already knew what the photographs revealed (since they had exchanged dirty words in a dazzle of confidence) and in part by that mortifying Bromsden mystique which made even the bath a marbled peculiarity, a known place, because only in that steamy privacy could one stand naked.

Paul came back often to that place where the wire sang in the wind till, rusted, it snapped and curled back, like red ash, to leave the pit available to lovers. Once he found a rubber slug there and a tongue of silver paper, as if the orgiasts had come to leave another puzzling clue. Eventually he gave up the place. When Alma asked him why he did not go and play on the common any more, he could only reply that it was not nice out there. Alma was reminded of her char, Mrs Battersby, who, walking home late one night, cut across the common and in a clearing saw a lady almost as fat as herself standing by a tree. Mrs Battersby hesitated a minute, thinking the woman might be ill, but the other sang out to her 'Get off my bloody pitch', at which Mrs Battersby, shocked (not knowing such things went on in Bromsden) and affronted (being taken for a tart), made off as fast as she might, not, as she told Mrs Riesman, knowing where to put herself. Alma was tinklingly amused and had retailed the story frequently ('Isn't it sweet?') at afternoon bridge and Tory teas, where it had been a great success. What a joke it was that anyone should suspect the amorphous Mrs B. of having sex! Mrs Battersby's husband had died of tetanus after stepping on a rusty nail at work. His death was so contorted that the doctors would not allow Mrs Battersby in to see him, even after he was dead. Paul had not been told these things about Mrs B., nor did he tell his mother of the photographs he had instantly glimpsed. Detached his knowledge was and abstruse, compartmentalized; like those five lines he could write about the Heights of Abraham, it bore no relation to anything else he knew. His mind was honeycombed with pockets of knowledge, but no glimmer of a language of life was there to make them into a single intelligence. Bromsden was like a tomb (not least because many of the children were still evacuated) and Paul's life was a solitary one. He had the confidence of his parents' love, but he was denied vivid contact with others; everything seemed either in the unreachable past (like history, which had no part of the present, despite the war) or in the unapproachable future (like sex of which he knew but in which he could not believe, since no one around him seemed to do it, though whispers and nudges and 'stories' gave Bromsden adults a spurious community) so that for Paul the present was a strange centre, silent in a raging world, wherein to be a good boy was all that really mattered. He turned to books to find life. He went through volume after volume with sick speed, hoping to find within them a knowledge which being simultaneously experience, could help him mesh with life. The books spoke to him in a cold voice, but with a certain precision, whereas Nat and Alma, speaking to him in the language of love, could only embarrass, since their explanations of life were so full of exhortation to virtue that life itself was obscured with the rash of values placed upon it. Paul found nothing hard in his parents' explanations, nothing around him to come up against and feel oneself really *in*, nothing except the empty streets he cycled through filled with that golden silence which was like his parents' love. He had no roots in the streets he cycled through; when he looked for reality he found it only in the love his parents promised him: from love he came, Alma would tell him, in love he was brought up and to love he would go. Nat was a shy man and left the boy's home education to Alma except for those set occasions on which he felt it his duty to 'talk to Paul'. Then his stiff tone was so formal that it seemed to Paul that his father was carving out the words on some stone tablet rather than speaking directly to him. There was no direct commerce between Paul and his father. The boy had no sense of direction at all.

Oh, how he would have died but for his Jewishness! 'Yid!' a boy whispered at school. It was like the first slap a midwife gives a baby. It goaded him into fretful life, though Paul hated it. 'Why do we have to be Jewish?' he asked his mother.

'Everyone has to have a religion,' Alma replied.

'Is being Jewish a religion?'

'Of course it is. You see, we don't believe that Jesus was the son of God, that's the only difference.'

Alma had no use for religion; it was truly for her one of those things one had to have, like a refrigerator, because it made things so much simpler: one knew where one was. She did not pretend that Judaism was what she would have chosen exactly, but it had been passed on to her and one had to find space for it. Liberal Judaism was the obviously suitable model, since it was trim and unobtrusive and looked British; its doctrine was 'sensible' and its dictates few: it suited those who felt they had to be something but did not really want to be anything. To Paul Jewishness was an irrelevant thing of which you had to be proud, as people were that their parents were street cleaners though they had no intention of sweeping the streets themselves. Nat endorsed this, for if one didn't believe in God or live in a Jewish community, what possible value was there in stubborn professions of faith? It was only when his father died that a certain change came over Nat. Suddenly one evening Paul was called into the front room and found his father sitting there with a prayer book in his hand. 'It's *Rosh Hashana*,' he announced severely. 'And I'm going to read some prayers.' Paul sat down and his father read out the prayers in a rapt mumble which the child, darkly watchful, heard as mere grunts and raspings in the throat. The next year Paul waited for the same thing, but nothing happened till *Pesach* when Nat gruffly informed them that they should not eat leavened bread and asked Alma to 'get some *matzo* in the house'. The next year, Paul waited for consistency and was greeted with toast for breakfast and cake for tea. 'Aren't we keeping Passover this year?' he asked Alma.

'We don't ever keep it,' she replied. 'Those things were all very well for a primitive tribe, but they aren't part of our religion.'

'Did you keep Passover at home?'

'Grandpa liked to,' Alma said. 'But Granny and I used to creep out and have tomato sandwiches for tea.'

'Weren't you ever orthodox?'

'We never had bacon for breakfast.'

'You don't much like bacon, do you?'

'Not unless it's crisp,' Alma said.

The day before he was due to go to Benedict's was a set occasion. Nat called him in. He said: 'Sit down.' Paul did, in anguish, having so much in loving common with his father which this formality destroyed, longing to cry out that he knew all that Nat was to say and that for him to say it was to destroy still more the natural common manhood between them. But Nat would warn him of older boys and to beware of any too close friendships and always to wash his genitals after sexual contact with women (as though it were a brothel not a public school he was to attend). Paul saw the sweat glistening on his father's forehead, under the straight grey hairline and ached for the man to stop. But Nat went on, made him who had never held a girl's hand shameful with useless knowledge. That night Paul dreamed that his penis was a bready roll which he could tear off and throw away and Jewishness with it. Without either he would be totally free.

TWO

The Fifth Form at Benedict's

1

PAUL'S FIRST term at Benedict's was delightful. There was
so much freedom. Friends seemed so easy to make –
Connaught, Williams, Harper, he knew their names in the
first day and they played together in Yearlings, the first-
year football team. He nicknamed one of the others 'Podge'
and the name stuck. There seemed no division between
him and the others; the only difference was in cleverness,
and there all the advantage was on his side. Some of them
seemed pretty 'dim', but he was indiscriminate in his
friendships. He took care that none of them got 'too close'.

One evening, one of his friends, Podge it was actually,
asked Paul if he was coming to Late Evening Service. Paul
hesitated. Then he said: 'All right.' Podge smiled and said
he and Marino were just on their way. Paul attended daily
chapel and saw no reason why he shouldn't go in the
evening too. It was fun to walk through the darkened
buildings to the Little Chapel where the services were
held. Several of them went from Mr Walker's house and it
seemed to form a bond between them. Paul liked singing
the hymns and the little electric organ piped in an evocative way. There was a slight smell of incense. Once he
started going on a Friday night he found it hard to duck
out; it might have looked funny.

The Friday Evening Service sermon was noted for its
'frankness'. It was felt that those who attended were
'serious about religion'. So the chaplain, Mr Trotter, talked

about sex. The 'frankness' of words like masturbation (uttered with much working of the Adam's apple) was sweetened with notions of service and dedication. The genitals became something sacred but not yet to be used, like that part of one's ration book which read: 'Do nothing with this space until further notice.'

One day during his second term Paul was walking back alone from the Scout Hut, where the younger boys learned to tie knots and light fires with not more than two matches, when he heard footsteps behind him. A lance-corporal in the Corps caught up with him and put a hand on his sleeve. 'Riesman, isn't it?'

'Yes.'

'My name is Newman. We ought to get to know each other.'

Paul noticed a rim of moustache on the boy's upper lip. He said: 'Look, I've got to brace.'

Newman said: 'How do you like going to chapel?'

Paul flushed and looked anxiously behind him. There was no one there. He replied: 'I don't mind it. Why?'

'You're a Yiddisher boy, aren't you?' grinned the other.

'Discovered,' Paul said lightly, turning in at the gate of Mr Walker's house. He was shaking. By what secret right had the other approached him? How had he given himself away? Why must he be nailed to his Jewishness? He thought of Podge, who kept a list of those who masturbated. However careful you might be, there was nothing you could do to escape detection.

Dr Riesman said: 'The secretary from the Synagogue phoned about your confirmation.'

'Confirmation?'

'I expect you'll meet some nice young people,' Alma said. 'There might be some pretty girls.'

'I believe there's going to be a dance,' Nat said.

'Daddy and I met at a dance.'

Paul said: 'I know.'

Nat said: 'Should be quite fun.'

'The classes should be very interesting,' Alma said. 'Rabbi Silverberg is a brilliant man.'

Paul had no argument against his parents. He could not tell them of the insincerity he sensed in them. He went to the classes. He went and learned more paragraphs of five lines suitable for exams. He went to the synagogue, he answered questions, repeated prayers, ate buns and drank tea, wrapped his Benedictine scarf round his throat and left again. But not one word he said was spoken in the language of his own person. Every part of life now was an examination, a formal test, like the scholarship to Benedict's which he had to go through to please his parents. No sooner had one hurdle been cleared than another went up; childhood was not life but an incoherent jumble of torments with no abiding logic to give them order or sense. The accepted order was the order, but why it was neither wit nor feeling could reveal.

The confirmation classes were continued during the term, by correspondence. The envelopes arrived on Saturday mornings. They were franked 'STUDENT'S EXERCISE'. When the letter fag handed Paul the first lesson, he was terrified lest next time it might be handed to the wrong person or that someone, noticing him stuffing it into his pocket, might ask why he did not open his mail at breakfast like everyone else. From then on he rose early on Saturdays before the first bell, and crept over to the housemaster's side to subtract the guilty buff envelope from the morning's mail. Then he crept back down the stairs to the boys' side, fearful of meeting the letter fag who, jealous of his servility, might report his irregular behaviour. He never even opened the envelopes, but locked them up till, on empty afternoons, he could take them down to the town and drop them, shredded, in a dustbin.

So his father would say: 'I had a letter from Rabbi

239

Silverberg. He's worried about your exercises. He doesn't seem to have received them.'

Paul said: 'I posted them.'

'I think you had better go and explain to him personally. You'll get an opportunity at the holiday classes.'

'Got a lot of work to do this hols.'

'You must allocate so much time to each task until it's done.'

Paul closed his eyes.

His father said: 'How's the reading going?'

'All right. When I have time.'

'Do take that sullen look off your face, old son. There's a good chap.'

2

At the beginning of the next term Paul forgot to take back his ration book.

Mr Walker, the housemaster, said: 'On several occasions I have in fact asked you to write to your parents for it, and on none of them have you in point of actual fact done so.' Mr Walker pursed his lips and crabbed his chalky fingers over the snowstorm paperweight on his desk.

'Well, you see, sir, I – '

'I will give you one more chance.' The housemaster plunked the snowstorm down on a pile of sixth-form history papers, and the plum-dark eyes in the white face came up to Paul's, which glared down at him. 'Really, you know,' he said, 'this is such a trivial matter, I have no wish to do anything further about it.' He smiled. 'Do write.' Paul glared at him.

A week later, Mr Walker was saying: 'Riesman, I still don't seem in point of fact to have received your ration book.'

'No, sir.'

'Have you in fact written for it?'

Paul said: 'No, sir.'

'Great heavens, you're not a stupid boy. It's not beyond your competence to ask your parents for your ration book, surely?'

'No, sir.'

'Then why have you not done so?'

'I don't know, sir.'

Mr Walker took his snuff box from his waistcoat pocket and tapped snuff on to the bridge of his thumb. He knit his brows. 'You'll have to be punished,' he said.

'Oh, yes,' Paul said.

'You'll dig in the house market garden for three hours every afternoon until further notice.' He sniffed fiercely. The cuffs of his nostrils were transparent as melting wax.

'Does that,' asked Paul, 'include the Lord's day?'

'Sundays are of course not included. Now you'd better go and phone your parents and get them to send that ration book.'

There was only one telephone in the school for the boys' use. It was in the school porter's lodge. Paul climbed up the eighty-nine steps from the quarry where Mr Walker's house stood to the road which led across to the main school buildings. The eighty-nine steps were quite a climb, and when you first arrived at Mr Walker's you thought you would never reach the top without your lungs bursting. New boys allowed a good ten minutes to get up to school. Now, in his third term, Paul could do it in four. The record was three minutes fifty seconds, by Connaught, including a leak in the downstairs bog, verified by the vigilant Podge.

'Hullo there,' Mac, the porter, grinned. 'What can I do for you?'

Paul smiled back: 'I want to make a phone call,' and burst into tears.

'Hey noo, what's all this?' Mac, in his neat blue uniform

emerged and stood out in the roadway. On the first-eleven ground, Big Green, a rattle of clapping could be heard.

'Got to phone,' Paul sobbed.

'Benedictines don't cry, you know.'

' – n't mean to.'

'Come on, noo, what's the number you're wanting?' Mac put a hand on Paul's arm and squeezed. Paul said: 'Parkside 2019. I'll get it.'

Alma said: 'Paul! Are you all right?'

'Yes, Mummy, I'm all right.'

'Is something wrong?'

'No, not really, I – I just haven't got my ration book.'

'Didn't I give it to you to take?'

'No, you didn't.'

'Oh dear, does that mean you haven't been getting enough to eat? I'll send it right away. How stupid of me!'

'It's all right,' Paul said.

'I'll go right now and post it.'

'No hurry.' Mac was standing by the open lodge door.

'Are you all right, darling?'

'Fine. I'm OK. If you could just send –'

'Of course I will. I'm *so* sorry. Do tell matron.'

'It's nothing to do with the hag,' Paul said. 'Well, good-bye, Mummy.'

He was short with his mother; Mac standing there killed the natural affection in him. Every emotion but coldness was unmanly.

Mac said: 'OK.?'

'Yes, thanks.' Paul walked off briskly, Mac smiling up the road after him. Some Walkerites were coming up the hill from the swimming baths, scarved with towels, hands in pockets. They had a clean closeness which made Paul feel an outsider. He blushed fearfully and averted his face. They were talking and smiling; probably, he thought, about him. Did they know about his punishment? None were

242

monitors, but Stewart and Simpson were both quite senior. What did they know about him?

Mr Wilkins, the house gardener, blinked through wire-rimmed spectacles.

Paul said: 'Mr Walker told me to report to you.'

'Report to me?' The man's eyes needled Paul. 'Oh yes. You – you can do some weeding. Between the beans over there.' Mr Wilkins wiped his hands down on his baize apron. 'I'll show you.' They stepped through the vegetables. 'Here.' The man pointed to the weeds which starred the crusty earth. Paul bent down before him and began to pull up the weeds.

For three weeks Paul worked every day in the garden, refusing to play cricket with the excuse that he was 'doing something for the House Man', finding a new shame to be secret with. He knew that his fear that people would ask where he was going was senseless, for the ferocity of the sentence might well have gained him sympathy, but he feared that once open, he would be vulnerable. Simpson and Stewart and the others could be naked with each other but Paul was ashamed of himself, and of everything of him that was true. Only with what was false could he be convincing.

One day, in the junior common room, Simpson, sitting in the place of honour on the big radiator, observed: 'I really don't know what the house is coming to.'

'In what way?' Podge demanded.

'Oh, I don't know. Wogs – and Hebrews.'

Paul was reading a paper.

Podge reddened. 'Hebrews? Who?'

Simpson's eyes gloated round the room. 'Oh – I don't know.' Paul felt the eyes on him. 'Marino mostly.'

Marino rolled his big, hazel eyes. 'Me?' he snorted, with a burst of alarm.

'Me?' mimicked Connaught. 'Me?'

'I'm not a Yid,' Marino said.

Podge, who was in the choir with him, said: 'You are.'

'I'm *not* a Yid,' Marino said.

'You're a roundhead,' Podge said. 'So are Yids.'

Paul read his paper.

'Circumcise ye my people Israel,' intoned Setna. 'That ye may pick them out in a crowd.'

'Yids wet their beds, Marino,' Connaught said. 'Do you?'

Marino started blubbing.

Simpson said: 'Leave him alone.'

Setna said: 'Typical Yid.'

Behind his face of conformity Paul worked feverishly to destroy the truth before it came out, as if by the time they realized he was a Jew he could, by good works, be one no longer. He cut pieces out of the paper which mentioned black market dealings by people with Jewish sounding names: he wanted to destroy the Jews so that no one would ever speak of them again. He covered up feverishly. Even his having to dig the housemaster's garden had to be hidden like a stigma.

Marino said: 'Coming up to school?'

Paul looked at the clock: 'S'pose so.'

As they climbed the eighty-nine steps, Marino said: 'Where do you go in the afternoons?'

'Where the fly buttons go in the winter-time,' Paul replied. 'MYOB.'

Marino glanced down and then the red-rimmed eyes looked conspiratorially at Paul and his mouth dropped open in a complicated smirk. 'I thought I'd dropped sixpence.'

Paul said: 'Come on if you're coming, I can't wait all night. Come on. I've got the Thing.' Mr Thingwall was the fifth-form master. He was never late. 'I can't wait, honestly.'

Marino panted after him. 'No, I say, Reecers – '

'Come *on*, we've got a couple of minutes.' They came past Mac's lodge, and could see the clock on Stinks Block.

'Podge says you go off and play with yourself,' Marino puffed.

'Really? Well he's wrong. What I do in the afternoon is go and hang my sheets in the sun to get the piss stains out of them.' Paul spat the words out at the boy as their ways parted.

Then from across the quad, Marino had the last word: 'Jew.'

3

Paul had to sequester Marino from the others, had to cut him out like a dangerous clipping. That Marino alone had actually said 'Jew' to him made him alone frightening. How could anyone be frightened of Marino, with his honking adenoidal laugh, his weediness at games and his bed-wetting? Yet Paul watched him, and Marino, even when Simpson and Harper were making him pig in the middle while they slung his pencil-box backwards and forwards over his head, could turn and look at Paul with a cringing knowledge, while he shuffled, tearful with laughter, between his two tormentors. Paul waited and offered him a game of ping-pong. Podge was playing with Petersen. Podge took his ping-pong very seriously. He never played without donning his gym shoes. Then he moved with surprising agility; the small white feet seemed hardly a part of the fat body, so tinily did they dance and squeak on the black floor, divorced from the still moon face and the cold blue eyes behind the thick spectacles. Podge won the last slamming rally and handed the bat to Marino with a sliver of a smile. Paul watched anxiously, like one who knows that the man he is following has the knowledge to betray him and may at any moment alert others. To Paul there were no trivialities.

He sought by every quick means to ingratiate himself

with his fellows. Because those about to be beaten earned a sick sympathy from the others, Paul even conspired to be beaten, as an atonement. He enjoyed it, enjoyed making no sound during the ceremony, hoping to earn some of that grudging admiration given to those who go bravely to their deaths. He could imagine the others lying in their beds upstairs, listening to the strokes, rigid with expectation. He treasured the part of the common victim. He made his communion with a stick.

At the beginning of each term he resolved to do nothing which might draw attention to himself: he would not masturbate and he would always play in house games, his loyalty would be above question. If from 'now' he did everything anyone asked, surely all would be well. 'Always remember,' Nat had told him, 'a Jew has to do twice as much to get half as far.' Paul tried, but the question remained: Twice as much what? He had to be twice as unjewish as the next man, that was the real truth. It was hard for a Jew not to be a Jew, that was why you had to work at it. Well, he did work at it: there was never a moment when he was not on guard not to be Jewish. He used a slang that included 'to jew', he used a language that made him a scab. He fought to be false to himself.

Though by the end of his time in the Upper Fifth Paul was five feet nine, he still liked to stand below the monitors and be a small boy again. He broke rules, but the fracture was not complete without the punishment too. He hated the system, but his revolt was meaningless without its notice. For to be noticed was to be accepted. He broke rules – to be naughty – but never conventions. As a bad boy he earned a certain respect which as a good Jew could never be his. As a bad boy, he was accepted and even welcomed by authority, since he enabled it to be authorative, but as a Jew he would merely be rejected. He did what was wrong to hide that he was what was wrong. Yet he knew that sooner or later Podge, who missed nothing, would recognize him as the Jew. Term after term, Marino decoyed their derision but some time it must find its proper target. Why should it be Marino's pencil-box which was flung into the middle of the floor during prep and why was it then Marino, a banana of humiliation, whom the monitor, Stewart, punished? Marino bleated 'Give a chap a chance' and the bright mimics (oh and Paul was one!) picked it up 'Give a chap a chance' – 'Give a chap a chance', till the compliant Stewart grinned and said "ush – simmer' and limped back to his officious desk (having been popularly ballocked in a house match) and sat down and looked across at Podge and said with stern complicity 'On with your work' and chucked back his hair vainly.

Paul observed Marino's victimization with disgusted relief. To groan at Marino ceased to be a thing you did to a person. Marino was not a person, he was a concept. You were anti-Marino not in order to hurt an actual boy but that you might earn a smile from Podge. No one pretended he could help being a Jewy wop, it was just one of those things. And as the terms went by Marino accepted his place more and more, he accepted it in the sag of his smile, the hawk of laughter with which he greeted himself, the servile contortions with which he acknowledged the smallest gesture of friendship. 'Marino tugging his greasy forelock,' Simpson, the Dickensian, called it. The house's animosity towards Marino changed into genial condescension: they had got him where they wanted him. The hardeyed Podge worked with remorseless patience against the pimples which plagued him. He would sit for hours with his trouser leg rolled up, coaxing and pressing a pimple to a head which, with a sigh, he popped. Then he went on to the next. He was an implacable enemy of what was foreign, for he was neither deterred by pain nor sated by pleasure. He was, because he was obsessed by corruption, incorruptible. As soon as he had finished with one trouble-spot, he was looking round for another. Paul knew that he must at all costs avoid clashing with him. He had to avoid clashing directly with anyone. If he attacked anyone it was to establish his solidarity with someone else: with athletes he derided weeds, with intellectuals athletes. He never attacked the present. He pointed out the differences between his contemporaries, so that there might be other distinctions than Jew and Christian, other antagonisms into which the house's venom might be directed. He tried to have something in common with everyone, while destroying what everyone had in common with each other. He imitated the vocabulary and the attitudes of his present companions, whoever they were. His education was in mimicry.

His own integrity was nothing. His cleverness was all he owned. As long as he could stay one of the house, he was safe. Which one was unimportant. To be accepted, that was all. If one spoke enough languages, one could be many, one could be at home anywhere. He aimed to hold the mirror of himself up to others and they could not but like what they saw in it, since it would always be a reflection of them. Even in his work this method was ideal. It was when he was being Cicero that he earned the best marks, not when he intruded his own phrases into his prose. Individuality was no virtue in a Classical education; it was not oneself that one presented but the Ciceronian image reflected in one's own work. The academic and the social obligations of a Benedictine education chimed perfectly together.

Only in his dreams could Paul not escape himself. A dream he had was of a great hotel where escalators surged to upstairs rooms and to corridors where nameless, faceless figures flitted, where doors opened into grey cells full of grey men, iron staircases spiralled down to groined night-clubs where laughter was and a hot obscenity of members. In this vast and joyless dome Paul wandered, believing it was his and yet aware that it was possessed by others. He owned it and dared not enter a room, dared not speak, was as lost in it as if he had never been there, endless though his visits were. He met his own shadow in the long corridors and cried to himself: 'But I own this place. It's mine.'

THREE

The Team Spirit

1

PAUL'S RESULTS in school certificate were rewarded with a Senior Scholarship by the Governors and with a study by Mr Walker. He was a member of 'Hall' now. His privilege was to wear the top two buttons of his jacket undone and to read *Punch* a week before the juniors. Those in Hall were also allowed to stay up late three times a week in order to work. Paul was sometimes able to stay up more often; since he and Simpson, now a monitor, were the only two scholars in the house, Simpson could be persuaded occasionally to miscount in the interests of professional solidarity. Paul relied on this dispensation, for he found himself incapable of doing compositions except at the very last moment. The Thing, who took the Under Sixth for Greek, used to say: 'And, my dear sirs, make sure you let me have it by Wednesday.'

'What time Wednesday, sir?' asked Weigall, who though six feet tall and already a monitor in Mr Easy's house affected, before the Thing, a fag-like devotion. The Thing grinned gummily. 'My dear sir, when I say Wednesday, what should I mean but Wednesday?'

'Yes, sir, but – ' Weigall was almost speechless with subordinate laughter.

'When does Wednesday end, my dear Weigall?'

'Midnight, sir,' Weigall gulped.

'Then midnight let it be, my dear sirs, midnight let it be.' So Paul worked till midnight and then hurried to the

Thing's room. In the moonlight, the Stinks Block clock (donated by OBs to commemorate the Rev. Bond's forty-five years as Fifth Form Master) shone out like something on a provincial town hall. Its big hand lumbered towards midnight. Paul began to run, fearing that the Thing might be sitting in his classroom with his watch out, ready to chide latecomers with, 'I make it Thursday, my dear sir', as legend had it he had once done. The room was empty. Paul slipped his prose into the middle of the pile on the Thing's desk; there was no point in announcing that his was the last. Deceit was natural now. He glanced at Weigall's to see how he had begun: '*οἱ μὲν οὖν Ἀθηναῖοι ταῦτ' ἐποίησαν ἀκονίτι.*' Yes, exactly the same. Good. Paul stood in the darkness of the classroom and there seemed to be generations of Benedictines there, generations who had crept in with their proses and put them on midnight desks, generations all of whom had started with the phrase '*οἱ μὲν οὖν Ἀθηναῖοι*'. Paul smiled to be part of that tradition, to be safely in it, to be growing up to resemble exactly those who had gone before. Yet only that morning he had sat hunched over the *Daily Express* to keep it from the others, from his friends, from Podge, Williams, Setna, Connaught and Harper. On its front page was an item: TERRORISTS SHOOT BRITON.

The house was dark. Only the head monitor was still up. A ruler of light underlined his door. As Paul passed, the door opened. 'Who's that?' the voice shone out.

'Me. Riesman, Stewart.'

'Why are you so late? Monitor's privilege to stay up this late.'

'Working, Stewart.'

'No business to be this late.'

'Sorry, Stewart.' Paul Riesman opened with infinite care the door into senior cubes. It was a long room divided into cubicles by polished pineboards. Paul took off his shoes and padded down to his cube. He could feel the burrs of tiny splinters catching in his socks. He blinded against a partition. It creaked. He found his door. He pushed it. Someone flung a handful of coins on the floor. They clattered and rolled. He couldn't get the door open. A coin rimmed round and round and round ringing on the floor. He barged the door. Laughter began. He smashed past the door. His chair had been put against it. The laughter and more coins rolled out. He felt for his pyjamas under his pillow. He couldn't pull back the counterpane. His locker was on the bed. He lifted it off, sensing the others waiting for the noise. It thumped. More coins fell from it to the floor.

The first voice said: 'Whu's playingk vit his shekels?'

Paul fell for the coins, to kill their dinning.

'Whu's vit his chekels playingk iss?' inquired another. Connaught? Setna? Podge? Williams? Harper? Peterson? *Marino*. No, it was all a mistake. That was it: they had mistaken him for Marino. In the morning they would apologize. Sorry, sir, just a little surprise we were preparing for Fritz. They had meant it for Marino. Paul undressed and got into bed. It was soaked with water. He hoped it was water.

He lay on the cold sheet while the anonymous sniggers scissored above him. Staring upwards he masturbated with an empty frenzy, imagining love.

2

He woke early and saw a grey world: grey trees, grey lawn, grey road, grey houses, grey silence of before dawn, grey cold coming in with the gasps of mist through the open window. He leaned out on his elbows and looked down past the lines of sill-less windows to the ground, where the grey flower-beds were spiked with frost. It must have been meant for Marino. Paul stared down the grey tongue of road. Not a sound disturbed the cubes. Presently Parch, the house butler, rode into sight on his bicycle.

A milk wagon, with the shakes, came up the road. Then came the mail-van. At least *that* didn't come today. But today would come today, though the silence still lasted. Paul leaned out. The face of the house was mottled with warts of lichen. He longed to see his body in the flower-bed at the bottom of the wall, pillowed in the grey soil. He longed to be down there, looking up at the shocked faces coming out like tongues from the upstairs windows. To be dead and watching, that would be perfect; to be dead and conscious.

Below, in junior cubes, the cracked clangour of Parch's bell renewed the day. Paul slipped into bed and lay shivering between cold sheets. The door opened and Parch's bell clanged out. 'Wikey, wikey,' he called, 'rise and shine.'

Paul stayed in bed while the others went down to wash. He waited till the five-minute bell, then he got up quickly and dressed. He stood before the door of his cube and looked up at the ceiling. 'Please, God,' he muttered, and stepped out. Only Marino was in the corridor, spreading urine-glossy sheets. He smirked at Paul. Paul blinked and half-smiled, contemptuous and ingratiating, before hurrying past.

The house lined up either side of the dining-room for adsum. The majority was there already when Paul entered. He went, head down, to his place at the top of the line opposite the serving hatch. Williams, the head of Hall, faced him. Podge, Connaught, Setna, Harper regarded him coldly. Marino came in, tie over collar, and earned a universal 'unnnn.' He stood next to Podge and looked over at Paul and gave a sudden leering bray. Paul stared at the floor, noticing things.

The door of Hall opened and the monitors emerged, led by Stewart. Simpson read adsum: 'Riesman?' 'Sum,' Paul choked the word out. Simpson, in glasses, looked up to see that Paul was really there, as though a friend might have answered for him. A friend!

Afterwards everyone dashed for the serving hatch, behind which Parch was waiting with porridge, scoop in one hand, the other on his hip. When the queue was almost dead, Paul went for porridge. He had to sit on the end of the top table. Williams ate bulkily and gave no room. Paul sat down edgily, murmuring 'Sorry' as he touched the other, apologizing for himself. Williams said: 'Wish some people wouldn't jew in all the time.'

'I say,' Podge said, 'have you heard the one about the man who went to sleep on the steps of a synagogue and woke up in the morning with a heavy jew on him?'

'Jewed funny,' Connaught said. Podge gave a quick laugh in which there was time for a glance at Paul who was feeding himself with heavy porridge. At the top end, the five monitors ate grandly. Between them and Paul was the mass of his enemies, buttering their bread. Yesterday he had sat in the same place, if a little more securely on the bench, and he had thought them his friends.

Connaught said: 'I think it might be jewdicious to make one's bed.'

Harper, a thick-thighed boy whose father was President of the Scunthorpe Trustee Bank, belched loudly and stood up. 'Thank God for my good dinner,' he said in a mock-Lancashire accent, 'that's what my old man always says. Coming, Podge?' he added in a more respectable accent. 'Right ho,' said Podge, bobbing up. Connaught lifted his legs over the bench and looked at his watch. 'I must brace,' he said to Williams. 'You coming up to make a bed?' Why did they need each other so much? What were they going to do to him? Paul watched Connaught to the door, noted the target where his trousers had been mended. Paul gave them all time to make their beds and then went to make his. No one saw him, but Setna was saying: 'It ain't vot you jew, it's the vay vot you jew it.'

'If jew vos the onnly boy in the verld,' Connaught sang back.

'And I vos the onnly girl, ve vould find such *von*derful tings to jew . . .'

Paul crept out, planting each foot as carefully as if he were on alien ground. He could not fight them. What could he do? He could register every detail, every difference between their methods, but he could not fight them. He leaned out of the landing window. On the opposite hill, Mr Burgess's house was thronging with boys. Why couldn't he be one of them? Why couldn't he be the bus driver in the red bus plunging down the hill towards the village? Or the man with the suitcase on the back seat? A suitcase! Could there be an escape? The reek of Marino's sheets came to his nostrils.

Paul went and locked himself in his study. He picked up his Sallust con and started to work at it methodically, writing in the difficult words over the top.

A voice said: 'Is the Yid in?' Podge.

'I don't know.' Harper.

'Jew don't?' Setna.

Paul took the Bible from the bookshelf and opened it above the Sallust. He read at the place he had turned up. 'Comfort ye, comfort ye, my people Israel.' Who was to comfort them? Who in the whole world cared to comfort them? The boys left the door. Paul clenched his hands on the steel tubing of his chair, grabbing himself down into it. Sweat salted his lips. Nothing. He collected his books together to go to chapel.

Opening his study door he upset a wastebin. It clanged and clattered across the landing and down the first flight of stone steps. Stewart erupted from his study: 'What the hell do you think you're doing?'

'Sorry, Stewart, I couldn't help it.'

'Look where you're going next time.'

'Yes, Stewart, sorry, Stewart.'

'Incidentally, about last night – '

'What about it?'

'No stopping up for a week.'

'Fine,' Paul said. 'That's the old British love of the underdog we all like to see.'

'Make that a fortnight,' Stewart said.

The wastebin was on the lower landing. Paul kicked its side in. The paint split like skin. Paul kicked the bin till the two sides met. He stamped on the round base till it buckled. Williams came out of his study and said: 'Stop that bloody noise, blast you.'

Paul picked up the battered basket. Stewart was watching from the top. 'Yours?' he inquired.

'It was a present actually, Stewart,' Paul said. 'Left outside my door.'

'Looks like house property.'

Paul took the bin into his study and tried to restore it, almost tenderly, to what it had been. When he came out, Stewart was still standing there. Paul smiled at him: 'Mustn't be late for chapel; that would never do, would it?'

In the break there was PT, taken by the monitors. When the exercises were over, they played football. Williams and Setna picked up sides. Riesman wasn't chosen. Murdock pointed him to Williams's side. Setna, who was goalie, gathered a shot and punted the ball hard into Paul's face. He went down hands up. When he had swallowed the first pain he lowered his hands. The game was going on. The blood rolled down from his nose and dottled the grass. The ball hit him again, from behind. 'Out the way, can't you?' Murdoch said. They made a game of kicking the ball against him, calling 'Out the way, can't you?' to flatter Murdoch into acquiescence. Riesman limped, sag-faced, off the field. Murdoch shouted. 'Come back here.' Paul returned. 'You can't just walk off like that. You're supposed to be taking exercise. Run about.' Blinded with tears, Paul ran about among the players.

At lunch they kept the vegetables away from him, daring him to ask for them. He didn't dare. They kept him thirsty and he dared not ask for water.

At the end of the table Mr Walker smiled among his monitors. 'How's the garden doing, sir?' one of them had asked. Abstractedly, the house man pursed his lips, his chalky fingers fudging a piece of bread. Did he know what was going on? What had started it all, Paul wondered. Palestine? Damn the Jews, damn them. They were damned. If only Hitler had killed every last one.

The house was a prison. The bars ran from roof to basement. The studies were small as cells. The boots of the boys going to football sparked on the stone steps. They bolted into the lavatories. The reek of them filled the house. The swing-door into the downstairs bogs banged. It banged again and again. The boys in the stalls strained and sweated to empty themselves. The house squeezed itself empty. The boys excreted from exercise and pleasure. Paul stopped in his study, rubbing splinters of blood from his nose, black as shot, and cracking them between his teeth.

At tea-time, Paul opened his food locker carelessly. His butter and jam had been leaned against the door. And fell. The butter went flat on the black floor. The jam rumpled into glass and red mush. The house sent up a universal moan.

''ush – simmer,' Stewart called. 'Clear up that mess right away,' he added loudly to Paul. The house cheered. 'Sim – mer,' Stewart said, grinning.

Then night was coming. Paul feared the night. He had been forbidden to stay up late. He would have to go to bed with the others. He would have to lie and listen to them. He sat in his study during prep, the curtain open, and watched night come inescapably down. Rain hissed in the quarry and tingled on the bicycle sheds.

After prayers, there was only an hour to lights out and darkness, which belonged to them.

3

Bang. 'Good night, Williams.'

'Night, sir.'

Bang, 'Good night.'

'Good night, sir.'

Bang. 'Good night, Connaught.'

'Night, sir.'

'Nice goal today.'

'Lucky, sir. Thank you, sir.'

Bang. 'Good night.'

'Night, sir.'

Bang. 'Good night.'

The housemaster's eyes rested for a moment on Paul.

'Sir,' Paul mumbled.

Bang. 'Good night, Harper.'

'*Good* night, sir.'

Bang. 'Good night.'

'Night, sir.'

The House Man went away down the line. The light went out. 'Good night,' Murdoch called.

'Good night. Night, Murdoch. Night. Night. Night.'

Silence of springs creaking. Were they going to attack him? The rasp of farting. If only he could die, turn his back and never see the stroke coming and die. Another fart. 'Was that a genuine one?' Harper demanded.

'Jewnuine,' Podge started up.

'Let's play a jewsy game,' Harper said.

'Jewsy, jewsy, jander,' suggested Marino.

'Who's a jewy Yid here?' Podge asked. 'Marino, are you a jewy Yid?'

'I'm not a jewy Yid,' Marino brayed delightedly.

'Connaught's a jewy Yid,' Podge suggested.

'I'm not a jewy Yid,' Connaught said, 'but I know who is.'

'Who is?'

'Shag is. He's a shaggy Yid.'

'Are you, Shag?'

'I'm not a jewy Yid,' Williams said. 'I say, Riesman, do you know any jewy Yids?'

'He couldn't be one, could he?'

'Riesman a jewy Yid? Of course not.'

'Perhaps he's a *greasy* Yid.'

'Greasy, that's different!'

'A greasy Pole Yid,' Connaught proposed.

'It's the Yids that make the poles greasy, isn't it?' Podge inquired.

'Poles are netcherally greasy.'

'Yids are, you mean.'

'Greasy and Yiddy.'

Connaught thought of a new line: 'Who's a Yiddlesex supporter here?'

'Three jewy cheers for Yiddlesex.'

'They've got Comptonstein and Yidrich,' Connaught said.

'How can you tell a Yid when you see one?' Podge asked.

'By the vay he loffs his shekels – '

' – his monnith – '

'How ah loffth mah monnith,' Connaught said. 'Shekels, shekels, shekels. I loff counting them.'

'Let's do Jews are,' Podge said. 'Jews are – Masterman?'

'I'm trying to get some sleep. Why can't you pack it in?'

'Masterman's got jewy blood.'

'Piss off.'

'Jews are – '

'Greasy,' Harper said. 'Jews are – '

'Hairy,' Williams said. 'Jews are – '

'Oily,' Connaught said. 'Jews are – '

'Dirty,' Setna said. 'Jews are – '

'Funks,' Podge said. 'Jews are – '

'Monnith-lovers,' Marino said. 'Jews are – '

'JEWY!' they all cried together.

The gas-chambers were like mammoth cinemas. The obedient queues stepped mutely, numbly forward into them. There was silence over the yellow land. It lay, dull daffodil, up to the horizon. The black queues slowly moved against beaten pewter skies. There was no barbed wire. No guards paced. The long lines of men and women and children shunted into the brazen tunnels. No one stirred from the ranks, no one wept, no one spoke. There was neither rain nor wind. No sound came from the ovens, nor did the crowds diminish. As one man stepped into the oven, another came into sight. From time to time, a face leaned out and looked back along the line, expecting the end, but there was no end. The pewter sky was as heavy as a shutter. There was no hope. Paul saw himself standing there in the queue. A man muttered to him: 'We should fight.' It was his father. Paul said: 'Fight the sky, fight the earth, fight the truth.' The dark foyer closed over the two of them. Paul said: 'Where's Mummy?' His father said: 'She's at home.' The darkness covered their heads. Paul said: 'It's no use now. Nothing's any use now.'

4

The trees were laden with damp. The rutted path, cancered with roots, gave no footing. The branches were furred with mist. Paul walked alone. He could draw no comfort from natural things. He leaned against a tree till the damp was drawn through his coat and welted his back. He barked his head against the trunk. He kicked apart a pile of leaves. A woodlouse, like a fat running blister, sped into the rot again. A bird sang. Paul did not know its name.

It was too late to learn natural things. Desolate autumn swelled no joy in him. Such comforts would never be his. There was no song in him. Behind the wood, along the leaf-slicked path and over the stile, past the masters' cottages, lay the school. Beyond the school lay Mr Walker's house, which called to him, which called to him in the only language he knew, with a voice he must recognize, a voice above birds and woods and natural things. What could he do but go back? Here in the wood, alone, it was cold. There was no freedom. What was possible? Palestine? 'I don't suppose,' Nat said to a neighbour on one occasion, 'that we should find anything more in common with them than you would, Mrs Paynter.' How that 'we' did take in Paul! And how the 'them' did exclude him! With whom then did he have something in common? With the cold trees and the wet leaves and the dusty mist in the branches? Mere poetry. With what then? With whom? With those who baited him, with Benedict's. There was nowhere else he could go. He had no real place. He had to be grafted on. He had to graft his way in. He had nothing in common with anyone.

A boy in shorts came padding down the path. He glanced at Paul and was past, down over the barbed wire and across the ribby field. Oh to call him back and say 'I'll be your friend', oh to call to anyone in the world and have them care! The boy ran on and into a dip and disappeared. Paul hated him. At length he palmed away the tree and started up the path. A black welt was starred on his back. In a grove of sticky saplings he stopped to piss among the golden leaves. Ah, if he could but rip off his face and hair and nose and his penis like a roll of bread and be but a grey sausage of nothingness, lying among the smelly leaves in a deserted copse!

After school, Paul knocked on Williams's study door. 'Hullo,' the boy called.

Paul said: 'Hope you don't mind, Shag.'

Williams was combing his hair, scurf scabs falling on to his knees. 'What the hell do you want?' he demanded.

'What's all this about?'

'What's all what about?'

'You know what,' Paul blurted.

'It's not my fault.'

'What have I done? What am I supposed to have done? How can I correct any fault like this?' The tears rolled down his nose. 'God knows –'

'We just don't like you. I can't help it.'

'I hope this gives you a lot of satisfaction, that's all I can say.' Tears were like swallowed threads. 'God knows there must be some concrete reason – something I've done . . .'

'You're always going round with people above you – monitors – Simpson –'

'I see. I'll try and correct that.'

Williams said: 'I know this is rather a beastly way.'

Paul shook his head. 'Doesn't matter now. Is there anything else? *Anything?* Sorry about this. I didn't mean to. Blub, I mean.'

'Look, I'll try and do something. Get them to stop.'

'Will you really?'

'I never really thought it would – go this far.'

Paul thought he had done it. He really thought he had done it, till the laughter began downstairs. He opened his study window and could hear Williams: 'What have I done?' he was snuffling, 'What have I done?' and blubbing, only he was laughing so much. Paul grabbed his hair and pulled. He grabbed his own hair and pulled and looked for the hank of it in his hand. He bit a nail and ripped it red and sucked at the sore blood. Podge was saying: 'What shall we do now?' Paul shut his study window. He glared at the real, brute desk: books as heavy as rocks, pens, ink, writing paper, dead as putty, calendar (forty-three days to go). Lexicon, pencils, two snaps of his parents in a hinged frame. On the wall a passe-partout framed reproduction

'Bridge at Arles' which Alma had given him with her love for his birthday. She had always admired Van Gogh: he was so passionate, and so pretty. Paul sat down hard in the sling-seated chair and pulled the writing paper towards him. Night was coming. He began to write, hard against the metal struts of the chair.

5

Paul said: 'Please, Stewart, may I go to the post?'
'What for?'
'Let me see. Oh, yes, to post a letter, Stewart.'
'Very well,' Stewart said.
The pillar-box was near Mac's lodge. Light shone through the leaded window and squared off the lawn. Beyond, the chapel stood out along the purple sky. One of the tall slit windows showed a candle of light. Paul posted his letter and stood for several minutes, staring at the chapel, like a hangar against the sky. He stepped on to the lawn (a master's privilege) and strolled across to the chapel.
The Ypres Memorial Door was not locked. The latch coughed. At the east end, a huge gilt cross hung suspended, no figure on it, a huge cross barnacled with stones. Paul passed down the long aisle. Flights of pews stepped up on either side. An electric lantern swinging on a chain over the vestry door was the candle he had seen. The rays struck the underside of the cross and seemed to ignite it: the golden flame soared to the pinnacle, up under the hoop of white dark roof. The altar steps were covered with buff carpet. A *prie-dieu* stood on the second wide step. Paul passed the massive organ, its pipes stretching like headless throats into the darkness. He stopped before the altar and gazed at the cross. He mounted the steps and the clack of his feet on the tiles died. He knelt at the obvious *prie-dieu*. 'God. God. God.' The cross was petalled with light.

It moved. It flamed. It flamed and moved with the light. 'Oh God, let me not be a Jew. I'll be good. I'll do anything. I will be modest and unselfish, only please let me not be a Jew.' He stopped and laid his head on the smooth wood. He looked up again and saw himself hanging from the cross, hanging head and neck down from the cross, and felt the driven agony of nails. He hung down over himself and mocked himself.

The vestry door coughed.

'What are you doing?' It was Mr Trotter, in mufti.

'Praying, sir.'

Mr Trotter swallowed his Adam's apple. He blinked several times. 'You should go to your usual place,' he said. 'In any case – er – the chapel is out of bounds at this hour. How did you come to be here?'

'I came up to post a letter. I – I came on afterwards.'

'If you wanted to pray you could have come to Late Evening Service. It is tonight, you know.'

'That's no use, sir,' Paul said.

'No use? Why is it no use?'

'I'm a Jew, sir. I used to go to LES but I can't any more.'

'I'm afraid I don't quite understand. Are you a *convert* to Judaism?'

'No, sir. I can't help it.'

'Can't help it? You sound as if you were – er – ashamed –'

'Do I, sir? Isn't that strange – ?'

'The Jews are a great race – Spinoza – er – Mendelssohn, Heine, Proust – er – Einstein –'

'Freud, Marx, don't forget Marx, sir, and Jesus. We mustn't forget Jesus, must we?'

'Jesus, too, was a Jew,' Mr Trotter agreed.

'Why aren't you?' Paul demanded.

'Me?' Mr Trotter tucked his muffler under the lapels of his grey jacket. 'Well, I'm – I'm a Christian.'

'Tell me, sir, would you like me to become a Christian?'

Mr Trotter said: 'Nothing would please me more, if you felt the – the call.'

'Do you think Jones minor felt the call?'

'What house is he in?' asked Mr Trotter.

'All the boys – do you think they "felt the call"?'

'Some grow up in the faith, others must labour to attain it.'

'Could I be a Christian, Mr Trotter, do you think?'

'Anyone may be a Christian if he wants to. That is the meaning of the Holy Catholic Church. No one is excluded. But you must want to – er – join for the right reasons, not simply in order to get away from what you are.'

'But I hate what I am. I *want* to get away from it. Isn't there a saying that Christianity is a refuge? To be a refuge it must receive people who're escaping from something. That's me. I'm a sheep, Mr Trotter,' Paul said. 'And evidently I've gone astray.'

'Sarcasm,' said Mr Trotter, 'is not a way to faith.'

'What is?'

'Humility. You must start with humility.'

'And walk into the gas chamber unselfishly,' Paul said. 'And just let people – '

'Let God,' Mr Trotter said. 'If you can't come humbly to God you would do much better to stay where you are.'

'I shall never be happy as what I am.'

Mr Trotter said: 'Happiness *isn't* everything. I'm not a clergyman, a chaplain, because it makes me happy. I'm a clergyman because that is what I must be – '

'It doen't seem to me to be fraught with misery.'

'Nor does being a Jew to me,' smiled Mr Trotter.

'Six million people – ' Paul cried. 'Six *million*.'

'Six million what?'

'Gassed, hanged, injected, murdered. And what do you care? What does anyone care?'

'Is anyone plotting to kill you?'

'They would,' Paul rapped out. 'They would. If it was in school rules they'd do it all right.'

'In school rules? What are you talking about?'

'It was in Nazi school rules. That's what I'm talking about.'

'You exaggerate, you know. There's good in these boys. You must see the good in them, as I do.'

'There was good in Pontius Pilate, but he's roasting in hell, I understand. Or shouldn't I believe everything I read in the Gospels?'

Mr Trotter said: 'I think this conversation had better end. I'm going to lock the chapel.'

Outside, Mr Trotter hesitated. 'Um – it's not all – um – gas and gaiters, you know, being a parson. You see, I – I can't sing and – um when I have to chant the responses, I'm, I'm very nervous. I'm frightened all day Sunday, thinking about having to sing them. I always think I shall be less worried next time, but I never am.' Mr Trotter swallowed. 'I – I don't know exactly what it is that you are frightened of, but I – I want you to know that you're not as alone as you think you are. We're all Jews one way or another.' He stepped off quickly into the darkness.

Paul said: 'No. *No*. That can't be what it means.' He walked back to Mr Walker's, but not across the masters' lawn.

At the top of the stairs, Stewart said: 'It doesn't take that long to post a letter.'

'You're right, Stewart. There's no deceiving you, I can see that.'

'I only gave you permission to go to post. Where've you been all this time?'

'I've been to chapel, Stewart. Any objections?'

On Saturday morning the STUDENT'S EXERCISE came. Paul woke early, from habit. The agonies of the last three days were insufficient to quench the tiny terror. They would find a way. He crept downstairs before first bell, using all his old silence as he went for the buff envelope. He knew it would save him nothing. He was like a murderer, badged with blood, who goes to destroy a tiny clue which is, in any event, no part of the prosecution's case.

From after lunch they were free. Freedom was a chasm of horror to Paul. For three days he had been alone. The afternoon yawned before him. Without the community of the boys, a desert of feeling, without action, a dictionary of fear was his only refuge. He went into the buttery where Parch was washing up the lunch plates.

'Give you a hand, Mr Parch?'

Parch's eyes protruded from under busy amber brows. He handed Paul the wet cloth. 'Givin' you a rough time, are they?'

'I'll survive,' Paul said.

'If you want to, you will.'

'You sound as if you were speaking from experience, Mr Parch.'

'Buried in mud for three days I was, at Wipers.'

Paul smiled, but Wipers was no joke. 'Who got you out?'

'One of my mates, corporal by the name of Sidebottom.'

Stewart was in the door of the buttery. He looked at Paul and then at his watch, as if Paul were a clock that ought to be keeping time. Paul glared at him. Stewart looked at Parch. Parch stuck out his lower lip, hooked thumbs in his belt, said nothing. Stewart said: 'Afternoon, Mr Parch.'

'*Good* afternoon, sir.'

Stewart stood there for a second and then left. 'And 'e's another,' Parch said.

Paul laughed. 'You're right there, Mr Parch.'

'Bet your sweet life I am. And that Walker's another.'

'The House Man?'

'Creepin' Jesus. And his old woman! Jee – *suss*! I wouldn't stay another minute if it wasn't for me pension. Thirty-five bob a week, after thirty years. Close, Christ, this lot they're as close as –' Paul was quickly busy with drying forks '– close as two fuggin' honeymooners on an iceberg.' Parch wiped his nose on his sleeve. 'This lot, blimey, you'd think I was Chancellor of the wadjamacall –'

'Exchequer.'

'Exchequer, that's it. Mr Parch, 'e says, how much do you spend on cleaning equipment? Cleanin' equipment! 'Ow much on this, 'ow much on that? You know the trouble with this lot? They ain't never known what's what. Ain't never seen nothing. I'll bet you 'e never put 'is 'and on 'er whatsit till after 'e'd *"proposed"*. Wilt thou be me lawful wedded fugh!' Parch spat. 'They don't know what it's all about. They just 'aven't got any idea, believe me.' His eyes bulged. 'You got a girl?'

'Not really, no.'

''Ow old are you?'

'Sixteen.'

'And you 'aven't 'ad a girl yet? You're wastin' the best years, believe me. Key 'oles is all very well, but you know what I'd do if I was you, Master Riesman?'

'What would you do, Mr Parch?'

'I'll tell you what I'd do. I'd get out of 'ere as quick as I could and I'd find me a girl to do it with. That's the trouble with you lot, got nothing to do with yourselves. Get it in, son, that's my advice, and the quicker the better.'

Paul hung the towel on the rail. 'Is that the lot, Mr Parch?'

'That's the lot.'

Climbing the eighty-nine steps, Paul looked down and saw Parch march into the bog, flies open, hand at the ready. Paul glanced across at the study windows. Masterman was in his study, even though he was not a monitor and should have been out like the rest of the house. As Paul watched, Masterman put something to his mouth. A second later a puff of smoke blew up and drifted out of the window. Masterman was smoking! It was incredible. He seriously considered whether he should inform Stewart.

Numbly, Paul went to Bookshop. There were no novels except in Everyman or Nelson's Classics. On a side table there was poetry: Keats, Byron, Wordsworth's Prelude. Testament of Beauty. In the shelf above, pressed between textbooks, was *Works of T. S. Eliot*. Paul went straight to it, bought it and left the shop. Mr Hastings-Howard, the English master, said that modern poets were very difficult and many people thought they were a lot of rot. It seemed to give Paul something in common with them; though he understood little of what he was reading, it was immediate to him, even as far as 'The rats are underneath the piles the Jew is underneath the lot'. It pleased him to find Eliot among his persecutors. Eliot was there on paper and had to wait till Paul was ready to attack him; the words were there and could never be denied, no good act and no good poetry could ever efface them and Eliot had it coming to him, though he knew it not. He was a killer and he had it coming to him. As for Podge, Connaught and Williams, they would no doubt stand aside and let the great Mr Eliot be their champion, as the strongest man available, and that was fine: Paul had no fear of meeting Mr Eliot after suitable training and ripping him up, coat of clerical cut and all. With this evidence on paper, Paul could afford to wait. He would come on Eliot from below and rip him out, the Jew underneath the rat, time no object. To be a writer, that was all one needed to be up with Mr Eliot. To be a writer one pouched one's pains, one enjoyed them. One was above the crisis; Paul felt his pain was no longer absurd, since it had a use and a place: it provided the goad that would drive him forward against the prissy master, no matter how long the road. He could enjoy his pains because they fleshed him with muscle against his enemies. He would never again exist on the solitary level of a simple being. He stood behind himself, armed with the invulnerability of one who from now on could delight in every wound.

7

Stewart banged the door officiously. "Ush – simmer. Answer your names.' What answer did one give to one's name? As for one's name, there it bloody was. There it bloody was: 'Riesman?' 'SUM.'

The roll ended. 'Doncaster, Phillipson, Greig' and the lower house stampeded for the ping-pong table. Marino, Podge, Setna, Harper, Connaught and Masterman all went into Hall. No monitor joined them. It might have been arranged.

Paul closed his eyes. The familiar terror reasserted itself. He wrenched open the door. Podge and Marino were looking at *Punch*, pointing out the jokes to each other. Setna was gluing a flap of rubber on to a ping-pong bat. Masterman sat on the table, swinging his legs. Harper and Connaught were planning teams for next term. Paul stood in the centre of the room.

Williams came in. 'Oh, um – '

'What ho, the Shag,' Connaught said.

'Um, I – '

'Don't go, Shag,' Paul said. 'We need you.' Paul went over and stood above Podge. 'Why are you doing this?'

Podge pointed to a cartoon in *Punch*. He and Marino

laughed. Paul snatched the *Punch* from Marino and threw it into the fireplace.

'I say, house property!' Marino squawked.

'House ballocks,' Paul said. 'Now you listen to me, all of you – '

'I'm jewing this pingers bat. Any objections?'

'I don't know if you're doing what you're doing just for amusement; if you are, I suppose you'd better go on till it stops being funny, but if you think you'll do any good – or change me – you're wrong. Why don't you hit me if you hate me so much? Come on, why don't you, all of you? Look, I'll tell you what – we'll start with the weakest, to ensure you all get a chance. Come on, Podge,' Paul said. Podge smiled at Connaught. Connaught was writing. 'Come on, Podge,' Paul said.

The door of the room was wrenched open. Stewart came in. 'Unnatural 'ush,' he commented. He picked *Punch* out of the grate. 'How did this get here?'

Connaught said: 'Come on, Harper.'

The two left the room. Harper was saying: 'I've got some cake if you like.' Podge and Marino followed, then Williams, sucking his knuckle. Setna muttered 'Get some hot water' and whistled out.

Masterman said: 'Hullo, Stewart.'

Stewart blinked and put down *Punch*. 'See the House Man,' he mumbled and went through the door to the private side. Masterman picked up *Punch*. Paul said: 'Think I did the right thing?'

'Why ask me? I don't care.'

'You're not – like them.'

'I don't give a monkey's ballock about either of you. You or them.' Masterman looked at Paul. 'You did OK.'

'Thanks.'

Masterman palmed himself off the table. 'This really is a bloody shitty hole,' he said.

Paul sat alone for a while, holding *Punch*, then he went

upstairs. A panel of light from Podge's study lay on the landing. Paul skirted it. Podge was saying: 'Now what shall we do?' Paul clenched his fists. It was going to go on. He would kill himself. He hated them so much he would kill himself. Williams said: 'I told you, the House Man said it would have to stop soon.'

Paul ran up to his study. He snatched the Van Gogh print from the wall and flung it out of the window.

At tea, Masterman said: 'I say, Riesman, are you coming to the English Club this evening?'

'Oh, I don't know,' Paul replied. 'Do you think they'll let me in?'

'They're discussing the British tradition.'

'What's that?' Podge inquired.

'Oh, the team spirit, isn't it?' Paul said.

FOUR

My Son, My Son

1

PAUL'S LETTER had arrived that morning at breakfast. 'The boy's written at last,' Nat observed, slitting the envelope.

'I hope nothing's wrong,' Alma said.

Nat read the letter to himself; it had been addressed only to him and he feared trouble:

Dear Dad,

I did not want to write this letter. I write because I must talk to someone, because unless I can speak, I need not exist. Here I do not exist. For days no one has spoken to me. I am the Yid. I never thought I would write like this. It was never my intention. A few days ago, I would never have dreamt of writing. In spite of occasional things, I have never really suffered till now. All my friends, or those I thought my friends, have turned against me. I have no one. They mimic Jews all day and mimic me too. I sit here and shiver. I am powerless. I do not know what I have done or why God has treated me like this. I do not know why there are Jews or why I must be here. I would sooner be dead. Perhaps soon I shall be. I can't hit them, since they do nothing directly. I am not a person. I am a thing: the Yid. It's true, isn't it? I *am* the Yid. I did not want to write, but I must talk to someone. Don't worry about this, I simply had to write for someone to see, or I should explode.

Love – Paul

'What's he say, Nat?'

'Oh, nothing really. It's – it's about money.'

'He's not in trouble?'

'No, not really.' Nat looked at his watch. 'Heavens, I must dash.'

'Nat, you're not working today?'

'Um, yes, forgot to tell you.'

'Nat! The Paynters are coming in for a drink – *Nat!*'

Nat blundered into the lavatory. Fury and shame rose in his throat and almost strangled him. Why didn't Paul hit them? Why did he have to write? When Nat was six, another small boy called him a Sheenie and Nat promptly knocked him backwards over his tuckbox. Now he crumpled his son's letter and thrust it between his legs into the lavatory. Paul should never have written.

In the train going down to Benedict's, Nat sat, in belted overcoat, muffler and old green porkpie hat, like a stranger. There was both meekness in him and a certain arrogance; he was shy of venturing beyond the bounds of the usual, emotional excess was abhorrent to him (his mother had always smacked him as a child if his hand moved while he was talking) and it was the vulgar show which he associated with Jewishness that most revolted and alienated him. He believed that everyone should act in accordance with his place in life and when he himself ventured into the unaccustomed, there was in him a withdrawn docility that seemed to assure the world that he had no critical or domineering intentions. Arrogance came with the conviction that he was doing his duty. Whenever Nat did anything out of the ordinary he did it because he felt he must; he enjoyed nothing unusual; even if he were asked to dinner by a grateful patient he would tell Alma that he felt they 'ought to go'. He was wary of hedonism, for socially its counterpart was that kind of Jewishness which led you selfishly to seek your own advancement without considering its effect on others. If one did only one's duty no one could complain; in his profession as in his private life, he did everything with rigid ethical propriety: he went quietly and unobtrusively about his business. Only one thing drew him out: his sense of duty; he would confront and challenge anyone and anything which he felt it his duty to oppose. For himself he would do nothing, he would do anything if duty called. He went down to Benedict's because he must help his son, but the journey was miserable and the prospect of an interview with the headmaster distasteful; Benedict's was not his school and he recognized how exceptional it must be for parents to arrive and confront the Head, indeed if it weren't for being Jewish he would never have had to do it himself. He resented having to be exceptional and therefore he resented, though he accepted it as a dutiful burden, the whole distinction of being a Jew. It was imposed on him from outside; it was his duty to be a Jew, not his nature. It was a thing he went about quietly and without joy. There was even pain in it, but a pain that must be borne with dutiful stolidity: Paul should never have written. Nat had given up general practice when the Health Scheme was introduced and was now an anaesthetist at Wimbledon Hospital; he had no belief in the rightness of pain, far from it, but he had little patience with those who could not bear even the prick of the needle without a cry: he fought to eliminate pain but he had a deep abhorrence of those who could not bear it when it was inevitable, for the expression of any emotion or lack of control deserved, in his opinion, only to be smacked down.

2

The headmaster of Benedict's, Mr Ronald Grosvenor Charlesworth, was sitting at his Sheraton desk when his secretary, Miss Worthing, came in to inform him that a Mr Riesman wished to see him. 'Oh dear, oh dear!' Mr Charlesworth blinked over half-moon spectacles. If there was one thing he hated it was being interrupted during the preparation of a sermon. 'Oh dear! Did he say what he wanted?'

'No, Headmaster.'

'Oh dear, oh dear.' Mr Charlesworth rose, rubbing neat hands. 'I do wish people would make appointments, eh, Miss Worthing? I suppose it must be a parent. There's a Riesman in my classical Under Sixth, I believe. He is one of my pupils for Greek Testament.' The headmaster walked to the fireplace and braced his hands out for the heat. He was a short, plump man with fine silver hair and a precise surprised face with a puckering about the nose and mouth which sometimes made even Miss Worthing avert her head, expecting a sneeze. Mr Charlesworth rubbed a small, brilliant shoe behind his calf. 'I did hope to finish those notes before the school match. Ah me! Well, ask the gentleman to come in. Really, he could have made an appointment. Still, ask him to come in.' The headmaster tapped his left forefinger against the pad of his thumb.

'Ah, Mr Riesman,' said Mr Charlesworth, rubbing his hands and inspecting them before offering Nat the right one.

'*Doctor* Riesman.'

'I beg your pardon? Oh, of course, yes, quite. Now. What can I do for you?' Far away, on Big Ground, a roar proclaimed the kick-off in the school match. 'Today we tackle Bradfield,' the headmaster explained. 'Now.'

'Mr Charlesworth, I have come down here today to put a certain state of affairs to you. A certain state of affairs affecting my boy. As you may know, we are of the Jewish faith.' Another roar from Big Ground distracted the headmaster. Nat waited, lips compressed. 'As you may also know,' he went on, 'this is not an easy time for the Jews in this country. There's been – trouble in the East End and elsewhere; including, so it would appear, Benedict's.'

The headmaster drew his trouser over his knee and pulled up his black silk sock. 'There are,' he observed, 'two Jewish boys in my own house. I have neither seen nor heard signs of any trouble.'

'The same would not seem to be so of Mr Walker's house,' Nat retorted. 'My son Paul is threatening to commit suicide.'

'Dear me,' said Mr Charlesworth. He rose and went to the window and stood with his hands clasped behind him. 'Dear, dear me.'

'I had a letter from my son this morning.' Nat raised his voice. 'I assure you that he would never have written if the situation were not intolerable, if there were anyone else to whom he could turn.'

'Doctor Riesman, this is a Christian foundation – '

'In which one must expect Christian behaviour, what?'

'Minorities are, I fear, bound to suffer in any community.'

'Mr Charlesworth, my son is being persecuted.'

'Christians too know what persecution is.' Charlesworth sat down at his desk and stared at the blotter with its embossed Benedictine crest: *Quod dedit dare debeo.* Outside the cheers rose and fell. Charlesworth swivelled to face his visitor. 'Doctor Riesman,' he said, 'what do you expect me to do?'

Nat's mouth cut a cold line across his face. 'I'm here to acquaint you with the facts, Headmaster, not to teach you your job. I hope you're qualified to do that without my advice.'

Charlesworth rose as Nat did. 'Doctor Riesman, I have had a great deal of experience with boys. I have lived with boys all my life. I can assure you that there is a striking disparity between the number of boys who threaten suicide and the number who actually take the step. From what I have seen of Paul, I fancy he'll not add to the latter.' Mr Charlesworth opened the door of his study. 'Have you a car?'

'I'll get a taxi, thank you.'

'My excellent Miss Worthing shall arrange it. Miss Worthing, would you be so good as to summon a taxi for Dr Riesman?'

Mr Charlesworth glanced anxiously at his watch. 'It may interest you to know that I am preaching tomorrow evening in the school chapel. I shall, in view of what you have told me, insert one or two hints about the proper treatment of these matters.'

Nat said: 'It's got to stop.'

'My boys are Christians, Doctor Riesman. They know how to behave.'

'History,' Nat said, 'would hardly confirm the syllogism.'

The headmaster, hearing another cheer from Big Ground, held out his hand. 'Good-bye. I beg you not to worry.'

'It's not my job to worry. It's yours.'

'Tea at a quarter to five, eh, Miss Worthing? It's muffins,' he told Nat, 'and I'm very partial to muffins. I always have muffins on Saturdays – and sometimes on Wednesdays too, eh, Miss Worthing?'

'Yes, Headmaster.'

'Miss Worthing knows my little weaknesses.'

'And your little strengths too, no doubt,' Nat said.

Mr Charlesworth slippered quickly in the direction of Big Ground, his small nostrils dilated. It really was most tiresome. If there was one group of people whom he found excessively tedious, it was Jewish parents. The trouble was, you admitted their sons to the school, as something of a dispensation, and then you found that they expected it to be run for their exclusive benefit. For one who found his ideal in the notion of a closed High Anglican society this attitude was especially unacceptable. Jews were less a problem than an intrusion: they destroyed homogeneity, they confused motives, they confounded doctrine, they were in effect living embodiments of successful and impudent dissent. If one believed in the justice of a hierarchical society, one must believe in the universality of that justice; there could be no successful exceptions, however much one might sympathize with individual hardship. If punishment was to entail absolution, as Mr Charlesworth was convinced it must, then justice must be absolute, from God. Universal Justice was inseparable from Universal Christianity. The presence of Jews threatened his authority, not so much by their physical as by their logical nature. Mr Charlesworth neither hated nor feared them: he deplored them.

'Ah,' said Mr Charlesworth, 'here is our friend Mr Hastings-Howard. How goes the fray?'

'We are leading two-one, Headmaster.'

'And who is our marksman?'

'Stewart, sir.'

'Ah, the admirable Stewart! Tell me, is not that our friend Mr Walker I see over yonder?'

'I rather think it is, sir, yes.'

'I must have a word with him. Well, Hastings-Howard,

I hope your exhortation to the troops at half-time will prove efficacious when the struggle is resumed.' The headmaster set off round the pitch.

'Ah, but here is our friend, Mr Walker.' The headmaster took Walker's arm. 'Walker, one moment – I – um – I had a visitor this afternoon.' The two men walked away from the match. 'A Dr Riesman.'

'Oh!' Walker said. This was in point of actual fact most inconvenient. Walker was thinking of applying for the headship of Moulton Abbey School. It wasn't much as schools went, but one had to start somewhere. A reference from the Head was, in the circumstances, vital, and now this had to crop up! Walker said: 'Um, to what effect?'

Charlesworth licked his lips. What a tiresome fellow Riesman was! 'You know what that kind of parent is like,' the headmaster began. 'Always imagining that little Ikey is about to run away or do himself a mischief. Personally, I believe boys should be left to work these things out for themselves, don't you?'

'Yes indeed, Headmaster.'

'However, our friend Dr Riesman arrived and I could hardly refuse to see him. Very well, he informed me, not without emotion, that his son was being subjected to an anti-Semitical campaign. He is a Jewish boy, is he not?'

'Yes, Headmaster.'

'I felt it my duty to mention this visit to you, Walker. What you do is, of course, entirely your affair. Nevertheless, I could hardly refrain from informing you of the good doctor's representations.'

The two men turned and went up the shallow steps away from Big Ground. 'Bene*dict's*,' chanted the crowd, and 'Oooh!'

Mr Walker's tongue slipped along his lips. 'I need scarcely tell you, Headmaster, that I was aware of this matter. To be perfectly frank, if I may – '

'Yes, of course,' said Charlesworth, consulting his watch for muffin-time.

'I have no evidence that there is any undue bullying. Boys have a natural sense of when to stop and personally I remain to be convinced that the treatment of Riesman will not, in the long run, have a salutary effect on him.'

'We shall see,' said the headmaster. 'And meanwhile we shall have to possess ourselves in patience and remember that when all's said and done' – the headmaster looked over the tops of his spectacles – 'these things are sent to try us.' The headmaster nodded. 'Well, I must be on my way, Walker. Good afternoon to you.'

'Headmaster.'

FIVE

The Only Girl in the World

1

THE OFFICE OF the *South London News* was between the
Globe Garage and Bill's Dining Rooms. A sign read:
SMALL-ADS BY WEDNES PLEASE: APPLY WITHIN. Paul
peered in through the smeary glass and then stepped
inside. There was a counter with a notice 'Smalls here' and
a hoop-backed chair behind it. The walls of the room were
stacked with damp back numbers. A sign on the counter
'Ring' pointed to a handbell. Paul crossed to the counter
and rang. No one came. Paul peered up the narrow stairs.
On the landing was a tin bucket with ARP on it. Paul
climbed the narrow, curl-edged lino stairs. In the yellow
upstairs office, three men were working.

'Yes?'

'Oh, I'm looking for Mr Peace. I've got an appointment.'

'I'm Mr Peace. Are you, let me see, Mr Riceman?'

'Yes,' Paul said. 'How do you do?'

'Wanting work, isn't it?'

'That's right,' Paul said. 'If there is anything.'

'You won't find anything very glamorous to do here,
sonny,' Mr Peace said. 'And I haven't had any instructions
about money. Are you expecting to be paid?'

'Not important,' Paul said.

'Not important!' said one of the other men.

'Perhaps expenses,' Paul suggested.

'We don't have no expenses here,' the editor said. 'If in
doubt don't proceed with the story if it's going to cost you

money. We'll fill the paper all right, always have. No one cares what's in it. They only buy it for the smalls and the flicks. Mr Carters and Mr Pratt,' the editor added, presenting the other members of the staff.

'How are you?' said the two together. Mr Carter, a thin-wristed man with a head the shape of an upturned walnut, nattered at an ancient Underwood, lower lip jutting. Mr Pratt, waiting for the machine, was doing his story in longhand. It was headed 'ALLEGED RAPE – Wandsworth Man Held'. The electric light began to tick. 'It's always about to go,' Mr Peace said.

'Er – what shall I do?'

'I'll tell you what I should do this morning, sonny. I should have a scout round the area, get your bearings. Then you can 'op along to the Magistrates' Court and have a listen, see what you can pick up.' Mr Peace smiled sadly. 'And I don't mean fluff.'

'You won't find any excitement here, laddie,' Mr Pratt said, looking up from his rape.

Paul walked and walked through grey streets. The trolley-bus lines were strung out along the main road, dipped under railway bridges where the trains drummed moisture from the roof, swung past grey factories and second-hand car lots; all was damp and darkening. The only colour was where advertisements were caked, like scabs, on hoardings and wall sides. Paul passed from Putney into Wandsworth, Wandsworth into Battersea, and always the ruck of hutch-houses, the slick of damp pavements. Paul walked and walked and drew no nearer to anything; there was nothing to approach: all was infinitely strange. He would have got on a bus and gone home but this was a job, this walking in grey streets, and had to be done. There was no solution to the greyness, no answer to it, no meaning to it. There it was. Paul passed tobacconists, greengrocers, Durex chemists, sweetshops, newsagents; everywhere was greyness, and where there was colour it was the scabs of the adverts, pick them and there was greyness: behind the Bonny Babies and the Young Lovers, the drab, smutty greyness. Paul passed schools as raw as prisons. BOYS and GIRLS: the words were graven in the brickwork like LADIES and GENTS: BOYS and GIRLS were dirty words; smut filthied them. Paul remembered Mr Hastings-Howard quoting 'Shades of the prison-house begin to close upon the growing boy' and adding 'These poets exaggerate a bit' while the Under Sixth laughed and their laughing went out through open windows into the clean Surrey air. Now Paul saw the system's extension; the monitors were not set over the juniors alone but over all the earth to govern it. Here the school windows looked on to rail-tracks and iron bars. The children spilled out for their break like mice and flung themselves against the railings. The white faces with their dotty eyes blanched Paul as he passed. One had passed such schools before. One had watched people from buses. One had said: 'It's not so bad.' Paul would have said the same perhaps, but for the ache of his feet, but for the duration of his grey pilgrimage, but for the knowledge that he must walk and walk in this callous hopelessness till time was up.

Perhaps the newspaper could help these people. If he were editor he could run campaigns, demand action, insist on – what? Improvements in building, new opportunities. The *South London News* would become famous. The People's Paper. Editor: Paul Riesman. The slogan: 'THE TRUTH SHALL MAKE YOU FREE.' The conclusion: To hell with literature!

Paul never went to the Magistrates' Court that morning. He didn't know where it was and it seemed an impertinence to ask. He feared people might say 'What do you want it for?' and he would have to reply 'Oh, just to watch'; while others suffered he would be content to notice them. In such surroundings one did not ask the way, for if one did not have to be, then one had no excuse for being there.

In romances it was all right to ask the way, 'Go I right for the Lady Guinevere?' but here, in brute streets, only jokers and perverts went where they need not, slipped into ochrous pubs at midday, to observe the inmates. Alma said of these streets 'they're so *depressing*' and made no further apology for avoiding them. The pursuit of happiness followed other ways. Paul felt his perspectives widening to embrace too much, till his senses were flooded with the myriad of his impressions; he was like a funnel through which the waters rushed and flooded fat again, so that the thin neck of him was tight, strangled from within, by the pressure pushing him out, exploding him; he had no time for words; the experience was too quick for him: the experience stormed him from within like a fever and though he fought to come in again with words, there was nothing in him but the churning of this grey experience as it pounded through the thin stem of his consciousness. He tossed his head and tried to draw nourishment from it but it flowed too fast; it flushed and drained him, it ripped out the careful dams of Nat's and Benedict's precepts and left him with nothing. He could say nothing of what he felt – a grey flood ripping through him – what was there to say?

Paul said: 'It's awful.'

'What is, darling?' Alma inquired.

'Everything. It's awful. Nothing's changed. The poverty – everything. It's awful.'

Alma said: 'You can't change human nature.'

'Human nature? It's not human nature I want to change, it's human behaviour.'

'Aren't the two related?'

'It's all so *ugly*,' Paul said. 'What are they doing, what do they think they're doing, these people? There must be something they can really do.'

'I should have thought,' Nat said, 'that they were doing exactly the same thing we're doing – trying to keep a roof over their heads, trying to get on –'

'Get on to *what*?'

'I don't mind a discussion,' Nat said, 'but I really won't be spoken to in that tone.'

'Get on to what?' Paul asked.

'They want to buy television sets,' Alma said. 'Switch it on, Nat, or we'll miss the Groves.'

'Happy families!' Paul said. 'Happy families!'

'Clever boy,' Alma retorted.

The week before the General Election, Paul was sent out by Mr Peace to get the man-in-the-street's opinion. He returned with a stack of interviews. Mr Peace glanced at each briefly then put it either on the table or in the wastebin. The yellow light still ticked on its thread of life. 'All right, sonny,' decided the editor finally, 'these'll do nicely.'

'What's wrong with the others?' Paul inquired.

Mr Peace said: 'This is a Conservative newspaper.'

Mr Carter's wrist lengthened out of his skinny blue jacket and he scratched the peak of his head. 'We aren't the *Daily Worker* 'ere,' he said.

Mr Peace said: 'This is a Conservative newspaper, sonny.'

Paul said: 'Yes, but the truth –'

'We don't get paid to tell the truth. We get paid because Mr Cook chooses to pay us to do a job.'

'Who's Mr Cook?'

'The proprietor, on account of whom you and I are here. We're not here because of the truth, we're here because of Mr Cook.'

'Who is Mr Cook when he's at home?'

'Mr Arnold Cook,' Mr Peace said, 'is Granny's Brown Gravy.'

'Granny's Brown Gravy?'

'Biggest gravy people in South London.'

'What does he run the *South London News* for then?'

'He likes to have an organ,' Mr Pratt said.

'And now, gentlemen, I think we all have our work to do.' The three men bent to their tasks in the old jaundiced light.

'And will you vote Conservative yourselves?' Paul demanded.

'The ballot,' Mr Pratt informed him severely, 'is secret.'

2

There were nine months before he went up to Cambridge and by that time he was determined to have written something that would be accepted. Day after day, when he got home from the paper, he sat in his room and tried to write. He stared down from his bedroom window at the TRADESMEN ONLY sign at the back entrance of the flats and waited for something to come. He waited emptily for something to come. When it did, it was always some-one else's. His imitation was of a high order (had not the Cambridge scholarship examiners been especially delighted with his prose?) but nothing issued from himself. His ignorance of life seemed irremediable. He sat in the centrally heated flat and stared down at the concrete rind of road which bounded Monmouth Court. He tried to write but had no language natural to him. His life was nothing to write about, for it was but an empty stare into the January day, a desolate passivity; nothing grew out of him, nothing grew in him, he himself did not grow. He was like a stake to which pretty flowers were tied; when people admired the full and confident blooms they failed to perceive the arid stick at the heart of the arrangement. Paul was girded with prizes awarded him for his cultivated exterior, but when he looked into the heart of the matter, there was a dead centre. He could not express himself, for he had no access to a language in which he could give himself expression. His language then was an obscure sullenness, the only blemish, Nat and Alma thought, on their charming son; his only real language was one of moods, of sulks, of hollow incommunicable despair which could issue only in trivial tantrums. When he thought of life, of earning an income, he was filled with nausea. He thought of going through life with the perpetual dirty secret, the inexpressible dark sweat of himself always having to be hidden, washed out like those tell-tale stains that ever reappeared. He had no substantial unity: his body was the suitcase in which he carried the pretty props through which his living would be achieved. He tossed off the physical in favour of a pure and acceptable mentality. When the mind functioned, the self vanished. All intellect functioned in a purely spiritual world. He looked forward to Cambridge as a place where only intelligence would count. When he thought now of being a writer, he thought inevitably of fame, of publication, of acceptance. He no longer thought of writing as a response to the problem of Jewishness, for he believed that his academic life would be all his life and that if he developed his mentality sufficiently, the question of Jewishness would never again present itself. He wanted to be a writer now because of the joys which might arise from seeing his name as having done something rather than as being something. It was for no very different reason that Nat so prided himself on the Dr before his name. Paul accepted the position of the writer as that of one who looked with humorous indulgence on the follies of the world and depicted them with a pen neither censorious nor didactic. He considered that a detached irony would be his attitude and he aimed at a prose which would leave the author unnoticed; his realism would be of a kind that left the writer quite unresponsible for the foibles of his characters since he himself would neither comment nor intrude. At eighteen he fancied himself an ironic man of the world to whom sex was a faint bore and human society an elaborate source of amusement. But though he believed for a time that this view originated in himself, when he came to express it in his writing he recognized at once, if with a leaden despair, its derivative inadequacy. Yet he wrote banal, Maughamian stories one after another. He had no other language. When he tried to express himself, he dried up. He sat in a sweat of lust and impotence. The grey tide which surged through him was incommunicable. Lust, desire, nausea, how could these be stories? Again and again he thrust away with sweaty shame the monstrous goitres which deformed him. He knew no language of life which could allow him to acknowledge them, for in Monmouth Court all was decorous gentility. Every dark truth that was in him seemed to possess a clean, Gentile equivalent which was its only proper form, just as in writing the limpid, disdainful irony of the Gentiles was the only proper form in which to externalize the black, inner anguish. One could not risk offending or embarrassing. But whence could originality come then, when the springs of his own being were tainted? Originality was impossible, since he had no language in which to take up the grey tide. Integrity was impossible, since to be integral with the Jewy truth in him would be to frustrate the very career on which he was set. Life itself was impossible, since to live it would be to destroy that ironic detachment which was the only hope of salvation. He had found the antidote to black Jewy truth and he feared and hated the idea of letting the poison into his system again. In deciding, during those unhappy days at Benedict's, that he would write, he had not decided to proclaim and be one with his Jewishness; he had decided to find a place outside it from which he could, as it were, disinterestedly defend it, though it was a position to which he was, by virtue of his literary eminence, personally indifferent. But where was this place? It was death. Only by being personally null could he attain to it. Pure mentality was death and he could not achieve it; he could not achieve it because grey horror and black lust would not die in him. He could not achieve it because of a girl called Julia whose name tolled the death of death. He had to open his eyes for her and admit he was not dead. Except for her, he could have died in the cold silence of those weeks when he tried to wrestle himself to death.

For several weeks he did not dare to phone her. The telephone was as heavy and repulsive as black pudding. One day he got as far as phoning Colin for the number, but then again a shutter of impotence restrained him. The flat was quiet as the tomb; to dial a number was like rolling a stone from the mouth of the cave, death had become so comfortable a state. But in the end he phoned.

They met at Lyons Corner House in Coventry Street. Paul waited nervously, looking quickly this way and that, in case Julia might come and go in an instant of time unless he spotted her. But he saw her a long way off, coming confident and erect, dark hair bobbing, through the slouching crowd. When she saw him she smiled a full real smile and held her head slightly to one side, a highlight of humour in her dark eyes. 'Waiting long?'

'Ages,' he smiled. 'No, not really. I got here early so as not to give you any excuse to escape.'

'Escape? I'm not interested in escape, not yet anyway.'

'How do you feel about eating?'

'I feel about eating that I'd like to eat.'

Paul said: 'Um, we could go to the Salad Bowl.'

'Fine.'

'And then I thought we might go to the pictures. I've bought a paper so we can see what you want to go to.'

'Well that just about completes the evening, doesn't it?' Julia said.

Paul said: 'We don't have to go to the pictures.'

'Come on – food. I'm hungry.' Upstairs, Julia said: 'How's the writing going?'

'Going, going, gone. I don't know – I never seem to do anything that's any good.'

'I'd love to see something.'

'It's no good,' Paul said. 'I don't just mean it's not much better than Nevil Shute, I mean it's not as good as *Peg's Paper*. It's horrible, Wagstaff, it stinks!'

'I'd love to see something,' Julia said.

'I don't think I'll ever be a writer. I don't think I'll ever be anything. Probably just as well.'

'Why?'

'Oh, because I'm not really a very nice person. The less I am the better.'

'What isn't very nice about you?'

'Lots of things. Nearly everything.'

'You seem pretty normal to me.'

'Oh, I'm normal all right, that's the only majority quality I do have.'

Julia said: 'What have you been writing about?'

'Life.'

'And what do you think of life?'

'I think it's death,' Paul said. 'And now for an encore –'

'Why do you always make a joke of everything?'

'One must have a sense of humour,' Paul replied. 'One must learn to laugh at oneself. Oh ho, oh ha!'

'Joke and rejoke,' Julia said. 'Soon you'll get so far away from yourself you'll be gone by the time you get back.'

'That I like, may I use it?'

'You can use anything you like.'

'Julia, you don't know what you're saying!'

'Maybe not, but I know what I am.'

'I think, as they say in Monmouth Court, I'm being got at. Am I being and if so, what are you getting at?'

'I'm only talking.'

'What, you mean there's something else people can do?'

'Why, do you lead such a dull life?'

'You mean "why do you lead such a dull life?" I suppose. The answer is I lead such a dull life because I don't know what other kind of life there is or whether they'd let me in when I got there. I gather they don't take Jewish members.'

Julia said: 'What I provoked!'

'The girl who pulls the stopper out of me is going to have a pretty unpleasant time.'

'But interesting,' Julia said.

'Clinical masks will be worn,' Paul said. 'And asbestos suiting. The only real danger will lie in the stampede for the exits. Personally there's nothing very dangerous about me.'

'Have you written anything about yourself?'

'I did start something that was sort of based – you know.'

'Let me see it.'

'Not bloody likely.'

'Please.'

'No, not till – '

'Not till what?'

'Not till I know you better.'

'How much better?'

'We shall see.'

Their eyes met and smiled. The naïve jokes and taunts and solemnities flowed easily between them. Paul was suddenly in a conversation such as he had never had before, a conversation in which deathly formality had no part. Suddenly he was able to reveal himself and find himself accepted and more demanded and so, with a rush, he flung his whole being at Julia, rushed to confide his whole life to her, willing in this great intimacy across the supper-table to gush out his brilliant anguish to this first living woman he had known.

They met again and again. Paragraphs of churning incoherent regret, indignation and desire poured from his lips. His eyes bored into hers, demanding her agreement and her sympathy. The torrent of his frenzied expression swept her out into a new life; they both went riding down it in a helpless and buoyant confusion. They kissed. They kissed

deep and the joy of living and of hope burst in Paul and
held him there on the top of the torrent.

'You're the only girl in the world for me, Julia,' he said.

'So soon already?' she smiled.

'You don't really take me seriously, do you?' he said
sullenly.

'I love you,' she said.

'You what?'

'I love you, Paul,' Julia said. 'I love you.'

'Julia, my God, Julia, Julia, Julia,' Paul said. 'Oh Julia,
my God!'

3

Julia read the manuscript which Paul had brought her. He
sat in the armchair opposite, watching every inflexion of
her face. Julia read nimbly, her eyes quick across the page.
The narrative had the tactless crudity of a psychiatric
transcript. No character was defined, nothing was recogniz-
able but the cast which held the hero in its iron clamp.
Blind hatred fired that figure, fired him yet more rigidly in
the posture which other forces contrived. The very phrases
which expressed that vicious pressure were other men's.
Only the ferocity with which the words were driven on to
the paper was Paul's own. The typed letters were sunk
through the paper, so that as Julia's eyes read the stale
words on the front, her fingers traced the fresh braille of
his hatred on the back.

Paul said: 'Well?'

'You poor darling, you poor darling.'

Paul said: 'It isn't me.'

'Poor Paolo,' Julia said.

'Well, will anyone publish it?'

'Why didn't you say Philip was Jewish?'

'Because he isn't. It's only a story. You shouldn't take things so literally.'

'He's a Jew except that he isn't Jewish,' Julia said. 'You tell us everything about him except the one thing that'd explain him.'

'Explain him, explain him. I don't agree at all. I don't see why that's the only explanation for him. He's nothing to do with me – he's just a character – ' Paul jumbled the sheets together. 'Just because I've got a club foot I don't see why I should only write about people with club feet.'

'But this boy thinks like a Jew – '

'God dammit why do you have to hang a bloody millstone round my neck? I admit I'm a Jew. I admit it. But I don't see why all my characters have to be Jews too.'

'They don't,' Julia said. 'Unless they're Jewish.'

'Oh my God, what I wouldn't give not to be Jewish!'

'Almost as much as you'd give not to be alive,' Julia smiled.

He kissed her. 'That,' he said, 'is not quite as true as it used to be.'

'I don't care how miserable you are,' she said. 'I still love you.'

'Come to bed with me, Julia.'

'No,' she said.

'You must,' he said.

'Must?'

'I need you. God, I hate this idiotic game. I want to get it over.'

'That doesn't sound very enticing.'

'I'm not enticing.'

'You're lovely,' she said.

'Lovely. My mother once called me thick-lips.'

'You've got a lovely mouth.'

'My mother doesn't think so.'

'Your mother's opinion really doesn't matter any more.'

'It does unless you come to bed with me.'

'Have you ever – ?'

'I've been to bed with a lot of good books,' he said. 'I love to go to bed with a good book, don't you?'

Julia said: 'You'll meet other girls at Cambridge.'

'I don't want to meet other girls,' he said, drawing a skein of her dark hair against his lips. Paul looked round the unfamiliar sitting room of 15 Woburn Road. Julia was a thing on her own, the neat set of her on the sofa, her legs angled to the floor, the cuff of her red corduroy skirt over her knees, the slant of her thighs secret from him, the white Angora sweater which fuzzed his jacket when he kissed her, the olive slimness of throat and arms, the red lips and the black eyes and the swoop of long black hair; that was all that concerned him in this room, not the cocktail cabinet or the chandelier, nor the hotel furniture which gave it domestic dimensions. Julia was no part of this, nor was he. Her parents were not people, he was not interested in what she came from. He and Julia were alone.

Paul said: 'Well?'

'What about – you know?'

'Oh that'll be all right. Come to bed, Julia – '

'No, I want to think about it.'

'Think about what?'

'That's my business,' Julia said.

'I want you, Julia, I want you.'

'I want to think about it,' Julia said.

4

They met at Lord's the following Thursday afternoon. Paul was waiting for her, the Benedictine scarf round his neck, though it was a mild summer afternoon.

'Essex batting, just my luck,' he said as she came up to him, head on one side as it always was that instant before they kissed on meeting. 'Well?'

295

'Sorry I'm a bit late. I went to see a man about a job.'

'Why do you have to get a job?'

'So I won't miss you too much,' she said.

'Why? What do you mean?'

'When you go up to Cambridge. What did you think?'

'I thought perhaps you were thinking you shouldn't see me again.'

'I'm going to see a lot more of you,' Julia said.

Paul said: 'Mound stand?'

'Free seats,' Julia said, 'who do you think you are?'

They strolled up to the nursery end. Young was bowling; his neat controlled jerkiness punctuated the afternoon. 'It's been a long time since I've seen you,' Paul said. 'It's seemed ages.'

'Me too,' Julia said. They sat down in a bank of empty benches. Paul put his arm round her shoulders and kissed her and pressed her mouth farther and farther back so that her eyes fluttered in alarm at what people might think till at last she closed them and gave herself entirely to the kiss.

'I do want you, Julia,' Paul said.

'All right.'

'What?'

'You can have me,' she said. 'Why haven't we bought a scorecard? I like to have a scorecard.'

Paul said: 'How? I mean when, where?'

'My folks are going out tonight.'

'God, I said I'd be home for dinner.'

'You can ring up and tell God you won't be after all.'

Paul said: 'Yes, I suppose so.'

'Well you might be a bit more enthusiastic.'

'I'll go and get a scorecard,' Paul said.

Julia took her sunglasses from her bag and inspected the scoreboard. With any luck they might see Denis batting before the close. At last Paul came back along the line of seats. He looked so pink and young. She started to clap vigorously. They were bringing Compton on to bowl.

They arrived at Woburn Road before Hannah and Isidore had left. 'Come in for a sec,' Julia said, 'they're dying to meet you.'

Paul said: 'Must I?'

'They would like it.' Julia led him into the dining-room. Isidore was pouring tinned cream on to his peaches. 'Mummy, Daddy, this is Paul.'

Paul saw a stocky, grey-haired woman in a black costume and a slightly bowed, glassy-eyed man opposite her, grey hair brushed over a bald patch at the front of his head. The man stood up, serviette dangling. 'How do you do, m'boy?'

'How do you do, sir?' Paul said. He walked to the other end of the table. 'Do forgive me for interrupting your dinner like this.'

'It's only supper,' Hannah said.

Isidore wiped his lips. 'You're a Yiddisher feller, aren't you?' he asked at last.

Paul flushed and clenched his hands. 'Yes, I am, yes.'

Julia said: 'Well, hope you have a good game.'

Hannah said: 'Be good – '

'And if you're not, be careful,' Isidore finished it with a giggle.

Julia shut the sitting-room door. They waited while Hannah fussed about and Isidore got the car out. As the front door shut, they stood together and were fixed in a kiss.

Julia said: 'Down here or upstairs?'

'I don't mind.'

'A bed's nice.'

'All right.'

'Have you got – you know – what we talked about?'

'Yes,' he said.

The strangeness grew between them as they climbed the stairs till both longed for this to be over, for them to have done it again and again, whatever it was, so that there might not be this strangeness between them as they climbed the stairs.

'Are we going to take everything off?' Julia asked.

'I am,' he said, hating every word that passed their lips.

Julia lay naked on the bed. 'Here I am,' she said. He looked and saw the small breasts of truth and the navel of truth and the black hair of truth and the straight legs of truth. There was no part of her that was not true to him, not to the tiny mole above the black triangle of hair. So they touched, though with the stall of contraception between them, and the unentrancing failure of the act itself was transcended, so that they lay there and went on loving.

Julia said: 'What do you think our baby will look like?'

'Christ, there won't be one.'

'No, I mean, who do you think he'd take after?'

'I don't want one,' Paul said. 'I don't ever want one.'

Julia gave a new smile. 'That's obviously not what you really think.'

'It's you doing that,' Paul said, frowning, 'not talking about babies. I don't ever want to have a child, not ever. We don't have to have one, do we?'

'We have not to have one.'

'Thank God for that.'

'But one day it'll be different.'

'It'll never be different for me,' Paul said.

'You ought to be flattered that I want your child.'

'There's one thing I'll never be responsible for,' Paul cried, 'and that's bringing a Jew into this world.'

SIX

The Escapers

1

HE REJOICED to be faithful to her. His faith in her was a positive thing; they had faith in each other. The uncertain days were gone, the strangeness on the stairs was gone. They were new for each other; neither wanted to keep any part of what they had been before. He talked occasionally of school, she of college, but these were but descriptions of scenery gone through, as eager lovers still find time to ask each other, 'What kind of a journey did you have?' Soon before he went up to Cambridge they lay right together and her eyes burned up at him and he came to dread what he had so longed for because he must leave her for it. She demanded nothing of him except himself; she insisted on his integrity as a living thing. She built his integrity with her love. They roamed through that summer London as through an unexploded and uninhabited island; nothing was old when they were together, nothing done before. They were innocent together, free of others, just the two of them. Julia was something so deeply important to Paul that he hated all thought of sharing her with others. He wanted always to be alone with her. He even fought against letting her meet his parents again, for fear of their love becoming ordinary. He wanted his love to be outside the social context of Monmouth Court. Not until September did he give in to his mother's request to ask Julia to dinner at the flat. 'At last we meet again!' Alma said, extending both hands to Julia.

Julia put her head on one side. 'Hullo.'

Alma said: 'Won't you come through?'

Paul went into the sitting-room, where Nat was reading. 'Well, Dad?'

'Oh, hullo, I didn't hear you come in. Is your friend here?'

'She is,' Paul replied. 'I expect Mummy is making her powder her nose.'

'Ah well, we have to be careful of our noses, don't we?'

Alma rustled in with Julia. 'Of course you remember Julia, don't you, Nat?'

'Now let me see. You were the one who did the fan dance, weren't you?'

Alma said: 'Now what about drinks? Julia? Are you sure? I think I'll have a little whisky. I've had the most exhausting day: we've been revising the mailing lists at the Association.'

'I thought those were femailing lists.'

'Nat dear, you might buttle.'

A few minutes later, the dining-room doors slid apart to reveal Mrs Battersby standing there in a black dress and white apron. 'Heavens above,' Paul exclaimed, 'hullo, Mrs B.! What are you doing here?'

'Dinner is served,' Mrs Battersby pronounced.

Paul said: 'We are grand tonight.'

'You know very well Mrs Battersby sometimes comes back in the evenings.'

'Not since we had the King and Queen to dinner, surely.'

'Clever boy!' Alma gestured Julia to her place. Julia sat down, giving Paul, opposite her, a quick wink. 'I hope you like cold *consommé* – I thought this warm weather –'

'What've you two been up to this afternoon?' Nat inquired.

'Went on the Serpentine, Dad,' Paul replied quickly.

'Can't you see Julia's caught the sun, Nat?'

'Need powder on my nose?' Julia asked Paul.

'Looks all right to me. I like 'em shiny.'

'As if I meant that! You should know me better,' Alma reproached her son.

'How's his rowing?'

'Paolo's? Not bad, apart from catching an enormous crab.'

'You should have brought it home. I like a nice piece of crab.'

Alma smiled: 'I don't suppose Julia eats shellfish.'

'I like lobster,' Julia said. 'I had it with Paolo the other night.'

'Paolo, is that what you call him?'

'It seems possible, doesn't it, considering that's what she's been calling me for the last half-hour?'

Alma said: 'You mustn't lead her into bad habits, you know.'

'Like calling me Paolo?'

'Like eating shellfish.'

'Are you thinking of their aphrodisiac qualities or what?'

'Clever boy! No, I expect Mr and Mrs Adler keep Kosher.'

'Oh *that*! Oh.'

'They do, but I don't.'

'The shop is Kosher, isn't it?' Alma inquired.

'Both shops are,' Julia said, 'yes.'

'I think my mother used to go to one of them,' Alma said.

Nat said: 'So we shan't see him in the Cambridge boat, you think?'

'Not this week,' Julia said.

'Just because you used to go out with a Blue!'

'A blue what?' Nat asked.

'Rowing Blue,' Paul replied.

'He wasn't a Blue,' Julia said. 'He was a near-Blue.'

'A green?' Nat suggested. 'I nearly got a green myself.'

'Well I won't even get a very pale shade of yellow, so you don't have to worry.'

'I only wish I was going to have my chance again –'

'Chance?'

'At the Varsity. Meeting new people –'

'I don't much care about meeting new people,' Paul said.

'Go on,' Julia said, 'of course you do.'

'I don't,' Paul said to her.

'I always understood that writers were supposed to be keen on meeting new people. You know Paul's idea of becoming a writer, I suppose?'

'I have heard of it.'

'Incidentally, I forgot to tell you: I met a fellow at the hospital last week who writes. Chap called Stanley Wicks.'

'Never heard of him.'

'Writes detective stories. He lent me one actually. *Sudden Death* – very good it was too. Only does them as a sideline, of course.'

'Of course.'

'Does very nicely at it, I believe. People like a good detective story.'

'People like the telly, but that doesn't mean I'm going to write for it.'

'There is the question of making a living.'

'God, how I hate that word!'

'Sooner or later you'll find that just because you hate things doesn't mean that you'll never have to face them.'

2

Julia hated the thought of Paul's going to Cambridge, but she knew it was inevitable and she forced herself to face it, hoping to vaccinate herself against the pain by facing it first while Paul was still there. But when he went the pain was far greater than she had ever imagined, far greater than

her job at the Haughton Advertising Agency could anaesth-
etize. The world was void of joy. Sometimes, in the tube
going home, the back of a head, the set of a pair of
shoulders would send hope surging into her throat that it
was Paul pressed there, like a fossil, in the rush-hour
crowd; but the head would turn, the shoulders shift and it
was not Paul. Paul was at Cambridge, happy. There was
no equivalence of pain between them, for Paul was happy.
When he wrote to her that he was bored and disappointed,
she was divided between sharing his disappointment, for
she loved him, and welcoming it, for she wanted him. He
had made no friends, the work was dull and repetitious,
the undergraduate clubs too exclusive or too dreary. He
longed for Julia to come up, if only for the day. She
refused. She believed that she should leave him alone for a
term, that it would not be fair to reclaim him too quickly.
During Christmas they did not make love more than two
or three times, hurriedly, while Hannah and Isidore were
at the pictures, and they had to listen for the sound of the
car in the road, always fearing the interruption of their
love, which came too with family parties and day after day
when Paul could not escape from Wimbledon. Too soon he
was going up again to Cambridge and now when he begged
her to come for a week-end, loneliness and confidence in
his longing made her accept.

They were strange to each other again, as they had been
on the stairs. She stayed in his rooms on the Saturday night
and he was so possessed by terror that someone – a porter,
his tutor – would come and knock on the sported oak that
he was impotent. The impropriety of what they were doing
quite destroyed him. He was sure that someone would
have noticed Julia's coming in and failure to go out; he still
believed that nothing to do with him could escape detection. Julia did not resent his fear, but she did not share it;
she pitied him because she could see how unlikely were all
the horrors which were so possible to him. He said he

loved her now, but Julia knew differently; she saw that his conviction that everyone was watching him was based on his own inability to forget himself; he was like a dreamer who, no matter how he tries, can see nothing in the foreground of his dream except himself. The monstrous, alien figure of himself ruined and distorted his relation to everyone around him. It was against this monstrous self that everyone conspired; he could see no one without seeing himself, a forlorn, goitrous figure, like a great balloon, vast and impotent. If only he could escape from this flaccid vision of himself and be directly in touch with nature and with others! 'If only we could go away from all these people! If only one could fill one's lungs just once with the air the Gods breathe!'

'We can,' Julia said. 'We can go abroad – to France or somewhere.'

'How can I?' Paul said lamely. 'What would Dad say? Anyway I haven't got any money.'

'I'm earning,' she said.

'I can't go on your money.'

'Don't be so bourgeois,' she smiled. 'You could get a bit out of him if you tried.'

'I suppose I could say I was going with Tom Wallace. He's that other Classics bloke I was telling you about. The chap from Rochdale.'

'I'll get the tickets and everything,' Julia said. 'You wouldn't have to do anything except turn up at the station.'

'I don't know – ' He lit a cigarette. 'I don't know how I could get away. I mean they'll ask so many questions – '

'Tell them as little as possible. And behave as if there was no doubt about it. Oh, Paul, I do want to spend a long, long time with you.'

'So do I,' he said. 'And just think of all the writing I could do. I shall have to think very carefully about what I'm going to say to the folks. I mean I shall have to find a really convincing excuse – '

'You'd need to give an excuse for being alive, wouldn't you?'

'If I was I would,' he replied.

Dieppe! Dubonnet advertisements on fading housesides! The poles of level crossings swinging up in the wide air! *Épicerie! Café! Charcuterie!*

'What's *charcuterie*?' Paul demanded.

'Place where you buy hors d'œuvres-y things,' Julia replied.

'I say, I always thought French trains had wooden seats.'

'You're thinking of French women,' Julia said. 'Only the local trains do actually.'

'Is there anything you don't know?'

'Plenty,' Julia replied. 'And I'm forgetting new things all the time!'

'Julia, what do you say we only read French papers all the time we're here?'

'Fine. Only I don't want to spend all the holiday reading papers, if you don't mind.'

'That isn't my idea at all,' he said. 'God, I just can't believe it, Julia, that we're really here. Honestly, it just seems too good to be true. When I left that flat this morning, I couldn't believe there wouldn't be a hitch. I don't know – a message at the station – "Will Master Paul Riesman return home at once, all is known" – something like that. And now we're really here.'

'For six whole weeks.'

'Six whole gorgeous weeks with whole gorgeous Julia. What more could anyone want?'

'Another six?' Julia suggested.

Paul said: 'Where's this place Slinky told you about?'

'Somewhere in the south; she'll give us the details when she sees us.'

Slinky met them that evening at the Deux Magots, 'as per arrangement'. She was wearing a fisherman's sweater and a pair of black tights. 'Darling!' she greeted Julia.

Julia said: 'This is Paul.'

'Hullo, Paul,' she said, holding out both hands.

Paul took one. 'How do you do?'

'Honey, I hope you don't mind, I've asked Ali to join us.'

'Who's Ali? Sounds fascinating,' Julia said.

'He's a blissful Arab. Let's have some coffee and I'll tell you all about this place you can go to.'

'*Trois cafés*,' Paul ordered. 'In impeccable French, of course!'

'The woman's name is Madame Fragonard,' Slinky was saying, 'and the village is called Les Marteaux.'

'Let me write that down,' Julia said.

'You get the bus from St Tropez.'

'*Trois cafés*,' the waiter said.

'She won't mind us not being married, will she?' Paul asked.

'This is France, darling, thank God. Over here everyone does it, only Ali doesn't know that, that's why I wanted to tell you about Les Marteaux before he arrives. You see, when I was there the lay wasn't Ali, if you know what I mean.'

Paul said: 'What's all this on the bill about Rendezvousing with the *Élite Intellectuel*? When do they roll up?'

'When the Yanks roll out,' Slinky said. 'Meaning never. J-P.S. stopped coming here when they printed the bills – and he *is* the *Élite Intellectuel*. There's Ali – he's the *Élite* too, but strictly *non-intellectuel*. Big boy! Over here!'

A very short, dark, frizzy-haired man came over to the table. Paul stood up and shook hands uncertainly. Weren't all Arabs anti-Semitic? Paul wondered whether he shouldn't come out quite bluntly and say he was a Jew.

306

Very soon Ali was explaining that the Arabs in Morocco did not hate the Jews because they were too busy hating the French. Paul said boldly: *'Nous sommes tous les deux Juifs.'* Ali shrugged and continued in diarrhoetically fluent French to abuse France, pausing only to order *fines* all round and a packet of *Caporal Jaune* for himself. A Frenchman at the next table joined in querulously and the conversation became general and heated. Paul thought how lucky it was that Britain had no colonial problems.

4

The village was turbaned about the hilltop. The vineyards frogged the lower slopes and between them and the sea the narrow road twisted among pinewoods. It turned and returned across the hillface and then drove between the ramparts into the heart of the village. The bus stopped in the wide square. On one side was the church; on the other, the café, its metal chairs and tables cool under the trellised vine which blinded the hot eye of the sun. Between church and café was a contorted elm, hooped by a wooden bench where old men sat. At the fountain, a girl was taking water in a thin-throated jug. The villagers came across to help unload the bus. Paul and Julia stood in the sun.

'Now what do we do?' Paul asked.

'Ask someone where Madame Fragonard lives, of course.'

'They won't know.'

'Of course they'll know. This is a village. They must know.'

Madame Fragonard's house was in a narrow alley down near the ramparts. The old houses leaned together across the cobbled lane. Wedges of sunlight cheesed into the grey stone. It was very quiet, though as they passed the butcher's they could hear the drumming of flies. Madame

Fragonard was a small woman with a smiling, doggy face and a manner at once friendly and acquisitive. 'It is as well you have come in June,' she told them. 'Later on' – she wrung her hands – 'I am booked solid, you know? Now, here is a room you can have. I call it the Andalusian Room. Andalusia, that's the south of Spain, you know? *C'est jolie, hein?*'

'I'll bet *c'est jolie* expensive too,' Paul whispered.

'I show you another.'

Madame Fragonard's domain was a labyrinth of small apartments, wittily furnished in the various styles which she had selected. 'I started with one house,' she told them, 'and gradually I acquired more. I bought the first one with the compensation when the bus went over the precipice, you know.'

'Was it your bus, Madame?'

'No, it was my husband driving it. Now here we have the Provençal Room. This is a room I would like very much for you to have, but unfortunately it is taken.' Madame Fragonard knocked briefly and went in. 'Ah, Monsieur Bergman, a thousand apologies. I was sure you had gone to the beach. Cosette told me you had gone to the beach. What do you think of that daughter of mine? She told me you had gone to the beach.'

'I did indeed go to the beach, my dear Madame,' replied the Swede. 'I returned to do some writing.'

'Monsieur Bergman is a Professor of Theology. A thousand pardons, Monsieur.'

Bergman, who was doing nothing more private than shaving, smiled dreamily and in his sing-song voice replied: 'My dear Madame Fragonard, you are welcome at any time.'

Madame Fragonard giggled and wagged her finger. 'Monsieur should be ashamed of himself. A Professor of Theology too!'

'Ah,' said Bergman, 'how little you understand of our

Scandinavian theology!' He smiled at Paul and Julia. 'You are staying?'

'If Madame will give us a room we can afford,' Paul said.

'She's a wicked old woman. You're a wicked old woman, Madame Fragonard. You give them a nice room – and don't cheat them.'

'Professor of Theology!' said Madame Fragonard reproachfully. 'Come' – she turned to Paul and Julia – 'I have just the thing for you.'

'You have to bully her. It's the only thing these peasants understand,' the Swede called out.

Madame Fragonard led them through a pass door into yet another of the tiny houses which, stepping down towards the ramparts, provided, at different levels and with different prospects, the many rooms of her establishment. She showed them now a low-ceilinged room scarcely higher than the door which gave access to it. 'The Blue Room,' she announced.

'*Mais évidemment, Madame.*'

'It's sweet,' Julia said. 'Isn't it sweet?'

'You can cook in the kitchen downstairs. It goes with the room, but there is a charge for the gas, you know.' The kitchen, down red-tile stairs, was a tall, narrow room, whitewashed and cool, with a plank table, scrubbed smooth, three chairs and a big wooden cupboard. There were two jugs for getting water from the fountain, crockery of fat earthenware and a drawerful of unmatched knives and forks. When Madame Fragonard was satisfied that no amenity or beauty had been left unrevealed she left them. Julia ran up the stairs. 'It's all ours,' she cried. 'All, all, all ours!'

Paul said: 'I'm going to grow a beard.'

'Like Lawrence,' Julia said.

'Like Gumbril,' Paul replied.

'Oi! No glooming.'

'Take your clothes off then.'

'*Now?*'

'Take them off.'

'Well, lock the door then.'

'There.'

Naked, she stood to attention in front of him. 'Well, here I am.' Her hair stood out crisply over her ears. She tilted her head on one side, smiling, and the hair shifted against her shoulder. Her skin was palest amber in the afternoon sun which just slanted in under the lintel of the tiny window. Her breasts were barely defined, the nipples as small as buds. From her navel to the hair below a faint line was ruled, beside it the little mole sprouted a single silky black hair. Paul raised his hands to her hips. The bones were curved out, and the belly between them was hollow, with a soft pulse in it. His hands trembled to touch her, trembled to believe in her. His hand passed up her side, barely feathering the pout of her breast, to her armpit. She cricked down to him with the shock of the caress and her hair tumbled across her face and her red mouth was there for him and the hair touched his shoulder and chest as he pulled her down to him and fell across her to enclose her, to lie enclosed in the hollow of her belly that was there for him.

5

It was a long walk to the beach, along the narrow earth road which split the vineyards. There were pinewoods nearer the beach and within the pines groves of cork. The bark was piled at the side of the road in long sections, like rusty guttering. They came through the pines, where the Swede always parked his car, to a deep ravine which sliced down, through thorn and cactus, to the sea. A white villa stood up on a high shelf above the cove. One day Paul and Julia walked to it and found it a hollow shell. In the garden tame flowers had gone wild among the trenches and barbed wire which controlled the place. Paul and Julia entered the villa, which was still luxurious with frescoes, great built-in cupboards, niches for statues. You could see down to the private jetty, far below, and the strip of rock where the Swede lay naked, like a white lizard.

'What a wonderful place to live,' Julia said. 'But awfully lonely. I'd be scared.'

'Of what?'

'I don't know. Burglars. Things that go bump in the night.'

'You wouldn't get any burglars here. Too far to walk. Even my blisters have got blisters.'

'Who do you think lived here?'

'What do you want?' Paul demanded. 'A nice piece of fiction? I don't know who lived here.'

'Needn't get ratty.'

'Some fabulously rich people, I suppose. Buckets of servants and champagne. *Le martini est sur la terrasse, Monsieur le Baron.* Probably collaborators.'

'Why do you think the place was wrecked then?'

'I don't know any better than you. I suppose the Boches did it before they left.'

They were in the nursery. Bears and rabbits and squirrels chased each other over the scarred walls. The sea gushed faintly on the rocks.

'I suppose this was the young master's room,' Paul observed. 'Oh, I don't miss much!'

Julia said: 'I'd give anything to have your child.'

'And I'd give anything for you not to have it.'

'I'm sorry.'

'Why can't you leave things alone? Why can't you leave me alone?'

Julia walked out on to the terrace. The sea was bruised with the shadow of clouds.

'Julia,' Paul said, 'I'm sorry. I didn't – mean anything.'

'You don't want me, do you?'

'Want you? Of course I want you.'

'You don't want to be me,' she said. 'You don't want to know what I'm feeling.'

'I want to be me, and I want you to be you.'

'You resent it when I want something.'

'As far as I'm concerned you can have anything you want. I don't want to stop you doing anything you want to do.'

'You don't love me,' she said. 'You don't.'

'Oh, Julia, don't let's talk like this. Don't let's talk like other people. We're not like them.'

'No,' she smiled. 'We're not, are we?'

They went down the steep path to the beach, hand in hand. The sand spread in a wide apron from below the rocks where the Swede was lying. Julia led the way to the far spine of rocks and they put down their towels and her blue bag.

Paul said: 'Look what I've found.'

'What is it?'

'Top of an old scent spray or something, isn't it?'

'Or a throat spray,' Julia said.

'Used by a famous opera star,' Paul suggested. 'Who threw herself off the rocks not an opera star's throw from here.' Julia had stretched face down on the sand. 'Do you ever listen to the Manny Finkelbaum Show?'

'Occasionally.'

'It's absolutely the thing at Cambridge. Do you want me to put some oil on you?'

'Mmm,' Julia said, rolling over. He poured the Ambre Solaire on to her darkening skin and smoothed it over her shoulders – dotted a drop on her nose – and into the fine graining of her breast, down to the strict line of her swimsuit. The tiny hairs came clear with the oil and the sun rusted the down on her arms. He bent down over her and kissed her. 'What about the Swede?' she whispered.

'He's not here,' Paul said. 'No one's here but us.'

312

'Someone is here but us. And anyway you've got no business to feel sexy: we've only just finished lunch!' They always went to bed after lunch, before coming on to the beach. In the mornings, he wrote.

Paul said: 'It's not what I feel; it's what you make me feel like.'

'What do I make you feel like?'

'You. In large quantities. I just – '

'What?'

'Could kill you,' Paul said. 'I could just – kill you.'

'Perhaps you will one day,' Julia said.

'Oh I love you, Julia. I love you.'

'That's nice.'

'Do you love me?'

'You'll do,' she said.

'Oh my God, Julia, where would I be without you?'

'Monmouth Court?'

'And now anywhere where there's a bed is home! It's the only thing no one's managed to spoil for me yet – you and me in bed!'

'And the Swede,' Julia said, 'makes three!'

'I'm warning you, my girl, it'll go hard with you tonight.'

'OK,' Julia said.

He went and played sandcastles, constructing causeways and castles on peaks of stone, looking now and again at her as she lay dozing. She opened an eye and watched him as a nurse might. Julia said: 'The bridge is going to go.'

'Oh, leave it alone, can't you?' he snapped. 'Now look what you've done.'

'I told you it was going.'

'Look, I know what's wrong. I do wish you wouldn't – '

Julia sighed and lay back on the hot sand and closed her eyes. Paul touched her foot. 'I'm sorry. I didn't mean any harm. Look – '

'Don't want to look now.'

'Oh, you might look.'

She opened one eye. 'Very good.'

The bridge slowly sagged. Julia's eye regarded Paul. He frowned and then laughed. 'You wouldn't believe I was Mr Sandcastle 1943, would you?' He grabbed her hand and pulled her up. 'And you'd be right. Come on, let's have a swim.'

Julia swam well but she would not venture out of her depth. Paul was far less stylish but he blundered determinedly out towards the point, calling Julia to follow. The sea was calm and from his flat rock the Swede surveyed them, his hands caressing his pale chest and shoulders. 'Come on,' Paul cried, 'it's lovely out here.'

'I don't want to,' Julia replied, tossing water out of her hair. 'You go.'

'No fun without you. Come on.'

'I'm tired now,' Julia said.

'You shouldn't talk so much.'

'Do you think I'm silly?'

'No. If you don't want to, you don't want to. I just think you're silly, that's all!'

Julia rose out of the water and was only knee deep. Paul wallowed in after her and they shuffled out of the waves. There was a pile of driftwood under the rocks. Paul stopped and extracted a piece of board. 'Hey, we could play cricket.'

'We haven't got a ball,' Julia replied. 'At least not one we can use.'

'What about this?' Paul held up the opera star's scent spray.

'Come on then,' Julia said. They played cricket in the soft sand. The oval scent spray bounced miraculously, breaking both to leg and to off. The game developed its own rules; runs were awarded according to the value set on the stroke by the bowler. For the first time in his life, when Julia clean-bowled him for a duck after scoring fourteen herself, Paul did not mind being beaten. They played another game. Paul bowled a full toss on the leg and Julia hooked it – and the bat – far out to sea. The bat turned over and over in the sun, like a severed wing. Paul swam out for it and the scent spray. When he floundered back to shore Julia was waiting for him, her hands hidden behind her back. 'The umpires have gone in for tea,' she announced. 'I've brought you yours, sir.'

'What's for tea, young lady? And a dashed pretty young lady y'are, if I may say so, by George.'

'Bananas,' Julia said, producing them.

'Bananas for tea!' Paul said. 'Stap me vitals. I shall have to have a word with the secretary.' They stood against each other and fed alternate bites into each other's mouths.

The Swede drew on a pair of canvas shorts and stretched his arms in a gesture of worship. 'Ah, nature,' he cried. 'How I worship nature. What pleasure I have had in watching you two dark, beautiful children here on the beach. You are children of nature. I am a Scandinavian, and above all in Sweden, we revere nature. We do not seek to transcend it. That is why we are not Catholics. Catholics do not recognize nature; for them the study of theology is the study of Catholicism, for me it is the recognition of God and nature, indivisible.'

'You're a Spinozan then?' Paul suggested.

'The greatest of the philosophers,' agreed the Swede. 'Freedom is the recognition of a certain kind of necessity – that is the greatest epigram in the history of human thought. Beyond a certain point it is ugly to resist. To be free one must comply. Then the whole world will be full of love, love and God and nature all one – that is the ideal. It is wrong to resist what the body desires, for therein lies the logic of sin. Do you follow me?'

'I think so,' Paul said, not sure whether he was annoyed or impressed by the Swede's apocalypse.

'One must test that what is wanted is necessary. There is that check, that it must be natural. But you, lovely Mademoiselle, you have your beauty because there is

315

nothing you do which is ugly and you make nothing near you ugly. Ah, that wonderful female acceptance! Woman, the vessel of nature!'

'My wonderful female acceptance,' Julia said, 'is extremely limited.'

'The most beautiful free love in the world is that practised between two faithful lovers. That is the limit which is perfect freedom. That is the ultimate revelation of Spinoza's genius. He was the Jew who saw the absurdity of Jewishness.'

Paul said: 'What's absurd about Jewishness?'

'The absurdity of the Jew lies in his freedom, his unnecessary freedom. He has no proper place. He belongs nowhere. His freedom is utterly spurious: it has no necessity. He is the bee who makes no honey, the spider that makes no web, the bird that has no nest. He has no object. He can never escape from himself. He is cursed with self-consciousness. His terrible necessity is the recognition of a certain kind of freedom. Nations, principalities and powers, he stands above them all, ridiculous. He is the whirlwind who scours the earth and can never rest. How right it is that his God spoke from out the whirlwind, voice without substance, the voice of the Jew throughout the centuries.'

'Immortal,' Paul suggested. 'We are immortal because we are without substance.'

'Substance is the only immortal thing we have. The unique Jew Spinoza saw that, predicted the law of matter's indestructibility when he taught the unity of God and nature – consubstantial, co-eternal, don't you sing that?'

'I'm afraid I'm a non-singer,' Paul said.

'You are in a state of innocence,' the Swede cried, raising his arms over them to the sinking sun. 'You do not understand and it is well. You are Adam and Eve, brother and sister, man and wife, flesh of nature. So far you are without taint. Never leave this place. This is your Eden. I am the serpent who has come between you, the serpent

316

fulfilling his nature, but you have resisted temptation. You have not pursued knowledge and it is good. Children of nature, stay true to life, stay true to nature, your mother. God the mother! That is the paradox of truth. Forget God the stern Jewish father and turn to God the mother, be true to nature and your own nature above and in all things.' Bergman began to walk away towards the rocks whence he had come. 'Adam and Eve,' he called. 'Adam and Eve.' He started up the steep path to the pine wood. 'Adam and Eve, never leave this place.'

Paul said: 'Do you think I should have said we were Jewish?'

'I shouldn't worry,' Julia said. 'Do you think he's cracked?'

'He's all very well as a visitation,' Paul said, 'but he must make a pretty peculiar don.'

'Adam and Eve,' the Swede called down to them and waved. 'Adam and Eve. This is your Eden.'

Eden. Eden. Eden. The word echoed in the ravine.

'It's all very well talking about Eden,' Paul said, 'but it wouldn't have hurt him to offer us a lift back.'

SEVEN

The Strangers

1

THERE WAS a newcomer *chez* Madame Fragonard. 'I hope you do not mind,' Madame said, 'but Mademoiselle will be sharing your kitchen.'

'I shan't be cooking very much,' the girl said. She spoke excellent English.

'Are you English?' Paul inquired.

'Swiss. Annabelle Gutmann. I am a radio announcer,' she explained, peeling white gloves from slender hands. She was wearing a black mohair skirt, coral shoes and a coral blouse. Her face was made up with exquisite care. Only the curved, thin nose defied concealment. 'I expect I shall disturb you very little,' she announced. 'I shall eat out mostly. Tell me, what is there to do here?'

'Swim and lie in the sun,' Julia said.

'Mmm. Well!' she clapped her hands together and touched the tip of her nose with a thumb. 'I must do some unpacking.' She went tripping upstairs.

Julia looked at Paul. 'Attractive?'

'Not to me.'

'She's got a good figure. Be fair.'

'You mean breasts,' Paul said. 'Good figure! You sound like Monmouth Court.'

'I mean she's got a good figure. Her legs are all right, aren't they?'

'I was too busy looking down the front of her blouse to notice.'

'You prefer her to me!' Julia mock-sulked.

'Don't be silly. I couldn't have anything to do with a woman like that.'

Annabelle had changed. She wore black ballet tights, backless cork-wedged shoes, and a man's shirt. She had tied her hair in a horse's tail. 'Now,' she told them, 'I feel more natural.'

Paul said: 'Do you want some supper?'

'Monsieur Bergman is taking me out,' the girl replied. 'All I hope is he won't make a pass. I'm very tired of passes.'

Julia said: 'I don't think you'll have to worry about Mr Bergman.'

'Did you know there was an artist living here in the village?'

'Nobody ever tells us anything,' Paul said.

'I'll introduce you.'

'Better wait till you've met him,' Julia suggested.

'I am waiting for my fiancé to come and join me,' Annabelle said. 'Until then I must find people to entertain me.'

'When's he coming?' Julia inquired.

'When I send for him,' Annabelle replied. 'I've come here to decide whether or not I want to marry him.'

'And how will you decide?' Paul asked.

'He is a very attractive man. I want to find out if the fascination lasts. As it is, I should hate him to go to all the trouble of getting a divorce and then have to tell him that I didn't want him.' She gave them a little wave. 'Well, see you later.'

'She is so sophisticated. She is just so bloody sophisticated.'

'I'm dying to see her fiancé, aren't you?'

Paul said: 'How the hell do you decide whether you want to marry someone?'

When Annabelle came down to breakfast next morning

Paul was already at work. She told him that she had arranged that they should all meet the artist for a drink at the café before lunch. He was a barrel-chested, close-cropped man of about forty-five. His eyes bulged from a square brick-coloured face. You might have taken him for a labourer. 'This is Roque,' Annabelle said, introducing them.

'What will you drink?' Roque demanded. 'No – you are new to Les Marteaux – I will tell you what you should drink. *Marcel, tu viens?* Pastis for our new friends and ice, plenty of ice. He is very mean with the ice.' Roque wrung his hands in the manner of Madame Fragonard. 'Where is our friend *le Suédois* this morning?'

'Gone to lie on his rock, I suppose,' Paul said to Julia in English.

''is rock? What is that?' Paul explained. 'Ah, so long as he does not want to lie on *this* Roque,' Roque cried, banging his chest, 'that is all right.'

'Roque wants to take me midnight bathing,' Annabelle told them. 'Do you think I should go?'

'What sort of things do you trust yourself to decide?' Paul asked.

'Midnight bathing, quite naked, you know,' Roque told Julia, 'it is quite wonderful.'

Julia said: 'It must be.'

'There is too little nakedness in the world. Look at this girl' – he gestured to Annabelle – 'she is never naked enough, that is her trouble. If women wore less clothes they would not look so silly. Ah, here we are. And the ice? Good, good.' The pale Pastis was poured into the glasses. 'Now we add the ice!' The liquid fumed around the ice. 'And the water!' The drink clouded up from yellow to foggy white. 'Now we stir – and we drink! *Le vrai Pastis du Midi!*' To Paul the phrase was an epigram. The artist raised his glass. '*À votre bonne santé,*' he cried. They all drank with splendid and uncertain abandon. The artist wiped his red mouth on the back of his hand and became more expansive. 'I live six months here in Les Marteaux,' he informed them, 'and six in Paris. It is perfect – like having two mistresses who can never meet. To each one protests "You are my first love" and one has the delicious pleasure of betraying each in turn with the other!'

Paul said: 'May we see some of your paintings sometime?'

'I would like very much to paint a picture of Mademoiselle.'

'He's already said he'd like to paint me,' Annabelle told them quickly.

'You I paint after our bathe and not before.'

'I shall have to keep my eye on you, I can see that.'

'No,' Roque brought out another epigram, 'I shall be too busy keeping my eye on you!' He turned to Paul. 'You are a painter?'

'No,' Paul said and blushed, 'a writer.'

'I know lots of writers in Switzerland.'

'I didn't know there were any writers in Switzerland.'

Annabelle pouted. 'I meet them at the Radio Station,' she said.

'Radio writers!' Paul said.

'They're very good, some of them.'

'They are not,' Paul said loftily, 'creative.'

Julia smiled. And yet he longed for acceptance by the *Evening News*. Roque inserted a cigarette into his mouth. 'Come, I show you some of my pictures.'

As the artist unlocked the door of his studio, he told them, 'I bought this place in 1934 for the equivalent of ten pounds English money. Come in. Come in. I paint down here. Through that window you have the light from the east and that for a painter is the best light you can have, and for love too, you know. I get myself up at five in the morning sometimes. Light is purest when it is young.' He began to stack pictures below the easel. 'This is not my best work, you understand, just what I happen to have here.' He put the first one on show.

Paul considered. How did one try to describe paintings? He had the idea that there must be some way in which these pictures could be verbalized. Then it would be possible to criticize them as literature. It should be possible to verbalize everything and criticize it as literature; then everything would be under control. Once everything could be literal, nothing could escape a painstaking mind: everything would be ripe for the killing bottle; it would then be a question of the right gas. The pictures succeeded each other. At each the three onlookers nodded. It was like an identification parade. Roque effaced each canvas with the next, waiting, so it seemed, for one of them to say 'That's the one!' Annabelle tilted her head prettily (she did have a good figure too) and looked knowing, as if she would recognize a good thing if she saw one. Julia stood with her feet slightly apart, her hands behind her back. She looked quite unaffected, but was there perhaps a slight formality in her face? Wasn't she 'doing something'? Could one look at pictures naturally? If only nothing went on in one's head! After a while, Paul asked: 'Will you sell these?'

'When I return to Paris, I will have a show, then I shall sell them.'

The conclusion presented itself: in that case they must be some good. Yet Paul felt total emptiness before these well-rendered cypresses and skilfully blocked cottages, before the whole sterile repertoire of Riviera charm. There was no harm in the pictures, even a certain skill, and since the Riviera was charming, what harm could there be in so presenting it? Yet these paintings were not enough to justify a man living as the artist did: they did not crown his freedom. There was no aspiration in them. They were trivial and they trivialized life. On the other hand, why, as Mr Maugham would have said, take a sledgehammer to kill a fly? Roque was unimportant. To Paul, however, he was not: he impersonated another man, the real artist, and kept him from the sun.

'These are minor works,' Paul said grandly, when the last had been shown.

Julia said: 'I liked the one of the harbour.'

'Wonderful sense of colour,' Annabelle said.

'I'd like you to show me some of your bigger things,' Paul said. 'You must have others.'

'In Paris, but not here. You must come to my studio in Paris.'

'I'd like to see what you think is your best work,' Paul said. He was determined to make the artist good. He wanted him to be good. His contacts with that world into which he longed to be accepted, the world of Art, were so tenuous, that he had to make any chance acquaintance in it a person of great achievement. He wanted to goad the artist into being worthwhile. He wanted to goad everyone to be his best.

'Come upstairs and we will have a bottle of wine. I have something special. Come, I insist.' They stumbled up the narrow stairs after him. Annabelle grabbed Paul's arm: her cork wedges were daintly precarious. She half-fell into his arms before righting herself.

'Oh, dear,' she exclaimed. 'What will your fiancée think?'

Paul said: 'Fiancée?'

'Hullo there, good morning,' a familiar voice sang out from the room they had just quit.

'Mr Bergman!' Annabelle cried. 'How did you get here?'

'My intuition told me you would be here.'

There were no right angles in Roque's living-room. The ceiling sloped upwards to the far end; the tile floor was a bright red wedge of colour under the uneven whitewash of the walls. In the far corner of the room was a single bed, with a headboard of bamboo rods. Hand-sawn shelves protruded over it, and beside it stood a brass-hooped barrel with a candle-holder fixed in the bung. Julia and Annabelle sat on the bed, facing the window. Their view across the valley was bisected by a long gutter of cork bark hung on two chains. The bark was filled with peppers and aubergines, peaches, grapes and oranges, limes and pineapples, lemons and figs. Paul turned to the artist with a smile. 'This,' he said, 'is your best work.'

'Everything you see in this room,' Roque said, 'was found by me personally on the beach. Except the settee, that was here when I bought the house. It is Louis Quinze.'

'I thought I recognized the face,' Paul said.

'All this I found on the beach too.' Roque drew back a curtain to reveal an iron range with many copper pots and pans slung on hooks above it. 'Except for the kettle. That is from Lille.' Annabelle clapped her hands. 'The simple life,' intoned the Swede. 'The simple life!' Roque produced a bottle. 'Riveèsaltes,' he told them, brandishing it before their eyes. 'The finest wine of Corbières.'

'The simple life!' the Swede proposed, and they all drank. 'These two, they are Adam and Eve. You should paint them as Adam and Eve. There is a subject for you. Adam and Eve in the garden of paradise, their own private beach!'

'I would like very much to paint such a subject,' Roque said. 'Why don't you join us on our midnight bathe? Annabelle and I would welcome you.'

'Roque! I haven't said I would come yet.'

'You wouldn't disappoint a man, surely?'

'You don't know Annabelle,' Paul said. 'She could disappoint anyone.'

'You!' the girl pouted at Paul.

'Tonight we will all bathe, yes?'

'Tonight we will all bathe, no,' Julia said.

'You are too modest?'

'They are Adam and Eve,' the Swede said. 'Do not tempt them to share themselves with others. They have only a

324

few weeks together and then Adam and Eve must die. Let them enjoy the garden together until then.'

'Bergman,' Roque said, 'you're an idiot.' He touched Julia's arm. 'You will stay for lunch?'

'No,' Julia said. 'We've got everything at home.'

'He cooks like a god,' Bergman said, 'with the simple fruits of the earth he cooks like a god.'

As they crossed the square, Julia said: 'You didn't think they were any good, did you, face? The paintings, I mean.'

'They were all right. With a place like that he doesn't need to paint. He doesn't need to do anything. He's *happy*. No one who's happy can be an artist.'

'Aren't you happy, Paolo?'

'Yes, I'm happy now,' he scowled. 'It's just that I shall never really be happy. I can't be. I know I can't. That's why I have to be a writer. It's just a hobby for people like Roque. For me, it's an affliction. It's not a question of decision. Nobody else is going to tell me if I've passed the exam or not; they've just got to recognize me, that's all. It's like a bloke who's sure he's got cancer. Whether or not the doctors agree with him doesn't make the smallest difference to what he feels, only to what kind of treatment he gets. No one can cure you of being an artist. Or of being a Jew.'

'You think of everything that's right in you as a disease.'

'That,' Paul said, 'is the advantage of having been to a really first-class public school.'

2

Annabelle said: 'Are you sure you won't come with us? It's a wonderful night for a swim.'

'Have fun,' Paul said.

Annabelle clacked down the steps to the street.

'Coming to bed?' Julia asked.

'Not for a minute.'

'I'll go on up. Will you be long?'

'No, not long.' He could think only of Annabelle, taking off her clothes. He could not want Julia for the strength of this vision, yet he did not want Annabelle but *was* Annabelle; he felt the power of being Annabelle, as if there were a part of him superfluous to himself, free with a wanton freedom to enter into others. What kind of vice was this, to steal into other people's skins and never put oneself to the open test? It was a strange infidelity to Julia to experience the breasts and belly and thighs of another woman, and yet to have done nothing. It was a new life in him, a kind of puberty. He rose and went upstairs, troubled.

Julia was almost asleep, the sheet drawn over her shoulders so that only a whorl of black hair was visible. 'What've you been doing?' she asked drowsily.

'Thinking.'

'What about?'

'Things.' Paul went to open the shutters. He leaned on the sill for a moment, looking down into the narrow street. The downstairs door opened in Madame Fragonard's next house. The Swede came out and hurried away down the alley. 'Ay ay,' Paul exclaimed.

'What's up?'

'*Le Suédois*. Off to spy on Roque and Annabelle.'

'*What?*' Julia sat up. 'He's probably gone to join them, that's all.'

'I don't think so,' Paul said. 'You forget: the Swede is an idealist.'

The next morning, when he had finished work, Paul and Julia went to the *Épicerie* to buy some Petit Brun for tea; as they came out, they saw Roque had taken his place in the Café de l'Ormeau. 'Looks rather sorry for himself,' Julia commented.

'*Post coitum omne animal triste est,*' Paul said.

'What does that mean?'

'It means "After bed everyone feels a bit sorry for himself" or herself, I suppose. I thought you were good at Latin.'

'Not where bed is concerned. I went to a nice school.'

Roque waved to them with jaded bonhomie.

'*Bon bain?*' Paul inquired.

'Not bad. Will you have something to drink?'

'Time I bought you one,' Paul said. He and Julia sat down but evaded Marcel's eye: they were too poor to buy anything for themselves. 'You did go for your bathe then?' Paul asked.

'For our *bathe*, yes.'

'Where's Annabelle this morning?'

'Anna*beau*,' Roque said. Paul roared with laughter. He threw back his head and roared with laughter. Roque shrugged. 'It is well known that Swiss women are very frigid.'

'Was Bergman with you?'

'Monsieur Bergman may not have great passion, but he has great tact.'

When Paul and Julia returned to Madame Fragonard's, Annabelle was in the kitchen. She was frying tomatoes, her red fingernails glossy with oil.

'How was the swim?' Paul inquired innocently.

'Wonderful,' she replied. 'It was a wonderful experience. But very cold!' She wrapped her slim arms round her body and unwrapped them to brush a pop of fat from her shining face. 'You really ought to do it before you go.'

'How did Roque enjoy it?' Julia asked.

'He was magnificent. He is the most tremendous fun to be with – and a wonderful swimmer. I couldn't begin to keep up with him.' Annabelle opened a tin of sardines. 'And then afterwards he kept me up talking till three-thirty. The trouble is, he's such a wonderful talker. You wouldn't think it to look at him, but he is an extremely *cultured* man.'

'No,' Paul said, 'I must say I took him for a primitive.'

Annabelle, fixing stray hairs up into her bun, peeked at Paul under her arm. 'Naughty!' she said.

Annabelle ate her tomatoes and sardines in haste and then rushed off to meet the Swede who had promised her a lift to the beach.

'If he weren't so damned keen on not spoiling our idyll,' Paul observed, 'I should not have the blisters what I have got.'

'You know, Paolo, we really ought to go on a midnight bathe.'

'I'm happy,' he said.

'It would be lovely to swim with nothing on.'

'I didn't realize you wanted to. We could have gone with the others.'

'Would you have rather?'

'No,' Paul said. 'Of course not. Not that I would have *minded* seeing Annabelle without her clothes on. Before she turned into Annabeau, I mean.'

3

It was like another escape to walk down out of the village in the moonlight. There was silence in the olive darkness. They walked delicately through the farms not to wake the dogs. In the ravine to the sea the roots caught the moonlight. The sea was very calm, pathed with silver. Paul and Julia stood on the edge of the water. They looked up at the villa, hollow-eyed as a skull above the cliffs, and round the skyline to the spine of rock which cut into the sea and dwindled below it, to the point. The seaspit was cold, but the sand was soft beneath their feet and they threshed quickly into deeper water, where warmth came to them. Julia plunged down into the water and Paul flung himself down and went after her, out into the bay. Free of the land, their bodies belonged to the sea and the slip of the clear waters which beaded them with its pearls so that they twisted and surged forward in an envelope of bubbles, one past the other, to the deep water, into the darker water, into the cold currents that grew unexpectedly warm out by the tip of the point and beyond the point where they would never have ventured in daylight; beyond the platter of the land-hooped bay they came aside each other, lipped and schooled each other. Julia swam tirelessly; she belonged to the water now she was in it deep. They were alive, even in languor, here in the water; here there was peace, but not slackness. Only the moontrails were slack moorings to the shore, but it was the unconscious real tide that made their mating in the dark water, not the moon's silver glitter.

They stumbled to the soft shore, falling, lurching, as if the land was not their proper place at all. Julia's breast rose and fell for breath. Paul went towards their clothes, but Julia caught his arm, fell on to her knees and kissed him there on her knees, while he stood proud up. Then they ran for their clothes. They rubbed each other with the towels, dressed and climbed the steep path to the woods. They stopped, panting, and stared down at the sea. Then they kissed and started to walk back to Les Marteaux.

In the room, Paul said: 'Pure existence. That's what it was, pure existence.'

'I love you,' Julia said.

Paul frowned. 'The fruit of the tree of knowledge,' he said, 'is speech.'

'I won't talk if you don't want me to,' she said.

'For the first time ever tonight, I really felt as if I might never have to speak again.'

'It must be nice to be a fish,' Julia said.

A week before they were due to leave Les Marteaux, Paul and Julia walked out, after supper, along the Col road. They stopped in a bend of the road and looked back on the village. The slate roofs scaled the heights; yellow lamps flowered in deep-cut windows; cypresses, like black shako-plumes, crowned the hill. The chaffing of insects in the vineyards made a gauze of sound between them and the village; they felt divorced and sad, sitting on the stone parapet of the roadway and gazing at the village.

'I wish we could stay,' Julia said. 'I wish we could get jobs or something and stay.'

'We can't. We've got to go back. It's no use trying to pretend. It'd be nice to be a fish, but we can't be.'

'You don't love me,' Julia said.

'It was your example. Oh, Julia, you can imagine staying here, but I'm not going to be like Roque, a kind of paper Tarzan. I know things. I don't want to know them, I don't want to be them – but there it is. You're different, you're pure. Perhaps you could stay here, but I'm not pure. I know too many things.'

'I'm not pure,' Julia said.

'You don't have – thoughts.'

'What do you mean – thoughts?'

'I don't know. I keep catching myself thinking the wrong things, knowing the wrong things and not able to forget them. I'm afraid – I don't know: I'm not the right shape.'

'You're a lovely shape.'

Paul jumped up on to the parapet.

'Careful you don't fall over, face.'

'It's a sheer drop of two or three hundred centimetres but I don't care.'

'Ass.'

'Oh God, I do wish we didn't have to go back. I do feel like that, honestly.'

'But you know we will go back. Going back is what matters. You don't really care about destroying us, do you?'

'Julia, you're the only thing in the world that matters to me.'

'Am I?'

'You're the only person who knows who I am. If I lost you I wouldn't be myself. Christ, Julia, I don't ever want to lose you.'

'I love you, Paolo. I'd do anything for you.'

Paul came to the end of the parapet and turned and looked down at Julia. He held down his hands to her and she reached up and touched his fingers. 'Catch me,' he cried and jumped out of the darkness. Julia drew back as he hurtled down and he fell past her into the road, crumpled on to hands and knees. 'Paolo,' she whispered at last, 'Paolo, are you all right?'

'I'm all right. Grazed my hands, that's all.'

'For God's sake get up.'

'You were supposed to catch me,' he scowled.

'I – I was scared – I couldn't have held you.'

'If you'd just stood still I'd never have fallen.'

'You came at me, like – like a buffalo.'

'If I get tetanus and die, it'll be your fault,' he said. 'You should have caught me. I asked you to. If I can't rely on you, who can I rely on?'

'You can rely on me. For the right things.'

'What are they? What are they, Julia?'

'Have you really cut yourself?' Julia asked. 'If so, we'd better go and bathe it.'

'Oh, it's only a graze; don't make such a fuss.'

'You might get tetanus.'

'I doubt it,' Paul said. 'Nothing ever really happens to me.'

Slinky said: 'How many days late are you?'

'Six,' Julia said.

'Six days! God, that's nothing. Remember when we had to dose Alyson?'

'I remember when we had to dose you,' Julia said.

Slinky scratched herself under the left breast. 'God, this bra's tight. Come with me while I buy another?'

'Paul's waiting.'

'Where's he gone?'

'Bookshop. I said I'd pick him up.'

'Why didn't he come with you? Embarrassed?'

'He just doesn't want to know.'

'Poor poppet! But honestly, darling, there isn't anything to worry about. Six months, yes, but six days, honest-lee!'

Julia said: 'I know I'm preggers, Slinks.'

'Well, there's only one thing for it – the old dose. No time like the present – except the past, of course. Now don't *worry*. Look, I'll tell you what: I'll pop in here for the quinine. You pop over the road to the Green Cross for the castor oil.'

Julia obeyed. She was not afraid of taking the stuff, though she expected it would give her a bloody pain, but she was filled with revulsion. She had delivered herself into Slinky's hands and how willing the girl was and how well equipped to destroy what was in her, to treat all that was true in life as a kind of hangover! Everything that was for life was alien to Slinky. Slinky would draw attention to her breasts, which were good admittedly, and she was so safely attached to them that she could afford to joke about them. Julia's breasts were small, and though she had a good figure she knew no one turned in the street to get

another look at her front. Slinky annoyed her into awareness of the individual features of herself: with Slinky, Julia
felt on show, split up like a cow on a joint chart. Julia
hesitated outside the Green Cross. Slinky was the sort of
girl who before a dance gave you sincere, girl-to-girl advice
on how to make the worst of your best point, so that you
should not compete too much with her. And now Slinky
was so keen that she should get rid of what was in her.
Julia wanted the child, not for morality's sake, but for
herself. Slinky came out of the chemist's and watched the
traffic, waiting to cross over. Then there was Paul to
consider, and his freedom to be himself. There was Paul
who could bear the thought of nothing, neither of staying
with Julia nor of returning to Wimbledon. There was Paul,
whom she loved, seeking refuge from life among books.
Julia went into the Green Cross and bought the castor oil.

Paul was conning a shelf of books in soft covers: *White
Thighs, Thongs, Love of the Lash, the Naughty Lovers*. He
longed to find a chronicle of debauches so enticing and so
delicious, so disgusting and so repugnant that a new
dimension of sexuality would be revealed to him. These
comings-together of dedicated hedonists did not fail to
prick excitement but, for all the efforts the authors and
their creatures made, a pale and fretful scratching filled the
books. Even verbally the possibilities of such a life were
soon exhausted. Repetition was its only form. The fantasist
could not be restrained from concocting naughty recipes,
for the ingredients were there and did have names, but in
the end they satisfied lonely appetites and suited only
those whose days were pappy with books and wan with
impotence. The concept of total eroticism was bogus,
reached only by the folding of repetitive mirrors. Paul
closed the books with a dull desire for that heady sex and
yet, for the life that was still in him, shuddered at it. He
walked to the door of the shop. It would need effort to turn

the complexity of faces and bodies which thronged the boulevard into the glazed mush of smilers who actually filled that waxy-fleshed pornographers' world. Yet Julia was pregnant and remembering that, how much better it would be to live in the safe solitary world of thongs, where one's pleasure could not have this unfair culmination! The consequences of an act should have some relation to the act itself; that pregnancy should cap six weeks of simple happiness was like receiving a life sentence for picking flowers in the park. It was impossible to think of the pregnant girl and the girl with whom he had spent those six weeks as one person: Julia had vanished with this other girl's coming. Julia was a stranger. Would he even recognize her when she came to the shop for him? Well enough, well enough. Oh, they were the same: the pregnant girl who carried his child and Julia, they were the same. No, he did not want to marry, he did not want to quit Cambridge, he did not want a living. He was only a boy. Oh, God, to have no respect for people, to be able to say, 'You've had fun and so have I, and now – good-bye!' How bitter it was and how unfair to have to stand by people! Perhaps she would not come back, perhaps she and Slinky – a fast car, a bus, the sickening wail of a hooter and then silence. Paul winced away the thought. If only one lived in a pornographer's world, where pregnancy never occurred, where orgasm succeeded orgasm without the need for resurrection, without the need for being alive between one and the next. What about all these carefree students swinging down the Boulevard St Germain, why were they different from him? Why could one not pitch women into the gutter, as surely they did, especially when a considerable literature proclaimed that they liked it? But Julia loved him, and he . . . What was love? Did he love anyone? The cinema across the boulevard advertised *L'Amour, Madame*: black silk stockings, hands on knees under night-club tables, footy-footy, as they called it in Wimbledon.

Was that the life, a series of affairs, of mirrors folded about oneself? The cycle of love: the French and how they handle it: Chapter one: Le first meeting; Chapter two: Le heart-to-heart; Chapter three: Le first assignation; Chapter four: Le first protestation of undying love; Chapter five: La Nuit D'Amour, breasts and bottom in the moonlight 'I will never forget zis night, chéri'; Chapter six: Passion 'Ah nevair knew eet could be like zis'; Chapter seven: Ennui and the sight of a new face, Zizi's jealousy; Chapter eight: Parting 'Eet was too 'ot not to, 'ow do you say, cool down'; Chapter nine: Le first meeting. That's the life, eh, Paolo? Fantasy and Fugue. That's the kind of book I want to be in. Open the soft covers, I want to get in. And what about Chapter ninety-three, what would that be? Ze first meeting, ze chorus girl, ze ze ze. One would go through life weighing each woman by the time it would take to crack her thighs. One's eyes would crinkle with nature's oldest craft, the tired professional eyes that never fought at an unfavourable weight, that risked nothing. And one's mouth, one's mouth would have the same cynical lips that said, on smug evenings at Monmouth Court, 'I was a Socialist at your age.' God, Paul thought, let us have the child! Let us give up everything and rightly have this child. For what? For what, after the great scene? To bring a Jewboy into the world and send him to the gas-chamber or to Benedict's. Bring a Jewboy into the world and be a parent — a named brand — a parent with do's and don'ts at one's finger and school fees every quarter. Bring a Jewboy into the world and be responsible for him, tell him, 'One must do twice as much to get half as far — that's what it means to be a child of mine.' Bring a Jewboy into the world and say, 'Tolerance, my boy, is what we must hope for, tolerance — and meanwhile punch them on the nose if they call you a name.' If they call you a Jewboy, if they call you a son of mine, punch them on the nose. Is that the life to promise my son, crouched away from the light that people may not think him pushing? I'll never do it, I'll never be father to a Jew, to a cripple, to a twisted, stunted, careful-how-you-go kind of child. And yet I can be father to no other. I can bring nothing but agony and shame to all who know me. Julia, Julia, fool to know me, fool to love me. The world hates me and I hate the world: I'd like to kick it to hell like a football, but I have no power against it, no rights in it, nothing. Poor Julia, that loves me, let us cling to each other in this tunnel of life, let us love each other, but while we wait to die, let us not, for God's sake, create another wretched thing to wait out its time too. Let us die out here, Jews, and be gone, for God's sake. Let us die, if we can, in each other's beds, for comfort's sake, but let us die, let us die.

Julia said: 'Hullo, face. Dreaming?'

'Oh, hullo. What happened?'

'I had to buy a bra, darling. Sorry we've been so long. What do you think of it?'

'Lush,' Paul said. 'Did you get the stuff?'

Slinky said: 'Easy as kiss your fanny, darling. The chemists round here reach for the stuff as soon as any woman under thirty comes into the shop.'

'It's nearly lunch-time,' Paul said. 'Do you feel like eating, darling?'

'I don't think I'd better. Not if I'm going to take this stuff.'

'God,' Paul said.

'Don't worry. I'll get rid of it. You have lunch with Slinky. You're hungry, aren't you?'

'Yes, I'm afraid I am. I wish I wasn't.'

'I'll go back to the hotel and take some stuff. You have lunch with Slinks.'

'Will you be all right?'

Julia nodded. 'I'll be all right,' and marched quickly away.

'This would have to happen,' Paul said. 'Bloody bad luck.'

'We may as well go to Raffi, shall we?'

'I don't care where we go.' He took her arm for them to cross the Boulevard. 'Tell me, how's Ali these days?'

'Gone back to Morocco.'

'Why's that?'

'Oh, I don't know exactly. Someone else's teethmarks in my bottom, I expect.'

Paul said: 'Do you ever want to get married, Slinks?'

'I'd like to have some kids one day. There's plenty of time for that though. I might get round to it one day.'

'We'd better decide what we're going to have,' Paul said. 'Here comes Gladys.'

They ordered Châteaubriands. *'Deux Châteaux, je commande,'* the waitress shouted down the hatch. *'Deux!'*

Slinky said: 'You look awfully mizz, darling.'

'I cave in easily,' Paul said.

'So do I, darling.'

'Are you ever serious about people, Slinks, really?'

'I could be, about the right person. I just haven't found him yet.' A black-jeaned, leather-jacketed young man with an oval, olive face came into the restaurant. His eye fell on Slinky, who had her back to him. Slinky said: 'Is my radar system deceiving me or is someone looking at me in a certain way?'

'Someone is.'

'Madame de Maintenant, that's me,' Slinky said.

The young man sat down at the next table and opened a newspaper. Paul said: 'I must be getting back.' He rose and put three hundred francs on the table. 'I'll leave you two young people together.' The young man turned over a page in his newspaper with ferocious diligence. Paul left the restaurant. He wondered how easy Slinky really was. Did she really go to bed with people and think no more about it? Then why shouldn't he, just once? The possible had an undefined lure. And if Slinky got pregnant she would get rid of it without regret; she wouldn't expect anyone to clear up her mess for her. Bed with Slinky would be like taking your turn at the fair. She would test your strength all right: once you had taken up the challenge you would have to make damn sure you hit the thing right bang in the middle and rang the big bell at the top that proclaimed you had passed the test and proved your manhood. Slinky one had to defeat. And one day she would retire, she said, and get married and have kids, and what would that make her husband? The one she didn't put the stopper in for. The one that gave her the kids. Slinky was like a cat and would be with her husband, the man with whom she would live her ninth life, secret, revealing nothing when what he did to her recalled other incarnations. Paul ran across the Boulevard St Germain and down the Rue Napoléon to the Rue Jacob where the hotel and Julia were.

EIGHT

The Return

1

JULIA WAS LYING on the bed in the room. Her lips looked brown in the dim light. Paul said: 'How do you feel?'

'Dizzy,' Julia said. Paul's head seemed to spin. He lay down on the bed and took Julia's hand. 'Christ, I'm sorry about this.'

'I feel so *dizzy*.'

'What can we do? Can't you take something?'

'It's like poison: there's no point in taking it if you don't want it to work.'

'This had to happen. It had to happen to me.'

Julia let out a gasp of laughter. 'To you it had to happen! You don't care a damn about me.'

'Julia, for God's sake – '

'You don't. You don't love me.'

'I ran all the way – '

'You don't love me. You don't.'

'I ran all the way back to the hotel. Julia, I do care. I do, darling.'

'Leave me alone. I've got such a pain. Such a pain.' She twisted away from him and drew up her knees.

'You don't love *me*,' he said, sitting on the side of the bed, his back to her.

'You're so selfish,' she cried. 'You're so damned selfish.'

'All right. All right. I'm selfish. I'm a Jew and I'm selfish. OK. OK, Julia. OK. Oh Julia, honestly, I don't want you to be in pain – '

'Don't you wish you had some anaesthetic with you? Don't you?'

'What?'

'Pain and pleasure,' Julia said. 'Jesus!'

Paul snatched an ashtray off the bedside table and slammed it on to the carpet. It did not break. He kicked it under the bed. 'I wish I was dead. I wish to God I was dead.'

Julia said: 'Don't worry. It'll be all right.'

'Do you really think so?'

'Sure,' Julia said. 'Nothing ever really happens to you, remember? You'll go up to Cambridge again OK. It'll be all right for you.'

He put his hand on her belly. 'One day it'll be all right for you, too, Julia. I promise you.'

'Do you, face? Can you really promise?'

'I do want it in a way, Julia, I do. It's just that – I want to want it, but I don't.'

'You won't have it,' she said, levering herself off the bed. 'I must go to the lavatory.' She hobbled out of the room. Paul was dead. His eyes glazed over with the pattern of the leaves on the dado. He lay dead. The door opened. Julia was pale as mutton fat.

'Any luck?' Paul asked.

Julia shook her head. 'Obstinate little bastard, your child,' she said.

2

The crowds at Victoria hurried for buses and taxis. Paul and Julia stood under the clock where they had met so happily, escapers, six weeks before. Paul said: 'How do you feel now, darling?'

'I don't feel any different,' Julia said.

'God, Julia –'

'It'll be all right. Don't worry about it.' Julia patted his arm. 'You'd better get along home. Your folks'll be wondering what's become of you.'

'Just so long as they haven't come to meet me,' he said.

Julia said: 'Will you phone me, Paolo?'

'Come to Wimbledon,' he said. 'Now. And we'll tell them. Now – together.'

'No, the curse is only seven days late. I'm not a fallen woman yet.'

'I'll phone you tonight.'

'Well, I suppose I'd better be – going.'

'Shall I see you tomorrow?'

'You'd better ring and see if I'm otherwise engaged.'

'Do you want a taxi?'

'I'll get a 2 bus.'

They walked out to the bus-port.

'Come out to Wimbledon, Julia. Please.'

'No, it's no good.'

'They'd forgive us,' Paul said.

'Oh, how sweet you are, Paolo!'

'They would, honestly.'

'Maybe they would,' Julia said. 'But you wouldn't.'

'You'd better go on this one,' Paul said. 'I don't want you to have to stand all the way home.'

'I'm going,' she said.

'Julia, I will make it up to you. I swear I will.'

'Make it up,' she said. 'Yes, I know.'

Paul turned and walked back into the station. In the Underground people kept staring at him. He stared back belligerently until he realized why: his ruddy beard. Poor old Gumbril! What a packet he'd caught. Serves him right, for playing the man. The beard had to come off. As Nat said, 'You can't expect toleration if you will assert yourself all the time.' Be modest, and while you're being modest, smile.

Paul took a taxi from Wimbledon Station. It was rather

fun to be home again. He wondered whether there would be any letters for him and what the gossip was. Had Penny Paynter been up to any of her tricks again? As the taxi breasted Wimbledon Hill it occurred to him in a flurry of panic that he was supposed to have been abroad with Tom Wallace. He began to reconstruct the whole holiday on the assumption that Tom had been his companion. The substitution was not too difficult or too implausible, particularly since his parents had never met Tom, nor so far as Paul knew anyone from Rochdale, and would not detect the falseness of the whole provided the detail was convincing and 'fun'. The whole question would not occur to them: why should two undergraduates spend six weeks in one small village – without classical connexions – in the South of France? Big questions were not much the vogue in Wimbledon. The question 'Why do we do as we do?' was a form of treason.

Paul embraced his parents with genuine pleasure and relief at their smiles (showing they knew nothing) and rushed upstairs to put his things in his room and found a new filing cabinet there by his desk and came clumping down again to thank his father whose gibes about 'the bearded pard' had to be endured and smiled at. 'There was no point in shaving there,' Paul said.

'Didn't you scare the girls off?'

'Weren't any girls.'

'And are we to have the barbed-wire entanglement till the end of the vac?' Nat inquired.

'Maybe.'

'I don't think it's quite the thing for the Hospital Ball.'

'Daddy got you a double ticket. We thought you might like to bring – well, I suppose it'll be Julia.'

'When's this?'

'September the fourth.'

'Wonder how the beard'll go down with the lady.'

'Oh, she – she won't mind.'

'Did you tell her about it?'

'Tell her? When?'

'When you wrote to her. I suppose you did write to her?'

'Oh yes, rather.'

'We thought you might have,' Alma smiled. Nat was smiling too. They were so happy to see him. Paul felt near to tears. He resented having to worry about Julia.

'Well,' he said when he phoned her. 'How goes it?'

'It doesn't.'

'Christ. Christ. Christ.'

'It's no use getting upset.'

'Have you taken some more stuff?'

'You don't get a pain like this from just sitting around.'

'God, Julia, I'm so sorry, darling. I'd do anything – '

'I miss you dreadfully,' the girl said.

'Me too,' he replied. 'How're your folks? They don't suspect anything, do they?'

'No. How about yours?'

'Oh, they're OK. Dad's got tickets for the Hospital Ball. Want to come?'

'When is it?'

'Fourth of September.'

Julia chuckled. 'I might be three months by then.'

'Christ, it must work soon, surely.'

'So must I,' Julia said. 'I start job hunting on Thursday.'

So their lives together were broken apart, not even the bud of life in Julia could hold them together; its presence served only to destroy Paul's peace of mind. If only it could be quenched all would be right again, all would be dead right. Paul made a firm start on his vacation reading: Cicero, Thucydides, Theocritus, Lucan, Horace, and Pindar: Taylor, Cornford, and Burnet. The dead words were on the page. It was another symptom of his fragmentation, of the dull devotion to death which was his hallmark. When he went up to Cambridge at the beginning of his first term he thought he would really learn something new, but here he was like a schoolboy, translating, reading other people's compositions, imitating, imitating and imitating above all death. Death in place, death in emotion, death in language.

The phone rang. Julia said: 'It's all right.' She burst into tears and hung up. Now everything was all right. Now nothing was not dead. He looked out of the window at the sugary blocks of Monmouth Court: now he was a normal son of Monmouth Court again. Now he was all right. The Swede had said on the beach at Les Marteaux: 'You should never leave this place.' Paul curled his upper lip and winced his eyes shut. What happened to Adam and Eve was this: they lost each other in the crowd.

3

Paul sent the stories he had written at Les Marteaux to various magazines and one by one, as the weeks passed before he was due to return to Cambridge, each of them was returned. He always hoped for one sentence of hand-written comfort, but he never got anything but printed rejection slips. Julia said: 'All the best people had hundreds of stories rejected before they became successful.'

'Yes,' Paul replied, 'and all the worst people had millions rejected before they became failures.'

His second year at Cambridge began aimlessly. His reading list was full of books he had duly read, but he remembered little; there was no reason to remember anything. Nat believed a First was a passport through life, but life seemed such a world away, even now when so short a time in fact lay between him and it, that Paul was indifferent alike to fear and to hope concerning his fate in it. There was nothing but dead drudgery in the proses and verses which he was still expected to compose; there was no harm in Cambridge, people were pleasant enough, the days passed easily in the drinking of coffee, making of tea, in reading James Joyce and talking about sex and God, but that any great influence was at work on him Paul regarded as absurd. Other people seemed busy enough, with their societies and their rowing, their diligent trips to the University Library, but Paul was bedded in boredom.

It was in this mood that he received a letter from Benedict's asking whether he would care to play in the Old Walkerites versus the House football match at the end of December. Connaught, Harper, Williams, Podge, and Simpson had all accepted invitations. 'I believe they were all here with you,' said his correspondent coaxingly. Benedict's! That at least was another world, that at least was something he would never have to go back to. Paul lit a cigarette; to smoke when he was alone somehow alienated him from himself. He regarded his Benedictine self with a sneer: 'Well, why don't you go, if you think you're cured? Why don't you?'

4

The eighty-nine steps curved down to the fag entrance of Mr Walker's house. Paul, in his college scarf, stood on the landing at the top and gazed down on the house. What was there to fear? What was there even to remember? What terrible things had they done to him? For three days, during one term of his time there, a few people had been nasty to him. For the rest, he had had his share of privileges and pleasures: so why the butterflies in the stomach, Master Riesman, as you stand at the top of the eighty-nine steps? He stared down towards the heavy grey block.

'Wotcher, Reecers?' It was Connaught.

'Hullo, David,' Paul said. They had been monitors together in their last year.

'Come down to play in this free for all?'

'I haven't come to play lacrosse,' Paul said.

'What are you up to these days?'

'I'm at Cambridge,' Paul said. 'You?'

'I'm doing agriculture, you know. Seen anyone else?'

'Not yet,' Paul said, 'but I'm hoping.'

'Hullo, there's Simpers!'

Simpson had arrived on his motor-bike. He removed his goggles and waved to them. 'Carry on smoking,' he said.

'Wotcher, Simpers,' Connaught said.

'Hullo,' Paul said.

Simpson unslung his boots from the handlebars. 'Do you think I shall be able to borrow some things? I've only brought these and my house-team socks.'

'I'm sure,' Paul said, 'you'll find a whole range of first-eleven colours laid out waiting for your inspection.'

'Anyone else here?' Simpson inquired.

'We're just going round to knock up the House Man,' Connaught said.

'I saw Harry in the garden as I came by.'

'So they've planted him out at last, have they?' Paul said. 'Plenty of lime around the crutch, that's the great thing.'

Podge and Harper were having sherry with the house-master. Podge was wearing a blue suit with a silver tie and a gold pin. He was an executive, so he told them, in ICI. He had come down from London on his mo-ped. 'They're jolly good things actually, sir,' he was telling Mr Walker, who, with his tongue prancing out to wet his lips, was doubting their ability to stand up to long journeys. Harper was wearing an Old Benedictine scarf. It looked as though he had wrapped himself in yards and yards of Neapolitan ice-cream. He had grown very fat. 'Ah,' Simpson said, 'I can see someone's been ripening you for Christmas.'

'Now then, Simpers, watch it,' from Harper.

'Oh, is that what it is?' Paul said. 'I thought he'd been specially pumped up for this afternoon's game.'

The head monitor came in when the visitors' team was

almost fully assembled and informed the housemaster 'The house waits'. Mr Walker looked nervously round and then nodded to his wife to lead the way. 'Must have been working out if he could afford to feed us,' Paul whispered to Simpson.

The faces of the house were turned towards the door of Hall, through which the housemaster and his party had to pass. Paul felt extremely nervous. He was sure he looked terribly Jewish. He folded his arms sternly while the head monitor read grace. When grace was finished, there was much scraping of benches and chairs as everyone sat down. Now the house butler was due to appear carrying the joint to the housemaster's table. Paul smiled at the thought of seeing old Parch again. The door of the buttery opened. A neat, thin, monkey-jacketed man entered. He placed the joint deferentially before Mr Walker, quite unlike Parch, who used to ram it down with a force which often silenced the whole room. 'Thank you, Veneker,' said Mr Walker, fretting the carving knife between the roundels of the sharpener. 'What's happened to old Parch?' Paul demanded of the monitor next to him. 'He's left,' replied the other, with a shifty look at the House Man. Mr Walker was licking his lips in earnest assessment. Simpson had just asked him how the garden was doing.

The senior changing room had been made over to the visiting team and while they were bedecking themselves in the various colours, from house teams to first eleven, to which they were entitled, Paul turned to Simpson for news of Parch. 'Has he retired or something?'

'Sacked,' Simpson said.

'Parch? What the hell for?'

'Embezzling.'

'Embezzling? Embezzling what?'

'You'll have to ask Harry.'

'That shit,' Paul said. 'I wouldn't ask him the time.'

'Oh come, what's wrong with Harry?'

'He is a tit.'

'The things you learn at Cambridge,' Simpson said.

'Isn't it awful? When was he sacked?'

'A couple of terms ago,' Simpson said.

'Without his pension, I presume?'

'I presume so.'

'How convenient! How too damned convenient!'

'Been pilfering for years apparently.'

'Coming?' Harper asked. His fat legs were bursting from his school fourth-eleven shorts. The boots on his feet, which were the only thing about him which had not grown, seemed so diminutive that you wondered how he could balance on them. Podge had brought a hanger for his blue suit and trees for his shoes. He too had grown fatter, but there was a cold restraint about him; he was one of those firm-fleshed fatties who still retain an unexpected agility. Connaught looked aggressively fit and started 'doubling on the spot', his boots striking sparks out of the changing-room floor. ''ush,' said a voice. 'Simmer.' Bryan Stewart was standing in the door of the changing room.

'Christ,' Paul said. 'The Thing from the Haunted Whore-House.'

'Everybody outside for PT,' Stewart cried, advancing into the room and beginning to throw off his clothes. 'No cheek from you, young Riesman.'

'No one told me you were coming, Bryan,' Simpson said.

'Ah, well, Simpers my lad, you have to save the best for last. Do you know the House Man just told me they haven't beaten anyone for two and a half years? Can you believe it? Don't know what the old house is coming to.'

'It's nice to have someone here from the Bronze Age,' Paul said.

'Still the same Riesman here, I see.'

'That old eagle eye of yours doesn't miss much, does it, Stewart? Though I must say it looks a bit odd in a pigeon.'

'There is something I could say to you, young Riesman, so I should shut up if I was you.'

Podge's blue eyes glinted behind his glasses. Harper winked. Paul looked at his watch. 'Well, we'd better be going up, I suppose.' It needed but one word and the old laughter would ring out against him. So now again he must shepherd them out of the room, must not leave except with the main body, lest behind his back the old taunts be heard again. Why had he not stayed safely in his new refuge? Why must he always try to reform the past when much the best thing was to forget, to make a new start? 'I will be modest, I will smile. I will deserve their toleration.' There could be no other departure from the premise of being Jewish than this repeated resolution. He could see himself coming down to Benedict's year after year to play in this match, always taunting his contemporaries to see if they had forgotten he was a Jew and always finding that they had not, that they would accept his cleverness, allow him even to deride them, only because they knew that when it came to it they could destroy him with a single truth: Jew.

Paul played centre-forward. It was the only position he really enjoyed. He scored two goals, one of them offside, but the thrill was the same – the ball in the net, the goalie in the mud and Paul's own Roy Bentley pose. That he did the scoring was evidence of his superiority to the anonymous team, just as his name on the spine of a book would be, for what could they compare to the name he had made for himself, Connaught, a farmer, Podge, an executive, Simpson, a laboratory boffin, Stewart, the Kenya policeman? If he could only succeed, if he could only be famous, that would show them, that would muzzle them, for he would have made another name for himself but Jew.

After the match there was tea in Hall for the two teams. Mr Walker came down to congratulate the visitors who had won 4–2. 'I fear,' he observed, 'that brawn was too much for brain.' 'Oh, sir, I say!' Connaught said. 'Can't allow that,' Harper cried. 'Sir,' Paul said, 'where is Mr Parch living these days?'

Walker said: 'Er – Mister – ?'

'Parch,' Paul said.

'Oh, um, I have the address in my study somewhere if you'd care to stop by later.'

'I would,' Paul said. 'Sir.'

'Well, Harry,' Bryan Stewart said, 'it was a bloody good game!'

'It was in point of fact most stirring.'

'You'll have to turn out next year, sir,' Podge said.

'I shall not in actual fact be here next year.'

'Why not, sir?'

'I have been offered the headship of Harnwarth.'

'Harnwarth? Where on earth is that, sir?' Stewart inquired.

'Very excellent little school in the north country,' Walker replied. 'Surprised you haven't heard of it, Bryan.'

'Oh, I've heard of it, sir,' Harper said.

Paul felt himself unreasonably shaken by Walker's news. He realized how deeply he relied on Benedict's. He had fancied that each year the same cast would assemble to honour his increasing fame. It was not that he had abandoned Benedict's to become a writer, but that he was becoming a writer to get back into Benedict's. He had thought that he despised Benedict's, that it was as if he had never been there, but now he saw how dependent he was: without the system his triumph over it was meaningless.

Mr Parch's house was in a row of smoke-blackened cottages near the station. A woman came to the door. 'Yes?'

'Um, is Mr Parch in, please?'

'Arthur. F'you.'

Mr Parch came out of the parlour. He was in his braces and there was a pipe between his teeth. His hair was whiter, but his brows were still that gingery shade Paul

350

remembered and the amber eyes bulged from under them.
'Hullo, Mr Parch,' Paul said.

''ullo, what do you want?'

'I was passing so I thought I'd come and see you.'

'Come in,' Parch said.

The parlour was stuffy with pipe smoke, the furniture
yellowed to almost the same shade as Parch's eyebrows.

'I can't stay, I just wondered how you were.'

'Alive.'

'I – I was sorry to hear about – it.'

'That son of a Hongkong whore,' Parch said. 'Three
months to me pension. Three months. And he wouldn't let
me work it out. Son of a Tokyo tart.'

'What happened exactly?'

'Bleedin' packets of Persil, bleedin' packets of bleedin'
Persil.'

'No pension at all?'

'Not a farthing. Not even my contributions. Not even
my bleedin' contributions.' Parch's thumb tamped the
tobacco in his pipe. 'I'd like to do that sod. I wouldn't mind
hanging for it. Not if I could really do 'im properly. So he
knew.'

'I've been up there, you know – playing football.'

'Oh yes? 'Course they done it to avoid 'aving to pay me
pension, stands to reason. Robbery, that's what it is.'

'What are you doing with yourself these days, Mr Parch?'

'Bit 'ere, bit there,' was the reply. 'What you doin' with
yourself?'

'I don't do it with myself any more, Mr Parch,' Paul said.
'I've found myself a girl to do it with.'

Mr Parch nodded gloomily. 'Creepin' Jesus. Talk about
creepin' Jesus.'

Paul said: 'Best advice anyone ever gave me, that was,
Mr Parch. Do you remember?'

'What was 'at then?'

'About finding a girl,' Paul said.

'Twenty-eight bob a week,' Parch said, 'that's what I'm getting. Twenty-eight bob a week. I look out of my window in the morning and I see that bloody great 'ill up there and the school on the top of it and I think – well, never mind what I think.'

Paul put his hand in his inside pocket, for his wallet. 'You know, Mr Parch,' he said, 'I left rather suddenly and I don't think I ever saw you before I went, did I?' Paul took out his wallet and pulled two pound notes from it. 'I'm afraid it isn't much, but – well, I'd like to give you this.' He held out the money. Parch's amber eyes twitched from Paul's face to the money and back. 'You're the first bloke ever done that,' Parch said.

'Done what?'

'Come back 'cos he's forgotten to tip me – and the last, eh?' Parch coughed his amusement.

'Ah, well,' Paul said, 'typical of these Jews to come back to pay their debts.'

Parch struck a match to his pipe. 'You're all right,' he said at last.

'Thank you, Mr Parch.'

'Yers, you're all right, got your life before you, you're all right, you've got nothing to worry about, you've 'ad the right start, even if you don't get anywhere at all, you'll end up higher than any of us could 'ave got 'owever 'ard we worked.'

Parch's wife came in. 'You'll have a cup of tea with us, won't you, sir?'

'Paul's my name. No, actually, I must be going. Got a train to catch. Um, I only called in to see how Mr Parch was.'

'He's all right,' said his wife.

'Cup o' tea, Cissy, eh?'

'I just wanted to know if the gentleman was staying.'

'No,' Paul said, 'it's very kind of you, but I really must

be going.' Paul took a step to the door. 'Well, cheerio, Mr
Parch.'

'I'll see you out, sir.'

Paul held out his hand to Mr Parch. The other took it
sheepishly, as if for a photograph. Paul held it and let go
and walked briskly out of the door, into the lavender
evening. From the top of the rise which climbed to the
station yard Paul looked back on the row of cottages and
there welled in him again a feeling of total love and total
impotence; he had so much that he wanted to give and no
means by which to give it. The whole world deserved his
love. He longed to lie down over the whole world and
warm and love it; its brutal, dull despair came to him
through the still evening air and he hated his own puniness,
his fatuous efforts to assuage a man's empty life with a
couple of quick pound notes; he hated himself for his
pretension and for his pretence that he was not pretentious.
He turned and hurried into the station, making sure, as he
ran into the light, that his return half was safe in his wallet.

NINE

The Final Analysis

1

PAUL'S TUTOR, Mr Wrightson, was a burly, jovial man of an aggressively hearty disposition. No one could have been less of an intellectual or less of a pedant; he and Paul regarded each other with a puzzled amiability which was the fruit of an awareness on both sides that nothing the one could say would have the faintest effect on the other. Mr Wrightson viewed most of his tutorial duties with humourous resignation, so that even if he was reminding you of the college rule that you must not throw milk bottles from third-storey windows into the Cam, he conveyed to you that he personally was quite indifferent to your misdemeanours. The contrast with Mr Walker's meticulous severity could not have been greater. Wrightson was a man, not the implement of a system. He stood on his own, smoked his own pipe and chucked his own weight about: he needed no systematic crutches. 'Any ideas what you're going to do when you go down?' he demanded of Paul during one of their infrequent meetings.

'I'm going to be a writer, sir,' Paul replied. He still could not shed his servile deference to those in authority.

'If you're going to be a writer,' said Mr Wrightson, eyes popping out over the top of his pipe, 'aren't you going to need some sort of a job to keep body and soul together? Or do you plan to starve in a garret like all the best people?'

'I suppose I shall need something, sir. In journalism, I imagine. I did a bit before I came up.'

'I usually suggest to my pupils that they go along and see the chaps at the University Bureau at about this stage, see if they've got any ideas that'd interest you. They're a good lot of chaps. Just fill in this form, pop it in the post and they'll drop you a line suggesting a time to go and see them.'

In the court, Paul stared at the form and the questions it contained. School? College? Father's name and occupation? University status? Clubs? University societies and status in them? Interests? Type of employment desired? There was only one thing of which Paul could begin to boast and it was the one thing he abhorred: School – Benedict's. That would give him a start with them.

'Oh, you're an Old Benedictine, are you? Do you know Basil Weeks?'

'No, I'm afraid not.'

'Secretary of the OBs' cricket club. Play cricket?'

'I did at school, yes. My top score for the house team was thirteen actually. Or was it fourteen? I forget.'

'Nice chap, Basil. He's with Lloyd's.'

'Bank?'

'He's an underwriter at Lloyd's.'

'Oh yes, yes, of course,' Paul said and straightened his OB tie. The man behind the desk was Mr Page, one of the secretaries of the University Bureau. He was wearing a Hawks' Club tie and his genial blue-eyed face must have been immensely reassuring to those who were entitled to go under the same colours. Paul did not doubt that he would do his best for him, considering what he was, but nor did he doubt that he would consider what he was. 'Now then, Mr Riesman, I see you're a scholar of your college.'

'Yes, sir.'

'And what do you think, shall you get a First, do you think?'

Paul smiled. 'It depends more on what the examiners think, sir.'

'What are your interests up here?'

'I haven't joined anything much. I write a bit.'

'*Varsity*, *Granta*, anything like that?'

Paul said: 'No, not really, no.'

'Published anything yet?'

'No, not yet. I'm – not very good yet, that's why I want to get a job.'

'What about the Army?' Mr Page asked, pulling a pipe from his blazer pocket. Did they *all* smoke pipes?

'Oh, I don't have to do that, sir. I had rheumatic fever when I was younger.'

'Very convenient,' smiled Mr Page. 'I see your father's a doctor.'

'So he is,' Paul said.

'What sort of job do you really fancy, Mr Riesman?'

'I wouldn't mind working for a publisher.'

'Wouldn't mind! Practically every undergraduate who comes into this room would give his eye-teeth to work for a publisher.'

'Wouldn't mind,' Paul said, 'was merely intended to be a becoming show of modesty. Actually I'd like it very much.'

'I'm afraid I can't extend much hope in that direction.'

'Well, journalism – '

'I'm sorry to say that the Press seems to have very little call for educated men, certainly we get very few applications from them and of course practically everyone who works on *Varsity* wants to be a journalist in one form or another. What do you think of *Varsity*?'

'It's all right,' Paul said. 'I think it's a bit silly in a way – clever people trying to make themselves into hacks.'

'You'd like to see a higher intellectual standard?'

'I always thought that was the idea of a university,' Paul said.

Mr Page said: 'What about advertising?'

'It's not really what I want to do. I suppose I could have a shot at it.'

'They make you do a sort of entrance paper, then you'd have to go for an interview.'

'I don't mind interviews,' Paul said.

'Well,' said Mr Page, 'I'll let you know when I hear of something that might interest you.'

'Thank you, sir.'

When Paul had gone, Mr Page uncapped his Swan pen. It was the same one he had used in his tripos. He thought for a moment and then began to write. 'RIESMAN, PAUL: Old Benedictine. Quite a presentable sort of chap, if rather full of himself in that mock-humble way that one finds rather typical of the Chosen People from whom he almost certainly springs. Doesn't seem to settle down very well with his fellows. I rather fancy he may have a chip on his shoulder. Wants to be a writer but hasn't done much about it, may be an excuse for not facing the future, a kind of escape mechanism you sometimes find among those spirits who fancy themselves too fine for this world. Difficult to see quite how he will fit into a job, may have rather too much idea of his own importance. A good deal of charm if he wants to, but rather a quirky individual. Not bad looking, despite obvious racial characteristics: raven hair, hooked nose, etc. Perhaps an employer of his own kind might care to take a chance on him?'

2

It was at a scholars' dinner that Paul met Thornton Ashworth. The dinner was held in the Senior Combination Room, a long, narrow and panelled room in which Charles the First had dined, perhaps at the same white-clothed table at which Paul sat, a Fellow on either side of him, enchanted by the iridescence of the candles as they struck bright coins of light from the college silver. It almost seemed that in the smoky recesses of the room Charles might again be seen, his eyes upon the same silver which, on his last visit to this room, he had so coveted and from which the wily Fellows of that day had, with their rich and loyal hospitality, deterred him, handing over only that which was too obvious to hide and then not neglecting to compose for the King's signature a humble deed setting out in full the nature and value of what he was taking, so that when the Fellows begged a later and less contentious monarch to restore what his warring predecessor had removed, there was a full record of Charles's depredations, which no soveriegn could ignore, and of the Fellows' loyalty to the crown which none could fail to honour. Nor had the present Fellows lost any of the generous guile of their ancient counterparts: hearing of a wartime plan to take over the college for an RAF training school, they held a farewell feast to which they invited the chiefs of the Air Staff, the heads of the neighbouring colleges and as many distinguished ex-members of the college as memory and *Who's Who* could supply. When this splendid company had been dined as well as rationing would allow and wined as well as generations of provident Fellows could ensure, the Master rose and addressed his guests; he referred in a tone of mild wonder to the changes which would possess the college, the tramp of boots in the courts, the barrack-room pin-ups in the rooms where Wordsworth worked, the vehicles parked on lawns it had taken six hundred years to cultivate and he harped, with remarkable candour, on the use to which the Fellows' garden might be put. He went on to congratulate the planners for deciding to take over his college instead of one of the country houses or schools which had served the Army and the Navy so well and he expressed his hope that the bombs which would surely fall on Cambridge would not fall on the personnel who would inhabit the college but rather on the near-by buildings of no military importance: King's Chapel, the Wren building of Trinity and the old court of Magdalene. Strangely, by the time the speech was over and the port in fluent circulation, a unanimous resolve was revealed in every guest's heart to do what he could do reverse the Air Staff's decision, nor was their combined strength unequal to the task, particularly since one of those present owned just such a country house as the Master had mentioned. The Fellows then had good grounds for the pride they took in their own wordly wisdom and there was about them such an air of confidence and of geniality, of contentment and security that Paul, finding himself now within the secure circle of their fellowship, wondered that he had ever doubted the value of Cambridge, regretted only that he would have to leave it and determined that by making a fresh start on the morrow he would strain every sinew to obtain a permanent place among this cultured and convivial company from which nothing seemed so distant as the mundane jealousies and the trivial irritations of the outside world. Even the younger fellows, of whom Thornton Ashworth was one, had about them, as they smoked their cigars, a detached and slightly forbidding serenity. Thornton Ashworth, across the table from Paul, spoke to Paul's neighbour, the Professor of Anatomy, with an ironic respect which placed upon the young Fellow's face more years than any beard or wrinkles could have, indeed his manner of speaking was so much his own and yet so much a manifestation of his surroundings that his face flickered in the candlelight between extreme youth and extreme age and his permanence in that place seemed predetermined. For all his obvious youth Paul found it hard to imagine a time when this candid figure, with its carefully modulated lips and its characterful yet discreet lick of hair across the forehead, had not graced High Table and spoken to Professors with grave but reverent disdain. When the cigars were finished and Thornton Ashworth produced a box of cigarettes which he offered to the immediate company, reaching across the table without undue regard for the tiered fruit, dates and nuts which adorned it or for those genteel niceties which, till this moment, might have led him to ask a waiter to offer the cigarettes to the gentlemen opposite, this large gesture seemed the signal for general movements among the diners who, rising from their places, went about finding for themselves companions more congenial or more refreshing than those with whom they had sat out the long meal. Paul merely leaned forward across the table towards Thornton Ashworth, feeling in himself an emulous respect which always prompted him to display his own intellectual irony at its most effective. Tom Wallace, the other Classics scholar of Paul's year, had wandered up the table, eyes screwed up shortsightedly in the quest for company, his small, dark figure swathed in a gown which, though still an undergraduate's seemed already to have lengthened in confident presumption of its owner's soon attaining a higher status. When Tom saw Paul, his eyes popped open and he raised his hand in a Caesarian salute. Thornton Ashworth curled his lips in a cold greeting and offered his cigarettes. 'I'm glad to see Socrates at the symposium,' he observed, his eyes confirming the amiable haughtiness of his words. 'He has got a certain Silenan quality, hasn't he?' Paul commented. 'On a dark night with the light behind him.'

'How's the book going?' Tom Wallace asked Ashworth.

'Unfortunately my duties towards the dimmer undergraduates of this college have somewhat lamed my creative zest. I suppose it's the fate of junior Fellows to spend their early years having their livers pecked by the most determined and hard-beaked vultures that the wit of the examining board has foisted on an unsuspecting college. There are times when I long again for the carefree raptures of research.'

'You don't look to me like a man who's spent very long in Tartarus,' Paul ventured.

'Do you know Paul Riesman?' Tom asked Ashworth.

'His reputation has not escaped me,' replied the other.

'What reputation?' Paul inquired.

'When I complained at the calibre of the pupils I had been given this year I was told that if I persisted in my complaints they would give me Riesman, at which I need hardly say that I desisted.'

'I don't believe a word of it,' Paul said, flushing with delight that the other thought him worth taunting. Thornton Ashworth leaned back and emitted a strange bray of laughter. 'Not,' Paul continued, 'that I can pretend that I find the Classical Tripos the most invigorating of disciplines nor, necessarily, Mr X the most stimulating of teachers.'

'Why don't you read something else?'

'I don't know. What, for instance?'

'Moral Sciences,' said Tom (who had plainly heard this line before) and Thornton Ashworth (who laughed to acknowledge the other's anticipation of him).

'What exactly does that include?' Paul asked.

'The Ultimate Nature of the Real,' smiled the other. 'The One and the Many, Freedom and Necessity, the Problem of Matter, the Analysis of Mind, Ontology, Phenomenology, Ethics, God.'

'Christ,' Paul said.

'Not this year,' Thornton Ashworth said.

'Next year, sometime, never,' Tom Wallace suggested. Tom presumed an equality with Ashworth which Paul would never have dared. It was difficult to believe now that he and Tom were actually scholars of the same year. During their time at Cambridge together, Paul had watched Tom draw steadily away from him in knowledge and achievement. Classics was a career for Tom; every hope of his was centred on it, there were no subsidiary interests to distract him (except women and even with

361

these he exercised a terminal restraint) and no other kind of success seemed to him even remotely possible; he plunged resolutely forward with the deliberate and ferocious energy of a man who has left one shore too far behind ever to hope to regain it and whose every nerve is geared to the attainment of what lies in front. He knew where he was going and he had trained himself with fanatical rigour for the course. Paul felt fat and out of condition next to him, strangely when the suspicion of a double chin was already showing under the other's red mouth. Paul said: 'Yes, I wouldn't mind switching. I've always wanted to do philosophy. Actually that's what my father said Classics was at university, but then he was at Oxford. Frankly I'd much sooner have done Greats.' He felt about ten years old. The port came round and he filled his glass. The Ultimate Nature of the Real! Paul had not failed to notice the sarcastic lilt of Ashworth's voice when he gave the list of subjects which Moral Science comprised and the very disdain with which he enumerated them suggested that somehow such questions were very old-fashioned and even ridiculous. Paul sensed the possibility of freedom from those questions of morality and of religion which shackled and hampered him whenever he seemed about to free himself from the empty legacy which his Jewishness had left him. 'It would be a mistake,' Thornton Ashworth was saying, 'to think of determination and freedom as necessarily opposed. I seem to hear in such an argument the clank of causal chains! The balls of the past (I take it we are all friends here) holding back the actions of the future. To think on that model is to regard the future tense as a reasonable one in which to cast statements about the past!' Thornton Ashworth laughed shortly and proffered his cigarettes.

Tom said: 'Will philosophy solve all outstanding questions this year?'

'The man who asks the question is in the best position to

answer it,' replied the other. 'The question which can be asked answers itself, the question which cannot be asked reveals its own absurdity. All problems which are real problems are capable of solution. Someone once said to Wittgenstein, "Professor Wittgenstein, I have a problem: I do not feel at home in the Universe." "That," replied Wittgenstein, "is not a problem, that is a difficulty!"'

Paul laughed delightedly. 'That is perfect,' he said. He was strangely excited. He had always been tantalized by the knowingness of others, the way in which they had, though open to no influences unavailable to himself, developed a cryptic sophistication (such as Tom had revealed in asking whether philosophy would solve all outstanding questions this year – a question which in itself was naïve and yet, with a trick of the lips, acquired an elusive and omniscient irony) and now he was aware of an opening in a school whose address he had never before known; opposite him, in the figure of Thornton Ashworth, he saw the impersonation of its principal.

3

Paul sought out Thornton Ashworth the day after the scholars' dinner and begged him to accept him as a philosophy pupil for the following year. Ashworth seemed amused at Paul's eagerness and warned him that he might be well advised to talk the matter over both with his father and with Mr Wrightson, who might not think too well of the seduction of a pupil from the trite path of the Classical Tripos into the thickets and snares of Moral Sciences, but when Ashworth went on to suggest that a fourth year might be advisable if he were really to master the subject, Paul was the more determined upon his course, since another year (if Nat was prepared to stand the racket) might give him a chance to recoup his university fortunes and would, in addition, put off the necessity of resigning himself to the mercies of Mr Page and the University Bureau. He wrote to Nat impatiently, praising Ashworth and demanding that he be allowed to do a fourth year in order to gain a thorough command of the new subject which, whether Nat agreed or not, he intended to read.

Paul began to read philosophy at once. The first book which Thornton Ashworth recommended was *Language, Truth and Logic*. No sooner had Paul begun it than he felt he had found in it the solution not only to all his problems but to all his difficulties as well. The book's icy articulation of language and the remorseless destructiveness of its arguments were alike agreeable to him. There was no outstanding problem which was not dealt with or eliminated. The world was the public world and all that was meaningful within it was patent and available to all; there were no secrets, save that there were no secrets. Paul was savagely in sympathy with the cutting derision for all systematic morality which fired the work; he felt the author to be his saviour from a world of tangled and ponderous pieties. He was cut free, in the exultation of discovering this new, clean, logical world, from all the sour memories which possessed him. For the first time, what he was learning affected his own life. He saw the irrelevance of so many of the burdens he had carried; stripped of this lumber, he felt capable again of drawing abreast with Tom Wallace, of pressing forward into life without that lagging sense of doing 'doing things' which had for so long possessed him. Nothing in Paul's past was relevant to this new philosophy. It was a fresh, sterilized scalpel with which he might excise all the scar tissue which still pained him with its adhesions. There was nothing he might not do. There was no reason on earth why he should be anything that he did not want to be. There was no reason why he should acknowledge his Jewishness. There was no reason why he should remain faithful to Julia. There was no reason to pay any attention to the rumblings of his own inner moral indigestion, it remained only to purge it, to ridicule it, to prune his own contradictory and nonsensical feelings till his personality had something of the cold and confident resolution which was so obvious in Thornton Ashworth.

When the next year started and he went to supervisions with Ashworth, Paul came to see that some of the positivistic views he had accepted were not tenable under rigorous analysis. But analysis itself was a method of logical dissection which could immunize any problem, however grave, and disarm any objection to that antiseptic approach to the world by which philosophy was clearing the lumber of metaphysics. Thornton Ashworth was somewhat amused by the vehemence with which Paul used the analytic method: when he employed it to show that all anti-Semitic statements were attempts to redefine 'Jew' unfavourably, Ashworth advised him to choose less tendentious examples. One did not become a plastic surgeon simply because one didn't like the shape of one's own face. Paul could not wholly scotch this tendency (later he said that the distinction between the causal theory of perception and naïve realism had no more natural significance than that between Jew and Gentile) but he did see that his personal emotionalism was an obstacle to that scientific detachment which analysis idealized. The analyst was a doctor of thought; it was hardly healthy for him continually to harp on his own symptoms. Unselfishness was vital to that stern impersonal school of conceptual surgery which he had joined. For here it was not a question of holding an opinion: one did not win an argument, one dissolved it. In effect, there were no problems. The contentious Jew gave way to the therapeutic white-robed figure. Paul came to copy the healing hand movements of the great consultants, he listened with a new suave tact to the problems of others. He felt himself to be part of a movement which would destroy for ever the superstitions and fears which differentiated men. He enjoyed the simplicity of his position: his own opinions were irrelevant, just as the doctor's spots were, to the problem of curing those of others.

Paul had imagined that the new philosophy had nothing to do with politics, but a logical extension of it revealed the futility not only of metaphysics but also of political systems: all social planning had to be scientific, dealing with each problem as it came up according to empirical rather than theoretical principles. Paul now felt himself absolved from the need for any personal stand; he did not have to be anything: there could no more be political than there could be absolute morality, for both were based on unverifiable principles. The philosopher bandaged the wounds occasioned by the wars of ideas. He was neutral as between the ideas themselves. He wanted only to put things right. The doctor sought to heal the body. His work was most perfect when his services were no longer required. The philosopher aimed to destroy the toxic content of language and reduce it to an antiseptic vehicle of communication. When this was achieved, he, too, rejoiced that his services were no longer needed. A doctor's intentions were above reproach, so too were a philosopher's, for he believed only what all men must believe: the truth, that it is true.

Paul's belief in the scientific use of language led him to employ in his stories a flat descriptive idiom in which no sentence was not, at least in principle, verifiable. When these stories were rejected as firmly as those which came before them, Paul was able to tell himself that it was not their demerits but their unorthodox narrative which had failed to appeal. It was no longer he who was rejected but his new school. He wrote less in any case, for there was nothing which could be said which could not be said in philosophical terms. Since language was a public vehicle, there was no excuse for private joy-riding. A writer was either a philosopher or an idiot. The analysis of the concept 'I' was a curiosity with which one might toy during breaks from more serious work. Scientific truth did not depend on the existence of any particular individual, hence the irrelevance of all personal statement or morality. Indeed a certain kind of individualism was a symptom of divorce from philosophy rather than of an especial interest in it. A certain kind of modesty was essential to the true philosopher.

Paul's academic life achieved a kind of unity. He talked about philosophy even with those to whom it meant nothing. One of these was a freshman called Mark Abrahams. Paul met him at a College play-reading. He was a short, thickset youth with a gift for mimicry. He was particularly adept at imitating the voices in the Manny Finkelbaum Show. He reminded Paul somewhat of Marino, except that he had no shame: he was a Jew and he didn't care who knew it. Paul took him back to his rooms for coffee.

'You're a Yid, aren't you?' Mark asked bluntly.

'Shright,' Paul replied. 'I take it you are.'

'You can say that again, boy. You're not one of the St John's Wood gang though, are you?'

'No, I'm not.'

'Where you from?'

'Wimbledon.'

'Wimbledon Shmimbledon, what's it matter so long as he loves his mother?'

Paul Said: 'Do you belong to the Jewish Society up here?'

'I went a couple of times, but they're very *frum*.'

'*Frum*?'

'I thought you said you were a Yiddisher feller,' Mark grinned. 'So this is Wimbledon.'

Paul said: 'I'm afraid I don't much feel any necessity to keep very closely in touch.'

'Either you're a Yid or you aren't.'

'I'm afraid,' Paul said, 'that I can't feel any call to be Jewish if I don't want to be. There's no ingrained trademark

367

on a Jew that makes him a Jew whether he wants to be one or not.'

'Vell, look who's talking,' Mark Abrahams said. 'You think the Yids in the gas-chambers went in because they wanted to be Jews? Listen, once a Yid always a Yid.'

'I don't agree at all. It's a perfectly plausible line to say that one intends to integrate oneself with the country one lives in. Other so called racial groups have done it, I don't see why we shouldn't.'

'The German Jews did it, shnooky boy, and look what happened to them.'

Paul said: 'I've never lived with Jews. I don't have anything in common with them. I don't even know the way they talk and that's what it is to have something in common.'

'What you've got in common is what you've got in common,' Mark Abrahams said. 'Your nature.'

'One's nature isn't all settled when one's born. It can change.'

'You're a Yid and you know it,' Mark said. 'Why fight it?'

'Because I don't feel any necessity to accept it. I don't want to be a Jew and I don't have to be a Jew and I'm not going to be a Jew.'

'So what do you get in exchange?'

'Freedom,' Paul said.

'How can you be free unless you can make other people believe you're free?'

'That's my job,' Paul said.

'And what about persuading yourself?'

'Oh, I've done that.'

'You're a Yid,' Mark Abrahams said. 'Do you deny it?'

'I don't deny anything – I just – dissolve it.'

'*Peee!*'

'Hullo, Paul,' the girl said.

'Good God! Penny Paynter! Hullo, what are you doing up here?'

'I'm in a play at the Arts, *The Same Old Story*. Surprised you haven't seen my name on the bills.'

'Oh. Well, Christ, this is marvellous.'

'What are you doing now?'

'Me? Mooching. Mooch with me?'

'Why not? I'm sorry you've shaved your beard off. I thought it was wonderful.'

'Did you see me in it?'

'No, not actually, but I think it was lovely!' She spoke with a husky perkiness that was rather charming.

'My mother thought I looked like Christ. She didn't seem to think that was a very good thing.'

Paul took Penny back to his rooms for tea. She took off her red duffel-jacket to reveal black trousers and a rough fisherman's sweater. She stood cheekily in front of Paul's bookcase. 'You won't find much there to interest you, I'm afraid,' he told her.

'Are you an existentialist at all?'

'Hardly at all,' Paul smiled.

'I think they're marvellous.'

'Have you visited the sexistentialists in their native haunts then?'

'No, actually, but one of the boys I was at RADA with was frightfully keen and he lent me books and things.'

'Things, did he? Did you understand them?'

'Bits of them. I believe fervently in Will, don't you?'

'Will who?'

'Will. I mean I believe that if you really make up your mind to do something you'll end up by doing it.'

Paul said: 'What have you made up your mind about?'

'Nothing yet, really.'

'Have you ever come across cases where people made up their minds to do things and eventually did?'

'Oh yes, hundreds,' Penny said.

'And cases where they've made up their minds and haven't done the things they made up their minds to do?'

'Oh yes,' agreed the girl.

'And how do you account for the failures?'

'They didn't make up their minds hard enough.'

'Which is established by the fact that they didn't do what they wanted to do. That's a circular argument, isn't it?'

'I love philosophy,' Penny said. 'What do you think about Christian Science?'

'It's based on a logical fallacy,' Paul said.

'Now that's interesting, because I believe in it. I think. I had a cold once I cured by Christian Science. I just willed that it should stop – and prayed as well, of course.'

'Together or one after the other?'

'Oh, both! And it worked wonderfully. It just went. Mind you, I tried it a bit later with laryngitis and it didn't work.' Penny laughed and fluttered her eyelids. 'But I believe in it all the same.'

Paul said: 'More tea?'

'No, honestly, I must be geting along to the theatre.'

'What about some supper after the show?'

'I'd love to but I promised I'd go to some party at a place called Maxton's Yard. I shall probably get raped or something awful! I say, why don't you come along? I shan't know a soul there.'

'I haven't been asked,' Paul said.

'Oh *that* doesn't matter. Robin Boyd asked me to come. Do you know Robin?'

'No.'

'He's a dear. Look, I must fly. Pick me up at the theatre at ten-fifteen. We come down at ten.'

5

Robin Boyd said: 'Gin or rum?'

Paul said: 'Look, I hope you don't mind –'

'Rum, please, Robin,' Penny Paynter said.

'You were wonderful tonight, darling.'

'Think so?'

'You only stole the show,' Robin said. 'Do you want sugar or ice-cream in your rum?'

'Just a dollop.'

Robin Boyd said: 'I expect you know everyone, old chap.'

'Oh, every bloody one, mate,' Paul said.

Robin said: 'Penny poppet, Bruce and Katie are already here somewhere and they're dying to talk to you.'

A year before, Paul would have left the party, but now, although furious at Boyd's ignoring him, he stayed. He dredged another rum out of the washbowl into which it had been poured and downed it at a gulp. Then he stormed up the narrow stairs. Somewhere a gramophone was playing. The upper part of the house was in darkness. Paul blundered into the room from which the music came. A girl said: 'Dance with me.'

'How can you see me?'

'I've been in the dark for a long time, kid,' replied the girl.

'So've I, baby,' said Paul.

They began to dance. In the darkness, Paul distinguished a large bed in one corner of the room on which several couples were already lying. He and his partner danced for several minutes, by which time Paul could see that she was a neat, rather pretty girl with large eyes and red, well-lipsticked lips. She danced with a fluffy independence.

'I've never danced with anyone quite like you before,' Paul said at last.

'Probably because you've never danced with a ballet dancer,' she said, still affecting the American accent with which she had greeted him. 'You don't dance so badly yourself.'

'Think not? My father – '

'What's your father, dear?'

'Nothing,' he said, 'he's nothing, he couldn't matter less. How about a drink?'

'Let's go outside,' the girl said.

It was even darker in the passage. Paul said: 'Drink's downstairs.'

'Never mind drink.'

She dragged him along the passage away from the stairs and pushed open a door into a bedroom. There was no light, but Paul could see one or two couples lying on the floor. The girl shut the door and turned against him. He kissed her and felt the roughness of her teeth against his tongue. She pressed forward against him. 'Well, hullo there,' she whispered at last. He pushed her towards the bed and they stumbled and fell on it. 'I say, do you mind?' someone said. 'Make room for a fellow-sufferer,' Paul said. 'Say,' said the girl, 'who's suffering?' He caught her round the waist and pulled her against him. Another girl lying with her back to him wriggled her bottom. Paul's girl said: 'I like you. I do like you. This isn't how I usually go with a feller.' Paul said: 'Me neither.' He pulled her blouse out of her skirt and undid the buttons. She had no slip on, just a brassière. 'Umm,' said the other girl, 'umm.' Paul fumbled with the catch of the girl's brassière. She was very slim; he felt the whole cage of her ribs between his hands. The brassière came undone. Her breasts were small but firm as apples. She said: 'I do like you, honest. You're special.' He let the blouse fall down over her flat stomach. His hands fondled her breasts. The nipples were rigid. She said:

'What's your name?' 'Paul.' 'I like you, Paul,' she said. 'I wouldn't let just anyone do this.' He put his hand under her skirt and slid it between her thighs and into her groin. The other girl said: 'Could you move over a bit? Honestly, you've got well over half.' 'Sorry.' The girl took his hand out of her groin and bit it. 'You're a naughty boy!' 'What's your name, naughty girl?' Paul asked. 'Julia, dear,' she said.

Paul sat up and held his head in his hands.

The girl said: 'What's the matter, dear? Not feeling too good?' She did up her buttons.

'Feel bloody,' Paul said.

The girl took the mirror out of her handbag. She peered at it in the darkness. 'What I look like!'

Paul opened the door ('Shut the door!') and went out into the passage. 'Nausea,' he said. 'Sheer bloody nausea.' He went into the lavatory and retched dryly. 'Julia,' he said, 'how too bloody funny for words.' Someone knocked. 'Is it?' 'It's me, dear. Are you all right?' 'All right, thanks, fine, out in a minute,' Paul said. He wiped his lips on his handkerchief. He looked at it in horror. He was bleeding. Oh, he was bleeding Julia's lipstick! Bleeding Julia. He opened the door. 'Hullo.' 'Are you all right? I was ever so worried.' Paul held his head. 'Poor you.' 'Christ, I feel awful,' Paul said. 'Hair of the dog? Best thing.' 'I couldn't.'

'Come on,' the girl said, 'I'll look after you.'

'Why?' Paul said.

'I like you. You're a nice boy.'

Paul said: 'God, I feel shitty.'

'Come on. We'll go and find somewhere to sit down.'

'Why are you chasing me?' Paul said.

'I'm not chasing you.'

'No, why do you bother?'

'I told you. I like you. You're special.'

'But I'm not,' Paul said. 'I'm not special. There's nothing special about me.'

'I can tell. You are special, honestly. I could tell when you came into the room.'

'I can't be special,' Paul said. 'Or I wouldn't be here.' He started to pull at her blouse. 'There can't be anything special about me.'

'Enough is enough,' the girl said, patting his hand away.

'Aren't we going to – you know?'

'Not in your condition.'

'Want to,' Paul said.

The girl kissed him. 'Not now.'

'You kissed me. Why?'

'I felt like kissing you, dear, that's all.'

'Get me a drink. A big one. Want a drink.'

'All right, dear. You wait there.'

'The difficulty of today,' Paul said, 'is how to be oneself and not to be oneself. One self, that's a paradox when you think about it, you can't be one self, that's to subscribe to the metaphor of causal chains, ensnared in causal chains, one self, immortal, invisible, God only wise, not Whys, my boy, but Hows, hows and gardens. Drunk. I am drunk. No, I'm not. I'm not drunk. I can think. I can talk lucidly, I am not drunk. I am not drunk. I will discourse on any subject with amazing lucidity. I will even speak with tongues. With tongues of fire. With fire tongs. Thank you. Time future is not contained in time past. Mr Eliot is a chiselling old faker with an anti-Semitic leer. An old anti-Semitic Lear weeping for the kingdom he never owned, carrying in his arms the daughter he never – he never did the hard work for. Did the hard work for! Good. Afflatus is upon me. I can see the whole world – a lovely series of non-monistic, non-monastic concatenations. Con – as in con, cat as in cat and tenation as in tenation. Ethics equals aesthetics, aesthetics equals ethics and the good is more or less equivalent to the beautiful. No, let us try to think lucidly about these problems which possess our – imaginatings. Ethics equals aesthetics. Then I would say this: a

374

beautiful work of art is no better and no worse and no different, mark ye, from a beautiful or good action. Fizz, Sic, and Viz. In a perfect life art would be superfluous. Art is not an embellishment of life, it is an alternative to it. The life and the art are one. The question recurs: what am I good at? A symptom, my dear Watson, of the fragmentation of modern life, to ask what one is good at. What am I waiting for? Let us ask that question. What am I waiting for? When will the signal come: education's over? Life is now officially beginning. Marriage follows, for no good reason, a living, middle age, a pension and death. All fixed, all set. Time future is contained in time-table. The conclusion, my dear Murgatroyd (an old chum of Watson's) is this: we are waiting for death. It is the only thing we know we are worthy of and thank God for it, thank God for a way out, lads, and don't all leave at once.'

'I've got your drink, dear. There was ever such a crush down there. One of the girls is doing a strip. I think she must be drunk. She's not like that really.'

'We're all like it, J – , we're all like it, my darling. All waiting to do a strip. That's the hard elemental life, that's the blight that man was born for. You should have been here, my sweet, I was philosophizing.'

'Honest?'

'As honest as I'm ever likely to get.' Paul gulped down the drink. 'Jesus,' he said, 'you shouldn't have brought me gin. I was drunking rim, drinking rum – '

'Drunking rim! What a funny boy you are!'

'Would you like to marry me?' Paul said.

'Marry you?'

'Share my bed and share my sorrows, would you?'

'You're kidding,' the girl said.

'No kidding till after we're wed. Definitely not – embarrass the parents.'

'You'll regret it in the morning, if you really are proposing, I mean.'

'I am – feeling out the ground,' Paul said. 'Will you tell me the truth?'

'What about?'

'Are you a virgin?'

The girl kissed his hand. 'I wouldn't be unfaithful to you. I love you.'

'You what? You love me? *Love me*?'

'Really love you,' the girl said.

'You haven't got the brain for the job,' Paul said.

'I'm not stupid. I don't see why you should say that. I'm not all that stupid.'

'How many men have you slept with?'

'I'm not telling.'

'How can I marry you if you won't tell me how many men you've slept with?'

'Do you always ask questions?'

'Always.'

'I couldn't marry someone who always asked questions. It'd drive me barmy. Are you a Jew?'

'What?'

'Are you? A Jew. Are you?'

Paul said: 'What an extraordinary question! What made you ask that?'

'I thought you might be, I don't know. Are you?'

'Why should I tell you?'

'I couldn't marry you without knowing if you were or not.'

'Let's say I'm not. No, I'm not a Jew.' Paul drank some more gin. 'No, I am not a Jew. What follows?'

'We'd be married in church,' the girl said.

'Anything else follow?'

'I wouldn't have Jew kids.'

'You wouldn't have kids.'

'What's the point of getting married if you don't have kids?'

Paul put his hand under the girl's skirt. 'There are things,' he said. 'No, you're right. What is the point? We

376

don't have to get married. We don't have to do anything. We're free. The free peoples of the world. Tell me, you're not Jewish, are you?'

'Me? No, 'course not, silly. My nose isn't crooked, is it?'

'Persuasive definitions,' Paul said. 'See my *Logick der Forschung*.'

'You *are* a Jew, aren't you, dear?'

'You know, just lying here like this, I could throttle you and leave you here and no one would know.'

'You'd be hung if you did,' the girl said.

'I don't think so,' Paul said. 'No one would ever know we'd been together. It'd be so easy to throttle you, you strange little beast.'

'I'm not a little beast. You're being horrid now.'

'Do you still love me? If I'm a Yid.' Paul's fingers were round the girl's throat. 'Will you come to bed with me?'

'Always asking questions,' the girl said, 'that's your trouble.'

'That's right,' Paul said, 'always asking questions and always expecting answers.'

'I can't answer your questions,' the girl said.

'Never mind: the man who asks the question is in the best position for answering it. You know who said that?'

'No, who?'

'A bloke called Wittgenstein.'

'Was he a Yid too?'

'I don't know. But I hope so.'

'You are, aren't you? You are a Jewboy, aren't you?'

'I am a Jew. I'm a Yid. I'm a greasy, smarmy, oily, central European, blackmarketing, cowardly, Semitic Yid. I don't expect blue-eyed maidens to love me for myself, for my black-hearted Asiatic, Levantine, old Benedictine self, I expect them to hate me and I expect I hate them and I wish them all in hell for what they have done to us and to all men. I hate them and I hate you for not caring about the six million you helped to kill and the six million you

377

don't care are dead and I expect you to think I'm a stupid, maladjusted bore because I can't forget the slaughterhouses you want to forget about and I won't be any of the things you want me to be and I've tried to be for the last twenty years and I'm not going to earn a living or be a good chap or any of the thousand and one bloody silly get-up-when-a-lady-comes-into-the-room things you want me to be and don't care if I am because you don't care if I'm alive or dead or care if anyone is alive or dead and I don't want good chums from among the good old Benedictine toss-offs and their decent wog-flogging ladies with their cheese-grater voices and their damned condescending crap and I wouldn't know how to even if I did. I will draw breath. I will draw breath out of the air you want to breathe and I won't apologize for it though I expect I shall but I don't want to – from now on I shall be my own self and if you don't like it you can turn me into Lifegoy soap like your Nazi chums but from now on I shall be something and that something'll be me, I shall be myself, oneself, so for Christ's sake stop tolerating me and if you want to blather about races, don't do mine any favours because if you want to kill it it's so much the bloody worse for you, mate, not for anything we'll do to you, not for any good scientific reason but because that's the way it is, chum, so much the worse for you if you don't respect what's good in us and in all men, I wouldn't have your shitty toleration on a bloody plate, you fairy-faced cretins who think you're something because you're the sons of Godstone poultry-farmers, a pox on you all, a pox on you bloody generation of nigger-beaters and Jew-baiters, do what you bleeding well like to us but keep out of my bloody way unless you've come to kill us because if you've just come to be around and be decent to us and show us your toleration, piss off and double quick. I've had friends from among you, you generation of crowd-pleasing parakeets, you fine-freckled liberals who only keep to your jolly decent rules when it doesn't hurt you to do it, you bloody ethical disputers with your it's-only-a-question-of-what-you-say mentalities and your gritty little eyes, oh, you're the boys all right that turn us into false-faced, old-school-tied Gentile impersonators. Look, I wish I had another drink. Look, I don't want to conquer you, I don't want to do anything to you at all except break those cruddy little knots of conceit and make you be men again and make you let other people be men again and women be women and not make me put my bloody hand up this poor little tart's skirt (oh, she's gone, well anyway), I don't want to be damned well like you in anything whatsoever and I think it's a filthy insult that you do yourselves and everyone else that you want everyone to be like you. Look, I don't know where it all started, all this cringing apologetic, I suppose it all started with the fear of death and the fear of torture and I know a Yid screams like anyone else and maybe worse because he knows that no one will ever come to his help and I don't know when I started to apologize for being alive and walking and eating and smiling and wanting a woman the same as anyone of you pure-blooded one hundred per cent white bastards and I don't know why and I don't bloody care any more and I don't care if you won't give me a job or a place in the jolly old club and I'll tell you frankly I won't work twice as hard to get half as far or three-quarters as hard to get five-eights as far, I resign. I resign forthwith from all ambition. I do not give a twopenny wotsit for the Ministry of Supply and I don't have any interest in being the first Jew to become anything in the whole wide bloody world and I don't care if the first man on Everest is a Swiss admiral or an albino chimpanzee and I don't care how many Christmas cards I get from people with names in Who's What and when people say to me, what are you a writer for? I shall reply because they wouldn't let me be a man. As far as I'm concerned this is a lousy hotel and the service is rotten and the wrong people are running it but I don't care as long as

I can get a meal sometimes and a bed with my woman in it, my own bloody woman, my own bloody Julia, even if I turn out too big a fool to be true, and as long as they don't run the thing on the rocks or anything like that I shall muddle along and write if I can, and if I can't, well, I shall have to do something else, but I shall be a man and mean something by being a man and be it with one woman who's my woman and not just anyone. Furthermore I will not take another sodding examination and I will not answer another stupid bloody question that someone else could answer just as well. I resign from trying to please any of you, examiners, employers, harlots, girls from the ballet, the lot of you. I resign. Make your own bloody world and be welcome to it, I don't care how you do it or what you do to each other, just leave us alone, leave us alone and let us get back to our Eden and the quicker the better. To hell with England, to hell with all of you; I shall, my Lord Mayor, address you further from warmer climes. Write to me, if you will, on postcards only please, care of GPO Palermo. Think what you like and say what you like and do what you like, but don't expect me to join you. One woman all my life, that's all I want and keep your hands off, all you helpful smutters, keep your hands off us (and keep my hands off you) because without you is where I wanna be. Thank you, friends, thank you for your constant attention. I hope I've bored the balls off you, because if you can't be my sort of person you can go and grow radishes. I give you notice, all of you, I quit. I quit. I quit. Nice word, quit.'

BOOK THREE

Process and Reality

ONE

Some Investigations

1

THE MAN SAID: 'Mrs Simons?'

'Yes.'

'Oh, good morning, my name is Superintendent Palmer. This is Sergeant Strangways. I wonder if you could spare us a few minutes?'

Susan cuffed back the hair from her forehead. 'I'm just in the middle of some washing,' she said. The superintendent said, 'Monday wash, is it?' and removed his hat, which was a blue fedora. Susan had an obscure sensation of having won some sort of victory: someone had once told her that policemen always kept their hats on in the house and the superintendent's revelation of his thinning hair and freckled scalp was an agreeable concession. Susan said: 'Would you like to hang up your coat?'

'No thank you.'

'No thank you, ma'am,' said the sergeant, a fair young man, with a squashed, doughy face, blue eyes. Susan said: 'In here, if you like.' The men went into the sitting-room, squeezing past Susan with a businesslike deference which made her hurry into the room after them. She said: 'Well, sit down, won't you?'

The superintendent sat down in the armchair beyond the fireplace. He nodded to Strangways to sit on a cane-seated kitchen chair by the bookcase. The sergeant sat down, crossed his legs and took out his notebook. He uncapped his pen and licked the nib. Starting at the top left-hand corner of the bookcase his eyes moved methodically along the shelves, stopping now and then at a particular book. Susan concentrated her eyes on him, anxious to distract him.

The superintendent said: 'Mrs Simons, we'd like to ask you a few questions if you don't mind.'

'What about?' Susan asked, big-eyed.

'Does the name Fletcher mean anything to you?'

'Fletcher? I don't think so.'

'Herbert Fletcher.'

'Oh, yes, sorry, yes, of course. It didn't connect for a minute. We haven't seen Herb in ages. He went back to America, didn't he?'

'When did you know him, Mrs Simons?'

'Oh just at the end of the war. He was a friend of my husband's.'

'Oh, yes? Tell me, when did you first meet this man Fletcher?'

'Has he done something wrong?' Susan asked.

'No one's done anything wrong so far as we know, Mrs Simons.'

'I suppose it was the way you said "This man Fletcher – "'

'When did you say you first met Mr Fletcher?'

'Just before the end of the war it must have been. He came here several times. Stan brought him here first. Stan Halloran.'

'Would that be the radio comic?' Sergeant Strangways asked.

'That's right,' Susan said. 'The Manny Finkelbaum show.'

'How did Mr Halloran come to bring Mr Fletcher here?'

'I honestly don't know. I think Stan thought he might be interested in a magazine which he and my husband were thinking of starting at that time.'

'That would be *Everyman*, would it?'

'That's right,' Susan said. 'What a long time ago that seems!'

'It isn't all that long,' the superintendent said. 'Did Fletcher have anything to do with that magazine?'

'I honestly don't know. I wasn't really in on it very much. They just used to hold meetings here, you know, to discuss things.'

'They being – '

'Oh, Stan and Ben and Sid and this chap Fletcher.'

'Sid – ?'

'Sid Forbes, another friend,' Susan said, with a glance at Strangways, who was writing very smoothly, with none of the snatches and hesitations of speech.

'This would be your local Party secretary, would it?'

Susan said: 'What's all this about exactly? Honestly, I do think I'm entitled to know. I mean, who's being accused of what?'

'We're just trying to clear up a certain matter, Mrs Simons. There's no question of anyone being charged with anything. Oh, I happen to have brought along a couple a copies of the first and I believe only two issues of *Everyman*. Do you recognize them?'

Susan took the two flimsy magazines with their bright, Ben-designed covers. 'That's them.' She flipped through the pages: 'SEE THE OTHER RANKS GET THEIR OVERALLS, WON'T YOU, CARRUTHERS?' She was about to hand the two copies back when the Contents pages was accidentally revealed. She read: Editorial Staff: STAN HALLORAN, Editor; Vice-Editors: BEN SIMONS, SID FORBES. 'Sid's name's here,' Susan said reproachfully.

'So it is,' said the other, 'but I notice that Mr Fletcher's isn't.'

'Oh, I don't think he was really in it, you know, I think he was just sort of interested.'

'In what?'

'Oh, the idea of a progressive magazine.'

385

'Progressive meaning what exactly, Mrs Simons?'

'Oh, left-wing, you know. We were all very left-wing at that time.'

'But not any more?'

'Not really, no.'

'Mr Fletcher, what did you make of him, Mrs Simons?'

'He was quite a nice sort of chap. I didn't see much of him really.'

'What did he do, do you know that?'

'Oh, some kind of war work. I never found out what exactly.'

'What do you mean, you never found out?'

'I don't mean I tried to find out, I just mean, you know, no one ever told me.'

'What made you think he was doing war work?'

'Oh, well – um – I don't know really. Nearly everyone was doing war work in those days.'

'Didn't he say anything about what he was doing?'

'Not while I was in the room,' Susan said. She caught Strangways looking at the *Collected Works of J. V. Stalin* and lowered her lashes reprovingly.

'Mrs Simons, I'd like to know a little more about the circumstances in which this little magazine was started.'

'Oh, it was an idea of Stan's and Ben's originally. They used to talk about it all the time when we were decorating. You wouldn't believe it, but this house *was* decorated once.'

'What was the idea of the magazine exactly?'

'Oh, it was just going to be a kind of progressive satirical magazine. Like *Punch*, only funny, Stan used to say.' Sergeant Strangway's lips twitched, Susan was watching him. 'First it was on and then it was off, you know what these things are like, snags always cropping up.'

'Did the snags stop cropping up before or after Mr Fletcher came to this house, Mrs Simons?'

'Now you're asking,' Susan said.

'Exactly. Tell me, at the time when Mr Fletcher first came to this house was *Everyman* in active preparation?'

'Oh, it's all such a long time ago, honestly. I couldn't swear – '

'We're not asking you to swear anything, Mrs Simons.' The superintendent took a pipe from his mac pocket. 'Just see if you can recall what stage things had reached when Mr Fletcher first came to this house.'

'I *think* I was pregnant,' Susan said. She broke into a smile: 'I wish you'd tell me what this is all about.'

'You were pregnant, Mrs Simons.'

'I don't think anything definite had been fixed,' Susan sighed. 'At that time it was just talk, you know.'

'And then sometime after Herbert Fletcher met your husband, this magazine was on again, is that it?'

'Oh, they talked and talked and eventually something got moving. I wasn't really in on it very much – except for making the tea and clearing up afterwards.'

'How many people used to come to these meetings?'

'Oh, Sid and Stan and Ben and Herb, that was all really. Later on someone may have come from the printers; I can't remember too well.'

'Mrs Simons, did your husband put any of his own money into this magazine?'

'I don't know, honestly. Why don't you ask him?'

'No doubt he'll help us if he can. Mrs Simons, did Mr Fletcher ever write anything for this magazine?'

'I honestly don't know. He may have done some photos for it. I know he was very keen on photography.'

'Oh, really? What sort of thing exactly?'

'I don't know exactly,' Susan said. 'I just remember Ben saying how good he was at it. They were awfully set on getting him to contribute.'

'Did he seem unwilling?'

'He was a bit nervous, I think.'

'Why was that, do you think?'

'In case his boss found out; the Yanks were a bit down on, you know, people having anything to do with progressive – things,' Susan said.

'Mrs Simons, you and your husband were members of the Communist Party, I think?'

'Yes,' Susan said huskily and coughed, hand to breast. 'Excuse me!'

'And are you still?'

'Yes,' Susan said, 'we are. In a way.'

'And Mr Fletcher, was he a member of the Communist Party, do you know?'

'I'm certain he wasn't,' Susan said. 'He was an American.'

The superintendent's eyebrows shot up. 'And are there no American members of the Communist Party?'

'Yes, only I'm sure *he* wasn't.'

'Then why were your husband and Mr Forbes so eager to get him to join the staff of their magazine?'

'Oh, but it wasn't theirs,' Susan said. 'I told you: Stan Halloran was the really keen one. It wasn't supposed to be an exclusively Communist magazine.'

'Mr Halloran was sympathetic to your husband's point of view though, wasn't he?'

'They were great friends,' Susan said. 'Stan was very left in those days, you know just at the end of the war – things were different. I mean we all had hopes – '

The superintendent crossed his legs. It was a major operation. 'Mrs Simons, how did your husband get on with Mr Fletcher?'

'Quite well. Ben didn't talk about him very much.' Susan lit a Player's Airman. 'I say, he hasn't been murdered or anything like that, has he? Herb, I mean?'

'No one's been murdered. Now correct me if I'm wrong, but I imagine the order of events was roughly this, nothing definite was done about this magazine, beside a lot of talking, until Mr Fletcher arrived on the scene, but very

soon after that serious moves were made towards getting
things started –'

'Yes, I think that's roughly right. I mean it was as if Herb
Fletcher was the man they needed to complete the team.
Not that that's the expression my husband would have
used!'

'Up till that time had Sid Forbes come into the discussions at all?'

'No, I think he was rather anti.'

'I see, but when the magazine started to be talked about
seriously, then Mr Forbes joined in, is that it?'

'Yes, he seemed to come round to Stan and Ben's way of
thinking.'

'And did he help financially at all?'

'Not that I know of,' Susan said.

'Were you at all surprised that Mr Forbes came round,
as you put it?'

'I was a bit,' Susan said. 'He'd seemed very anti at one
time.'

'Now Mrs Forbes – ah, Mrs Simons – you had a party
here on the night of the General Election, I think?'

'How on earth do you know that?'

'Nothing secret about it, was there?'

'Oh no – Well, people were in and out, you know. We
knew a lot of people in those days.'

'Tell me about the party, Mrs Simons. Was there any –
trouble that night?'

'I suppose you're referring to the row between Stan and
the others. I don't remember what it was all about. I was
very upset about it, that I do remember. Stan left in a bit
of a huff.'

'And was that the last you saw of him?'

'Stan? No, we saw him several times after that, but
things were a bit chilly, after the row, I mean.'

'Who picked the quarrel, Mrs Simons, can you tell us
that?'

'Oh, honestly, it was such ages ago.'

'Eleven years,' said the superintendent, 'not all that long.'

'I couldn't say,' Susan said. 'Eleven years is a long time to me.'

'Now, what about Mr Fletcher, did you ever see him again?'

Susan bit her knuckle. 'No, now I come to think of it, I don't think I ever did.'

'Did your husband?'

'Not that I know of. He never said he did.'

'Was your husband out very much in the evenings at this time, Mrs Simons?'

'Yes, quite a lot. Almost every evening after he joined the *Worker*.'

'Which was when?'

'Not long after this.'

'He's since left it again, I believe?'

'Oh yes, nearly four years ago. He's got his own business now.'

'But he still contributes, doesn't he?'

'Yes, of course,' Susan said. 'Surely you must know that. It's no secret.'

'No, quite. Why did he leave, Mrs Simons?'

'Because we weren't making enough money.'

The superintendent smiled. 'I imagine you had something to do with the move.'

'I wasn't exactly against it,' Susan said.

'No, quite. Tell me, Mrs Simons, where did he find the money to start this business of his?'

'I don't know. The bank, I imagine. He's doing very well at it anyway.'

'Yes, nice business running a press. Rum thing for a comrade though, isn't it, designing Christmas cards?'

'I imagine he knows what he's doing.'

'Oh yes,' the superintendent said, 'no one's ever doubted that your husband knows what he's doing.'

2

Mr Sonny Minster said: 'Well, first of all, Mr Riesman, I want you to give me a little sort of background on yourself so we can know where we go on from here.'

'Well, I came down from Cambridge about eighteen months ago but for the first six months of that time I had a travel scholarship, so I haven't really been in London all that time, and then since then, well, apart from getting married, I haven't really done anything very much.'

'Apart from getting married – I like that! So what do you think of married life?'

'I like it,' Paul said.

'Wait till you've been married as long as I have, feller, and then see if you like it. But seriously, tell me, what sort of writing have you done, so far I mean?'

'I've written a novel,' Paul said, 'but no one's accepted it yet.'

'A novel, eh? What's that about?'

'Oh, it's only a light thing, a sort of two-level satirical thriller.'

'Two-level eh? Sounds interesting. But tell me, have you done any writing in the entertainment field at all yet?'

'No, not really.'

'You see that's where the big money lies today. It's a tough world, show business, I mean, I don't have to tell you that.'

'I'd very much like to write some films,' Paul said.

'Well, you've come to the right place. I signed for one of my writers only this morning to go to Hollywood on a two-year-contract at two thousand dollars a week. That's a lot of money today.'

'Or any day,' Paul said.

'I handle a lot of writers from this office, I mean I've been in this business a long time and I'd say that today the opportunities for writers are greater than ever. I mean, for instance, people haven't begun to understand the potential of what television is capable of in this country today. I signed a couple of my writers this week – Nat Vincent and Jerry Lodz – for a thirty-nine half-hour series at three hundred and twenty-five guineas a time, well I mean to say, that's a lot of money today.'

'What sort of thing was that?'

'Sort of a little comedy idea I thought up. I put it up to Danny Baldini and he sort of played around with it and then we sort of found a formula and now it's a quarter-of-a-million-dollar project; well, that's the sort of thing I want to get you into. I mean, we've got to find the right thing for you and then, well, who knows? I mean, I want to start getting you a hundred and fifty, two hundred pounds for a half-hour script; I mean, the top writers on my books are getting outgoings from this office of up to fifteen thousand pounds a year, some of them, and that's what I'd like to be able to do for you, you see what I mean?'

'Mr Minster,' Paul said, 'I don't want to earn five thousand a year, I'd like to just start off by earning five hundred. Basically, I want to be a serious writer.'

'Well, of course, I mean, I set up a film for two of my writers last week, I mean, I don't say this happens every week, but this was with MGM and this was a single picture deal and over sixty thousand dollars were involved there, now I mean, this is a couple of really serious writers.'

'Mr Minster, do you think there's anything I could do immediately to earn some money? That's really why I've come to see you.'

'What I suggest is, you leave it with me for a few days and I'll sort of dig round and see what I can find. I'm sure we'll be able to sort of sort something out for you. I mean, you've got to have faith in yourself at this stage and sort of believe in yourself. I mean, I had a young feller come into this office, fresh from school just like yourself, you know, and within eighteen months he was earning over four hundred pounds a half-hour script, well, I mean, I can't guarantee that sort of success for you naturally but I wouldn't be surprised, from what you've told me about yourself, that you'd end up in exactly the same way. I mean, that young feller, he's a top writer today, just like you could be.'

3

The man said, 'Surely it is Colin Adler, isn't it?'

Colin said: 'Yes. I'm afraid – '

'Don't you remember me? Saul Marowitz.'

'Oh *hullo*,' Colin said. 'I didn't recognize you for a minute. You've lost a lot of hair or something.'

'Look who's talking. What are you doing round here? Same as me, I suppose, come to spit in the foundations of this monstrosity.'

'Not exactly,' Colin said. 'As a matter of fact my firm are, um – '

'Who did you get fixed up with in the end?'

'I'm sort of attached, you know, to the Family Lovers' – '

'Oh, Christ,' Saul Marowitz said. He was wearing a short, belted trench jacket with a fur collar and carried a satchel fastened with a metal pin like a music manuscript case. 'Well,' he said, 'I hope you didn't have anything to do with the design of this bastard.' His thin fingers plucked at a sore place on his chin. 'I must say I thought we'd seen the last of the mausoleums of King Lombard.'

'It's not all that bad,' Colin said. 'I know there's been a lot of criticism in some quarters.'

'Colin, this is *bloody*,' said the other, eyelids twitching down over his quick, grey eyes. 'You must admit it.'

'It's what the clients wanted,' Colin said.

'Ah! What the client wants, Mr Marowitz, is what it is our job to supply, as our old friend Mr Airye used to say. You know what my father would have done with that man? Thrown him through the window, believe me. So you're working with the enemy, eh?'

'Enemy?'

'The unarchitects,' Marowitz said, pulling a cigarette from the zippered pocket of his jacket. 'Smoke?'

'Never use them,' Colin said.

Marowitz crossed his legs and scratched the top of his head with the thumb of his cigarette hand. 'You still married?' he asked.

'Certainly.'

'Kids now, I suppose?'

'Two,' Colin said. 'Eight and five. What about you?'

Marowitz shook his head. 'Negative and negative; I take life too seriously to get married, you follow. Anyway I believe in the celibacy of the architect.'

'I see,' Colin said. 'Um. What are you doing these days?'

'I live just near here. Come round and I'll show you what you missed being in on.' Marowitz started off down the road, his head pushed forward, the satchel bumping up and down with the over-emphatic movement of his arm. Colin trailed unenthusiastically after him and nearly tripped over his umbrella in the effort to keep up.

Marowitz's studio was chaotic with drawings and bits of models, torn sheets of rendering paper and photographs cut out of glossy journals. Marowitz pushed a pile of papers off his table. 'Um, yes, well, this is a place we could start. This is one of the first things I did out there. A small project, housing for three hundred workers from a light engineering firm. My father used to say "Integrity in architecture is building the people with the housing". And

Christ, were some of them *bloody* out there. And I don't mean the blacks. Did I have battles? To begin with, I annoyed them because I wouldn't allow any architectural drawings to be imported into Kenya from this country, projects, nothing, except from people who'd lived out there a minimum of six months, preferably a lot longer. Look, I'll tell you, this idea of an international architecture, it's all based on a false premiss.' Marowitz lit another cigarette from the butt of the last. 'Chain-smoker, bad habit. Do you love people, Colin?'

'I beg your pardon?'

'Do you love people? To build you've got to love people, that's my experience. My father loved his people. You know he didn't even like working for clients that weren't Jewish. I mean, he was a *Jewish* architect. Does that mean anything to you?'

'Not really,' Colin said.

'No, OK, that's going a bit far, he always went a bit far, but I think there's something in that, I mean working for *people*, you know, making people your own people before you do anything. I tried to do that with people in Africa. The first thing I did, I got all these workers together and I told them, we're all going to build some houses. At first they were *bloody*, but eventually I forced the firm to pay them while they worked on the site, you see what I mean? We didn't just put up stables for people: we got the people to make something *grow* for themselves. You know what I'd like, Colin, I want to get everyone to stop what they're doing for a year and pull everything down and start again, in this country, everywhere, keep things, change things, learn to belong to things and belong in them, that way you'd get all the *real*, organic love that would really hold people together.' Marowitz prodded aside some papers and pointed to a smudged rough. 'Here's a problem I solved *bloody* ingeniously. It was basically a bastard idea I got doing card-houses; foldover housing. Do you ever build card-houses?'

Colin said: 'Occasionally. I say, look, this is all frightfully interesting but I'm afraid – '

'Home to the wifey and kids?'

'I must, I'm afraid,' Colin said.

'We must have lunch and talk,' Marowitz said. 'I still need some people to help me force these *bloody* people to understand and then there's this theory of the interdependence of love and architecture I want to work on.' Marowitz drew out a cigarette. 'You know, architecture is the Jewish priesthood. There's still an opportunity to build with a kind of Mosaic loyalty to people and their Gods, i.e. what they live in. Living in God is a *bloody* significant expression.' Marowitz jabbed out his old cigarette, mashing his thumb-pad into the ember without apparent feeling. 'I believe that the modern Jew in particular – the atheist Jew who can't help being religious – I believe he can understand and tackle the problem of alienation better than anyone else. We've suffered longer than other people and the suffering has become creative again, you know?'

'I'm afraid I'm still not altogether clear what it all amounts to when it actually comes to design.'

'What was the last building you designed?'

'I helped on a restoration job for our golf club,' Colin said.

'Golf club.'

'It was bombed in the war. My firm gave me leave.'

'My father killed himself. Right? Did you know that? He killed himself because he couldn't get his kind of work and he wouldn't work on the wrong thing. He died in the wilderness, you see, I mean it all ties up, with this Mosaic tradition I was talking about. I think the time has come to do the right thing.'

'So do I,' Colin smiled. 'I must be getting home.'

TWO

Time Future and Time Past

1

TESSA SAID: 'Colin, where have you been?'

'Sorry, Tessers. I met a chappie I used to work with. Fellow called Saul Marowitz.'

'I remember *him*,' Tessa said. 'What's he doing nowadays?'

'Oh he's been in Kenya most of the time, far as I could tell. He's gone very, you know, peculiar. Glad I didn't, you know, go with him, really. I say, Tessers, you know the evenings are getting a bit longer, I shall be able to get out in the garden again soon.' Colin rubbed his hands together and advanced into the sitting room. 'Kids all right?'

Tessa said: 'James was a bit sick after lunch.'

'Oh, poor Jimmy, what was it?'

'My cooking, I expect.'

'Now that I take leave to doubt.' Colin smiled at her and sat down in the chair by the fire. The room was everything they had planned, the shelves either side of the mantel, the velvet curtains in their box pelmets, the wine-coloured carpet and the rich, comfy three-piece suite. Colin broke into the evening paper with all the eagerness of a man opening an unexpected gift. Tessa said: 'I did say you'd go up.'

'Tell me, Tessers, what do you think of the idea of a man being wedded to architecture?'

'Wedded to *what*?'

'This chap Marowitz, he doesn't sleep with women, so as to keep himself pure for architecture. What do you think of that?'

Tessa wrinkled her eyes and put her head on one side. 'I don't think it would suit my man,' she said. 'Now go on, pop upstairs like a good boy.'

Colin sighed and pouched the paper down the side of the armchair.

'I wondered if you'd come,' Anne said heavily, putting down her Enid Blyton. Two fair plaits hung down on to her chest, bracketing the small face with its large, dark eyes. 'I said you wouldn't but Mummy said you would.'

'And Mummy was right, wasn't she?'

'As usual,' Anne sighed.

Colin lowered himself on to the edge of the bed. Crossing his legs, he caught himself between his thighs and bit his lip to hide the shameful pain. 'Well, what have you done today?'

'Played,' Anne said. 'And went for a walk.'

Colin picked up a small rubber doll with eyes which had once opened and shut and had long ceased to do either, remaining a permanent Marilyn Monroe. 'Well, um,' he said, 'I didn't do anything very exciting today either.'

Anne said: 'I'm looking forward to school again.'

'Why are you?'

'Him,' the child said gloomily, pointing through the wall to her brother. 'He's been *awful* today.'

'You mustn't talk like that about your brother,' Colin said. He leaned over and kissed his daughter. 'Time you went to sleep.' He put one hand behind his neck and stretched. 'Well – um – I'll depart.'

'In peace but not in pieces,' Anne said.

Colin turned out the light and left the room. Everything was quiet in the house now, nothing jarred the peaceful world which he and Tessa had fashioned for themselves. He had all that he wanted. 'In peace but not in pieces,' the childish phrase rang in his ears. James was asleep, Babbit (Bunny Rabbit) grasped in his hand above the bedclothes, his head averted from the light of the door so that all Colin saw was Babbit and the sheen of the child's fair hair. How lucky for them that neither of the kids would be dark! Colin stood above the sleeping boy. He hoped his son would be strong. To have a son was such a responsibility. When Anne was born, Colin felt relieved, reprieved almost, but with the arrival of James, he felt an inescapable pressure on him. Women might live in the pavilion of life, but men went out into the sun and took their stance and faced the bowling; he could leave Anne to be instructed in women's ways by Tessa, but the boy was his to educate. He watched the soft uncomplicated child growing up and a bitter dread was born in him of the day when his innocence would be finished, when fighting and Jewishness had to be learned; he often tried to anticipate it, by making the boy 'tough', by having mock fights with him and by teaching him the right way to hold a cricket bat, which James quite failed to appreciate, regarding his father with a somnolent and puzzled expression till Tessa, irritated by Colin's tone of nagging mateyness, snatched James away and put a comb through his hair and sat him down to have a story read, while Colin grumbled jocularly about having a milksop for a son.

'What's James been up to today?' Colin asked as they sat down to dinner. 'Anne said he'd been awful or something.'

'Oh, only yelling.'

'Oh.' Colin frowned and started to carve the boiled silverside. 'He really shouldn't be crying still, should he? I mean he's five years old.'

'He banged his head, sweets.' Tessa put the carrots and potatoes on the table and sat down. It was the first time she had been able to relax all day. Suddenly she was very tired. She opened her eyes wide and moved her head to one side to take a fresh purchase on life.

'I was just trying to remember when I last cried,' Colin said. 'Funny thing, crying. I wonder why one ever stops? Do you think it could be that one doesn't resent things any more?'

'What sort of things?'

'Well, I mean when you get hurt as a child you resent it, don't you? You think it isn't fair, but then when you get a bit older you learn to take the rough with the smooth, come to realize that if you trip you bang your knee and that's all there is to it, isn't that it?'

'It's different for men,' Tessa said.

'When was the last time you cried, Tess?' Colin forked a couple of dumplings on to his plate and sat down. 'You know, I think we might invest in some new chairs, don't you?'

Tessa felt like crying then. A passion of exhausting despair rose in her and she wanted to burst into tears because of that dull interrogative tone in which Colin spoke, apparently to her, but in fact to himself. 'There is one thing I'd like to invest in,' Tessa said, 'if we can afford it, and that's the Times Library.'

'Yes, I wonder if we shouldn't join more things.'

'What sort of things, sweets?'

'Well, I mean – um – now they've got the synagogue definitely going, I wonder whether we shouldn't join that, for the kids, I mean.'

'Do you think we should have much in common with the people?'

'I'm wondering whether we aren't getting a bit, well, isolated.'

'Do you feel isolated, love?'

Colin flushed at his wife's tone. 'Well,' he said, 'once I've got the garden in good shape, you know, we shall need something to occupy the evenings.'

'I'm quite happy to put my feet up and listen to some records personally.' Tessa speared another slice of the silverside. 'I thought I might help Bunty up at the hospital when the kids go back.'

'Good plan. Perhaps I could do something like that too.'

'*Colin.* What could you do?'

'That's a good question,' Colin simpered. 'What could I do?'

Tessa regarded him with a shocked eyebrow and her old thin smile, the edge of her lip turned up almost at right angles. He had looked just like Isidore. Tessa said: 'Don't you worry, sweets, there're a lot of things you can do.'

Colin looked up and his eyes were red-rimmed and half-old. 'What?' he said.

Tessa said: 'How many people can design houses?'

'I don't design them.'

'You do.' She rattled her fork down on her plate in sudden sickness. 'You know what's the matter with us, don't you, my boy?'

'What?'

'We're getting middle-aged and sentimental.'

'We ought to have Saul round, you might like him better this time. He's – got something. Funny, really, I was rather impressed, this housing he's doing, course it's all a bit – cranky – but it's impressive in a way.'

'You have him round if you want to,' Tessa said.

'Funny really, to think we might have worked together all this time. I wonder if I've done the right thing, Tess.'

'Of *course* you have. You've done wonderfully. You mustn't let these people upset you.' Tessa gave him another thin smile. 'Pass your plate and you can have some sweet if you're a good boy. Now don't *worry*. It's all very well for him – he's married to architecture, but you're not! He can do what he chooses!'

Colin leaned back and waited for his wife to bring the sweet. Of course Marowitz was a complete crank, bit his nails, smoked too much, wouldn't get married, one couldn't base oneself on a chap like that. But the synagogue now, if

401

only he could have had a shot at that, if only he had been able to try his hand at something really – really what? Really at the limit of his powers. To live at the limit for a while, to do something which aspired to a height of its own, to stand up again, that would be to be young. Again? Colin saw himself standing again in the back of a truck as it drove across the desert in the brick-red of evening; dream-like he saw himself, with the wind in his hair (there wasn't much of that left) and manhood in his stance, holding the bar of the hood. Colin cocked his head back as Tessa returned to the room.

'I wonder if it's cowardly,' he said.

'If what is?'

'I don't know,' Colin said, 'I was just thinking.'

'You don't want to do that,' Tessa smiled.

After dinner they watched Panorama. 'Television's Window On The World': the words wound round the distorting curve of the glass and disappeared. How many distortions, Colin wondered, did life come through before it appeared encapsulated in the picture on the set, in the smooth voice of the commentator? What would it be like if there was no BBC? It was a sudden shocking thought. There didn't have to be a BBC.

'You are in a funny mood tonight, sweets,' Tessa said.

'Am I?' Colin sat up with a blink of surprise.

'Yes, have you forgotten you usually make us some coffee?'

2

Julia said: 'Hullo, face, how did it go?'

Paul kissed her and threw his mackintosh down on the divan. 'I don't know. This bloke Minster talked a lot about five thousand a year but we'll be lucky if we see five hundred.'

'Five thousand a year, eh?'

'Who wants five thousand a year?'

'I wouldn't mind five thousand a year,' Julia said. She grinned. 'Don't worry, I don't want five thousand a year.'

'He says I've got the makings of a top writer. In a couple of years he could make a Jerry Lodz out of me.'

'Jerry Lodz?'

Paul spread his hands. 'Jerry Lodz, that's what the man said.' He kissed Julia. Offhand, he asked: 'Any news about the book?'

Julia shook her head. Paul's novel *Mornings at Eight* had been rejected by three publishers and he was waiting with a gloomy joy for its rejection by the fourth. Yet he and Julia were very happy. Only the book's bi-monthly rejection brought pain into their lives. After the novel's first rejection Paul's confidence died: he sent it to an agency to find out if there was any hope at all of publication. He hesitated long. After two weeks of agony, Mr Davidson, of Moss, Freeman, and Davidson, rang him up and asked him to lunch at the Savile. Mr Davidson was portly and urbane. Paul wore the suit in which he had been 'confirmed' and his old Benedictine tie. Mr Davidson wore a tweedy suit, knitted cardigan and a blue, spotted bow-tie. He bought Paul a sherry, told him he thought *Mornings at Eight* was a rattling good yarn and lamented the slump in the book trade. He pressed Paul to smoked salmon and the *escalope de volaille* and warned him that he would be lucky to make a hundred pounds from the book, particularly with the present crisis in the trade. Over coffee, a brandy and a cigar ('No thank you, sir', from Paul) he reminisced about the great days when an author could earn a living and wondered how anyone made a penny out of writing today. He asked if Paul had a job, tutted and phutted when told no and offered, with avuncular scepticism, to try and get him a few little commissions.

Paul left the Savile in a transport of joy. Mr Davidson

had simply assumed he was a writer, no question of it. He was in. Mr Davidson had accepted him, first shot, and called him 'my boy'. He was even going to find him work. 'Have lunch again,' he had said on parting, 'enjoyed it muchly.' Paul went about London smiling with the contentment which filled him, smiling not only because of Dr Davidson but also because of Julia doing the shopping, cooking the meals, smiling because of their being able to go home properly together after the pictures, smiling because of the big bed in the dingy bedroom and the love they made in it.

For six months Paul had travelled on his own with some money which his college had given him, through the advocacy of Thornton Ashworth, and during that time the need and love he felt for Julia grew in him till his drunken resolve on that night in Maxton's Yard hardened and was confirmed. He wrote begging her to come to Paris when he would be there. She agreed eagerly. A telephone conversation between Nat and Hannah Adler revealed Julia's intention and one day, shortly before her departure, Julia received an invitation from Nat to join him for tea on Saturday afternoon. He suggested Gunter's.

'Ah, Julia, I'm glad you were able to come.'

Julia said: 'Oh, that's all right. Thank you for asking me.' She was wearing her new green coat with a fur collar and had seriously considered a hat. She looked at Nat, in his black overcoat and bowler hat, with quizzical composure. 'To what do I owe the honour?' she asked.

Nat said: 'My wife and I are rather worried about the way things are going.'

'What way are things going?' Julia asked.

'I understand that you're thinking of going to Paris.'

'That's not quite right,' Julia said. 'I'm not thinking of going. I'm going.'

Nat's lower lip jutted out. 'We'll just see about some tea.' The tea was ordered and then he proceeded. 'My wife and I are very worried about it. You see, Paul's very young, and – um – '

'Dr Riesman, do you know how old your son is?'

'He's only just starting out in life. He's still preparing . . .'

'I should have thought he'd had just about all the preparation he can stand.'

'There are a lot of faults that need ironing out before he can take his place as a responsible adult.'

'You've had twenty-three years to iron them out, why don't you give someone else a chance?'

'Far be it from me to try and dissuade you from such a task,' Nat said.

'I know him and I've waited a long time for him and I'm going to have him,' Julia said.

Nat gave a thin smile. 'I shouldn't be too confident about that.'

'I wouldn't advise you to try and stop me,' Julia said.

'I think you're making a packet of trouble for yourselves.'

'You're a doctor, do you really want your son not to sleep with anyone until he's married? Do you?'

Nat said: 'I don't think this is the place to discuss this.'

'What is?' Julia demanded. 'The gents' in Leicester Square?'

Nat said: 'My wife and I are very fond of you and we don't want you to be hurt any more than we want Paul to be.'

'Fond! Hurt! Oh, that's as far as your vocabulary of life goes, isn't it? You can't imagine anything that's bigger than fondness or deeper than not being hurt. You want to insulate everyone from pain so they can't feel *anything* any more.'

Nat said: 'The young always think they have a monopoly of feeling.'

In Paris Paul and Julia met joyously at the Gare des Invalides. They lay against each other in the taxi, the fur collar of her green coat glistening with tears and the wetness of Paul's mouth against her neck and their hands touching and moulding each other till they stumbled into words and laughing and waited in that quiet time of the taxi's honking and snuffling through the traffic to the hotel in the Rue Jacob. Paying off the taxi was in a dream, the driver's mouth opening and shutting and his head tucking down towards the clock and all quite pointlessly since he might as well not have been there and was left clutching his fare, take it or leave it, while Paul and Julia blundered up the stairs to the room, together on the stairs, together through the door, together on the bed whose rosy spread seemed to fill the whole room with its glow, so that cold January was absent. Cold January had no part in their loving on the red bed, in their regard of each other cold did not exist; Julia's hair, all crisp about her ears as it was when he loved her best, was the coaly sun and her lips, puffed with the love of him, with love for him, and her dark eyes, as bloomful as plums (flicker of lids against his cheek, the touch of lashes), this was the whole God-filled sky for him, and her nude, slim body, stretched on the bed.

As they dressed, Julia said: 'And this time it needn't ever stop. There's nothing to stop us.'

Paul said: 'Thank God you're here, Julia, I don't know what I was doing without you. Honestly, I don't.'

Julia said: 'Where shall we dine?'

'Raffi, shall we?'

At Raffi, Paul told her about his lunch there with Slinky and how he had wondered then whether Slinky would have slept with him and how he no longer cared. 'God, the world's a big place when you're alone in it,' Paul said. 'It's so terrifyingly big and now it's just us-big again.'

'Us-big,' Julia said, 'that's nice.'

'But I've learned how to write,' Paul said.

'You always knew.'

'No, I've written a book that'll be published,' Paul said. 'I knew it would be published the first sentence I'd finished. It reads like a published book.'

'You didn't mention it – you never told me,' Julia said. A twinge of uncertainty needled her.

After supper they went back to the room and Paul read her the manuscript. It was light, sunny and written with a somewhat formal style which was at once distant and professional.

'You see?' Paul said huskily. 'It's not about me at all. At last I've really got out of myself.'

'You know,' Julia said, 'I believe it will sell. Not that I know, of course,' she added hastily. 'I mean, we shall have to be patient.'

'I shall have to finish it first, I suppose,' Paul grinned. 'But I know exactly what happens. It's as good as finished really.' Paul mouthed a Gauloise. 'You do like it, don't you, Julia?'

'I think it's terribly good,' she said.

'And you see? It isn't about me at all. I don't really find myself interesting any more. What do you think of that? I think you're interesting, but I don't think I am. That's what this trip's done for me, you know, I realize I'm not all that important. I think it's partly Thornton's influence on me. He's made me realize that no problem is unique and if it is it isn't a problem –'

'It's a difficulty,' Julia grinned.

'And at the moment I have no difficulty,' Paul replied.

'Here we go again,' Julia mock-sighed.

They could not afford to stay indefinitely in the hotel in the Rue Jacob, so Julia asked Madame Nulli, the patron's wife, if she knew of a cheap flat. By chance, Madame's sister, a Madame Poulain, had two rooms free in her apartment in the Rue de Crimée. The rooms were separate, through a glassed door, from the rest of the flat and there was a basin-room with a tile-topped dresser on which

Madame Poulain, a small, white-haired woman with a spaniel face, not unlike Madame Fragonard's, assured them they could cook. The living rooms were small and the bed narrow. The view from the window was on to an ash-patched square scabbed with the funereal remains of summer allotments. The only vivid thing was a contrivance like a cross betweeen a porcupine and a Christmas tree upon which the used wine bottles of the flat-dwellers had been spiked. 'Look,' Paul said, 'a bottle tree!'

'Nine thousand francs the month,' Madame said.

'Perfect, excellent,' Paul agreed.

'My husband comes down the passage to get the coal,' Madame told them from the door, 'but you don't have to worry about him – he's blind!' And with a cackle of contemptuous amusement she made off down the passage, her slippers hissing against the polished pine of the floor. 'Nice sense of humour, the old girl,' Paul said. 'I must ask her to a funeral some time, she'll be the death and soul of the party.'

'We're really together,' Julia said. 'At last, we've got nothing to worry about except ourselves!'

Paul said: 'What do you think about getting married, Julia?'

'I have thought about it, I must say. Are you still terribly anti?'

'Didn't you get my letter, from Barcelona?'

Julia said: 'No. Let me see: there was Naples, Rome, Fes – '

'But God, I – I *proposed*.'

'You proposed, did you?'

'I can't understand it, you not getting that letter, honestly.'

'Well, tell me the good news, when were we married?'

Paul said: 'It's only a convenience, isn't it, getting married? It won't make any difference, will it?'

'No, we just won't have to worry so much about me getting preggers.'

'Oh, you won't if we're married,' Paul said. 'That's the way it goes.'

'Not unless we want to,' Julia said.

Paul said: 'I don't want a child yet, Julia.'

Julia said: 'Just so long as I can have one some time.'

'You can have someone else's.'

'How much energy do you think one girl's got?'

Paul leaned on the sill of the window and looked out on to the happy gloom of the courtyard. 'I've never seen a bottle-tree before,' he said. 'That really is a revelation. To come and live in a part of Paris I never even knew existed before and find a bottle-tree growing in the courtyard. It's all as ugly as hell, Julia, and I don't think it is at all, and that's the way life ought to be. Just you and me against all this.'

'We will have a baby one day though, won't we? I promise to look after it. Oh, Paolo, I know it'll look just like you and I shall love it so much.'

'Do you think we can get married in Paris?'

'Mummy'd be awfully upset if we didn't get married in synagogue.'

'Your sister wasn't, was she?'

'Susan? Yes she was, in Cricklewood.'

'I thought they were *Communists*,' Paul said.

'It was only for the parents,' Julia said. 'Would you mind terribly if we were?'

'It's all the publicity that turns me up,' Paul said. 'Announcements and receptions and all that.'

'We won't have any of that, just something very quiet.'

'Oh God, you only have to listen to us talking to hear what marriage does to you. I dread the whole thing, Julia. One ought to live in flagrant sin and keep the public out. We ought to walk around naked all day, perferably in an advanced state of sexual excitement. Oh, Julia, things won't change when we're married, will they?'

'I don't know until we get there,' Julia replied. 'I don't see why they should.'

'I don't feel as if there's anything else that has to be done. I feel as if the thing's complete between you and me.' Paul made a face. 'I'm *scared*, Julia.'

'I'll look after you, face. I always have, haven't I?'

That three months in Paris was, for Julia, happier even than Les Marteaux had been. She had no fear of the future. It promised not an escape from life; but life itself. She missed only the sun. Paul was no less happy; each day the pile of carefully typed sheets grew thicker, each day his confidence that he would be accepted was increased. He read through the manuscript constantly, not a little surprised at the mannered effortlessness of the narrative, amused at the tight-lipped jokes which punctuated its pages, so that he wondered whether coming to it fresh from other reading, he would have recognized it as his own. As these weeks passed, Paul began to regard marriage with less horror; he was, by the nature of what he was writing, more reconciled than ever before with the public world, less baffled and overborne by it since now he could for the first time measure his work according to public standards and find it satisfactory. With *Mornings at Eight*, he was ready to emerge into publicity, allowing that he had written no masterpiece, but prepared at least to claim the title 'writer'. To be a writer now, with *Mornings at Eight*, would not be to occupy the solitary role of an unhappy Jew getting back at his enemies, but the right to an aloof, rather patronizing seat in Pall Mall from which the procession of life could with advantage and impunity be observed. One would preserve, of course, one's liberal principles, sign letters to *The Times* about obscenity and homosexuality, canvass with humanitarian dignity for the admission of Negroes to the club. One would know one's wines, play one's rubber with some excellence in the squeeze and no interest in the money and with a cynical curl of the lip pity those whom circumstances had forced to the indignities of commerce. One would live pleasantly in a small flat (or even house) in Chelsea where one would entertain one's intellectual acquaintances with an individual but wholly tasteful hospitality, taking time only to do one's daily stint, in copybook script, of course, and pen a few letters to one's eminent contemporaries: 'Dear L. This morning a finch sat on my window-sill as I began to write to you and I was filled – as I am more and more – with a sense of the rareness of things – ' Oh yes, *la vie littéraire* was something to look forward to. These would be long philosophical controversies, in impeccable prose, with Thornton Ashworth, which would make Gide and Claudel look like a couple of Marble Arch maulers. 'I cannot but think that Wittgenstein's Heracleitanism . . .' And, of course, obituaries! What fun it would be writing obituaries! 'The artful cadences of his prose certainly had a silver age lilt but in the majesty of his vision and the loftiness of his hopes there was unmistakable gold – writes P. R.' On matters of aesthetics one would express oneself but rarely and then with reluctance: 'I do not call a man frank when, although he possesses a perfectly good suit, he insists on parading naked: I call him a fool and even, at times, a knave. The writer who assures me it is his duty to tell all is at liberty to do so, I ask only that he refrain from telling it to me.' With luck one might, if one could find friends in the right places, do a little novel-reviewing for one of the chic weeklies: 'Mr Y.'s brand of *Stimmung* may not be everyone's cup of Château Latour, but to one who, like the present writer, must confess to an omnipresent *nostalgie de Langue d'Oc . . .*' Oh, it would be a full life!

When the time came to pay the rent, Madame Poulain claimed that they had agreed to pay ten thousand francs a month. When Paul protested, she said that the extra thousand was for fuel. Julia kept shaking her head and saying 'Non, Madame' until Paul became quite impatient with her and told her, 'For God's sake, shut up.' Eventually, with a maximum of ill-feeling, a compromise was reached, not without impassioned speeches from all parties. When Paul and Julia returned to the hotel in the Rue Jacob, Madame Poulain had already phoned Madame Nulli to inform her of the perfidy of her two guests, with the result that Madame Nulli forbade them with many curses and cries of 'voleurs' ever to cross her threshold again. It was a sad ending to their stay, for it was in that hotel that they had spent their first night together and now they would never sleep in it again. 'It's the end of an era,' Paul sighed melodramatically. 'And I'm glad.' But really they were not.

The wedding took place in London, at the same synogogue in Cricklewood where Ben and Susan had been married. Alma's first actual meeting with Julia's parents was during the discussion about where and when the ceremony should be held. 'They're really rather sweet,' she said afterwards. Both Paul and Julia were eager to find somewhere to live at once; neither wanted to go on a honeymoon. 'It seems rather ridiculous,' Paul said, 'when we've just spent three months in Paris.' He was having to live in Monmouth Court until after the wedding and the weeks of waiting were hateful and humiliating.

Nat said: 'You could go back to Paris for a bit.'

'All we want is to get the whole thing over.'

Nat said: 'Well, you let me know what you decide. I must be getting along.'

'He's getting just like Dr Dale,' Alma said. 'Always having to dash off!'

Paul was left alone with his mother. He felt a desperate pity for his parents, a sense of having failed utterly to be what they wanted. His life was couched from beginning to end in terms they could not accept, so that now they must call the week after the wedding 'the honeymoon', must fasten the right terms to actions and feelings that were not fitted for them and Paul hated and pitied them for it, for fitting him and Julia in silly hats and making them join the party. Alma said: 'This is a big step you're taking. You're sure you're doing the right thing?'

Paul said: 'I'm not doing anything. It's being done to me.'

'That doesn't sound very hopeful.'

'By you,' Paul said. 'By you and you and you. It's nothing to do with me or Julia.'

Alma sagged: 'I'm sorry,' she said. Paul said: 'I dare say we shall all be much happier when we're married.'

'I think it's – *expedient*,' Alma sighed.

It seemed to Paul that the wedding had nothing to do with him. It must, he mused, be rather the same when you are about to be executed. He honestly thought, standing there with the four-poster canopy over them, that he would have married anyone whom they supplied. When Julia took her place next to him, he looked curiously to see who had been provided for the part. That she smiled and whispered 'Hullo, pudding' was proof merely of good casting. When the ritual wine glass (wrapped in a paper bag and slotted in a mahogany box) was put under his feet and he stamped on it like a man in a brothel, he was amazed to hear the shout *Mazeltov*! go up; looking round with the sheepish air of one who never thought to win a prize, he saw Isidore and Hannah Adler, Ben and Susan, Colin and Tessa, his parents, Mr and Mrs Paynter, and for a moment wondered what they were doing there, till someone touched his arm and there was something he had to do.

At the luncheon afterwards, he preserved the same detached air, saying in his speech that on the whole he preferred funerals to weddings, since it was so much less likely that a mistake was being made. He was conscious of the glassy, toothy portrait of himself which had so far fooled everyone into believing he was really there and he came to reinhabit his body with a serious and urgent fear that some irremediable harm had been done to it in his absence. He felt he belonged to these people, to Julia's parents, whom he had hardly acknowledged as real before, to his own parents, as ever gleaming proudly at what was of no interest to him and he thought then of standing on the beach at Les Marteaux, and Julia on her knees kissing him, and he felt then a sick awareness of how far they had travelled out of Eden.

Alma had insisted that they let Nat book them into the Royal Norfolk at Hastings for a week. 'If you don't like it, don't hesitate to come straight up to London on the next train,' she told them. 'We shall quite understand. Only I know you'll both be tired and a good rest won't do either of you any harm.'

When they returned from Hastings they went to live in a furnished room in Kensington. Within a few weeks Julia and Alma, who had teamed up for house-hunting, had found what Julia reported as 'a gloomy dungeon in Fulham'. Alma called it 'a dear little semi-basement flatlet in Chelsea.' Paul wanted only to be settled and agreed, after the hastiest inspection, that it was just what he wanted. Hannah Adler was less easily satisfied. 'You'll have the damp in here, you can be sure of that,' she told her daughter, 'and no fresh air, you'll catch everything there is to catch. You couldn't let a baby sleep in this atmosphere.' Alma said: 'They have got central heating and Dr Riesman seems to think it'll be all right as long as they don't stay too long.' Hannah Adler shrugged her Persian lamb shoulders: 'I don't understand the young people nowadays. You know what this place is? This is where they used to keep the coal in the old days.' Alma said: 'I think the children will probably like being a little Bohemian.' Hannah Adler said: 'Never mind, wait till you sell your first book, then things'll be different.' Paul put an arm round his mother-in-law for the first time. 'That'll be the day.' Hannah patted his cheek. 'It won't be long,' she said. 'And if ever you're a bit short, you just let me know.' Alma said: 'Now, Hannah, Issy wouldn't like it if he knew you were giving his money away!' 'It's not his money,' Hannah Alder said. 'I worked for it just as much as he did.' Alma smiled and craned her head down to the tiny mirror in the dungeon hallway to fix her hat and said how nice it was that they had a Flaxman number and not a Fremantle because that was so much better for 'prestige reasons'.

'Whose prestige, Mama? Yours or mine?' Paul asked.

'Clever boy!' his mother said. 'Well now, Hannah, I wonder if we shall find a taxi at this hour?'

'I'll drop you,' Hannah said. 'Where do you want to go?'

'Is your man still waiting? Extravagant girl!'

'The tumult and the shouting dies,' Paul said as he closed the door behind the two mothers, 'the captains and the kings depart.'

Paul and Julia had been obliged to buy the outgoing tenant's furniture and fittings. They gave the place a dowdy personality which Paul found not altogether disagreeable. The money had been realized from some savings certificates which Isidore had bought during the war as dowry for each of his daughters. There was a little left over and Paul had a few pounds of his own, as well as the rump of his college money: they could live. And now at last, Paul thought, they would be left alone.

3

Susan said: 'Ben! I've been so worried. Where have you been?'

Ben smiled. 'Am I late or something?'

'Been arrested again, old boy?'

415

'What makes you ask that?'

'You don't have to be so innocent,' Susan said, 'they've been here.'

'Who have, Susan?'

'The police, The *super*!'

'Aha. Been leaving your barrow outside the palace again?' Ben slung his overcoat on the hook. 'Matter of fact I was late at the office. Dave and I were going over some of the Christmas figures, see which lines had done best. The returns are just beginning to come in.'

Susan said: 'So how's business?'

Ben said: 'Don't ask!'

Actually Ben's business was doing very well. The dining-room at No. 24 had a new Swedish table and chairs from Heal's. A car was definitely on the cards. Ben's mother was at once proud and ashamed of her son's enterprise. 'What would your father have thought? A son that manufactures Christmas cards!'

'You *sell* Christmas cards,' Ben said.

'I only take a few each year, for the *goyim*,' Mrs Simons said.

'Well, I print a few each year for the same people,' Ben said, 'and a few for the deviationists.'

'Your father never sent a Christmas card in his life,' Mrs Simons told him, brushing invisible crumbs from her vast bodice.

'Ah, but I could make him a special price today.'

'Don't have to use that tone of voice when you're talking about your poor father, God rest his soul.'

'What tone of voice is that, Mum?'

'He was a good man, Benjamin.'

'Did I say he wasn't? Did I?' Ben laid his hand on his chest and was open-faced with inquiry at his mother, but the old woman did not accept his openness. 'Christmas cards,' she said scornfully. 'Whatever next? Next thing it'll be crucifixes!'

Ben said: 'I'll see you right, Mum, don't you worry.'

'You don't have to talk vulgar just 'cos you're talkin' to me.'

'OK, Mum, you win,' Ben laughed.

'Yers,' said his mother. 'Shockin', talk like that to your mother.'

Ben stared gloomily at the fair wood of the new table. His eyes were tired and there were crescents of bruised shadow under them; the brows remained bushy and aggressive, the only firm feature in a face tired at the end of a long day. When Susan came in with the supper he leaned back with a quick jauntiness that was suddenly irritating. 'Don't get up,' Susan said.

'Well now, what's all this about the police, Susan?'

'I expect you know as well as I do. They wanted to know all about that chap Herb Fletcher who used to come here.'

'Aha,' Ben said.

'Ben, they're not going to arrest you, are they?'

Ben chortled. 'Arrest me? Whatever for?'

'I don't know.' Susan batted her eyelids funnily. 'Spying,' she suggested.

Ben said: 'Nice piece of steak. Don't worry, girl. No one's going to arrest yer 'usband.'

'What's it all about then?'

'I suppose they're checking up on someone.'

'Well who?'

'Hard to say. They're always on at King Street these days. If it isn't one thing, it's another. I suppose the Yanks've been on to them.'

'What do you think they suspect?'

'I suppose Fletcher must've – been up to something – drinking vodka in the Library of Congress or some such heinous offence.'

'I thought it was hay-nus.'

'Hee-nus, hay-nus, what it is to have a wife with a high-class education!'

'What time did they call on you this morning?'

'Oh, I don't know, about ten, I suppose.'

'You might have tipped me off.'

'I tried to phone you,' Ben said, 'but they said you were engaged.'

'Ben, I wasn't on the phone all morning. Do you think our phone's being tapped or something?'

'A cabbage, two cauliflowers, quarter of mushrooms and three pounds potatoes. Got that down, Reg? That's it, boy. Straight to No. 10 with it, lad, and shoot to kill if they try to stop you. Come off it, Susan, who'd want to tap our phone?'

'The superintendent looked very businesslike. You'd think something absolutely *ghastly* had been perpreprated.'

'Perpreprated? What on earth's that? You mean, terpretaped.'

Susan giggled. 'Perpretated, isn't that right?'

'Preterpated,' Ben said, 'An outrage has been preterpated, that's what they say, isn't it?'

Susan said: 'No, seriously. He was awfully grim. Perhaps they think *Everyman* was a cover for passing information . . .'

'Susan, honestly, you're getting too E. Phillips Oppenheim for words. I think you ought to stop using the public library, it's obviously poisoning your mind.'

'I wish we could afford *The Times*,' Susan said.

'Afford it! We *can* afford it. Essential business reading. A man in the Christmas card game has to be alive to all that's best in the world of the intellectuals.' He still said in-tee-lectuals, with the first 'e' long.

'In-*tell*-ectuals,' Susan said.

'And teperpated to you,' Ben said.

Susan said: 'Ben, I suppose there wasn't anything fishy going on, was there?'

'What do you mean, Susan?'

'They thought you'd sort of inveegled – invaygled – this bloke Fletcher into coming in with you.'

'Inveegled – invaygled, did they? That's too deep for me.'

Susan snatched the plates off the table and stormed out of the room. In the kitchen a plate crashed to the floor. Ben smiled and ambled out to see what had happened. He leaned against the doorpost, his hand on the shelf where the pots were kept. Susan looked up from where she had gone down on her haunches. 'It's all your fault,' she shouted. 'It's all your fault.'

Ben shook his head. 'Honestly, Susan,' he said.

THREE

The Thaw

1

PAUL SAID: 'Do you have to wear your specs all the time?'

'I don't wear them all the time,' Julia said. 'But if I'm going to do your typing I have to wear my specs. Finish.'

'I never knew you wore them so much, you never used to.'

'I never used to do your typing,' Julia said.

Paul slumped into an armchair, feet over the arm. 'How's it going?'

'All right. I think you've done an awfully good job.'

'It's an awfully good job you do,' Paul said.

Julia was typing some ghosting which Paul had done for a firm of brewers whose chairman had been asked to write a piece on his firm's centenary for a trade journal. Mr Davidson had procured him the job. The other ghosting work which Mr Davidson had found him had been well received and the agent had been good enough to say that if some more lucrative work of a similar kind were to come along Paul would be one of the first of his clients to whom he would offer if: that this hack work came from the same man to whom *Mornings at Eight* had seemed so acceptable eased Paul's conscience at agreeing to do it. In any case, one had to live. It was this simple consideration which had taken Paul to Mr Minster. Mr Minster had no part in the literary world. He was strictly commercial. He belonged not to the Savile but to Coombe Hill. He was interested not in writing, but in money. There were no aesthetic

420

pretensions about Mr Minster. If it made money it was good, if not, not. Paul was under no illusion about the kind of brothel to which he had offered himself, but he was prepared to shelve his virtue if the money was right. It was all very well to talk about one's integrity, but what did it amount to? Why was it so worth preserving as a thing in itself? It was galling for him and Julia to have to stand in the rainy queue for the pictures because they were hoarding the extra one and sixpence that would take them both straight in. Julia did not complain, but now they were married Paul felt he would like to be able to give her what other married men gave their wives. When he said 'My wife is waiting' he wanted the man to whom he was talking to think of a chic, attractive girl watching for the taxi to roll up at the door, not of a girl going rusty becaust she had waited too long and too often in the rain. When Paul visited International Projects Limited, which was the name of Mr Minster's brothel, he did so with a conviction that he could keep separate the integrity of his art and the rewards of commerce. He found it difficult, under logical analysis, to see what the borderline between them was, except that one did 'art' for less money and for more discriminating people. He still wanted to do it, but he saw no reason why the jobs one took so that one might pursue one's art should be, by tradition, the most menial and unattractive ones. If one had to be a harlot it was as well that the beat should be an expensive one. Doubtless when *Mornings at Eight* was accepted new possibilities would be revealed in the literary world, little sinecures would perhaps be forthcoming so that he might devote his full time to writing, as the saying was, without the distractions of having to live. And eventually, of course, success would come. But what was success? It was selling the film-rights of the artistic novel he had been pensioned off to write. It was money. In the end all that people judged success by was money. When you were young, they said, you didn't mind discomfort, you could devote yourself wholeheartedly to what you wanted to do, but when you were successful you could show that it had been worthwhile only by the money you were now able to command. To prove it, you had drinks at Claridge's, lunch at the Caprice, you spent four months in the Bahamas each year, you played baccarat, you backed plays, you spent week-ends with statesmen. You remarried.

It had come about now that Paul and Julia spent at least one evening a week at Wimbledon with Nat and Alma. They arrived for supper and stayed to watch television. To begin with they had enjoyed it. Both Paul's parents did their utmost to make them feel welcome and Paul found pleasure in his parents' company since at last he need no longer have it all the time. It was rather like Old Boys' day.

Once or twice Nat and Alma came to Fulham to 'visit the children'. Alma wore her fur coat and kept it on all evening. 'Of course,' she commented, 'this is a sweet little flat to live in for a short time, but I do hope you'll be able, for your own sakes, to find something else soon. Anyway, of course, you'll be looking for a bigger place eventually.'

'Why, Mama?' Paul asked.

'Oh, well, you'll need a little more space, I dare say. There's no reason why art should always starve in a garret.'

'This is a garret?' Paul said.

Alma pursed her lips. 'I think Julia will know what I mean,' she said.

Paul gritted his teeth as Julia smiled pleasantly at his mother. 'I don't want to move,' she said. But it seemed a public announcement. Secretly there was a pact between the two women. They talked to each other on the telephone.

For a while it was pleasant to play at married couples, but Paul came to resent the very pleasure which they all took in their evenings together. On the way home from

Wimbledon he went abruptly sour. 'What's the matter now?' Julia demanded.

'We shouldn't go there. We shouldn't enjoy it so much. I don't want to be like that.'

'That's a lovely dinner service. Your mother's never got it out before.'

'Yes, isn't is a pity we didn't have a big wedding with nine hundred guests – we could have stocked up for life too.'

'I didn't want a big wedding,' Julia said.

'You wanted a wedding, though, didn't you? You wanted that all right.'

'Oh, Paolo – '

'I just knew where it was all leading to. I just wish I *didn't* know where it's all leading to: the television in the bedroom.'

'Look, I don't mind if we never go to Wimbledon again. They're not my parents.'

'I wish they wouldn't take so much trouble, I wish to God they hated us.'

They got off the bus at Lots Road and cut down towards Tregunter Road, where the flat was. When they were together they always walked with their arms round each other. 'Oh, it is all right,' Paul said then. 'It is all right. I am happy, Julia. I just wish there wasn't anyone else in the world to disturb us, to keep trying to change us. I so love our flat, don't you?'

'Of course I do. It's a dear little flat. I only wish the kitchen was a bit bigger, that's all.'

'Nothing wrong with the kitchen,' Paul said.

'It gets terribly hot in there. I have to keep running out for air.'

'Do you good. The exercise'll keep you young.'

Julia said: 'One day I want to have a wireless, don't you, Paolo?'

'What do we want a wireless for?'

'Concerts,' Julia said. 'And I expect you'd like to have the Manny Finkelbaum Show.'

'Oh, that's gone off,' Paul said. 'Lost all its old spark. I don't think Stan Halloran cares any more, you know what I mean?'

'They ought to get you to write it.'

'That's not such a bad idea.'

'Ben, you know, my brother-in-law – he used to know Stan quite well. We ought to have them over one evening.'

'Ask them. I don't think I've ever talked properly to a Communist. How come he knows Stan Halloran? I shouldn't have thought they came out of the same stable.'

'Ben knows a lot of people,' Julia said.

'I don't suppose we shall ever be able to go to the States once they've been to dinner.'

'Why not?'

'I expect he's followed everywhere by a member of the FBI, don't you?'

'Why should anyone from the Federation of British Industries want to follow Ben?'

Paul stopped and put both arms round Julia and kissed her. 'You're a peach,' he said. 'I adore you.'

'And I adore you,' Julia said. 'Nothing's wrong really, is it?'

'Always have to have the commercial, don't we?' Paul said.

2

Paul felt quite nervous before Ben and Susan arrived. He had never spoken to Ben except in the impersonal atmosphere of the wedding and he was conscious now of the shakiness of his own social attitudes.

One day, during the war, Paul had been waiting at a bus stop with his father. When the bus came it was full. Paul was very upset. 'If only we lived in Germany,' he said, 'we could have turfed some people off and got on ourselves, couldn't we, Daddy?'

'If we lived in Germany,' Nat Riesman said, 'we'd be in prison, or even worse.'

Paul was silent. Now whenever he thought of violent social change he thought of that day in the bus queue and it seemed to him that the state of England, uncomfortable though it might be in certain respects, was all right. For if the social order changed too violently, what good would it be that one had been to a good school and to Cambridge, what good that one's father was a doctor? However much one hated aspects of these things they were what Mr Minster would call 'credits'. Social change was all very well, but it must be social change on the medical model. A Dr Riesman must be in genial charge, not for what he got out of it but for the respect it earned him, the blameless Schweizerian eminence from which he could regard the mortal struggle. In the end, Paul realized, it was the fact that he got nothing out of it that excused and dignified the doctorial role. It was the desire to see change and yet not to be a victim of it that made Paul a literary socialist; despite all the trivia of life, one went on coolly operating, loved even by the sweatiest strugglers. In America, the doctor occupied a high social position, much higher than in Britain, and the reason for this was clear: the destruction of the upper classes left the professional classes in a magisterial position. Once a decent social revolution had been encompassed, the writer and the doctor would, with the universal respect of all, lord it in saintly benevolence. The writer as doctor was the ideal to which Paul aspired, the man whose devotion to his kind of medicine was above suspicion, the man who, no matter what social changes took place, never struck, but patiently, in the face of whatever obstacles, pursued his remedial tasks, careless of his social position and yet safe in it and respected. He had revolted against Monmouth Court and all it stood for, and yet he was following in his father's tradition and even, since he had given Nat *Mornings at Eight* to read, soliciting his good opinion. Like the doctor's professional code, Paul's political philosophy was based on the reverence for life. 'I don't see,' he said to Ben, 'how you can support a régime which cares nothing for human life. It seems to me that we've all got to agree that if we agree on nothing else, we agree that it's not worth shedding human blood in order to achieve political ends.'

Ben did not argue with this view. He sat as ever when under attack with a tucked-in smile on his face, his arms folded. 'I don't want to see people killed any more than you do,' he said.

'And yet you're always talking about liquidating people?'

'I am? When did I ever say anything about liquidating people? You've got to realize that the problems of a whole economic system are a good deal more complicated than the question of how to arrange them round a dinner-table so they don't tread on each other's feet,' Ben said. He spoke still with the same small smile on his face, but there was an impersonal quality in his voice. Susan sighed and talked to Julia about clothes. How many times had she heard these arguments since she had been married to Ben? That patient, unyielding voice had been wheeling away, neither persuading, nor being persuaded, for years and years and years. Ben never seemed to tire of his duty, nor did he any longer take pleasure in it. He was a professional. His weekly cartoon never failed to appear in the *Worker*, and never failed exactly to mirror the party line. He was indifferent to the reaction of those outside his own world. Ben was faithful to the *Worker*. It meant something to be able to say 'our paper' and not to have scabbed on it. He smiled at boys like Jerry Lodz, who had been in the YCs with him, but in his heart he despised them. Ben hated no one, he had no sentimental socialist animosity against any individual: the new literary leftism excited only his derision, for this was a personal, quirky and untrustworthy philosophy (which had not failed to be discussed at a branch meeting), the only fuel of which was envy, a political motive too easily blunted by success, by recruitment into that very class which kindled the first hatred, by money. Ben watched the slow degeneration of Halloran into a pop entertainer without the scornful and admiring jealousy which had ridden Susan; he expected it, that was all. Ben was amused at people's efforts to avoid the inevitable; he took no joy in their eventual subservience to it, he merely took it as one more reason for keeping faith.

Susan's fidelity to the party, such as it was, sprang from quite other roots: it was 'marriage', for which Ben had so often professed no use, that kept Susan to the party line. Bourgeois sentimentalism held her faithful to a revolutionary doctrine. It was a private rather than a public allegiance. Her Communism had nothing to do with politics: she was rather shaken if people assumed it had. When Superintendent Palmer called again he was more explicit about the purpose of his investigations. 'We're concerned, Mrs Simons, with what may amount to a matter of High Treason.'

'Of *what*?' Susan batted her eyelids.

'We've been asked for our help by the American authorities in tracing the movements of this man Herb Fletcher both in the years at the end of the war and quite recently –'

'I told you, Superintendent, I haven't seen him for years –'

'He was in this country last year, Mrs Simons.'

'Herb was? Well he never came to this house.'

'He never returned to the United States. It's the belief of the American authorities that he may have gone to Europe, perhaps eventually to Soviet Russia.'

'Well, it's nothing to do with me,' Susan said. 'I promise you.'

'Is your husband out a lot, Mrs Simons?'

'Ben? Oh a bit, you know.'

'Ever go away for several days at a time?'

'He may have been away for a night every now and then. Yes, he has been a couple of times. Had to go up North or something.'

'Ever go abroad?'

'Only for holidays last year. First time we'd been able to for years.'

'Where did you go, Mrs Simons?'

'We went to Biarritz.'

'Via?'

'Dover-Calais.'

'Via Paris, Mrs Simons?'

'We did go to Paris for one night, yes.'

'Mrs Simons, you strike me as a pretty reasonable sort of person. I'm very keen to avoid making any trouble for your husband, but I can only do that if I'm absolutely convinced that there's nothing further he or you can do to help us get to the bottom of this business. I'll tell you frankly. The Russians have made astonishing advances in ballistics since the war. The Americans believe that they couldn't have done this without certain leakages of information from allied sources. Do I make myself clear?'

'Do you really think if I was passing information to anyone – honestly, Superintendent, the whole thing's fantastic. I've never known anyone who *had* any information.'

Superintendent Palmer said: 'Yes, you have, Mrs Simons. From 1943 until 1951 Mr Herbert Fletcher was involved in secret work which would be directly relevant to ballistics and to missiles in particular.'

'Look, I don't know anything about ballistics or anything else.' Susan lit a Player's Number Three. 'Honestly, I don't

428

believe any information was passed to the Russians in the first place. I don't know why you think that all their achievements must be due to spies and secret agents.'

'Sounds quite like the Party talking, doesn't it, Mrs Simons?' smiled the superintendent. 'You see, what I was trying to tell you was that I am only concerned to try and help you. I dare say you're afraid I'm trying to trap you into something, but I'm not, I assure you.'

'Oh no.'

'After all, there's nothing I can trap you into, is there?'

Susan said: 'You don't know that.'

'I can promise you that if you can remember anything – anything that might help us trace this man and the channels by which he escaped from this country, we shall exercise the greatest discretion in the use we make of that information if it affects your husband in any way.'

'If you're trying to suggest my husband's a spy, I think it's the most ridiculous thing I've ever heard of. Do you really think that open members of the Communist Party would be so incredibly stupid as to be spies? It doesn't hold water for a minute. Life just isn't that simple.'

'That's where you're wrong, Mrs Simons,' Superintendent Palmer said. 'It often is that simple, I wouldn't place too much faith in that argument. Oh, by the way, does the name Hilda Klein mean anything to you?'

'I've never heard of anyone called Hilda Klein in my whole life,' Susan said.

Now she sat in the dungeon, as Julia called it, and listened to Ben explaining why the changes in the Party line were proofs not of its uncertainty but of its continual ability to embrace new historical perspectives. The window of the dungeon was beaded with steam from Julia's cooking (she had had to open the kitchen door every now and then to avoid suffocating) and Susan was reminded of the night when she had been banished to the kitchen of No. 24, leaving Ben and Sid alone in the front room. She experienced the same claustrophobic dismay: what was she doing here? who were these people? who was Hilda Klein? why had the police come to No. 24 and how many times would they come again? Listen next week for the next thrilling instalment, one might say, but this was her life and she seemed to know nothing of it, this was herself and suddenly it was not the same. She was a pinpoint of uncertainty, living backwards and forwards with equal doubts. At least before she had been confident of the past and now a man came and asked questions about it, was not quite clear on one or two points, and she wondered herself what had really happened, whether the past was really something she could be confident about and since the past was herself, was a fan spread out with herself at the crux of it, she felt she must get a grip on it, lest its blades, no longer spread out attractively, should break up, shatter, splinter and leave her naked, vulnerable and absurd. This was what Eve felt when she discovered her nakedness. She found she had a past in which she had done things she did not understand, in which things had had meanings she had never given them and yet which were held against her. Susan felt the need for flight, the need quickly, quickly, to make a whole new past to cover her nakedness.

'You can't defend the Hitler-Stalin pact, surely?' Paul was saying.

'If you want the causes of the Hitler-Stalin pact, so called, you'd do much better to blame it on Munich and the whole pre-war policies of the Conservative Government. If they'd gone in with the Soviet Union – or just let France go in – and beaten Franco out of Spain, the whole history of Europe might have been different.'

'But I thought that the course of history was inevitable,' Paul said heavily. 'Surely nothing can change it.'

'That's just where you're wrong, you see.' Ben was smiling. 'The *eventual* course of history is inevitable, if you like to look at it that way, yes, but it's like a race. Because there's a mile to go doesn't mean everyone has to finish the distance in the same amount of time.' Ben grinned at Paul. 'You're too impatient, you people.'

'Who people?' Paul said.

'You people,' Ben repeated. 'Always want results within twenty-four hours.'

Paul said: 'I'm just myself. I'm only interested in comparing the various ways political theorists go on about things.'

'Doesn't sound much of a life to me,' Ben said.

'I can't see how you can tie yourself to a system that tells you what to think. I mean that's absolutely incomprehensible to anyone with a philosophical training –'

'Just shows you the advantage of not being educated.'

'There I agree,' Paul smiled, glad of a truce. It had seemed to him at the beginning of the evening that he might be able to persuade or argue Ben out of the Party, after all a philosophical education must enable you to do something and surely nothing so well as refute the fallacious, but no sooner had Ben come smiling into the flat, with that slight side to side swagger of his, than Paul had felt utterly naïve and unknowledgeable. Ben had been in the game too long. Paul tried all sorts of attack in order to find a weak place in the other's defences. 'For any writer,' he said later, 'the thought of living in the Soviet Union is enough to give you the creeps.'

'There seem to be plenty of writers in the Soviet Union who don't think so,' Ben replied.

'Not being able to write what one wants to write, it must be frightful.'

Ben said: 'Aha. What are you writing at the moment?'

'Oh I've written a novel, you know.'

'Aha. What's that then?'

'Oh, it's only a light thing – it's called *Mornings at Eight*. A sort of comedy thriller.'

431

'Aha.'

Paul said: 'I felt I had to get something published. I mean once one's got something published, you know, one's in and then one can start doing, well, more serious things.'

Ben was smiling faintly. Julia said: 'You shouldn't disparage your own work. It's a lovely little book and very funny too. I think Ben would like it. *You* will,' she said to her sister.

'Why, what's it about?'

'Spies,' Paul said.

'Oh yes,' Susan said, 'I shall enjoy that. Anyone called Hilda Klein in it?'

'No.' Paul was puzzled. '*Hilda Klein*? What made you think that?'

'Nothing,' Susan said, her eyes on Ben who had swivelled away to look at the books in the shelves along the dungeon wall.

'I don't suppose Ben approves, do you?'

'What's that?'

'People writing funny books.'

''Course I approve of people writing funny books. You write any kind of book you like, boy.'

'What sort of books do you like?'

'I like all sorts of books,' Ben said. 'Zola, Malraux, Gorky – '

'But natch,' Susan said.

'No, but writing in English who do you like?'

'I don't read a lot of novels,' Ben said.

'Howard Fast?'

'Yes, I like some of his stuff. Read his *Spartacus*?' Paul shook his head. 'Oh, you should. T'riffic some of it.'

'Graham Greene?'

'Yes, very good, some of the earlier ones. *The Confidential Agent*.'

'Oh yes,' Paul said, relieved that Ben had mentioned one he had read. 'Very good, I agree.'

'*The Confidential Agent*,' Julia said. 'What's that about?'

'Spies,' Paul said.

'Let me see,' Ben said. 'Anyone called Hilda Klein in that one?'

3

Washing up, Paul said: 'I'm sure Ben won't like my book.'

'What does it matter whether Ben likes it or not?'

'I don't know. There's always such a gap between what one feels and what one says. You know, I just feel Ben'll ignore us and it. I mean, it won't shake him and it won't please him. It won't do anything to him.'

'Why should it matter whether your books do anything to Ben?'

'He's a central figure of our times,' Paul announced. 'No, he makes me feel terribly stupid, honestly.'

'You're not stupid.'

'I should say I'm not. I'm the original "very clever boy" in heavy Jewish italics, but I still don't feel I'm really in on anything.'

'You're really in on me,' Julia said.

'No, I'm serious: Julia, do you think I could ever be a Communist?'

'They wouldn't have you. You're the most undisciplined creature I've ever come across.'

Paul said: 'I think that's a fault.'

'I'm sure Lawrence wasn't disciplined.'

'It's no comfort to me to share that characteristic and no other. You might as well say Hitler had black hair.'

'Hitler had black hair,' Julia said.

'*Hitler*. Christ, I remember seeing the Belsen pictures and thinking it can't go on, something has to be done, something has to be done all the time about it, all the rest of my life I'll be doing something about it, and yet here we

433

are in our comfortable dungeon, a Flaxman number, plenty to eat, cinemas and here I am writing about comedy spies. There's nothing so terrible about anything we do. It's just that the whole way we live, all the things we stand for, all our invisible exports and imports, the whole bloody register of our lives is a complete outrage. I've got no guts, Julia.'

'I don't know what you're talking about.'

'What's the spiritual value we wouldn't deny? What do we really stand for, what would we rather die than say yes to? What are we really convinced about?'

Julia said: 'I don't know. I know I love you, that's enough for me.'

'You'd stick to that under torture?'

'I couldn't help it,' Julia said. 'I might say that I didn't love you, but it wouldn't make any difference.'

'You're a good girl, Julia. You're the only thing that means anything to me.'

'Would you deny that you loved me?'

'I don't know. I don't know. I don't know what's wrong with me. It's as if all the words which fit everyone else perfectly leave little gaps and chaffs and blisters when I wear them. No words feel really comfortable to me. I mean, I know they're the best things we've got but I don't really feel at home in them.'

'Professor Wittgenstein,' Julia began, 'I do not feel at home in the universe – '

'My, but you are learning!' Paul grinned. 'No, but seriously: words don't relate us to anything any more – all they do is make us think the unthinkable and drive us all rotten, with impossible ideas. In the end we aren't capable of anything except words, words, words.'

'You might dry the saucepan, saucepan, saucepan,' Julia said.

'God, I wish I wasn't a writer, Julia. I wish to God I

could shut up and want a child instead of just wanting to have my book accepted.'

Julia said: 'Paolo, Paolo.'

4

Susan said: 'Ben, are you being followed?'

'*What?*'

'It's a simple English question,' Susan said.

'Ah, that would account for it. You know I don't speak simple English. Very high-flown, that's the boy.'

'Ben, are you? Being followed?'

'Of course I'm not. I don't know what's got into you.'

'Look, Ben, you can't tell me that Superintendent Palmer of Scotland Yard, no less, called at No. 24 to discuss the weather.'

'Did I ever suggest such a thing?'

'Ben, he mentioned High Treason.'

'Well, that's nothing to do with the weather, is it? If he said High Treasson, I expect that's what he called about.'

'Are we guilty, Ben?'

'Of what, Susan?'

'Anything, anything at all? I mean, what about the kids?'

'They're not guilty of anything.'

'I hate you sometimes, Ben. I hate you with all my heart.'

Ben said: 'I'm honestly not quite clear what it is that you're so worried about. *What* about the children?'

'I feel as if the whole of the past's gone sour on me.' Susan's face puckered tearfully. 'As if there isn't anything I can trust any more.'

Ben said: 'Nothing's going to happen.'

'If anything happened to us,' Susan snuffled, 'I don't know what would happen to the kids.'

'The family'd look after them,' Ben said.

'Ben – '

'Look, I told you, nothing's going to happen.'

Susan said: 'I think I'll get a job.'

'Aha,' Ben smiled, absent-mindedly.

'I'm sick and tired of being stuck at home with nothing to do.'

'And what about the kids?'

'I'll get someone to come and look after them.'

'And where's she going to sleep?'

Susan said: 'Or you could stay at home and look after them for a change. Anyway, Sall's at school most of the day.'

'And what about the holidays?'

'I told you: we can get a foreign girl.'

'A skivvy, *nuch*,' Ben said.

'If I went out to work we could pay for Sall to go to St Cecily's where Julia and I went.'

'This is an education?'

Susan said: 'I don't think much of the school Sall's at at the moment. They don't seem to be teaching her anything.'

'Perhaps she doesn't want to learn anything, Susan.'

'Well, I want her to learn something.'

'What's the use of all the stuff they're supposed to learn?'

'Ben, surely your own kids – surely you want the best for them?'

'And what's the best? St Cecily's school for young ladies yet?'

'I don't care what you say, I'm certain Sall would learn a lot more if we sent her to St Cissy's – she'd have a better chance in life – '

'A better chance to do what, Susan?'

'Look, we've waited for – I don't know – years and years for things to change, but they don't change. Just think how big the Gentian Press would be if you'd started immediately after the war. It's no good always waiting till things are miles ahead of us. If Sall's going to go to Cambridge – '

'To Cambridge now.'

'I always wanted to.'

'So Sall has to. Honestly, Susan – '

'Why should we always be in a minority? Why do we always have to do the right thing? Why do you have to hold everything back because of your own cock-eyed view of the world?'

'OK, Susan, you do what you want, girl.'

'Ben, I only want what's best for Sall.'

'Then who cares if you wanted to go to Cambridge? I don't see what it matters going to Cambridge.'

'You get something out of it you don't get out of anything else – '

'Oxford and Cambridge, the Lourdes of England,' Ben said. 'So what do you get out of them? "This bottle of Beaujolais is *chilly*! You'll find that philosophers . . ."'

'Didn't you like Paul?'

'Yes, he's all right. He's just not relevant,' Ben said.

'He's a damn sight more relevant than we are,' Susan said. 'In England today.'

FOUR

My People, Israel

1

'OH, MR RIESMAN, PLEASE'

'Speaking,' Paul said.

'Oh, Bruce Davidson here.'

'Yes, Mr Davidson,' Paul covered the mouthpiece. 'Julia, it's Davidson. Yes, Mr Davidson?'

'Well, look here, I think I've got some rather good news for you.'

'Yes?' Paul nodded vigorously at Julia.

'Someone seems to like this book of yours, do you see? In fact, not to put too fine a point on it, they want to publish it.'

Paul said: 'Good God!' Julia burst into tears, the tears rolling into her smile as she stood there with the potato-peeler in her hand. 'Good God, well, *who*?'

'Francis Winter,' Davidson said.

'*Francis Winter*? Well that's – that's wonderful.'

'It's not a bad little house,' Davidson said. 'But I'm afraid they won't come forth with much of an advance – '

'I don't care about an advance,' Paul said. 'Just so long as they publish it. I mean, when do you think it'll be?'

'Oh, Octoberish I should think.'

'This is absolutely wonderful,' Paul said. 'It's the most wonderful thing that's ever happened.'

'I expect they'll be ringing you shortly, they've got a few points they'd like you to look over and they want about two thousand words out of the first section – '

'I'll rewrite the whole book, as long as they promise to publish it. There's no doubt about that, is there?'

'None whatever. A publisher's word is still his bond, thank the up above.'

Paul put the phone down. 'Well,' he said, 'we've done it.'

'Meet my author husband,' Julia said.

'They're actually going to publish it!'

'It's a bloody good little book.'

'Francis Winter too, he's not bad.'

'He's bloody good, don't start running down your publisher whatever you do.'

'You know it might make a film,' Paul said.

'It'd make a bloody good film.'

'You're very bloody today.'

'I'm feeling bloody!' Julia grinned.

'God, it's actually happened. It's really happened. Christ, this'll show those bastards – '

'What bastards?'

'Those bastards at Benedict's. This'll shake 'em, they'll know I'm going to get them sooner or later, by Christ this is going to make 'em look pretty stupid.'

Julia said: 'You must phone your mum, she'll be terribly excited.'

'I'll kill those bastards before I'm finished. God, honestly, this is like – I don't know – it's just too much, I mean I don't know who to tell first. Yes, you're quite right. I must phone my mother.'

2

The taxi went down Commercial Street.

'Mr Samuelson.' Hannah Adler tapped on the window. 'Mr Samuelson, will you turn left here, please, for a minute?'

Mr Samuelson nodded and swung the taxi down Quaker Street.

'Where we going?' Isidore Adler demanded, sitting forward anxiously.

'It's all right, Issy,' Hannah shouted. 'I just want Mr Samuelson to go down Brick Lane to show Paul where I used to live.'

Isidore Adler had gone very deaf. He lived now in a sealed world of fears and doubts. 'Shouldn't go down here, then,' he said, 'not if they're Fascists.'

'There aren't any Fascists,' Hannah said. 'Tell him there aren't any Fascists. Right here, Mr Samuelson.' They were in Brick Lane. Hannah sat forward, her face next to Paul's. 'I'll show you where my mother and father had the shop in a minute,' she told him. 'Oh dear, oh dear, of course they had terrible bombing round here, everything's changed, you know what I mean, dear? Saul Street, yes, Pelham Street, the next one's – Hanbury Street; there, what did I tell you? That's where I used to go to school, in Hanbury Street. And the shop – the shop should be somewhere here on the right, dear, No. 52.'

'They're coming back, you know,' Isidore whispered to Paul.

'Who are?' Paul smiled.

'The Fascists.'

'*No.*'

'Lot of trouble,' mumbled Isidore, nodding into silence.

'There it is,' Hannah Adler said. 'There it is. That's Grandpa's shop, where the shutters are up. Oh, I do wish we could stop for a minute.'

'Let's stop for a minute,' Julia said.

Hannah tapped on the partition. 'Could we stop just a minute, Mr Samuelson?' The taxi pulled into the kerb 'Whatsamatter?' Isidore said sharply. 'Why've we stopped?'

'We're going to get out for a minute, Issy, have a look round.'

'Not safe,' Isidore said. 'We shouldn't stop.'

Hannah smiled at Paul. 'I've got a big man to protect me.' Paul smiled back and shouted to Isidore: 'You don't have to worry, I'll protect her.'

'Gangs,' Isidore Adler muttered. 'Fifteen thousand people –'

They climbed out of the taxi, Hannah Adler bulky in Persian lamb, diamond earrings. 'You can see why we always had to go out and play in the street,' Hannah Adler said, 'there wasn't room in the house!' Hannah walked up to the shuttered shop. Boards were nailed across the door and iron bolts were rusted into the shutters. On the lintel the paint had cracked. Hannah Adler squinted up. 'Can you see the name up there?'

Paul said: 'It looks like it begins with an L –'

'Liepman's,' Hannah Adler said. 'There you are. What did I tell you? Liepman's. That was my name before I was married. Liepman.'

Paul put his arm round his mother-in-law. 'You don't say.'

'It was Liepman. I was Hannah Liepman.'

Isidore Adler's face appeared round the cab door. 'Shouldn't stay too long,' he said. The face looked cautiously up the road and then retreated into the cab. Hannah Adler was holding her hands clasped together, joggling them slightly up and down. 'Oh, it brings it all back to me,' she said. 'It brings it all back.' Paul watched his mother-in-law in a loving agony of envy. 'Morry Ginsberg used to live over there, No. 22. He's a very big man now in the fur trade. Oh I could tell you some stories about Morry Ginsberg, believe me!' Paul loved his mother-in-law as she stood transported in this narrow street where the cabbage leaves from the market were blackening in the gutter. He loved her because she loved what was true, because she acknowledged the truth, because she came from this street where Jewish people lived, where people were born Jews

441

and grew up Jews, where they did not doubt or think of escaping what they were. 'Oh, it used to be dreadful,' Hannah Adler said. 'You wouldn't believe it. My brothers had to fight their way home, sometimes. You know what they used to do?'

'What?' Paul asked.

'They used to take off their slippers, you know, the little black slippers they used to wear, they used to take them off and they used to hammer their way through, that was the only way they could get home, in their socks, and hammering their way through with their slippers.'

Paul said: 'Well, would you like to come and live here again?'

'Now? *No.*' Hannah Adler huddled into her fur coat. 'The rooms were so *small* and so *cold.*'

'I'd like to have a room down here,' Paul said. 'I'd like to come down here to write.'

'Oh no you wouldn't, dear, not really.'

'I would,' Paul said. 'I'd love to belong to all this.'

'Not if you had to live here,' Hannah Adler said.

Julia said: 'Your parents'd have a fit.'

'I wish I came from here,' Paul said. 'I wish I came from somewhere.'

Isidore Adler's face came round the door of the taxi. 'Stopping here the night?' he inquired.

'I'm enjoying myself,' his wife said petulantly. 'I don't come down here every day.'

'If we're going to see Uncle Otto,' Julia said, 'I suppose we ought to be getting along.'

Paul helped Hannah Adler into the taxi. The love he felt for her was the love for something which did not depend on him. He had never known such love before, the love of naturalness, in spite of Persian lamb coats, the love of family because it was family, the love that could be given because no spiritual blackmail demanded it, a love that was the natural result of a relation, not a substitute for it.

442

Hannah Adler did not substitute love for life. She did not gauge her day by the love she sucked and wheedled out of it. She did not unbalance life with a flabby feminine love-longing, with love-expecting and love-sighing and love-loving, the great empty, sexless love-loving which centrally heated the flat in Monmouth Court. The taxi rolled down a hard street between stunted houses and this was where Hannah Adler sprang from, this was the street where she went to school, this the one where grandpa bought *chola* on a Friday night, this where they went to synagogue: 'The Great Spitalfields Synagogue', the name made in stone. This was real, this was the solid reality of where life started and what life came from and so they went into Whitechapel High Street and down to Bethnal Green where life ended in the old Jewish cemetery. It was a community. Here in the old Jewish East End which now, as they sped down the Mile End Road, seemed so empty and so finished, there had been a community, so that a child knew what he was about, born among his own people, knew what moulded him and what he might become, born in a community which might be frightened or intimidated but in which people remained, not fainting against each other for love, but Jewish, Jewish though they all die for it, together. Paul watched the quick buildings fall behind and his eyes were full of tears. Each bombed patch was full in the fiction of his mind, full not of English literature but of life, so that his imagination gripped and swelled in him and was part of him, not a way of acceptance but a way of belonging. He had been robbed for so long of what was so simple, of his own people, of people, of a community which did not support itself on love-loving but on life-living. He put his hand on Julia's knee and thanked God, in the silence of their smile together, that he had married into this family which took him and said, 'Fine, you're Paul, you're one of us,' and not 'Do you love me?' It was wrong all this love-talking, it was the shoe-horn that eased you out of life, that

443

made loving where you came from and loving what you went to and loving what you did all your life. In a community, imagination could be of real people, thinking could be of real things, writing could be of the truth, not of funny spies or witty clerics or whatever, but of real people, who lived on paper as they lived in life. Then the writer too would be of the community, not a smiler, not a smiling cynical aloof too-fine-for-this-worlder, but a man whose words were bullet-hard, a man who came from something and was going to something, who came from a woman's womb and lay between a woman's legs and died with his real children round him. But without a community where did one start and where did one end? With oneself and only with oneself and life was so short for oneself. No great knowledge ran from father to son – father to son, instead all was uncertainty, doubt, fear and love-mush. Now, as Mr Samuelson turned the taxi into the drive of the Old People's Settlement, with all his heart Paul ached not that he was a Jew but that he wanted to be one.

3

The Settlement was in a cold building with much glazed brick in corridors and on staircases, linoleum on broad floors, heavy, dark chairs and tables and chipped, enamel bedsteads. The superintendent, Mr Levy, was a jolly hand-clapping man made brusque by overwork; the clumsiness of the old people made him pout and stamp and squeak about expenses and breakages and the troublesomeness of the patients' senility, so that the inmates grumbled and huddled against him, muttering, and irritated him still further. To Otto Kahane, however, Mr Levy was polite, since Otto preserved a certain independence; not only did he service the superintendent's clock every Sunday but he was also called for on Tuesdays by a chauffeured car sent by Sir Samuel Goldstein in which he was taken to that benefactor's house to wind and give a clean bill of health to the great man's collection of clocks. When he returned, the chauffeur always carried a box of good things into the Settlement after him, which the inmates came to enjoy on the following *shabas* eve. On the whole they felt no gratitude to Otto for the comforts he brought them; they merely resented less the privilege he enjoyed. Otto spoke but seldom, in a husky but thin voice, having little to communicate to others and caring less, since nothing could affect him, what they should say to him. As the years passed he had fallen into step with time till it seemed his own intimate possession, as though he alone, at the tips of his sensitive fingers, in the throbbing of his temples, had its very pulse and could not be interrupted by words, by life, for the communion he had with it.

Otto waited without pleasure and without rancour for the visit of his relations. The lounge had flowers every Sunday, given by Sir Samuel Goldstein, and it was nice to see them there against the scarred shoulder-high panelling. Most of the old people had visitors one Sunday or the next, though there were those like old Mr Jankower who sat Sunday after Sunday watching out of the leaded window and knew no one would come. Otto would say in his thin voice: 'You and I, Mr Jankower, it's not when is someone coming to see us but when are we going to see them, eh?' And Mr Jankower would shrug and nod and be amused and angry all in one and then he would say: 'I teenk a walk, Mr Kahane. What would you say to a walk?' Usually they went to the Bethnal Green Museum, two old Jewish gentlemen on gnarled sticks walking slowly round the glassy exhibits, as much a part of the museum as the museum itself: 'Jews, middle European *c.* 1920–30, fragments of a lost civilization, in poor condition.' So now when Mr Jankower came into the lounge where Otto was waiting for his visitors and stood near by and stared out of the window, Otto fretted his hands together, wondering how he could disappoint Mr Jankower. Mr Levy's clock was cradled in the black apron Otto always spread on his knees when following his trade so that no tiny cog or screw could fall to the floor. Mr Jankower turned away from the window and glanced at Otto and then at all the people with their guests who filled the lounge and he shrugged and nodded with that resigned anger of his at which Otto had to nod too and smile sadly, waiting to betray the old man whose whole week had been shaped maybe towards the moment when he would say: 'I teenk a walk, Mr Kahane. What would you say to a walk?'

Hannah Adler said: 'Otto dear, how are you?'

'Hannah.'

'Hullo, Otto dear. You remember Julia, don't you? And now I want you to meet my new son-in-law. Paul, this is Uncle Otto.'

Paul said: 'How do you do, sir?' and looked hard into the raisin-dark eyes of the old man.

Otto nodded. 'How are you?'

Mr Samuelson came into the room with two large boxes.

'Brought a few things for you,' Hannah shouted. She had got into the habit with Isidore. 'Chicken and smoked salmon and a few tins, in case they keep you short, and some fruit and a sweater my sister Rosie sent you. You remember Rosie? She sent you a sweater.'

Otto said: 'Very kind of you, Hannah, you really shouldn't take such trouble.' Out of the corner of his eye Otto saw Mr Jankower who turned away coldly and stared out of the window.

Isidore said: 'Well, Otto. Seems a nice sort of place.'

'Yes,' Otto said. 'It's all right.'

'Are they treating you all right?' Hannah said.

'Everything's fine,' Otto said. 'Anyway, I won't be here much longer.'

'Where're you going?' Hannah looked worried.

446

'Upstairs,' Otto said with the shadow of a smile. 'I hope!' In that moment Paul saw that the old man really was a relation of Isidore's, in that quick, sad smile.

Hannah pointed to Mr Levy's clock. 'Someone given you a clock to play with?'

Julia winced at Paul. Otto said: 'I do the clock for Mr Levy every week. I used to be a clock-repairer, a watch-maker, in Poland, you know.'

Paul said: 'Whereabouts did you live in Poland, Uncle Otto?'

'Poznan, in Poznan.'

'Where the riots have been?' Paul said.

'Yes, where the riots have been.'

'Riots?' Isidore said. 'Who's rioting? Fascists?'

'No, this is in Poland,' Paul shouted. 'A sort of revolution, in Poznan.'

'Gangsters,' Isidore Adler said.

'Have you ever heard anything from the family?' Hannah Adler demanded.

Julia said: '*Mummy –* '

Otto shook his head and his eyes held Paul's. 'When you've got no family any more, you don't care any more. The world's as big as your family. For me the world – ' He waved his hand vaguely. 'It's not very big.'

'We're your family, dear,' Hannah Adler said, patting the old man's knee.

Otto nodded. 'Sure, Hannah, sure. Of all the things I wish in my life I wish I had a son to comfort me in my old age, you know? Do you have any children yet?'

Paul said: 'Not yet.'

Hannah said: 'Please God in a few years – '

Otto said: 'Don't be selfish too long, you know what I mean?'

Paul nodded. Julia saw Paul nod. Isidore was nodding too, half asleep on his hard chair. A nurse said: 'Would you like tea?'

'Yes, please,' Hannah said. 'I've brought a Fuller's walnut cake, Julia, it's in the box. You'll find a knife too.'

'The people in the camp,' Uncle Otto was saying softly, 'the ones that had children in America or England, their names aren't dead, not like mine'll be soon. Soon there won't be any Kahanes any more.'

Mr Jankower's figure could be seen hobbling down the drive. Otto saw his friend going down towards the gate alone, shrugging and nodding to himself in the afternoon sunlight.

Hannah said: 'Thank you, nurse, we'll have it on this table, I think.'

Someone shouted out. 'We was first. *Nurse* – we was first. Some people – I don't know!'

Paul said: 'Uncle Otto, after all you've seen – I mean, been through, you know, I don't know if it's all right to –'

'He doesn't mind, dear,' Hannah Adler said, cutting fat pieces of cake.

'If you – would you really want to bring a child into the world? Knowing what might happen to it, knowing what can happen to a child just because it's a child of yours –'

'What *did* happen,' Otto said. 'I had a son, Mosha, a fine boy. He was killed fighting in the Warsaw ghetto. That was a fine thing, to die fighting for one's people.'

'They die, they get killed,' Paul cried. 'What's the point of it all? What's the point of bringing anything more into the world?'

'You talk like Hitler won the war.'

'He did win,' Paul smiled. 'He beat me anyway.'

'You know, you give grief to an old man because you are dead who should be giving me hope, you lie dead next to me and you want your seed to be dead, and that gives grief to an old man. I am – what do you say? – a museum-piece, but you – you are alive, you have a community –'

'But I haven't,' Paul said. 'I haven't got a community. I don't belong anywhere any more than you do, Uncle Otto.'

'You have a wife, you have a lovely wife and a great country to live in – '

'That hates us – '

'You dare to talk like this of a country hating you when you know nothing of what such hatred is. I see people come visit here, people with good life in them, with families, with a whole community ready and allowed to live for each other, I wonder why they have death in their faces and fear hatred from each other when they're alive and could have families and the truth of blood between them. The dead have no pity for the living, believe me.'

Paul said: 'I want to do something about the dead, Uncle Otto. I want to – clear that up before I go any further. I want to *do* something.'

Otto said: 'Forgive me, Hannah, but tell me, young man, you know how to give your wife a child?'

'I think I have an idea,' Paul smiled.

'That's simple then,' Otto said, 'that's all you have to do. That's what the dead can't do any more, give meaning to life, you know.'

'Meaning?' Paul smiled faintly. 'What meaning?'

'The meaning of life,' Otto said, 'is life. To give meaning to life, you give life.'

Paul said: 'If only one had the courage – '

'Oh, stop it, stop thinking so much and start doing. Thinking is fine about some things, but thinking about life, that's God's work.'

'God's work,' Paul said. 'I hope he's proud of it!'

'Pride and shame, they're not for God. I Am That I Am, that's what it is to walk in the way of God, you follow?' Otto put the clock on the table beside the walnut cake. 'It's not difficult, within your limits, to be like God. It's very simple: simply to be what one is.'

4

Paul said: 'We ought to go down and see Uncle Otto every Sunday.'

'He doesn't much like it at that place, does he?' Julia said. 'Poor old boy, he must be very lonely.'

'Yes, I suppose he must.'

'I feel a bit guilty about it really. I mean it was partly my fault that he stopped living with Mummy and Daddy.'

'Your fault? Why?'

'Oh, it was him or me in the end. Daddy got ratty about all the expense of sending me to college and then I got angry about Otto not pulling the chain – '

'Not pulling the chain?'

'He never pulled the chain in the lavatory,' Julia said. 'I know it sounds silly – '

'It doesn't sound at all silly. Poor old Otto. The home-spun philosopher who didn't pull the chain. God, you'd think after coming out of a concentration camp he'd never shit again, you know? You'd think he'd just sit in judgement – ?'

'Instead he shit in judgement,' Julia said.

'*Julia.*'

'Shocked him again.'

Paul said: 'I get very shocked when people pick up my habits.'

'You don't have to tell me.'

'You're annoyed with me about something. What?'

'I'm not annoyed with you.'

Paul shook his head. 'You are upset about something. What?'

Julia said: 'Nothing new.'

Paul said: 'I have to give up all my freedom, don't I? I

have to give up everything I value. It's all very well for Uncle Otto – '

'You want to visit him and you don't listen to anything he says – '

'Look, I listened, I understood what he said, but that doesn't mean I have to accept it. He's not a writer. He doesn't know what it's like to need freedom – all he can think of is kids, but I want to be something – '

'You shouldn't have married me,' Julia said.

'It wasn't my idea,' Paul shouted.

'You *proposed*. You told me, you proposed.'

'I never wanted to get married. I only did it because – because I thought it wouldn't change anything, but it has: it's changed everything.'

'You promised we could have one some time.'

'Have one! Have one any time you like only don't expect me to love it.'

'I don't expect anything from you.'

'You hate me,' Paul cried. 'You hate me, don't you?'

'Like last night, I hate you,' Julia replied.

'Oh, my God, Julia, I'm sorry. We're so lucky, we're just so damned lucky to be alive and free and yet – I don't know – we're too free, I feel so damned free I can't do anything. I can't bear the thought of having committed myself to anything. I want to do everything at once.'

• 'Just have a baby,' Julia said, 'and you need never feel free again!'

Paul said: 'I could give so much. Everyone could give so much. Not love-mush. I don't mean that. I mean they could look at each other. They could stand up and look at each other and want *nothing* from each other. Every day everyone should go up to someone and look them in the eye and say "I want nothing from you, I'm me and you're you and that's it". That's what respect is: to look at each other properly. But the whole thing's so stinking and so corrupt, you can't say a clean word without it having a dirty meaning. I want you to have a baby, Julia. I want to, honestly.'

Julia said: 'You don't, but you're trying very hard to. I do understand, Paolo, honestly I do.'

'I do want to. We must. I know that. I did learn something this afternoon even if you think I didn't.'

'I do want one, Paolo.'

'So do I. We have to. Otherwise Hitler just goes on winning, the way he goes on winning in everyone else's lives. God, what a futile answer to six million dead – a baby squalling! But it's the only real living answer we've got. There's too much damned freedom in this world, Julia. Freedom's like contraception, it makes you think about what was never intended to be thought about.'

'I hate it.'

'Freedom?'

'Contraception.'

'I never thought it could matter, but it does matter, it makes the whole of life ridiculous. It puts one more damned real thing into words and lets everyone yammer about it. God, all the work it takes to talk oneself back to where one started from. All the strings and strings of words you have to use to get yourself free of the old love-mush and word-mush and be alive again.'

Julia said: 'And after that, I think I'll go upstairs and have a bath and prepare myself for the defeat of Mr Hitler.'

FIVE

MacDonald Smith and Associates

1

ANGUS REYNOLDS SAID: 'Coming for a spot of lunch, Mrs Simons?'

'Why, Mr Reynolds,' Susan fluttered, 'how nice of you to ask me! Shan't be a sec. I just want to finish this letter and then ay'll be with you.'

'In that case,' said Angus Reynolds, 'ay'll wait.'

He sat down on the sofa and crossed his long legs, hands deep in pockets, an eyebrow raised. At last Susan pulled the letter out of the machine and sighed. 'Another redskin bites the dust. I'll just pop into the little girls' room and then I shall be all set.'

'Hurry not.'

The little girls' room of MacDonald Smith and Associates had pink brocading and Regency stripes. The brocade was dimpled into the wall with tiny silk-covered buttons and along the top of the mirrors above the basins was a row of the bare bulbs you see in theatrical dressing-rooms. A deep carpet extended even into the throne room. Susan did her lips carefully and washed the carbon bruises off her fingers. She had been with MacDonald Smith and Associates for a month and she was adoring it. MacDonald Smith and Associates were Public Relations Consultants. Mac himself was a tall, slim young man with curly black hair and an easy confident manner. Angus was his chief associate and Susan's immediate boss. He was not as tall as Mac but he had the same lazy confidence, the careless but well-groomed appearance, sleek dark hair slightly rough and masculine over the ears, blue eyes and a mobile mouth, lips somewhat tight, above a firm, semi-cleft chin. Susan came out of the little girls' room and saw him sitting there, chin tilted up, the blue eyes staring up at the sextuple Forrest Modern chandelier. Angus bounded to his feet. 'All set?'

'All set.'

'Let's be moving then.'

They went through the purple-carpeted, Liberty's furnished waiting-room with its piles of expensive magazines – *Vogue*, *Harper's*, *Design*, *Domus*, *Fortune*, *Epoca*, and *Elle*. MacDonald Smith and Associates had a large suite in the former town house of a famous Victorian statesman. When you came out of the thick walnut door of suite five, you were at the head of the great staircase which swerved down to a marble-tiled entrance hall where there was a desk and a commissionaire.

Angus said: 'Well, what do you think of us all now you've been here for a bit? Settling in all right, as they say?'

'Apart from my boss,' Susan grinned. 'He's an absolute stinker.'

'We shall have to see about getting rid of that chap,' Angus said. 'I've noticed he's a bit of a menace. No, seriously, any grouses?'

'Not really. What about you?'

'You're a great ornament to the office,' replied the other. 'Even old Mac said so.'

'That surly Mr MacDonald?'

'*Précisément*.'

'He's a honey,' Susan said.

'Bright boy, old Mac. Barelli's OK with you?'

'Smashing,' Susan said.

Barelli's was a place of booths and check tableclothes where the food was expensive and excellent and yet the customers could feel that they were not being extravagant because it was just an unspoilt little Italian place. 'Ah, Mister Reynolds. It is such a long time since you came to see us.'

'Hullo, Signor Barelli. Got a place for us?'

'For you, Mister Reynolds, and for the charming lady, I think so.'

'Barelli's an old devil but his food tastes all right,' Angus said. 'What'll you have?'

'You choose for me,' Susan said. 'I never know what to order.'

Angus carried on a fluent Italian conversation with Barelli and then turned to Susan: 'We'll just have to hope you like it, that's all.'

'I'm impressed,' Susan said.

'I wouldn't have sweated blood if I didn't think you would be. Actually, it's not often I talk Italian any more.'

'I've always wanted to be able to speak Italian,' Susan said. 'It's such a musical language, isn't it? Where did you learn it though?'

'Oh, I picked up a bit at Oxford, didn't read it or anything, but I was interested and of course once you know Spanish –'

'I've always wanted to go to Spain.'

'Lovely spot, we went there last year.'

'What, *all* of you?'

'Oh, we left Camilla with her grandmother, my wife's mother, you know, but Geoffrey and Davina came along. They both love the car, luckily. Had the times of their lives; they're fair both of them and of course that's rather rare in Spain and they made the most tremendous fuss of them.'

'I'm hoping we shall all get abroad this year. Ben and I had a few days at Biarritz last year, but of course it's not enough.'

'I wouldn't be without my three weeks on the continent

for the world. After all, that's what we work the other forty-nine for, isn't it? What think you of the *canelloni*?'

'Yummy.'

'Francesco's the only man in London who makes 'em like the real thing, usually they taste like freshly boiled cigars!'

'What a macabre imagination you have! It's positively Charles Addams.'

'He's a honey, isn't he?' Angus tilted some more chianti into Susan's glass. 'I want to ask you a favour, Susan.'

'Of course, what?'

'Old Sir George Gort's coming to London next week and I rather want to keep him sweet – '

'What do you want me to do – play the beautiful spy?'

'Oh no, Gee-gee's far too U for anything as blatant as that; anyway he'll have his wife with him. No, I thought we might take him to a show, a musical, I should think, and go on to dine somewhere.'

'What do you want me to do?' Susan inquired.

'Come and act as hostess, the usual offices, as they say.' Angus finished his chianti. 'He's a nice old boy but it will mean working all evening.'

'As long as it's not all night,' Susan said.

'That's not quite our line yet, though I dare say we shall have to run to it if competition gets much hotter. Look, think it over about Sir George. If you feel you can't leave hubby or anything like that, dinna fash yersel'. I dare say I could drag old Joyce up to town but it's a bit of a bind for her, what with sitters and all that sort of show, apart from the fact that she doesn't really know Sir George. I thought we might get Kenny Stocks to join us for supper after the show and put the two men together, for mutual benefit, as they say. Strictly an un-Barelli's gathering, by the way!'

'I should like to come very much.'

'So be it. I'll see about the details and check the table reservations, as they say.'

'Good evening, Mrs Simons.'

'God, you gave me a shock!' Susan put her key back in her bag. 'I had no idea there was anyone –'

'Your woman was good enough to let us in.'

'Honestly, just let me get my breath back!' Susan closed her eyes and breathed in deeply. Sergeant Strangways was at the books again. 'I'll just – take my coat off.'

'I'm sorry if we gave you a shock,' Superintendent Palmer said.

Susan came back saying 'Well now, what can I do for you?' and closed the door firmly so that Françoise, the French girl, shouldn't hear anything.

'Mrs Simons, we're still trying to clear up one or two details about Mr Herbert Fletcher.'

'Honestly, I think I've told you everything I know about him about three times over.'

'Mrs Simons, has your husband ever talked about leaving the country?'

'We talked about going to Palestine at one time, but apart from that, no, never.' Susan sat down and took out a packet of Rothman cigarettes and lit one. 'We're entitled to discuss things, aren't we?'

'In this country, certainly. Tell me, have you made any holiday plans this year yet?'

'No,' Susan said. 'Not yet anyway.'

'Mrs Simons, your husband –'

'I don't know anything about my husband,' Susan said. 'I don't know anything about him –'

'Mrs Simons –'

'Why can't you leave me alone? Why can't you leave me alone? I don't know anything about my husband. Look, why don't you talk to him? He should be here any minute. If I had any idea why you were persecuting us – '

'I'm sorry, Mrs Simons, I can see you're tired. If you'd rather we called at your office – '

'Why are you going on like this?'

'We have a job to do, certain investigations to make.' The superintendent took out his pipe. He smiled as he lit it. 'You know you are still a member of the Communist Party,' he said. 'I would have thought you might have some idea of the sort of things we are interested in about you.'

'I've never done anything more sinister than hand out leaflets at factory gates,' Susan said. 'I don't have anything to do with the Party any more hardly.'

'Then isn't it rather foolish of you to stay in it?' inquired Superintendent Palmer. 'Tell me, does your husband have a passport?'

'Yes, of course.'

'Get it for his holidays last year, did he?'

Susan said: 'I honestly don't know. Surely you could check up easily enough?'

'Oh yes, rather, I just wondered if you knew offhand. Well, we'll be getting along, Strangways. Let me know if you're making any plans for foreign travel within the next few weeks, won't you?' The superintendent smiled. 'And don't forget – if you think of anything you forgot to tell us, give us a ring. We should hate to have to disturb you at the office.'

Susan finished her cigarette and flattened it in the Wedgwood ashtray. It occurred to her that she would need a new dress for this evening out with Angus and old Sir George. Something delicious and slightly naughty! She went upstairs to settle Jonathan. He was pretending to be asleep, but as soon as Susan came into the room he sat up and said: 'Hullo, Mum, I was waitin' to see if you'd come.'

"One small boy who ought to be asleep.'

'Oh! Mum!'

'I wish you wouldn't call me Mum, Jonty. Call me Mummy.'

'Call me Jonathan then.'

'Clever boy,' Susan said.

3

'*Susan*. Great of you to make it,' Angus said. 'You look absolutely divine, honestly, smashing, as they say.'

'I'm glad you like it,' Susan said. 'The firm's paying for it.'

'Good for you! You look absolutely wonderful. Have a cocktail.'

'Mmm, dry Martini.'

'Olive or onion? They call 'em Gibsons with an onion. It's quite the fashion, they tell me.'

'In that case, by all means let it be a Gibson,' Susan said.

'Good for you.'

Angus turned to call a waiter. Sir George and Lady Gort had not yet arrived. Angus had arranged that he and Susan should meet a quarter of an hour early, to make sure the old boy didn't have to wait around. 'Essence of PR is that you're a very busy man and we've got all the time in the world.'

When the drinks came, Angus said: 'We'll down these, shall we, and have the decks clear when the old boy arrives.'

Susan said: 'What're we seeing or shouldn't I ask?'

'I thought *Salad Days*,' Angus said. 'Lovely little show. I hope it isn't *déjà vu* as they say, as far as you're concerned.'

'I've been dying to see it, but Ben wouldn't take me to it in a month of Sundays.'

'Oh, why's that?'

'He doesn't approve of that sort of thing.'

'What sort of thing is that?'

'Oh, you know, escapism.'

'I'm all in favour, personally. Escape while one can, as they say. "Gather ye rosebuds while ye may, old time is still a-flying!" I've already seen the show with Joyce and I can't wait to see it again!'

Sir George Gort was a tall, kindly faced grey-haired man in his sixties, his wife a rather plain woman of about fifty-five with newly permed brown hair, a Harvey Nichols dress and a rope of good pearls. While she was powdering her nose, Sir George consulted his evening paper gravely: 'Terrible thing this earthquake in Turkey,' he observed. 'Yes, rather,' Angus agreed. 'The terrible suddenness of the thing,' Susan said, Sir George shook his head mournfully at the picture of corpses and fallen masonry. 'Yes,' he said, 'it's a terrible thing. It's going to hit Lloyds pretty badly.'

'Well, what about a drink now?' Angus said, as Lady Gort returned. Sir George folded his paper and smiled at his wife. 'Yes,' he said, 'by all means let's get down to the serious business of the evening.' 'Now, George, you're not to drink too much.' 'Me, never!' Sir George said, with a wink at Susan.

Susan found it strange to be sitting in the darkened theatre with Sir George next to her and Angus only two seats away and know that the last time he had been there it was with his wife and now it was with her. Of course the whole thing was completely innocent and yet it was unusual. When the interval came it was to her that he addressed the jolly questions, which he might well have been asking his wife, some of which he certainly had asked his wife, standing in the same place, smiling down at Joyce with one eyebrow cocked, just as now he was smiling at Susan.

'It really is a honey, don't you think, the show?'

'I'm adoring it,' Susan said.

'The young man's from Cambridge, isn't he?' Lady Gort was looking at the programme. 'The one who wrote it.'

'You didn't know him, did you, Angus?' Susan inquired.

'He was a bit after my time. In any case,' Angus smiled, 'I was at Oxford, you know. There is a difference.'

'Good man,' said Sir George. 'Where were you?'

'Oriel,' Angus said. 'I went up in '38, just in time for Master Hitler.'

'And I did the same thing in '13 for another gentleman, though not quite of the same name!' Sir George buried his nose in a silk handkerchief and emerged to say: 'Time we were resuming our places, I suppose. See what these intriguing young people are going to get up to next!' As Angus stood back to allow Sir George to go in first, the older man said: 'I can't tell you, Mr Reynolds, what a pleasure it is to see a show in which nobody gets their brains kicked in. Long time since I've been to the theatre.'

'I'm extremely glad you're enjoying it, sir. Incidentally, Sir George, I've asked Kenneth Stocks to join us for a spot of supper after the show, as they say. He was very eager to meet you again.'

'What a nice idea! What a very nice idea! Yes, I should like to see Kenneth again. How very thoughtful of you!'

The dinner party was no less successful than the show. Angus had ordered the meal beforehand: *Pâté de canard, Saumon au Champagne*, cold sirloin of beef *en gelée* with a green salad followed by ice-cream or *Gâteau Succès*. Sir George refused the beef, pleading that it was too late for so large a meal, but agreed to sample the Château Latour '47 which Angus had ordered. Nor did he refuse an excellent cigar with his coffee. Angus leaned back and relaxed while Kenneth Stocks and Sir George talked and puffed; the evening had been perfect. Afterwards Sir George insisted on dropping Kenneth Stocks home in his car before returning to Claridge's. Stocks had his own car

461

just round the corner but was wise enough to accept Sir George's generosity.

Angus said: 'Susan, you're a born hostess!'

'Oh, Mr Reynolds,' Susan fluttered her eyelids. 'Do I get a taxi home on the firm?'

'Don't be silly, I'll run you.'

'It's right out of your way, isn't it?' Susan said. 'Yes, please.'

Angus took her arm. 'It was a wonderful evening.'

'It's difficult to believe these things really achieve anything. I mean the number of dinners he must have been to, you'd think he'd see through them.'

'It's not really a question of him seeing through it, Susan. We're not putting anything over on him, we're just presenting ourselves in the best possible light – nothing wrong with that. I mean, we're not secretly getting him to manufacture arms for the Russians or anything like that.'

Susan said: 'No, I suppose not.'

'This is my bus,' Angus said.

'Very nice too.' It was a Rover.

Angus said: 'You know, Susan, you were really great this evening.'

'You'd better drive carefully. You must be a wee bit over the top.'

'We must do it again.'

'Don't forget we want to present this thing to the public in the best possible light,' Susan said. 'What does your wife think of you being out at night?'

'Joyce? She doesn't mind.'

'I'll bet. I'd mind if I were her.'

'You and Joyce aren't the same sort of woman.'

'I'd like to meet her,' Susan said. 'Have you got a picture?'

Angus said suddenly: 'It was very dishonest of me, arranging this evening.'

'Angus – '

462

'No, it was. I don't mean it wasn't perfectly reasonable and businesslike, because it was. Mac thoroughly approved and I think he'll be jolly pleased with the results. Old Kennie Stocks will've asked Gee-gee in for a nightcap and we should be able to interest them both in this new anti-Nationalization caper, no, that's not the point. The point is, you were very useful and decorative and I couldn't have done anything like such a job without you, but that wasn't why I asked you. I asked you because I wanted to see you.'

Susan said: 'Surprise, surprise. There's nothing wrong in that.'

Angus nodded. 'There is, you know.' He stopped the car by the side of the road and turned to her. Susan said: 'No, I don't think you ought – ' 'Just for a minute, let's just talk for a minute,' Angus said. 'Please.'

'Angus, for God's sake let's get on.'

'There's nothing wrong in talking.'

Susan said: 'Christ, don't you realize?'

'Realize what?'

'I'm not – so far from your position.' She opened her bag and took out the Rothman cigarettes and lit two, one for him.

He said: 'I'm in love with you, Susan.'

She shook her head and gave a little coughing laugh. 'I feel very peculiar. I've never quite – been in this state before.'

'Good heavens, you don't think I make a habit of it?'

'Would it matter if you did?'

'It's never happened before,' he said. 'Perhaps you aren't aware what a big thing this is to me. How much it hurts me to fall in love with you.'

'Thanks very much.'

'I'm a married man,' he said. 'I'm *married*.'

'So am I married,' Susan said. 'I'm just as married as you are.'

He shook his head. 'No, you're not.'

'Just because you're a Catholic – '

'You don't know what a new world suddenly appeared to me when you came to work in the office. You've destroyed my whole world.'

Susan said: 'What is it I say now? Would you like to tell me about it? Isn't that the right thing?' She put her hand on his shoulder. 'Angus – '

His eyes came round full of tears. Yet his mouth was very hard. There was more flesh on his face than on Sid Forbes's, but for a second, except for the suspicion of tears, Susan was reminded of Sid, the shadows under the cheekbones, the ridge of the mouth. 'I suppose it was bound to happen,' he said.

'What was?' Susan asked. 'Words? Nothing's happened yet, has it? Except we're sitting here talking.'

'That's what love is – partly, talking. Like praying.'

'Yes, and if one wants to talk enough one always ends up by finding someone, isn't that it? You were bound to find someone sooner or later.'

'I suppose so. It's a long time since I've been able to talk to anyone about what I want to talk about.'

'What about your priest?'

'He's inside my world. I couldn't really expect him to help me escape from it, could I?'

'You don't really want to have a world at all, do you? That's the real point, isn't it? You want to be free.'

'I am free, that's the whole trouble. I don't seem to belong to anything, really fit with it, I mean.'

'I know just exactly how you feel,' Susan said. 'But exactly.'

'The more charming you are – not that I'm all that charming – '

'Yes, you are; you're terribly charming – '

'The more charming people think you the less you can be yourself. You deceive yourself, you represent yourself falsely and then you can't let yourself down, and inside you get lonelier and lonelier – farther and farther away from the world you're supposed to be in. You can't admit anything and you can't get anything out.'

'It's very late. People always feel like this when they're tired.'

'No, this has been coming on for years. And as soon as I saw you, I knew I couldn't hold back any longer. I had to make a grab.'

'It's been a very gentlemanly grab so far.'

His arm went round her shoulder and she leaned in under his mouth for him to kiss her and it was a hollowing, trembling quake of excitement for her, to feel the hard ridge of new lips against hers. She sat back in her place with a shudder and opened her bag for cigarettes. He pressed the bag shut and put his arm round her. She shuffled across the seat and pressed herself against him, her hands against his shoulder and on the back of his neck, remembering adolescence.

Angus said: 'I think we'd better have that cigarette after all, don't you?'

Susan sniffed. 'We don't know much about each other, do we? I always used to think you could know so much about other people. Or p'haps I didn't think there was very much to know. But there is, isn't there? There's a whole world to know.' She shrugged her shoulders. 'I don't seem to know anything. I mean even about my own husband. You can't even trust the past, can you?'

'One forgets languages one used to be able to speak,' Angus said. 'That's the most humiliating thing there is. To have been fluent and then to start stumbling and stuttering.'

'Are you "losing your faith"? Is that the right expression?'

'It's not losing one's faith that matters, it's dropping it. Then one's really alone. That's the finish.'

'Do you doubt though?'

465

'It's not doubt exactly. It's that I can't give them everything I should be able to. I can't speak the language right out – it's as if other words of other languages keep creeping in. There's a kind of pocket of otherness in me. It's' – he grinned suddenly – 'it's not very interesting.'

'I'm a Titoist too,' Susan smiled.

'We're two of a kind then.'

'I'm quite serious, you know. I used to be a Communist.'

'Good heavens! Really? I say, you're not still, are you?'

'No, I've – lapsed.'

'What about hubby?'

'He's still in,' Susan said. 'Theoretically I am too.'

'It beats me how anyone can stay in that organization.'

'It beats Ben how you can stay in yours.'

'There's no comparison between the two,' Angus said. 'I believe in something – '

'Do you think we don't – didn't – ?'

'Well, well,' Angus said, 'just fancy, you and I belong to the two biggest organizations in the world.'

'Neither of which would very much approve the present conversation.'

'No,' Angus said. 'Here, we'd better get you home, or we shall find hubby waiting on the doorstep with a shotgun.'

'But I'm married already,' Susan said.

Not understanding, Angus said: 'Do you think he'd be very angry if he knew about this conversation?'

'Knew what?'

'The way we'd been talking.'

'Ben? He shouldn't be. He's told me often enough he doesn't believe in marriage.'

'Being a Communist I don't suppose he believes in anything much, does he?'

'He believes in things all right. What about your people? Would they be very angry?'

'My people?'

'The Church and your wife – '

'I don't suppose they'd approve, no. But we haven't strictly done anything wrong.'

'What about kissing?'

'Kissing isn't a mortal sin, if that's what you mean.'

'I wish everything was a lot more – dangerous, don't you?'

'Dangerous?'

'Important.' Susan tossed her cigarette out of the window, reminded suddenly of Superintendent Palmer, who thought many things important. 'I think love ought to be terribly important.'

'It is,' Angus said. 'It's the only really important thing, different degrees of love, that's what makes us human beings.'

Susan said: 'Ben doesn't think so.'

'Nor does Joyce.'

'That's unusual for a woman.'

'Joyce is an unusual women, so I gather,' Angus said shortly.

'In what way?'

'Hates bed. She's never enjoyed it. It's rather funny, isn't it? Like the centipede with the wooden leg. It's rather a joke – a man with a frigid wife.' The words rattled out like bullets rapping against the metal behind the targets in a range. They were aimed at Susan, but they ended up against something far harder, far more unyielding than Susan; they went through Susan liks bullets, but fell harmlessly unimpressive from their final butt. 'She doesn't hate me. She doesn't think she hates me. She hates it. She doesn't complain or anything. She just doesn't like it. She can't see why I care so much. Not that I show it any more, of course.'

Susan said: 'Stop the car.'

'No, it's late.'

'Angus, please.'

'No, I don't want to talk any more – '

'That wasn't what I was thinking of – '

'No, Susan, it's no good.'

'What did you mean when you said you loved me?'

'That I wanted to be with you. I don't know; what does one ever mean? To love someone is to want to be with them, I suppose.' Angus accelerated. 'To exist with them, live with them, come alive with them. I don't know.'

'Straight on down here and the third on the right. Stop at the top of the road and I'll walk down.' Susan took the mirror from her bag and inspected herself. 'You wouldn't have a divorce, would you? Even if you could, I mean?'

'No,' he said, 'I wouldn't.'

'Well,' Susan said, 'we really seem to have the maximum number of difficulties between us, don't we?'

4

For nearly a week Angus and Susan made sure they were never alone together. If Angus spoke of her, Susan avoided looking him in the eye. Even when Gee-gee notified them that he had decided to go along with Kenneth Stocks on the anti-Nationalization plan, neither Angus nor Susan referred to their evening out together. Then Mac had to ask them out to a celebration drink and neither of them could quite refuse. After twenty minutes and two martinis, Mac said: 'Well, I can't stay here boozing all night. I must dash. Have another and tell Denis to chalk it up. Can't call a minute my own these days – I'm glad to say! If you'll excuse me, I'll be pushing and leave old Reynolds with the married women as usual!' He winked and hurried out of the pub.

Susan said: 'Have you been talking?'

'Talking? What about?'

'Us.'

'To Mac? Good God, *no*. I haven't said a word to a soul.
I mean, if anything got back to Joyce –'

'What?'

'I don't honestly know. She'd be frightfully upset.'

Susan said: 'I dreamt about you.'

'Dreamt about me? How about another?'

'Gibson,' Susan nodded. 'You needn't worry. It was a
very decent dream. You could show it to anyone. Strictly
U certificate. I dreamt I was at home, living with my
parents, and you phoned and asked me to go out and I was
terribly excited and everything and I asked Mummy if I
could have a new dress and she said "yes, I don't see why
not" and everything was going perfectly and then my father
came in and said "I thought you were married" and that
was the end.'

'Very crisp, as they say.'

'Let's get out of here,' Susan said. 'Let's go for a walk or
something.'

'Shouldn't you be getting home?'

'Françoise is doing supper.'

'We mustn't be too long.' He tilted back his drink and
swallowed it in one quick gulp. The stretch of his neck, the
convulsion of the swallow and the quick blink as his eyes
came down to her again were strangely intimate. She
wanted to put up her fingers and stroke that curve of
throat. 'Right,' he said, 'let's be pushing.'

They went into Green Park. It was a golden summer
evening. There were many people strolling about, many
couples lying on the ground. 'Another version of public
relations,' Angus observed.

Susan said: 'Didn't you ever do that?'

'Ours was a very intellectual courtship,' Angus replied.
'Joyce was more interested in the things of the spirit.'

'It's funny, isn't it,' Susan said, 'the way things start and
the way they end up? The things that one thinks matter

and the things that finally do, they're never the same, are they?'

'Yes, one starts out very big and one ends up very small.'

'Have you ever been with a tart?' Susan asked.

'It wouldn't be any good,' Angus said. 'I couldn't enjoy it. It wouldn't do anything for me.'

'Do you think I could? Do it for you, I mean?'

'No one could, Susan. Um, let's cut back to the office now, shall we? I've got to collect some papers.'

'Oke.'

Angus let them in with his passkey. They went up to the deserted suite. Typewriters had been gloved for the night, filing cabinets shuttered, chairs slotted under desks. It was out of hours.

Angus came out of his office. He looked at Susan and put his briefcase on the desk and walked up to her and kissed her. He put his hand on her breast. Their lips parted. They gasped and drew back. They sat down together on the sofa. She wanted to give herself to him. She twisted and pressed against him. No one could come. She pushed her shoes off. They fell suddenly on the thick carpet. Barefoot, she thrust herself against him, her feet straining against the arm of the sofa.

The telephone rang, rang.

His lips slackened against hers and he pushed her off.

The telephone rang, rang.

Susan tidied her hair, bent for her shoes.

The telephone rang, rang.

Angus picked up his briefcase, checked his papers.

The telephone rang, rang.

Susan fitted her shoes and stood up.

The telephone rang, rang.

Angus said: 'Come on.'

'Sssh.'

'No one can hear.'

The telephone rang, rang.

'Hm, silly of me.'

'You can't help thinking – can you?'

The telephone rang, rang.

They hurried out of the office. They clattered down the marble stairs. The whole empty office building was full of ringing telephones. They ran past the commissionaire's desk, Angus fumbling for his keys. Outside he pressed her hand and they went quickly different ways down the quiet street.

SIX

Men on the Run

1

MR MINSTER SAID: 'I think I've got a bit of sort of luck for
you, feller, if you know what I mean. I've just been
speaking to Sid Forbes of Royalty TV Productions about
you and he thinks maybe he's got something for you.'

Sid Forbes's address was in Soho Square. Paul was
shown into a large office important with framed citations
from the Film Renters' Guild, the *Cinematographic
Weekly* and the TV Critics Poll. Mr Forbes was sitting
behind a wide desk. He observed Paul coldly before
offering him a hand. 'Sit down, won't you?' he said, lighting
a cigarette from a gas lighter. He leaned back and narrowed
his eyes as the smoke flared from his nostrils. 'Look, I don't
know how much Ben has told you about all this – '

'Ben?'

'Ben Simons, he's your brother-in-law, isn't he?'

'Yes, but – '

'Oh, you don't know, maybe. He told me all about you
and mentioned you were tied up with Sonny Minster.
How's he doing for you?'

'Well, actually not very much yet, but it's early days. I
mean, my first novel's only just been accepted.'

Sid Forbes said: 'Look, what we do from this office, for
the most part, is packaged TV films. At the moment we've
two series projected – *Man on the Run* and *Dexter FBI* – I
heard you were doing some kind of crime writing so I
thought we might's well have a talk. Both these series will

be largely American controlled, but we shoot them over here because it's cheaper. Both series will comprise twenty-six half-hour films, to start with, and there may be more if they catch on. Our idea is to angle them transatlantically, if you follow me, so that they'll have a market on both sides of the ocean. We've got quite a lot already and what we want from you is some synopses of exciting stories which don't require us to re-stage the Battle of Jutland. With our budgets we just can't do that kind of thing.'

'I think I've got the general idea,' Paul said.

'Now look, since we're not familiar with your work I'm afraid I shan't be able to offer you quite the same terms as I should propose for an experienced writer – '

'I'd much sooner you talked to Mr Minster about that,' Paul said. 'I leave all that sort of thing to him.'

Mr Minster phoned Paul to say that he had agreed with Sid Forbes that Paul should prepare as many ideas for the two series as he could; for each accepted idea £40 would be paid, regardless of whether Paul did the script; if he did the script (and the first one would have to be on approval) another £100 would be paid. Paul did three ideas for each of the series and three of them were accepted. His trial script was approved, though Sid arranged that he should work with the director, Hubert Young, since he had some ideas on the way the script should be presented. Young was a crew-cut, canvas-trousered, nail-chewing New York intellectual for whom all intellectual considerations were irrelevant on the job itself: then he cared only about the commercial acceptability of what they were doing. His constant objection was 'I don't think they'll like that.' He would pace up and down the room, smoking Pall Mall cigarettes, until suddenly he would snap his fingers and say 'Here's a thing I remember Hitch saying' and then a satisfactory solution would be found. Hubert was anti-McCarthy and believed that the Rosenbergs had been framed and yet he would resist any attempt of Paul's to introduce into *Dexter FBI* the suggestion that the Communists whom Dexter was so ruthless in discovering could possibly have any tiny grain of idealism, however misguided, in what they were doing. 'They're all spies for our purposes,' he would say. 'We don't want to confuse people about which side is black and which is white. People don't want to have to worry about their own reactions. We have to pat them on the back and tell 'em whatever they think, they're right. Now, to get back to this script of yours, you've got too many dissolves here. I wonder if we can't think of a way to get round this one after Scene 18. Here's a thing John Ford once did . . .'

Meanwhile Mr Davidson, unaware of Paul's new job, phoned one morning when he was with Hubert Young. 'He said would you phone him in the morning,' Julia said.

'He didn't give any indication of what it was about?'

Julia shook her head. 'I didn't like to ask.'

'Why not?'

'Oh, he doesn't really know me. He'd sooner talk to you.'

'We don't have any secrets,' Paul said. 'Got the curse?'

Julia shook her head. 'No.'

'We don't have to tell people yet, do we?'

'Not for ages yet. We needn't tell them till I'm three months.'

'I don't want you to get fat, Julia.'

'Never mind, I shall have a lot more bosom, that should cheer you up a bit.'

Paul said: 'It will make a nice change, I must say.'

'Horrid, you are!'

'You said it.'

'You don't have to be quite so enthusiastic.'

'I say, Julia, if I get a few more of these films and things and old Bruce Davidson's got something more for me, I don't see why we shouldn't buy a car in the autumn.'

'There are going to be quite a lot of things we shall need,' Julia said. 'I mean, Mummy'll probably give us a

pram and I expect your folks'll want to give us something – '

'Christ, why can't they leave us alone? I don't want them
to keep giving us things. They're so damned generous.
They're so damned nice to us. Why? Why?'

'They're your parents, that's why,' Julia said. She looked
at her watch. 'Well, I suppose if we're going to have any
supper at all I'd better make my way into the burning fiery
furnace we call a kitchen.'

Paul said: 'I'll do the supper if you like.'

'I don't mind doing it,' Julia said.

'Oh, Christ, I wish we had someone to cook all our meals
for us – '

'We will one day.'

'Hell, we will,' Paul said. 'I'm not going to start employing people to do that kind of thing for me.'

Julia said: 'I shall need some help when I first come
home from hospital.'

'Oh, somebody's mother'll be down here using Persil,
you can be damned sure of that. Otherwise I'll do the work
myself. I don't want any *chars* around here. I've seen
enough people humiliated with that name.'

Julia said: 'I'll pop and get you the mop.'

'Anything to stop me writing,' Paul said. 'Anything to
stop me being what I want to be.'

Julia said: 'What's happened to the famous Riesman
sense of humour?'

'Disappeared with the famous Riesman sense of
independence.'

Julia said: 'What independence?'

'We were independent in Les Marteaux,' Paul said. 'We
were free to be ourselves and nobody bothered us.'

'I expect we shall be exactly the same again when we're
making enough not to have to worry – '

'When I'm making enough,' Paul corrected her. 'In Les
Marteaux we had *room* – '

475

'Well, we're not going to stay in the dungeon all our lives, are we?'

'Room to breathe, I mean. I don't know – I don't see where we're going. I don't see what it's for. It's not for its own sake, the way we're living, and it's not for the sake of anything to come. One reaches the prime of life – '

'The prime of life we've reached already!'

'*Marriage*,' Paul said. 'And there's nothing we do anything for, there's nothing there. Years and years of education for nothing. For Hubert Young to tell me that we've got to give them what they want us to give them. Educated for what? Nothing! There's nothing to *function* in.'

'There's me,' Julia said.

'It's not enough,' Paul said. 'God, all one's done to become a writer and all there is to write is *Man on the Run*. Do you know when I started this writing business, Julia? When I was on my own, when I thought I should never talk to anyone again, when I thought I should never have a friend again, when I had to write to live at all, I thought. And now what am I? The Dostoyevsky of *Man on the Run*! Even my parents like what I write! Writing is just a job like any other and its success is the same success as in anything else. How much money you're making.'

'I don't want you to write anything except what you want to write.'

'But can't you see that depends on living the way I want to live?'

'I don't want to stop you living any way you want to live either – '

'*But you do*. You do.'

Julia said: 'You won't be happy till I'm in tears, will you? That's what you want. I don't mind where or how we live. I'm not afraid of doing anything.'

'No, I am,' Paul said. 'I'm a funk, because I won't really stand up wholeheartedly and face things in a really total way. No, let's face it, I'm funking new things every day.'

'You don't funk things.'

'You know a writer's like a man on the run; he's like a man on the run with a secret he has to deliver, with a message engraved on his body, it's so much a part of him, and it's so important he should deliver it. He starts off with the message quite clear and he tells himself it doesn't matter what he does on the way as long as eventually he gets the message through and so he pretends to be all sorts of things, he takes all sorts of humiliations and makes all sorts of pretences so that he can get this message through, and he goes on and on, breaking all the vital principles which he's got written on him just to get to a position where he can reveal them. Getting through with the message is all that matters to him, never mind how corrupted or contaminated he gets, and so finally he gets through, he finally really makes it, he's famous, he's in a position to reveal his message and he strips off his clothes and he says "Look, this is what I *really* wanted to say all this time. Here is my real message to you all. This is what it's all about." And he turns slowly round so that everyone can see the message. And there's nothing there. He's arrested for making an exhibition of himself, because all they can see are the syphilitic sores and the sycophantic sores that he's contracted during his journey to the place where everyone can see and hear him. The message was the man and when he's been corrupted his message is no longer worth delivering, a few right words among the corruption. Unless a man lives right and gets there the right way, his message is not worth delivering and when the time comes it'll be obscured and rotted by what he's become. The writer and the work and the life are one. Tara. Thank you. End of speech.'

Julia said: 'Why do you always want to end with a laugh?'

'I,' said Paul, 'am a man on the run. And, after all, everyone has to know how to take a joke. That lets me in everywhere. The jester is the great survivor. Everyone knows that.'

2

It had for many years been Ben's practice to deliver his weekly cartoon to the *Worker* office on Wednesday morning and call in on Thursday evening to look at the block. The cartoon appeared on Friday. If something of great importance occurred on Thursday, Ben would stay in the office on Thursday night to draw a new cartoon relevant to it. At the beginning of August he called as usual on the Thursday evening and was asked to go up and see the Deputy Editor, Bill Ditchling, a rumple-suited, balding man with old-age freckles on hands and forehead.

'What ho,' Ben said. 'What's the trouble?'

'Oh, look, it's about the old cartoon this week.' Ditchling pushed Ben's drawing back across the desk at him. 'We're thinking that perhaps something about this Aswan dam trouble'd be more central to the present situation than what you've done here.' Ben's rejected cartoon showed Gomulka, Gerö, Gottwold, Khrushchev and the other Communist leaders, all the same size, smiling and holding out their hands across Europe, while on the other side a vast American GI in steel helmet with an atomic weapon in his revolver holster was pushing aside the tiny figures of the Western leaders. The caption was 'SATELLITES!'

'I think it's spot on,' Ben said. 'Don't you?'

'We don't feel it's central to the present situation,' Bill Ditchling said. 'Look, we're down to four pages tomorrow, Ben, and we want the whole paper to make the same point.'

Ben said: 'Is there anything wrong with this?'

'Of course there's nothing wrong, boy. It's a question of all punching at the same spot, see what I mean?'

Ben said: 'Will you use this next week?'

'I can't make any promises. You know how things change on the paper, Ben. After all, it's not so long since you were with us all the time – '

'OK, Bill,' Ben said. 'Fine. Well, I'll be pushing. See what I can think up.'

'Good for you,' Ditchling said, reaching for the cartoon Ben had already done. 'And we'll hold this over for another time.'

'I'll take it,' Ben said.

'I'll file it, then we can have it when we want it.'

'I'll take it, shall I?' Ben picked up the cartoon and rolled it into a cylinder. 'OK if I use Jerry's old office?'

'You mean Ernie Saunders's office. Yes, that'll be all right.'

'Oh yes, of course, that's right. Well – be seeing you, boy.' Ben grinned. 'Jerry's in Siberia of course, isn't he? I'd forgotten.'

Ditchling said: 'Well – um – if you're going to let us have something tonight – only two hours to bedtime.'

Ben phoned Susan to tell her that he would be late, but she was not yet home either. Françoise took the message. Ben sketched and doodled for a long time before any idea came for the new cartoon. The electric clock jerked with slow speed towards the deadline. A kind of lethargy still possessed Ben, bent over the drawing-board, the heel of his hand dark with lead. The deadline would come in silence. Every deadline he had waited for had come in silence. Egypt. The uncertainty he felt was the uncertainty of the Party. He would not admit any personal uncertainty. The pencil belonged to the Party. Ben wondered what kind of cartoon Bill Ditchling would draw. During all the years that Ben had been at the *Worker* full time it was very seldom that his work was not accepted. When it had not been, he had agreed instantly, if a fault was pointed out, that it wouldn't do; but now he took the rejected cartoon

and unrolled it and smiled. It was spot on. Ben shrugged
his shoulders and pressed his hand against the drawing-
board, depicting quick figures and then pencilling them
out. Trams and trolley-buses. Trams in the Mile End Road.
It was a long time since he had boarded a tram in the Mile
End Road and now he was travelling in silence, lonely,
without the familiar whine of the metal on the tracks,
without the pitching and the swaying and the workers in
greasy caps jostling against the basket-weave of the seats.
There was no one else on the bus. It hummed silently,
with the guides coming from above, the power coming
from above, a concentration of power from above driving
the empty conveyance. It was no longer the set of the rails
between cobbles which held the vehicle on its course, but
the driver, in uniform, steering where he would and where
he could, with the power flowing in from above and nothing
set in the firm ground to grip and see him right. Ben
messed through the trolley-bus he had drawn. What was
he thinking about? The clock jerked towards the silent
deadline. And if he missed it? Nothing would happen. For
so long he had expected that something would happen, but
the deadline came and nothing did and now he was thirty-
five. He drew the Aswan dam made out of piles and piles
of dollars and pounds and what the dam restrained was a
great sea of Arabs. Ben labelled them ARAB FREEDOM.
Below the dam Dulles and Eden were smarming up to
Nasser. Behind his hand Dulles was saying: 'I ONLY HOPE
IT HOLDS.' Ben dashed off his signature and stood up,
rubbing his eyes. The boy knocked on the door. 'Ready
yet?'

'Here we are,' Ben said. The boy looked at it and winked.
'Spot on!'

'You see what Bill Ditchling thinks,' Ben said. 'before
you incriminate yourself.'

The boy went out, whistling. Ben walked to the window
and looked out across Farringdon Road. Our paper. That

was the way he had always thought of it, all the years of his youth. And it still was his paper; he had no mind to desert it, even if others had, Doug and Jerry and the others. Israel and Egypt. He scratched his bald forehead, high up. Funny how lonely one could feel, suddenly, staring down into a seven-thirty street, with the market dead opposite and only the odd car going down Farringdon Road, and feel not that one wanted to leave the paper, not that one disagreed with anything or could disagree with anything, but that one might, that the day might come when one would. Something had to happen in one's lifetime. He thought of Susan as she had stood that night by the bed in Bognor and of the Party when he had first joined it, when men stood shoulder to shoulder at the barricades and Mosley and his muscle men came strutting between the tram tracks in the Mile End Road. Everything had fitted then; he had been fitted for everything. Now he felt tired. Susan had a job outside him; the Party too. He went to the door of the office and looked out. He went quickly, like a spy, down the corridor and ran down the stairs and out into the street. He turned away from the *Worker* and walked briskly in the direction of Ludgate Circus. He wanted a drink. He did not actually want a drink but a drink was the nearest thing to what he wanted. It seemed to him now that he was in a foreign country, that his excuse for being anywhere had been withdrawn. He was not afraid but he was alone. The electric clock seemed still to be jerking forward in front of his eyes, the clock that meant nothing, that registered no time. Strange that one should resent so much being set to work on another cartoon when one had always accepted it as part of the job. Perhaps if he hadn't used Jerry's old office, he would never have been so conscious of the waning necessity which held him to the Party. It would have been better if Jerry had been shot, if those who deserted the Party were shot. That would restore the necessity, for to stay alive one would have to

481

serve the Party. As it was, you could walk down a street away from the Party and no one followed, no one could touch you. Ben was ready for the shot in the back of the neck. So he thought of drink and of Hilda. Where was Hilda now? In Poland perhaps, in Hungary, who knew? A sweet agony of love for Susan rose in him and swamped the picture of the girl he had known. The sweetness of his love for Susan was sickly to him. When a phone rings and you want the person at the other end to answer and the phone rings and rings, it seems at last to be answered: the refusal to answer begins to be heard as a feature through that insistent ringing and the whole world grows glass-clear with the ringing. Intuition was untrustworthy, a thing to be ridiculed, the idea that hopes and fears unite and reveal people, but strangely in the hollowness of his own hopes and fears Ben was privy to a world he had never acknowledged; he longed to be answered, and in the ringing of his own mind, the hopeless ring against which he pressed himself, the world grew glassy clear for him, so that he saw Susan with someone, huddled outside that ring, and he saw his own life a mere splinter, a freak. The Party would never come to power, not in his manhood. He was a man, a man still muscled from the pits, a man who did not give in. And because he was a man the axe that split him had an awful edge; because he was a man who had been knit together in his manhood and who had been one, the knots in him like knots of woods, hard arteries of strength, unsplittable, because he had seen his life as one thing and exulted in that oneness, the axe that split him cut in silence, in an agony of silence, so that he knew what hit him, wishing that the bullet had come first, in the back of the neck, before the axe fell. His mind was opened by the axe that fell in the hollowness of the eight o'clock street, the axe edged with the knowledge that his wife was perhaps with another man, and that it mattered. It mattered that the only thing which had come to be for him was being destroyed. He had expected so much, waited for so much, and this was the only thing which had really come to be, his marriage; his marriage alone gave him place and time and reality. But now, aware of his divorce from Susan, released by the Party, his mind slewed with greasy uncertainty across the surface of life and he was ready for the bullet. He was ready for the bullet which did not come and so he walked on in the unwanted hours of reprieve when the deadline had been passed in silence. The line of death had been passed through and he lived still, suddenly conscious of his own absurdity.

3

Colin said: 'Can there be an argument against violence?'

'Of *course* there can,' Paul said. 'The whole notion of justice depends on there being an argument against violence.'

'I don't see why if someone is stronger he shouldn't have his way.'

'Good old Will of the stronger,' Paul said. 'I never thought I'd meet *him* again.'

'No, if someone is stronger than I am surely he's entitled to what I've got? That's the natural law, isn't it?'

'What is this natural law? I don't see that it adds up to anything other than if someone is stronger than I am, he's stronger than I am. That's not a law, it's a tautology.'

'Tautology?' Tessa said.

'Says the same thing twice,' Julia said. 'That one I've learnt.'

'But surely, if someone comes up to you and demands your wallet and he's got a gun and you haven't, that's the end of the matter, isn't it?'

'Nonsense. You send for the police. Surely the whole evolution of society has been the history of arguments against violence.' Paul turned to Julia. 'You're supposed to be the historian, you ought to know.'

'It's a long time since I did any history.'

'You ought to remember *something*.'

'Battle of Hastings, 1066.'

'What's the point of having a baby and then not being able to remember anything to teach it? It's crazy. It means we all have to start with the same ignorance and work our way out of it, all because of people like you not remembering what they were once taught.'

'Thanks very much,' Julia said.

Paul said: 'Quite frankly, I don't see where it comes from, this feeling that there can't be any argument against violence.'

'From people who want to be violent,' Julia said.

'Good. That's very good, darling. Yes, that's right.'

'Praise from the maestro,' Tessa said.

'But good heavens, I don't want to be violent,' Colin said.

'Perhaps you do,' Julia said. 'Really.'

'Why should I want to be violent, Prunella?'

'Because you're losing the argument,' Paul suggested.

'But I'm not in an argument.'

'He's always throwing things at me,' Tessa smiled, cutting the lemon meringue pie.

'You are in the argument. We're all in the argument,' Paul said. 'Only some of us don't realize it.'

'What argument?' Tessa inquired. 'Do help yourselves to cream.'

'Look, simply to be alive in a certain way is arguing for one side or another.'

Colin shook his head. 'I don't follow any of this –'

Paul said: 'We all live in a certain way, rely on certain luxuries, want certain comforts, we all live on certain assumptions; even the assumption that we're not going to lift a finger makes us just one more argument in favour of not giving a damn about anyone. We can't get out of being responsible. Simply by living, you're arguing in favour of the way you live, whether you like it or not. The only way not to argue is to be dead. The trouble is, most people think they can be ostriches until the last minute and then provided they wake up before we go over the precipice everyone'll excuse them for having been asleep, but it won't do. It's no use suddenly getting indignant when you haven't bloody well bothered to do the right thing earlier on. It's no use switching off the telly when something bad comes on, you've got to go up and bash the people who've put it on and tell 'em they've got you against them – '

'Go up and bash them, exactly – '

'You really do want to hit someone, don't you?'

Colin said: 'You said bash – '

'There's so many better ways of bashing people than hitting them. Only we always wait till the burglar's climbing in the window and then we say: What else can we do besides bash him? The answer is take more trouble over him before he gets to the stage of climbing in the window.'

'I suppose you're in favour of all this psychological business. Personally I think six of the best is a great deal simpler – '

'Colin, you're not serious – '

'Why not, Prunella?'

Paul said: 'Look, it's got nothing to do with psychologists at all. It's a question of finding a way of making everyone *valuable* to everyone else. Of giving them a sense of real *community*, not by waving flags or talking about "the people" or whatever, because every big name covers a false relation, but by creating the possibility at least of everyone standing in the community and having a relationship with his neighbour that will really hold and endure under fire.'

Colin said: 'What sort of relationship does hold under fire, do you think?'

Julia and Tessa were looking at Paul with a glinting expectation which was not unmixed with amusement.

'I don't know,' Paul said, and the two women breathed out and smiled openly and looked at the remains of the pie and smiled again. 'There must be some way,' Paul ploughed on, 'there must be some way in which people can trust each other and meet and conflict as human beings should by living instead of killing.'

'What about the sex war?' Julia proposed.

'The sex war,' Paul said, 'is greatly over-subscribed already. It's a question of respect, of looking at people and recognizing the Gods in them –'

'Good old Lawrence,' Julia said.

'You're being exceptionally silly tonight, Julia.'

'Thank you very much.'

'It's no use,' Paul said, 'it's no use because no one really cares what anyone says, no one is prepared to act on it. We talk and talk and nothing ever changes because of what we say, because the words aren't related to the people who hear them. All people want is to be entertained. That means one hears words and sees things and doesn't feel any need to act. If only we could stop talking and live out. If only going into action didn't always mean killing. If only we could make each other alive. If only we didn't spend so much time passing judgement on others. Values come in when life ceases to be lived.'

There was a silence and then Tessa said: 'Shall we have our coffee here or in the other room?'

4

Colin said: 'Quite a good evening, I thought.'

Tessa said: 'He's very intense, isn't he?'

'Stimulating though, in his way. I was quite intense myself at one time.'

'Were you, Colin?'

'I still can be,' he smiled. 'No, I was. About architecture, I mean. Meeting that chap Marowitz made me remember. We must have him out some time, I think you might find him very stimulating.'

'I'm too old to be stimulated.'

'I say, we are getting middle-aged, aren't we?'

'If you mean settled, yes, I suppose we are.'

'Perhaps we ought to unsettle. What do you think, Tessa?'

'In what way? Move, you mean?'

'I don't know. I might leave the Family Lovers', for instance.'

'What, before we've paid off the mortgage?'

'We could sell the house, or what we own of it. I worked it out: the Society still own the dining-room and wc and the garden as far as the birdbath.'

Tessa said: 'I would like to feel the dining-room was ours.'

Colin said: 'I was thinking of working with Saul Marowitz again, if he'd have me.'

'I should think he'd be glad to have you.'

'*Well*: it's a long time since I've done any independent work.'

'What about the golf club? Everyone was terribly impressed.'

'Yes, but that was just a restoration job, putting things back to what they were like before the war; working with Saul would be rather different – I don't know – perhaps our roots have gone too deep.'

'Too deep for what?'

'Moving. Getting out of the rut. Most of Saul's work is done abroad. He's got a big project on in Israel at the moment.'

'Oh, Colin, *no*; not with the children.'

'Everything's very quiet there again now.'

'There's always the danger of a new flare-up,' Tessa said.

Colin said: 'I am getting in a rut though. There's no doubt about that.'

'And a very nice rut it is too. What's wrong with our rut?'

'You know, it's really a bit, well, alarming, but I could hardly follow most of the stuff Prunella's young man was talking about this evening. Could you?'

Tessa said: 'He'll mellow.'

'I only hope he doesn't upset Prunella. He seems a very temperamental cove.'

'Personally I'd always back the woman in a marriage. She'll bring him round.'

Colin said: 'So you don't think I ought to leave the Family Lovers'?'

'I thought you were very happy there.'

'Perhaps I'm not meeting the challenge of the age, I don't know.'

Tessa said: 'What about meeting the challenge of your wife instead?'

'That's not a challenge,' Colin said, 'it's a pleasure.'

'I expect Master Paul would think that was wrong too.'

'I'm sure he would,' Colin said. 'Maybe he'd be right.'

'Colin, what are you talking about?'

'I don't know, Tess. Taking off pyjamas?'

'I think we might,' Tessa said.

5

Susan said: 'Nice of you to come home.'

'Sorry,' Ben said. 'Working.'

'Working at what?'

'The *Worker*; they didn't like the first cartoon I did.'

'This take four hours?'

'I – had a drink somewhere,' Ben said.

'With Hilda Klein?'

'With Hilda Klein?'

'You 'eard,' Susan said.

Ben said: 'What have you been up to?'

'Me? In what way?'

'What time did you get home?'

'Usual, Just after you phoned.'

'Aha.'

'Who was the drink with?'

'No one.'

'Well, it doesn't seem to have cheered you up very much.'

'I'm very cheerful, Susan.'

'Have you been with the superintendent again?'

'I've been having a drink, I told you. Smell.'

'Beer.'

'Shright.'

'Horrid. Ben, tell me about Hilda.'

Ben said: 'There's nothing to tell.'

'When did you meet her?'

'We were kids together, that's all. Long before I met you.'

'Was she in YCL?'

'Yes,' Ben said.

'And where is she now?'

'I don't know. I haven't seen her for a long time. She went back.'

'Went back where?'

'To Poland, I think, or Hungary. Wherever she could.'

'Was she still in the Party?'

'I think so,' Ben said.

'Did you go on seeing her after we were married?'

'I did see her a few times. You may have met her yourself. Fair with brown eyes.'

'Fair with brown eyes, eh? Attractive?'

'Not as attractive as you, Susie, my dear!'

Susan said: 'Right, my boy.'

'What is all this?'

'Were you in love with her?'

Ben threw back his head and laughed. 'Were you in *love* with her? I told you: we were kids together.'

'Did you sleep with her, Ben?'

'Look, Susan, it was twenty years ago nearly.'

'Did you?'

'What's wrong?'

'I said: did you?'

'I may've,' Ben said.

'Surely you know. Surely you know if you slept with someone or not.'

'We probably – look, I don't see what this has got to do with anything – '

'Ask the superintendent. Or do you want me to ask him?'

Ben said: 'I honestly don't know what you're talking about.'

'When did she go back?'

'A few years ago, I don't know.'

'When?'

'In fifty-one.'

'The year of the great exhibition,' Susan said. 'Very appropriate.'

Ben said: 'I think we'd better turn this in.'

'She took something with her,' Susan said, 'didn't she?'

'Took something with her?'

'Something to do with Herb Fletcher?'

'What is this, Samson and Delilah?'

'She did, didn't she?'

'Don't be ridiculous.'

'Ben, I think it's time I knew something about what's been going on – '

'Nothing's been going on, nothing whatever's been going on, you bloody fool.' Ben clenched his fists. 'Don't think I don't know what this is all about.'

'You slept with her after we were married, didn't you?'

'No,' Ben said. 'No, I didn't, but I wish to Christ I had.'

'Charming! Perfectly charming!'

'Where'd that one come from?'

'What one?'

'*Charming. Perfectly charming.* Too West End to be true, you are.'

Susan said: 'That reminds me. I'm going to the Public Relations Ball in a couple of months' time.'

'Fine. Right. OK. When's this?'

'End of October some time. I'll tell you the exact date.'

'Jolly decent of you,' Ben said. 'And who's the lucky man?'

'There's a party of us going from the office. We shall probably take a few clients as well, you know. All very works outing.'

'Aha. Well, fine. OK, Susan.'

'You can go out and get drunk again if you want to.'

'You think this is drunk? You've led a very sheltered life, girl, that's your trouble.'

'Ah, well,' Susan said, 'we can't all have Hilda Kleins, can we?'

Ben said: 'Don't be a fool, will you, Susan?'

'I can't help being,' Susan said. 'Remember?'

6

Paul was sitting in the dungeon reading through one of his scripts of *Man on the Run*. Julia came down in her dressing-gown. 'Aren't you ever coming to bed?'

Paul said: 'Christ, this is dreadful.'

'I don't think it's dreadful at all. You do it terribly well.'

'That doesn't make it any less dreadful.'

'Don't read it then, come to bed.'

'In a minute. Julia –'

491

'What?'

'Did I talk too much tonight?'

'You always talk too much, you know that.'

'No, did I?'

'I think you rather overwhelmed them.'

'It seems to be the only thing I can do, talk.'

'You can come to bed.'

'It's not enough,' Paul said, 'it's not enough.'

'Well, thanks very much.'

'Try to understand, for God's sake.'

'I do understand; you should never have married me, I should never have got pregnant, the whole thing's a ghastly mistake.'

'What do you want me to be?' Paul shouted. 'What d'you want me to *be*?'

'I don't want you to be anything.'

'And you're getting your wish, aren't you? That's just what I'm going to be: nothing.'

'I don't mean that and you know it. You're right: you do talk too much.'

'Thanks a lot for your loyalty.'

'Why try and make what I say mean what I never intended?'

'The function of criticism,' Paul replied.

'No, why do you have to turn on me all the time?'

'Because you're the only person I can hurt.'

'Why do you want to hurt me?'

'I don't. I just want to make an impression on someone.'

'You've already made an impression on me, remember?'

'I'm so damned boxed in,' Paul said. 'I wish I could get out more, talk to people – '

'I'm not stopping you. Get out if you want to.'

'This is my place,' Paul said. 'I pay the rent. *Remember*?'

Julia said: 'I thought you were so happy – '

'I am *happy*. But happiness is a way of talking about the

past not the present. It's a kind of death, to be happy, it's living in the past.'

'Well, I think it's jolly nice to be happy.'

'Yes, but it won't last unless there's some kind of reason – some kind of *necessity*. I don't know, perhaps our life's really a lot too easy, perhaps we don't have enough to do –'

'I feel as if I have plenty to do,' Julia said.

'Meaning I don't do enough, is that it?'

'You're all right,' Julia said. 'I'm not entering any complaints yet.'

'All we need is money, isn't it? If only we had packets and packets of money, everything would be all right. We could have a car and a telly and ten months' holiday a year –'

'Look, I've never complained *once* –'

'Oh, I know, I know, I suppose in a way I wish you had. I wish I had someone to blame beside myself.'

'I'm beside yourself,' Julia said.

'Her favourite position,' Paul quoted.

'Come to bed, Paolo. Hm?'

'Well, just this once.'

SEVEN

Two Deaths

1

THE NURSE SAID: 'It'll be all right if you don't stay too long.'

Paul touched Hannah Adler's arm. She said: 'You take your father in, I just want to have a word with the sister.'

Paul looked at Isidore, a bent figure in a heavy coat, with a frightful little smile underlining his stubby cheeks. 'Come on,' he said loudly, 'we can go in.'

Otto Kahane was dying. He lay against wedges of pillow, the skull ready beneath the punctured tent of skin which hung over it. Otto rolled his head towards them, his eyes as big as eggs.

Isidore said: 'Look who's come to see you!'

Paul said: 'Hullo, Uncle Otto. I don't suppose you remember me – '

'P – ' the old man pouted.

'Paul, that's right.'

Isidore Adler was looking nervously round the room. There was a slim cylinder beside the washbasin. Isidore lowered his head towards it suspiciously. ''Sis for?' he inquired.

'Oxygen,' Paul said. 'Why don't you sit down?'

'Right standing,' Isidore said, nerving himself to look at Otto. 'My wife's outside.'

Otto's lids came over his eyes.

Hannah came in.

'I think he's dead,' Isidore simpered.

'Don't talk nonsense,' Hannah Adler said, putting a huge basket of fruit on the bedside table. 'Hullo, Otto.'

'He's dead,' Isidore said to Paul. Paul shook his head impatiently: 'I don't think so.'

Otto's eyes opened. He saw Hannah and moved a hand along the sheet towards her. Hannah took it and pressed it. 'That's right, dear,' she said, 'it's me, Hannah.' She nodded. 'He knows who it is.'

Paul said: 'Why don't you sit down?'

'Prefer standing.'

'Sit down, Issy, don't be ridiculous.'

Isidore frowned and walked to the window.

Paul said: 'It's a very nice room.'

'Oh, they look after them very nicely here.'

The door opened and Mr Levy, the superintendent, came in. He was carrying his clock. 'Oh, good afternoon, excuse me,' he said, 'I didn't realize – '

Hannah Adler said: 'That's all right, Mr Levy. I don't suppose you remember me – I'm Hannah Adler.'

Mr Levy's cheeks rounded. 'You came to visit Mr Kahane, I remember.'

'And my son-in-law,' Hannah said.

'Afternoon.' Paul nodded.

Otto Kahane saw Mr Levy and smiled. Mr Levy held up his clock. 'I brought you the clock in case you wanted to know the time.' Mr Levy put it on the table beside the fruit basket. 'He's very fond of this clock,' he told Hannah with a smile towards Otto.

Otto said: 'Going all right?'

'Going very well, Mr Kahane, don't you worry. Going very well indeed.'

Otto nodded and opened his mouth, the lips gumming: 'Good, good.'

'The trouble Mr Kahane used to take over my clock!'

'Same with me,' Hannah said. 'He lived with us for a long time, you know, before he came here.'

'Yes?'

Isidore was looking out of the window. He muttered something and looked reproachfully at Hannah.

'And I don't want to hear anything from you, my boy.'

Mr Levy said: 'Well! I don't want to intrude on a family gathering. I'll come back and see you later, Mr Kahane.' Otto nodded and his lips peeled apart again. Mr Levy smiled chubbily. 'Don't go away, will you? That's right.' He smiled quickly round the room and went.

Paul watched the old man on the bed. Now that he was here, there seemed nothing very frightening in death; such an end as this was without agony and in due time. It was a thing about Otto which could be accepted: one felt neither pity nor guilt: the old man was going and one had come to see him off. It was a family duty. It demanded no expenditure of emotional capital. One was not supposed to love Otto (and so could afford to, discreetly), one merely attended him, and that was good, as when Hannah had said: 'You take your father in', that too was good; though Paul felt no love for Isidore he was related to him and that was enough, he despised him perhaps – since he owned North London shops – but he no longer shrank from him. He sat in this room in Bethnal Green and felt right, with a man dying opposite him, since nothing unnatural was being asked of him; his presence was his membership in the family. Love was superfluous because, in this dying, there subsisted the orderliness of tradition, however little one believed in anything, so that the spiritual burden did not fall on and cripple one but was borne by all. Happiness and unhappiness had no part in this, for this, till the moment of death, was life. Simply to be there (wasting time!) was life, one's bottom on the chair, the body in the bed, Hannah Adler in her Persian lamb coat, Isidore Adler thinking about the money the special nurse was going to cost him; all these things were true without love and gained a hardness from that truth. If only one could forget the

496

mushy phenomenalism of bourgeois love and toleration and be at home in the hardness of life! Then one might strut through life like a man, with the brute ground beneath one, that there and me here, instead of living in this phenomenalistic amalgam, inside out and outside in, with only a matter of words between you and death. Paul bitterly hated his past, saw that the aversion he had felt from his parents was unfair to them so far as it came from what they did, which was the best they could for him, loving him as they did, right only where it turned from what they were, what they argued for. You couldn't blame them for their arguments, only for the premises, for Monmouth Court, from which they were argued. But to change all this was not a matter of words.

Hannah Adler said: 'I think we ought to be going.'

Isidore said: 'Taxi waiting?'

'Yes, dear, Mr Samuelson's waiting.'

'Meter tickin' up,' Isidore said.

Paul put his hand on Hannah's shoulder. 'What does the doctor think?'

Hannah pursed her lips. 'He won't be with us for long, dear,' she said. 'I had a word with the nurse. She'll let us know.' She leant down and kissed Otto's cheek. 'We're going now, dear. I'll come and see you again tomorrow, please God.'

Otto nodded and the lips peeled apart. 'Right.'

Paul took the old man's hand. 'Good-bye, Uncle Otto.'

'P – ' Otto said.

Paul nodded and patted the hand and put it back on the sheet.

Isidore said: 'Um, good-bye then, Otto. Take care yourself.'

In the corridor the visitors passed an old man sitting on a stool. When they had turned the corner, the old man rose and went to the door of Otto's room and looked through the glass. He looked up and down the corridor and

pushed open the door. Otto opened his eyes once more
and saw Mr Jankower, who came without a word and sat
on the chair by the bed. The nurse came and peeped on
tiptoe through the glass, but went away. Mr Jankower
closed his eyes.

2

Julia was typing. The supper was on and she thought there
might be time for a few pages of the fair copy of *Dexter
FBI* before Paul returned. She remembered the blistering
lumpiness of the first thing of his she had ever read; and
now he had a novel coming out in a few weeks' time and
TV producers paid for his services. This success had not, as
she had once feared, taken him away from her, rather it
had closed him up against her. She typed on a sudden chill
of uncertainty; although he remained closer than ever to
her, there was a sullen hostility in him that had grown and
grown since their marriage. She spun the paper off the
roller of the machine and lifted her glasses to rub the pinch
of them.

Paul said: 'Wotcher.'

'I didn't hear you come in.'

'Well, I have. What're you doing?'

'What does it look like?'

'You always seem to have your glasses on nowadays.'

'Only when I'm typing,' Julia said.

'Then don't type. I can do it.' He threw the evening
paper into the sofa. Julia took off her glasses. 'How was
Otto?'

'I do not think he is long for this world,' Paul said. 'He is
sur le point.'

'I suppose he's – '

' – had a good innings?' Paul suggested.

'You hate me, don't you?'

'You hate me, I hate you. Caesar hates the Belgians, the Belgians hate Cotta – '

'Well, you have come home in a nice mood.'

'Sorry. I apologize. I should come from a death-bed scene doing the fandango, eh, what?'

'You might lay the table,' Julia said.

'Right, ma'am. At your command.'

Julia called out: 'Any news?'

'Oh, the usual rumblings about the Nasserite menace, lifeline of Empire, and all that. They're going to have some kind of conference from which we shall doubtless emerge vindicated, valedictory and vanquished.'

'Mmm, you must have been asked that question before today.'

'Thank you for that touching tribute to my spontaneity.'

Julia came down the three steps from the kitchen, wiping her forehead. 'Hot in there.'

'So you've said.'

'Am I not allowed to say that I'm hot? You don't exactly keep mum about what you're feeling.' Julia picked up the paper. 'My God, I know that man.'

Paul said: 'Whom do you know?'

'Neil King.'

'Who the hell is Neil King?'

'Shut up. He's someone I used to know.'

'Shut up, eh?' Paul said. 'Thanks a lot.'

The paper said:

Captain Neil King, 2nd Parachute Brigade, was killed near Famagusta today when the car he was driving hit a mine and went over off the road. The car fell fifty feet into a rocky field. Captain King's driver, L/Cpl Hamer, was thrown clear and is in hospital with a fractured skull. Captain King's home was in Abbey Road, London.

The headline was 'TERRORISTS KILL BRITON'.

Julia said: 'It makes you feel very peculiar.'

Paul said: 'Who was he anyway?'

'Someone I went out with a couple of times. He was horrid.'

'Then what's so awful?'

'Just because he was horrid doesn't mean you want him to be killed. Anyway, he was rather unusual – '

'Unlike me.'

'If you were killed,' Julia said, 'I'd say the same thing for you any day.'

'When did you know this chap?'

'Before I met you. When I was at college.'

'How well did you know him?'

'Not very. He wanted to go to bed with me. So it was that or not seeing him again and in his case it was the latter.'

'Why didn't you? Go to bed with him, I mean?'

'I didn't like him.'

'You go to bed with me,' Paul said.

'You silly bugger,' Julia said, 'You really are.'

'Is he Jewish? He doesn't look it.'

'Half. He was a very twisted individual.'

'Unlike we straight up and down Yids, what?'

'Perhaps you'll feel better after supper,' Julia said. 'I certainly hope so.'

Paul said: 'How did you meet him?'

'He picked me up,' Julia replied. 'At a party.'

'Did that often happen? You getting picked up?'

Julia said: 'If that offends your sense of delicacy you could say I met him at a party. I thought you preferred the rugged approach.'

'You seem to have a very strange idea of me suddenly.'

'He always drove like a lunatic,' Julia said, glancing at the paper again as she put the casserole on the table.

'It doesn't matter how you drive, if there's a mine in the road there's a mine in the road.'

'All the same he's the sort of person who would hit a mine, when you come to think of it. I mean it *fitted*.'

'What do you think fits me?' Paul said. 'What kind of death do you think would fit me?'

Julia smiled at him for a second and blinked and smiled again. 'You,' she said at last, 'there's no doubt about you. You'll die in bed.'

'On active service, I hope,' Paul smiled.

'*Sans doute.*'

'You can trust old Riesman to find himself a pretty cushy battlefield. You're beginning to know me too well, old girl, that's your trouble.'

'Don't turn everything against yourself, Paolo. I thought we'd passed that stage.'

'I don't think I shall ever pass it. God, Julia, you're lucky, you're pregnant with something worthwhile, something actual and real that's going to come out exactly what you want and believe and hope it'll come out . . .'

'Please God,' Julia said.

'God, it must be a beautiful thing to be a woman and be able to fulfil oneself, to have the pain and really produce something out of it, that must really be something. Instead of knowing that all the birth pains one has won't produce anything better than *Dexter FBI*.'

'They will.'

'They will *not*. They will *not*!'

'That's up to you,' Julia said.

'I don't know what I'm doing anything for,' Paul said. 'When you have a baby, you have a baby and that's it. But what do you have a book for? It's an awful feeling that before one's first book has been published even, one's going wrong and can't stop.'

Cyril King said: 'I'm glad you could do lunch, Adler. I wanted to talk to you. You know I lost my boy last week.'

'Yes, I –'

'I hope you don't mind, that's why I wanted to talk to you. I don't have many people in the business I can talk to. You see, Adler, I've made a fool of myself – I hope you don't mind me talking to you like this –'

Colin said: 'No, sir.'

'Don't call me "sir" will you? I don't mind Cyril or Mr King, whatever you like, only not sir. I'll tell you why. My boy called me sir. When he called me sir the way he did the blood used to run cold in my veins. My son hated me, Adler. He hated me.'

'I don't believe that, sir, Mr King.'

'Yes he did. There wasn't anything I could do for that boy that could stop him hating me. I did everything I could for him, I sent him to a good school, to Wellington – he had everything he wanted. If he'd wanted to go to the university I would have bought a college for him. But the more I did for him the more he hated me. He hated being tied to me, he hated being nearly free, you know? He was almost a goy and it drove him crazy. Mm. Well, have some more wine.'

Colin said; 'Fathers don't have an easy time.'

'You've got kids, haven't you?'

'A boy and a girl,' Colin nodded.

'Your wife's a Jewess though, isn't she?'

Colin said: 'Um – yes.'

'You're a wise man, Adler, you're a wise man.'

'One doesn't control these things.'

'One controls these things,' said the other. 'One has to control these things. You know, I was a fool, I married for love, Adler, and that's a very foolish thing. You can have love without being married. I've done everything the wrong way round, you know what I mean? I've got a Gentile wife and a Jewish mistress and a dead son. A son who hated his father and even died before him he hated him so much. You wouldn't believe this, but my son was a very artistic boy. Whenever we'd pass a really ugly building you know what he'd say? "One of yours, sir, I presume?" He wanted to kill people, my son, in the end that was all he wanted. He hated life so much he just wanted to kill people, that's all he wanted, and I think he was just as keen that they should kill him, you know? He didn't belong to anything, he didn't die for anything and he didn't kill for anything. He was a freak, you know? That's what I was the father of, a freak.'

Colin said: 'You aren't necessarily a freak because you don't get on with your father.'

'Don't you get on with your father, Adler?'

Colin said: 'Not always. I mean, I – '

'I apologize. There's no reason why you should tell me. Tell me, Mr Adler, what did you think of me when you first met me? Were you scared of me?'

'Not exactly,' Colin said. 'I don't think I was *scared* – '

'You know, if I was giving advice to a young feller today going in to see a big man about a job, you know what I'd say to him? I'd say: "If you feel scared when you get in there, just imagine he's somebody's father." It doesn't matter how ruthless you are, if you're a father you're weaker than the poorest man in the street.'

'What your son felt isn't your fault,' Colin said.

'Adler, Adler. You know what I didn't do for my son? I didn't give him anything that wasn't mine. I couldn't give him anything that wasn't mine.'

'I don't understand – '

'No? When I was a boy down in old Montague Street my father would take me to a synagogue on a Saturday and we'd meet people and talk; you know it was like my father gave me the whole world, oh, believe me, it wasn't much of a world, but it was a world you didn't have to buy your way into, you didn't have to be anything except a Jew to belong to it, you didn't have to thank your father for anything, because you had your own right of entry: you belonged in your own right. I loved my wife, Adler, and when she was pregnant with Neil I was glad. Now I look at her – and she's still an attractive woman, believe me – and I think to myself: what the hell did I marry you for? I don't dare any more, Adler, I don't dare to touch her any more. Well, well, you don't want to know about an old man's troubles. Tell me, Adler, were you in the Army, during the war, I mean?'

Colin said: 'Yes. In the Middle East.'

'My son always thought I should've been in the Army in the first war. I was just over eighteen when the war ended, you know, but he thought I should've volunteered. It always upset him I was never in the Army. Maybe he wished I'd've been killed, I don't know. During the war he always called me "General", you know. Still, that's all in the past; now I want to talk to you about an idea I've got.'

'Of course,' Colin said.

'There's one last thing I want to do. I want to build a building. I want to build a building to commemorate my son. I want it to be a kind of memorial to the son I might have had, not blaming Neil, blaming me. I remember when you first came to my office – what was it, ten years ago? – I remember I told you like I always tell new people in the firm, this isn't an artistic organization, remember? Well, I don't withdraw any of it. I won't gamble with other people's money, that's not my job, but now I want to give you a chance, Adler, I want to give you a chance to do something for me. I'm going to arrange for you to have time off and I want you to design me a building, a great building, Adler, to commemorate my son. I've already got the site in mind. Have you got a minute now? I'd like to show it to you.'

'My time is yours,' Colin smiled.

The Bentley came smoothly into the forecourt of the Savoy. Mr King opened the door and patted Colin inside. 'Where I told you,' he said to the chauffeur. The great car creamed through the city streets and down towards Aldgate East.

'Down here I can breathe,' Mr King said. 'Down here it's like the smell of the sea for me.'

Colin said: 'I don't really know this part at all well.'

'This is where we came from, Adler. This is where we all came from.'

Colin said: 'Yes, my mother came from round here.'

'Certainly. I knew your mother. A fine woman. I remember your mother when she was a little girl. Hannah Liepman, isn't that right?'

'Hannah Liepman,' Colin agreed.

'This is the place.' Colin looked out on a brick-strewn site stretching across the bomb-flats to the back of a garage. Rusty weeds fluttered in the crevices of old foundations. Colin could hear the drumming of traffic in Whitechapel High Street. 'This is where I want to build a fine building,' Cyril King said. 'You can design the finest building you can think of. Under a hundred and fifty thousand pounds, not including the site.'

'What do you want it to be?'

A club. A place where people can come. That's all I can tell you, I want it to be a place people can come and be part of. A kind of *club*,' King said. 'A place where people can come and belong.'

'How did you know my mother?' Colin asked.

'Down here everyone knew everyone, that was the kind of place it was. Oh, I'm getting sentimental about it; all right, in many ways I wouldn't come back here on a bet, you know, but here was the place I last felt – part of something.' King took Colin's arm and led him away from the Bentley across the uneven ground. 'I want you to create something for me; I don't know what I want, I just want a great community centre, not just for people round here, but for every one of our people to be able to come to.'

'Well – um – it'll need thinking about.'

'I want it to be a fine piece of architecture. I want it to be called "The Jews' Club" and I want it to be a fine piece of art, I want it to be something my son would look at and not say "One of yours, sir, I presume". I want it above all not to be like that.' King stumbled and grabbed Colin's sleeve. 'A library, an art gallery, a restaurant, a synagogue, everything, that's what I want it to have and everyone will be welcome, Jews and Goys, anything, but it'll be Jews' Club. I'm confused about that, about the membership, maybe we'll have to talk that over, but one thing it must be, a great building that belongs to its people.'

'A great building must belong to its people,' Colin said.

Back in his office Colin could hardly believe what had happened. It was an opportunity so tremendous that it reduced him to impotence. For years he had done virtually nothing and now he was called upon for a masterpiece. He phoned Saul Marowitz and asked if they could meet later that evening. There was no one else who could help him. Marowitz suggested that he come to the studio immediately after work. Colin hesitated and then agreed; he couldn't remember how long it had been since he had spent an evening out on his own. He phoned Tessa to explain. Tessa said: 'This is all rather unexpected.'

'Yes, something rather fantastic has come up. I'll tell you about it when I get home. It's – it's a commission.'

'*Colin*. Who from?'

'I'll tell you all about it later. I'm – um – in a bit of a daze at the moment about it.'

To engage oneself to that kind of thinking again, after all these years, was an agony. Colin took a big drawing book out of his cupboard and sharpened a pencil. He sat there in the office after everyone else had left the building, the light encircling his drawing block, and concentrated: he concentrated on forgetting all that he had been for twenty years, tried to remember what had made him see possibilities of architecture in everything he saw, tried to remember how he and Saul had ridden down the Edgware Road on the top of the bus and torn the buildings down as they went. He decided to wait and talk to Saul before he started.

'You mean he just offered you this job. Just offered it you, just like that?'

Colin nodded. 'That's what it seems like.'

'Jesus,' Saul Marowitz said, 'Jesus Christ almighty.' He tilted the whisky bottle into his glass and slewed it round for Colin. 'This is a something.'

'Um – what do you think the first thing to do is?'

'Get a contract,' Marowitz said.

'That's not what I expected to hear from you. I thought you were an idealist.'

'I'm not an idealist,' Marowitz said. 'I'm a fanatic.'

'What would you do if you were given this job?' Colin asked.

'Walk,' Marowitz said. 'I'd walk over every inch of that site and every inch of every street that you could see that site from and I'd talk to every person who'd ever see that building and ever use it and ever want to use it and I'd learn what it was to be a person that would use it and what could be made of those persons. I think I'd probably go and live down there in the East End for the whole time I was working on that aspect of the thing and listen and watch and live. That's a start on what I'd do. Christ, Colin, you've got a chance to do something – something bloody terrific.'

Colin said: 'Go and live in the East End. I don't know what my wife would say about that.'

Marowitz said: 'Leave her.'

'My dear chap – '

'Leave her for as long as it takes. That's what I'd do.'

'I don't see how living in the East End is going to give me some magic ability I wouldn't have at home.'

'It's not a question of ability, it's a question of integrity.'

'Oh *really*.'

'Why have you come here? Why have you come here tonight?'

'Look here – '

'Give me a bloody answer, will you?'

'I thought you – '

'All right, you thought me. You thought me because I'm insane enough to be the only person you could come to about the biggest chance you've ever had in your bloody life.'

'Um – look, if you think I'm imposing myself on you, I – er – don't have to stay, you know.'

Marowitz said: 'Have some more whisky. Of course you know where this Mr King of mutual knowledge ought to be building this club of his. In Israel. And it shouldn't be commemorating his bloody son, it should be commemorating my bloody father. Still, that one we will let pass. I think personally I shall be going out to Israel soon to work on a low-price farming community out there; I've managed to interest them in my new technique – '

'If it's low-price,' Colin smiled, 'I expect you would find some takers out there.'

Saul Marowitz said: 'He ought to build this club in Israel to welcome the immigrants. A club for newly arrived immigrants and he should never be allowed into it himself. Forbidden to Cyril King, Esquire. Like Moses and the Promised Land. Yes, why don't you agree to do the building on the condition that he never set foot in it?'

Colin said: 'Well, to get back to the point: you think I should go and live in the East End?'

'Certainly. Go back to the past and see what it stands for in the future, that's your job, as I see it. We don't want any bloody monuments.'

'That may be what the client wants,' Colin said.

'He's given you a free hand. He's allowing you to be an artist, now you give him what *you* want.'

Colin said: 'Yes, quite.'

4

Colin chewed and sucked at the bleeding cuticle of his right forefinger. It was very late. The train on which he was travelling was certainly the last. The nightscape was unfamiliar to him. Cyril King's commission had put him into an unfamiliar world. Colin considered: a great building, something that would be favoured in the *AR*: 'Club in the East End – architect Colin Adler. This club, designed to accommodate a theoretically unspecified number of members and casual visitors, has several unusual features including . . .' Including what? The thing was simply a castle in the air. King was a bit off his chump at the moment, otherwise it would never have been mooted even; it was a fatuous idea really, completely unrealistic. In any case, there weren't any Jews in the East End any more; it was all very well for King to mosey down there in the old Bentley, but who else would want to? Marowitz was right really. The project would be far better removed to Israel. And then one would have to go and live in Israel, no doubt! What would Tessa think of *that*?

Tessa said: 'I'm afraid I don't see why you have to go to Israel to build the same building you could build just as well in England.'

'It was only an idea of Saul's originally.'

'Do you think we could discuss it in the morning?' Tessa said. 'I don't really think anything very valuable is likely to come out of talking about it at this hour.'

Colin said: 'Fine.'

Colin had some work to finish at the office before he could give his full time to the consideration of King's project, so he and Tessa were able to discuss the whole matter during the following evenings. She could just believe that Colin was serious about going down to live in the East End but that they should all pack up and go to Israel was quite out of the question. Colin had not so far mentioned Marowitz's Israel idea to Cyril King but he believed now that he should. 'I'm sorry,' Tessa said, 'but I don't see why you should at all. He's asked you to do a building in the East End and now you want to persuade him into some crackbrained idea of going to Israel. Even if you do a wonderful building there, and I'm sure you would, it wouldn't do you any good.'

'People are as likely to see it there as anywhere else. More so, if anything.'

'Honestly, Colin, I think you could be talked into anything! I don't want to stop you doing anything you think you ought to do, only I do think we shall have to work things out sensibly. Anne's only just settling in at St Monica's, and I don't want her upset; I really don't think we can just up sticks and go off to Israel – '

Colin said: 'I don't want to.'

'Well, honestly, I don't see why other people should run our lives!'

'I agree we couldn't very well take the children to Israel with the present situation in the Middle East. But I could – um – go on my own, I suppose.'

'I don't want you running off to Israel and getting yourself killed, that wouldn't be fair on the children either.'

'Or me,' Colin smiled.

'Or *me*,' Tessa said. 'I was without you quite long enough during the war. I'm not waiting next time!'

Colin said: 'This whole discussion is a bit theoretical anyway. I don't suppose King'll want this thing in Israel in a million years.'

But he did. And it was an excited Marowitz who phoned to tell Colin so. Cyril King had said it was one of the most brilliant ideas he had ever heard; it clarified for him the whole object of his generosity: reconciliation. And what better than that of Jew and Arab? It might seem to be a hopeless objective, yet it was one that had to be reached if Israel was to survive. He had asked Saul to come round and see him and wanted Colin to join them. Saul was wild-haired and nervous when Colin came in. He knew he had been unethical in approaching Cyril King behind Colin's head, as he put it. 'I've been thinking and thinking about this thing and it seemed to me I had to talk to Mr King. I saw suddenly what this could mean, particularly at a time like this. I believe this would be a gesture of *today*.' Marowitz gestured with his hands. Mr King mumbled:

'That's what your father would've said. You know,' to Colin, 'I can hear his father speaking when I listen to this boy.' 'Yes?' 'I can hear his father speaking, that's no exaggeration.'

Saul said: 'The East End is a museum today.'

'Basic reconsideration, that's what's needed,' Cyril King said, piercing a cigar. 'Basic reconsideration. Tell me, Mr Marowitz, where do you think a suitable place would be? In Israel, I mean?'

'I've got several ideas about that, but I don't really feel that I ought to come any farther forward than I have done –'

'Nonsense; Adler doesn't mind, do you, Adler?'

'I'm very happy to have Saul work on the idea,' Colin said. 'Couldn't be happier in fact.'

5

Julia came back into the bedroom. She was very pale.

Paul said: 'Time, is it?'

Julia said: '*Darling* – oh God, oh my God, darling. Paolo.'

'What is it? What's happened?'

Julia said: 'The curse. I think the curse is beginning.'

'Christ, what do we do? How far's it gone?'

'It's hardly – it's, you know, just a spot or two.'

'Well, what do we do? Call the doctor or what?'

'Yes, I suppose so. And I really ought to stay in bed, at least till after he's been.'

'Stay in bed?'

'It may mean two or three days.'

'You stay in bed,' Paul said. 'Stay in bed for a week for all I care.'

'You want me to lose it, don't you?'

'Never mind what I want. Now, what about breakfast?'

'Just some tea and toast.' Julia lay down in the bed.

'What about some porridge?'

'Only if you're making it for yourself,' Julia said. 'I am sorry, honestly.'

'Now, don't worry. It'll be perfectly all right. You don't think anything's – gone wrong yet, do you? I mean, we can always start again, you know.'

'I want this one,' Julia said. 'This time I really want this one.'

'So do I,' Paul said.

He was good at looking after invalids. He boiled Julia an egg, cracked the shell and peeled it. He made the porridge and buttered the toast before putting it on the tray. This kind of tenderness restored him and calmed him. He wanted nothing more except when the complexity of outside events foisted ambition on him, when other women, like Slinky, made him aware of the possibilities of destroying what one was happy with. He was shocked to hear of Susan and Angus, shocked as though he had never slept with Julia before they were married, shocked as though he had never really believed in even the most innocent forms of marital infidelity. It was a gloomy liberation, to realize that even those marriages which seemed most secure could so easily be split. And now he did fear that Julia would lose her child. He feared it since he knew that if she did lose it, he would leave her. He looked anxiously at the tray to see if he had forgotten anything; it would be a shame to spoil the effect. He went upstairs, pushed the door open with the tray knee-propped, and went into the bedroom. 'Breakfast for one please, James,' he announced.

'Where's yours?'

'I don't want anything. Go on. Have yours while it's cold.'

'You are sweet,' Julia said.

'Are you OK? No further alarums.'

She shook her head. 'We're holding our own.'

'That's all we've got to do,' Paul said.

Julia said: 'You do love me, don't you?'

'I want to,' Paul said. 'I want to always.'

'Don't worry, Paolo, you're quite right; we can always start again.'

'No,' Paul said. 'You're definitely going to have this one, even if you have to stay in bed for a week.'

'I think if I get through this all right we ought to tell people, I'd like to tell Mummy and your mum. She'll be so excited.'

'Then kindly keep your legs shut,' Paul said. 'And don't let go.'

'It's not quite as simple as that.'

'Let's pretend, shall we? Just this once. Let's try and be ourselves for just a little bit longer.'

6

The cemetery trees were black stubs against a wild afternoon. Whips and curdles of cloud blew up in the sky. The party was small: Hannah and Isidore, Mr Levy, Mr Jankower, Paul and Sir Samuel Goldstein's chauffeur, Harris. Sir Samuel was in the Bahamas. Mr Levy and Mr Jankower had come in the superintendent's car, an Austin Seven. Hannah Adler had Mr Samuelson. Mr Samuelson remembered the old gentleman and joined the party in the chapel. Before the body was brought out, one of the attendants, a cheerful little man in a black uniform, asked whether anyone wanted to see Otto before he was nailed down. Hannah said: 'One of the men.' Isidore looked away. Mr Jankower did not look up. Paul said: 'I'll go if you like.'

The coffin was on a triple trestle, the lid open. Otto Kahane lay there, small, in the coffin. Paul looked at the dead man. The mortuary was cold, with white bricks. Outside, the wind seared the stiff trees. Paul looked down at the face of Otto Kahane, the first dead man he had ever seen. Paul smiled and nodded to the corpse, as if to be on terms with it, to acknowledge its state, before beginning to think. To think of death, to have the right words to say over the dead, these were not things for which any liberal faith could prepare one. 'Death,' Paul remembered, 'is not a part of life; it is not lived through.' The dictionary of Otto Kahane was closed, nothing could ever be looked up in him again, what you could learn from him was now known or never would be. Humanism ignored death; death belonged to a harsher language and could be spoken of only in terms which transcended individual life. Of death

514

one could only speak unselfishly. It seemed a great service to those outside that he had come into this chapel of death, a great service that he should go for them, but here it seemed a great impudence that before this shut book of Otto's life, there should be no more understanding review of him than 'Pool old chap' which Paul did mutter.

In the minutes while the others waited, Paul strove to find some expression adequate to the moment. To build a quick God in order to mourn Otto, that was a sham; instead he reached back even to Benedict's, lacking words in his own faith, yet feeling words were called for, rituals. At the great ends of life the piecemeal liberal was powerless, he had nothing to say. When you stood before a corpse which had travelled so harsh a road and found you had nothing to say, then you knew your liberalism. One could swear nothing for Otto that was not perjury, make no promise that one would not break, offer no farewell that was not empty. All that he could say to Otto in truth was this: 'If it's a boy, it shall have your name.' For the child had not been lost in Julia.

The attendant said: 'All right?'

'All right,' Paul said. Recognizing the inadequacy of his response, he was resolved, walking behind the grave cart, that he must make something of Otto's death. Life must recognize brutality or always be surprised by it. Life must recognize death or live unworthy of it. There was, to be sure, nothing the happy man thought about less than death, but nor was there anything the trivializer was more eager to forget.

If Alma had been at the funeral she would have said: 'He looks very peaceful. He looks so – *content*!' Paul wanted to say: 'He looks very dead.' But because he is dead, we are alive. The old dictionary goes down into the pit with the scars on it and in its death we are alive, and a great people. So long as we acknowledge our dead, we are a great people. One could never pay off Otto or say what it was one had learned from him. Without him, one would have been different, but how one could not say; as well ask from whom each word one spoke was first learned.

EIGHT

Satellites

1

BEN SAID: 'What's wrong with it this time?'

'I didn't say anything was wrong,' Bill Ditchling said. 'All I said was we shall have to wait and see.'

'Look, I've had my work in the paper every week for the last goodness knows how many years and now suddenly three times in five weeks there may not be enough space. What is this?'

'There are other considerations beside your feelings on this paper, Ben.'

'I would have thought SATELLITES was spot on, still – '

'Ben, you know the situation in Eastern Europe is one in which we can't afford to give any encouragement to disruptive elements – '

'All right – you give me the answer. What do you think about Poland and Hungary, Bill? What do you think the solution is?'

Ditchling said: 'What the Communist Parties are doing at the moment: de-Stalinization.'

'Then why won't you print SATELLITES? It's exactly about de-Stalinization. Equality within the Socialist camp. That's exactly what it's about.'

'We want you to concentrate on the Suez issue. I don't think we want to comment prematurely on what's happening in the People's Democracies. We all know that Britain and France are building up for an attack on Egypt, that's

517

where our comment ought to be centred. On the imperialists.'

'I was trying to contrast the imperialist and the Socialist methods of dealing with smaller states.'

'We want you to concentrate your attack on the imperialists alone,' Bill Ditchling said. 'There's no knowing where the present situation may lead to.'

2

Susan said: 'What do you think we ought to do then, Sir George?'

'I'll tell you what I think we ought to do, my dear. I think we ought to go in and take Master Nasser's pants down and give him a damned good thrashing.'

'Don't you think there'll be trouble with the Yanks if we do that, sir?' Angus inquired.

'We've been harried from pillar to post ever since '45. It's time we did something really decisive.'

'What about the Russians though, sir?'

'I should think they've got enough on their plate, haven't they? Trouble at home, what?'

'I thought that was popularly supposed to drive people to make trouble elsewhere,' Lady Gort observed.

'I think we're all getting much too serious,' Sir George said. 'Why should anyone in their right senses want to come to a delightful dance like this and then talk about politics? Come on, my dear, let's have another dance if you can stand the wear and tear!'

'You know very well you're a very good dancer, Sir George,' Susan said.

'In my youth it was one of those vital accomplishments like good manners which seem not to be taught any more these days. Dear me, I'm beginning to sound rather like Colonel Blimp, aren't I? Senility creeping in, I fear.'

'You've got a good way to go before senility, I should say, Sir George.'

'Ah, that's only through having such a pretty partner that I give that impression.'

'I'm glad I have such a rejuvenating effect.'

'Certainly,' her partner smiled. 'I haven't done a reverse spin for years.'

'You don't think there'll be a war then?' Susan said.

'Oh dear, oh dear, how you women do love to talk about the grim things of life! No, I don't think there'll be a war, not unless we dither about and let the Russians take over the Middle East without a fight. The only thing to do to a bully, my dear, and believe me I've had some experience of them, is to stand up to him. It's the one thing he doesn't expect and in this world it's the unexpected that pays dividends.'

3

Nat said: 'It's a pity that nationalization was ever thought of. Personally, I blame Attlee for the present situation as much as anyone. This notion that you can just pinch things and regard them as yours dates entirely from the time Labour came to power.'

Colin said: 'They did pay compensation.'

'They established a government's supposed right to grab anything they took a fancy to. I said it in '44: nationalization's nothing more nor less than pinching what doesn't belong to you and making it legal. And that's exactly what Nasser's done now.'

Colin said: 'I suppose the Communists put him up to it?'

'It's a completely foreign idea anyway,' Nat said. 'The whole idea of nationalization.'

Alma said: 'I do hate politics, don't you?'

'I do,' Tessa agreed.

'They just go round and round in circles and they never get anywhere. Why people can't just leave people alone, I can't understand.'

Colin said: 'It's a pretty return for saving them from the Germans.'

'You can't expect friend Nasser to show any gratitude for anything,' Nat said.

'It's not in the Gyppoes' nature in any case. I was out there in the war, you know, so I've had some experience of – um – Egyptian gratitude, fleas in the beds and all.'

'Obviously we've got to impose a solution on the Middle East sooner or later. If we don't do that it's just going to fester.'

'Yes,' Colin said. 'I'm inclined to agree with Ted Bradshaw – um – in what he said. If you can't bloody well look – um – after what's yours you haven't any bloody right to have it.'

'The usual Bradshaw bluntness,' Nat smiled with a quick glance at Tessa and Alma. 'But I can't quarrel with the sentiment. The fact is the time has come for drastic surgery and that's all there is to it.'

4

Sid Forbes said: 'Hullo, Ben! Come in.'

'Not got anyone in, have you?'

'No,' Sid said. 'Come in, make yourself at home. There's only me and the old woman sitting by the fireside.'

Ben said: 'Fine.'

'What's happened to your old woman?'

'At a dance,' Ben replied. 'At a *Ball*.'

'Fancy!'

'Very fancy, boy, Public Relations, at the Dorchester *nuch*!'

'Come in. Have a drop of Scotch?'

'A drop of Scotch would come in very useful. Wotcher, Ethel, how are you, girl?'

'I'm all right, Ben.'

'What's the well-dressed wife and mother doing with herself these days?'

'As a matter of fact, we're starting again,' Ethel Forbes said.

'Starting again? Starting what again?'

'She's gone and got herself pregnant again,' Sid said with a salty smile. 'Don't ask me how.'

'*Mazeltov*,' Ben said.

'Here y'are, Ben.'

'Ta, well, *lechayim*; when did all this happen?'

'About four months ago it would appear,' Ethel replied.

'Well, how's yourself, Ben? What's new?'

'I've just come from the paper. Merry old mess up there.'

Sid said: 'They don't seem to have the boys any more.'

Ben said: 'You can't get anything out of them, you know?'

'Bloody Khrushchev,' Sid Forbes said.

Ethel said: '*Sid –* '

'He's all right.'

'Sid or Khrush?'

'They're both all right. Let many flowers contend.'

'I wouldn't give much for my old man's chances at the Chelsea show.'

'Bloody Khrushchev.'

'What's he done to you, boy?'

'Bloody big talk,' Sid Forbes said. 'Always blowing his mouth off.'

Ethel said: 'He's been overworking. It always makes him like this.'

'You know what he's done to the Party, Ben? He's turned it into a blasted *discussion* group.'

'He's pickled,' Ethel said. 'You don't want to pay him no mind.'

Ben said: 'I wouldn't put it as bad as that.'

Sid said: 'I've had my lot, Ben. I'm turning it in.'

'He's only talking.'

'Leaving the Party, Sid? Why, tell me?'

'Because you're leaving too, aren't you, Ben?'

'What's the matter, can't do anything on your own account, is that it?'

Sid said: 'You didn't ever belong in the Party, Benjamino.'

'I don't like that name, *Sidney*.'

'You know what Khrushchev's going to do to you lot? He's going to kick you into the sea.'

'What lot?'

'Israel, the Yids – the whole of them – splash, into the sea. My advice to you, Ben, is get out while you can still walk.'

'He's been on the bottle all evening, don't pay any attention to him.'

'You're scuttling and everyone has to scuttle with you, that's your trouble, Sid.' Ben knocked back his whisky. 'I don't want to take your confession.'

'The Yids are finished with the Party,' Sid said.

'Then they've lost the last bloody chance they'll ever have.'

'Do you know what the *leader* thought of the Jews? Do you? Finito, Benjamino.'

Ben said: 'You'll be sorry in the morning.'

Ethel said: 'It's Independent Television; it drives them all off their heads eventually.'

Sid said: 'He's knocked the stuffing out of the old guard, that bastard, that's what he's done. You've seen 'em. Don't know where the hell they stand. Taken a hell of a pasting for years and years and now they don't get any support even from their own bloody corner. It's the biggest stab in the back since Trotsky, Ben, that's what it is. It's the end of the movement we knew.'

Ben said: 'I don't think so at all. We're seeing what we've all expected for years – increased freedom within the Socialist camp and increased repression in the capitalist.'

'Well, that bugger Khrushchev's made a right mess of everything, if you ask me.'

'Then we shan't ask you, comrade,' Ben said. '*Lechayim!*'

'Ben, get out while the going's good, that's my advice to you. The game's over, boy, and we're too old to start again.'

'That's not the story I've heard.'

'It's not going to happen in our lifetime, Ben.'

Ben said: 'What is all this, Sid, you trying me out or something?'

'You've rumbled it, Ben. It's all a cunning plot we cooked up in King Street to see how trustworthy old Simons is. I'm too busy, Ben, that's the truth of it; I'm too busy. I'm getting a transfer before it's too late. You won't be needing me anyway when the time comes. I shall have been superannuated.'

'How long has all this been going on here?'

'We've started again,' Sid said. 'It's a free country, isn't it? Is it or is it not a free country?'

'It's a free country,' Ben smiled.

5

Julia said: 'Hullo.'

'Julia, my dear, what a lovely surprise.'

'We thought we'd pop up,' Paul said. 'On the spur of the moment while moments still have spurs.'

'Come in,' Alma said, taking Julia's hand. 'Your brother and his wife are here. They came in for coffee.'

'I've done something absolutely crazy,' Paul said.

'What?' Alma led them into the sitting-room. 'Look who's here! Isn't it a lovely surprise?'

'Look out of the window,' Paul said.

Colin said: 'I say, what's all this about? Hullo, Prunella.'

'Well, what?' Alma asked.

Nat and Alma were at the window.

'That,' Paul pointed out. A Morris Minor was parked by the kerb.

'You haven't bought a car!'

Paul said: 'Well, I thought with Julia in her present condition –

'Her present – '

'Oh, Julia, no!' Alma threw her arms round Julia and kissed her. 'I could squeeze you.'

'That's a good imitation,' Paul said.

Colin was very red. He shook Paul's hand. '*Mazeltov!*'

'And a new car as well,' Nat said. 'Things must be improving in the literary world.'

'Underworld. This chap I've been working with, Hubert Young, he's going back to the States soon so he let me have his car, *not* at a bargain price incidentally.'

'Well, this is lovely,' Alma said. 'Would you like some coffee?'

'No, nothing, honestly,' Julia said. 'We just thought we'd pop up and show off our new possessions.'

'Bless your hearts!'

'After all,' Paul said, 'we shall probably all be dead within a month, so we may as well enjoy it while we can.'

Nat said: 'Don't tell me the British are wrong again.'

'Not quite,' Paul replied, 'but it looks as though they will be any moment.'

'Now don't let's spoil the evening with politics,' Alma said. 'If you men are going to talk politics, I suggest the girls go in the other room.'

Colin said: 'You don't really think we ought to let Nasser pinch the canal, do you?'

'I don't think we should start talking about killing people

and force being the ultimate persuasion and all that bogus moralizing.'

'Just let him have the canal, what?'

'I don't see what it matters.'

'I don't suppose you would.' Nat went on. 'But then you find it hard to excuse anyone for being successful.'

'Just who has been successful, Dad?'

'The canal was built because of the hard work of the French and the British and I don't see why they shouldn't be entitled to the fruits of that hard work.'

'Hard cash, you mean.'

'I suppose you'd prefer the Russians to take over the Middle East?'

'I don't see that we have any God-given rights there.'

'It hardly comes very well from us to be disloyal at a time like this.'

'I think it comes well from anyone to be disloyal when something fatuous and wrong is being done.'

'The basic assumption of all your arguments seems to be that Britain is always wrong.'

'Whereas you are renowned for the flexibility of your attitude, what?'

Nat said: 'I don't propose to be spoken to in that manner.'

Colin said: 'Um – what do you think the prospects are in South Africa?'

'There'll be a bloody massacre,' Paul said. 'Or Fascism.'

'I was referring to the Test matches,' Colin said.

'When's the big day?' Alma demanded.

'Seventeenth of April, near as I can tell.'

'Oh, I'm just so excited. I think it's wonderful.'

'You look much too young to be a grandmother!'

'That's exactly why it'll be so marvellous to be one, isn't it?' Paul called out.

'I suppose,' Tessa said, 'you'll be looking for a bigger place now, won't you?'

Julia said: 'Not for a bit. I think we shall manage perfectly well.'

'We'll have to,' Paul said.

'Not very healthy for a new-born baby, I should have thought.'

'Oh, the sooner it gets used to dungeon life the better,' Paul said. 'After all, it'll probably go to jail sooner or later for un-British crying.'

Colin said: 'Um – when's the book coming out, Paul?'

'First of November,' Paul replied. 'Only a week.'

'Well, I hope it's a great success, lots of reviews and all that sort of thing.'

'I only hope we're alive to see them.'

'Oh dear, we are a grim Jim tonight,' Julia said.

'As long as we stand firm,' Nat said, 'you'll be alive to see them all right. I've always told you: if people try to muck you about the best thing you can do is to give them a bloody nose. It's amazing how effective the old remedies remain.'

'There are other ways of changing people.'

'But none so well-proved, believe me.'

'I'm sorry, but I don't see why people should be killed, just because Eden doesn't like Nasser's face.'

'It'd be a pretty rare man who did like Nasser's face, I should imagine.'

'It's never you or me who's killed,' Paul said, 'it's some wretched Egyptian taking his dog for a walk and two paratroopers who drown in a sewage farm; you never think of that, do you?'

'I know what war's like,' Nat said.

'Then why are you so bloodthirsty about it?'

'I've had a number of things said about me in my lifetime, but that's the first time I've ever been accused of being bloodthirsty.'

'It's the *effect* of what you're advocating. You don't mean it to be, but it is, just as the effect of Eliot's verse was to

526

make people indifferent to millions of people being murdered.'

'The world is a much bigger place than you think. It can't be run according to the principles of Paul Riesman, however pleasant that might make it.'

Paul said: 'If Eden beats up Egypt it will be the final betrayal of everything people thought they were fighting for during the war.'

'I think I'm entitled to – um – have a say in that,' Colin said, 'and I don't agree with it at all. If the Egyptians' way of showing us gratitude for saving them from the Germans is – um – to pinch what's ours, I think they ought to be taught a lesson.'

Alma said: 'I do agree. Who was it who said "My patience is exhausted"? because I do think he was so right!'

'It was Hitler,' Paul said.

6

Angus said: 'Enjoying it?'

'Oh, it's a wonderful dance, I'm having a lovely time.'

Angus whispered: 'I love you, Susan.' Susan pushed away from him, looking very stern, and then burst out laughing and came close again. 'Come back to the office afterwards. I've got a bottle of champagne.'

'I've got to go back anyway, to change.'

'I know.'

She squeezed his hand. 'Oh, Angus, Angus.'

'I say, I think old Mac's quite smitten with you tonight.'

'No, he knows I'm your girl, doesn't he?'

'I hope not,' Angus replied. 'He's a funny chap, old Mac, I wouldn't like him to have too clear an idea of what's going on.'

Susan said: 'Perhaps we shouldn't go back to the office.'

'Be all right. I've told him about that. Long as you tell people things they never believe them.'

'That doesn't sound the right attitude for a PR man.'

'You always want to tell as much of the truth as you possibly can – people get bored before they get suspicious.'

'You seem to have eet all worked out.'

'I 'ave got eet all worked out.'

It was lovely rustling through the empty office. Angus looked more handsome than ever, Susan thought, the beard beginning to roughen his chin, his hair tousled from the car ride.

'I think it was very successful, don't you?'

'Rather,' Angus agreed. 'You were the absolute belle of the ball, as they say. Gee-gee was happy as ye sandboy.'

'He's a character; I only hope he's right about there not being a war. It's just the sort of thing that would happen just when one's nice and settled in a job and everything.'

Angus released the cork of the champagne bottle. 'Glass, quick.'

'Angus, be *careful* – '

'Everything under control. There we are. Cheers.'

'*Lechayim.*'

'*What?*'

'Good health,' Susan said.

'Cheers.'

'Mm – gorgeous! Let's stay here all night.'

'Nothing I'd like better.'

'Oh, I adore dances! I'd like to go dancing every night, and theatres and restaurants!'

'You'd get awfully spoiled.'

'A girl likes to be spoiled.'

'A girl as pretty as you deserves to be.'

'Oh, Angus, Angus. I don't ever want to see anyone else again.'

'Careful, you'll turn my head.'

'That's what girls are for, to turn men's heads.'

528

'Well you've certainly turned this one's.'

Susan put her champagne glass on the floor. 'Kiss me?'

'Like that?'

'And again.'

'I love you, Susan.'

'I wish we were on a wonderful cruise in the South Seas somewhere, don't you?'

'"When you begin the beguine . . ."'

'"It brings back a night – "'

'"Of tropical splendour,"' they both laughed and kissed again.

Susan said: 'I think I'd better get changed. If we're not careful we shall be caught here by the cleaners – '

'I'll go in the other room,' Angus said.

'You needn't.'

'Susan . . .'

'I'd like it,' she said. 'I'm not all that bad to look at.'

'That isn't my worry.'

'I want you to,' she said seriously.

'Susan, Susan, you're much too beautiful. It shouldn't be allowed.'

'I want you to know me,' she said. 'I want you to.'

'I love you,' he said.

'Kiss me. Now, like this.'

'I love you. I shall never forget you.'

'I won't ever forget you either.'

'I wish I didn't believe in anything. When I'm with you, I feel as if you're the only real thing in the world.'

'I like it when you talk like this. I like it more than anything in the world. I want you, Angus, you know that, don't you? But honestly, to hear you talk – in a way it's more satisfying – '

'Thanks very much,' he smiled.

'It's not a question of sex with you,' she said. 'You've given me what I need, I don't need anything else.'

'I shall never forget you,' he said. 'I shall never forget this evening.'

'Better take me home,' Susan sighed. 'Pity poor Cinders on a night like this!'

7

Ben poured the contents of the bottle out into his tumbler. Above all one must never be surprised; to be surprised was to be the servant of events. Everything was expected: Sid had packed it in. Just like that, he had given in. He had chosen the wrong kind of freedom. The new freedom given to Eastern Europe, to Poland and now to Hungary, had swept him into indifference, into feeling that the Party did not need him any more, that the sacrifices of the last years, the social isolation, the bitter, small-cast politics within the Party itself, were all unnecessary, since the Party's confidence in its rightness had all the time been misplaced or so that bastard Khrushchev said. Now who was talking? This was Sid's point of view. There was no need to feel isolated oneself. Sid wasn't the Party; the Party was still there, the *Worker* was still there, the Soviet Union was still there. The isolation was Sid's, the feeling of pointlessness was Sid's. What remained for oneself? That one was a Jew. It was the only thing really embedded and inexorable, that one was a Jew. Now who was this talking? Only Ben, only Ben, tipping the bottle into the tumbler. The thoughts of a drunk man were thoughts which had no value. The Russian brilliance was nowhere more clearly shown than in this, that they ignored what a man had said when he was drunk. The drunkard drivelled, about man, about life, about love. The drunk man threw himself from the window because his wife danced with another man; he was pitiful, but he was wrong; even though he felt deeply, he was wrong. Just as the Jew was wrong. Now who was talking?

Jewishness was a kind of drunkenness. Jews weren't much for the bottle. Unlike Sid, who had to sit at home with a bottle now he had scuttled. Ben was sitting with a bottle because it was three in the morning and his wife was not yet home. Ben's world was dissolving because every new freedom gave him pain where he had denied pain to be possible. They wanted their freedom, let them have their freedom; let them destroy everything that had been built up for them. At the crisis, one thought: what the hell? One thought, let them go their way. Bloody Hungarians. If dining and dancing means so much to you, dine and dance. I've given my life to make something greater than dining and dancing but if that's what you want, have it: 'Go on, get out, get out, if that's all you care, get out. I don't care, call yourself what you want, do what you want, be what you want, if you can. Go on, get out.'

Susan said: 'Ben!'

'Go on, get out,' Ben said.

'Darling, what are you doing up?'

'Go on, get out, darling, go on, get out.'

'Steady, old boy. Are you sloshed?'

'You don't like us, you've never liked us, so go on, get out.'

'Do you know what time it is?'

'Time to get out,' Ben said.

'You'd better get upstairs to bed, my boy. The children'll be down in a minute!'

'To hell with the Party,' Ben said. 'Let's all be happy. Above all, we must be happy. Is everybody happy?'

Susan said: 'Bed for you, my boy.'

'Get out,' Ben said. 'Go on if you want to, get out.'

Susan said: 'I must see you at lunch-time.'

Angus said: 'Well, it's a bit difficult.'

'I must,' Susan said.

'I'm supposed to be lunching with Mac. It's about this anti-nationalization release.'

'What about after work?'

'I don't want to be late home again. Joyce was a bit upsetipoo last night.'

'I must see you.'

''Ullo, 'ullo, 'ullo, what's going on here?' It was Mac.

'Susan's got a bit confused about dates,' Angus said. 'And she's gone and arranged for us to lunch with this shipping man.'

'Oh, we can talk about Gee-gee this afternoon, old son. You go and live it up with your shipping magnate.'

'I'm terribly sorry,' Susan said.

'Anything for a lady, eh, Angus?'

Angus had brought his car to the office and suggested that they drive out of the West End for their '*Tête-à-tête*, as they say'. If Mac spotted them eating alone together it would be a bit awkward for all parties concerned.

They drove around uncertainly. 'It's funny the way once you start worrying about being seen there doesn't seem to be anywhere you dare to go. The old guilty conscience, I suppose.'

Finally they went to a Greek restaurant in Streatham High Street.

Susan said: 'I'm sorry I was a bit hysterical about seeing you.'

'That's all right. Don't give it another!'

'I'm afraid I'm in a bit of a mess.'

'You are? In what way?'

'Ben's chucked me out.'

'Oh. What happened exactly?'

'He was drunk.'

'Well – um – why don't you go back? He'll probably have forgotten all about it.'

'No, I can't until he asks me to.'

'In that case – I – I don't quite see what I can do.'

'Do you want me or not?' Susan said. 'Because I'm – free.'

'Susan, I've explained – I'm a Catholic, I've got a wife and children – '

'Can't you stop being a Catholic? Why do you have to be one if you don't want to?'

'One can't live simply in accordance with what one wants – '

'Why not? There's nothing to stop us.'

'I can't, Susan.'

'I suppose that's why it always has to be married women, is it?'

'Always – '

'You 'eard,' Susan said.

'I thought you understood – '

'I do understand. I just wonder if Ben will. He can be very vindictive and we were in the office together under rather peeculiar circs, weren't we?'

'Are you trying to blackmail me, Susan?'

'I'm just trying to think what's going to happen.'

'But dammit, we haven't done anything,' Angus said.

'Judges have filthy minds.'

'What are you after?'

'I'm not going to be left in a ditch, not by anyone.'

'You said yourself he was drunk; if you ask me, he'll have you back like a shot. I expect he's forgotten the whole thing by now.'

'I haven't,' Susan said.

'But surely, I mean – *you* haven't got any right to be angry with him.'

'When we haven't done anything?'

'Legally. Legally we haven't done anything wrong. Susan, I know you think I'm behaving like ye olde cad but I promise you it isn't really like that; I do love you, I do really, and I always shall.'

9

'If you can stand it, I can,' Paul said.

'She sounded so miserable, poor old Susie, and there's nowhere else she can go.'

'Fine,' Paul said. 'She'll make a nice change when you're too fat for use.'

'No!'

'We shall see, my pretty maid.'

'I bet you would too.'

'You bet your life I would too.'

10

Mac said: 'Come inside, Angus, me boy, and tell me all about it.'

Angus said: 'All about what?'

'Ye shipping maggers.'

'There wasn't one,' Angus said, shutting the door.

'Wasn't there though? Have I found you out on amorous dalliance bent?'

'Of course not.'

'Only jesting.'

'Susan's very attractive though, isn't she?'

'Highly curvy,' Mac said.

'What would you say if I told you I thought we ought to get rid of her?'

'Ask why.'

'Would it surprise you if I told you she was a Communist?'

Mac said: 'Frankly, yes.'

'Well, she is.'

'And?'

'Just think what Gee-gee would think if he found out.'

'Why should he find out?'

'I found out,' Angus said. 'Look, the last thing I want to do is get rid of Susan. I like her enormously. But let's face it. Anyone'd give quite a lot to have Gee-gee's account, and all they have to do is drop the old hintipoo that we're red-ridden or something – you know what these boys'll do to get their hooks on someone like Gee-gee – and Robert's your male relation!'

'It's going to be a bit awkward though, isn't it? Giving her the old surgical boot.'

Angus said: 'Let me have a chat to her.'

'Do that small thing, old son. I hadn't thought about old Gee-gee, I must say. That could be damned messy. The old smear technique, jolly difficult to get round.'

'Particularly when there's fire as well as smoke, as they say.'

'Right-ho, Angus, me boy, the girl must go. Sad, but there it is. And now let us turn our tiny minds from curves to media, shall we?'

Angus said: 'Couldn't be happier.'

NINE

A Sunday in November

1

THE *Sunday Times* news summary said: 'For the fourth day yesterday French and British bombers of Middle East Command bombed air bases and military targets in Egypt. There is little news this morning from Hungary where it was reported yesterday that Russian troops were withdrawing from the country. Some unconfirmed reports this morning talk of gunfire in Budapest, but there is no confirmation of this from official sources. The Israel High Command announces that Israeli forces have halted their advance in the Sinai peninsula ten miles short of the Suez Canal.'

The *Sunday Times* 'Crime Bag' said: 'MORNINGS AT EIGHT by Paul Riesman: An amusing romp among double, treble and quadruple agents in the Espionage market. Mr Riesman has an ear for dialogue, marred at times by facetiousness. Plenty of excitement and laughs though. Mark: Beta plus plus.'

Paul said: 'It just would have to happen like this, wouldn't it? Today's the big day. Paul Riesman's comedy hit – three lines in *The Times* and nothing in the *Snobserver* at all. I wish to God Winter'd postponed it for a couple of weeks – '

'You should be jolly glad to be in anything.'

Susan said: 'Good morning, what's the news?'

'He's got a jolly nice notice in the *ST* and he's bleating.'

Susan said: 'What about Suez and things?'

'Mad,' Paul said. 'They've all gone absolutely mad. Apparently there's a rally this afternoon in Trafalgar Square.'

'We going?' Susan asked.

'I don't think I'd better,' Julia said, 'not if there's going to be crowds.'

'I'm going,' Paul said, 'no matter what anyone else is doing. There's a brave dragoon, eh?'

Julia said: 'I'd like to go.'

'No, not in the crowds.'

'I honestly don't think it'd be a very good idea, considering all things.'

Susan said: 'I'll come with you.'

'Right. Two-thirty it starts.'

The phone rang.

Paul said: ''lo?'

'Congratulations,' Nat said.

'What on?'

'Haven't you seen the *Sunday Times*?'

'Oh, that. Pretty half-hearted.'

'Very good for the libraries,' Nat said. 'I was talking to a chap at the hospital about it the other day – '

'He writes detective stories,' Paul said. 'I remember.'

'I see your friend Bevan is speaking this afternoon.'

'Yes, you coming?'

'He usually manages to choose a good time to put his oar in, I must say.'

'The time for dissension is past, what?'

'The country is at war,' Nat said.

'I shouldn't say we're at war if I were you, Dad; you'll find yourself arrested for sedition.'

Nat said: 'Well, congratulations about the book, anyway.'

'Thanks,' Paul said. 'It's nice to have something unimportant to talk about, isn't it?'

'You shouldn't be so tough on him,' Julia said.

'Oh, I wish I'd never written the book. I wish it hadn't

537

come out now anyway. It's so – I don't know – humiliating. To have a book come out at this sort of time and have it be about nothing. I've mucked it all up. Just think, if one had brought out the right sort of book – '

'What sort of book is the right sort of book?' Susan asked.

'The sort of book that makes one entitled to speak. Christ, just imagine English writers leading a revolution! The Society of Authors forming two and a halves, Blooms-bury armed to the tits, and the Pen Club building barri-cades in the King's Road, with a cry of "the Adephi, Edward Garnett and Saint Connolly!" Three cheers for *la vie littéraire*! And I'm in it, oh, I'm busting to be in it. I can't wait to be bloody in it. And it's a living disgrace. At a time like this it's a living disgrace.'

2

'Well,' Colin said, 'they've certainly given the Gyppoes a caning. Our chaps, I mean – um – the Israelis.'

'I've very glad we decided not to go out there just the same,' Tessa said.

Colin said: 'Well, they had it coming to them, didn't they? The Gyppoes. They've been provoking us for years.'

'Us!'

'Our chaps. It makes one feel one ought to have been out there, helping them.' The last time Colin was in action he sent two men to climb the shallow slope on the far side of a *wadi* to keep watch while he and the rest of the party unloaded their equipment from their truck. The two men went up and were shot. Colin had never been able to persuade himself that he shouldn't have gone up himself. He followed up vigorously with the rest of his section and engaged the German patrol; neither his nerve nor the correctness of his orders had ever been questioned. Two men were dead (the Germans left one dead and one wounded) and Colin was mentioned in dispatches. No one but he himself could have accused him of anything and if it hadn't been his last time in action he would probably have forgotten the incident, but as it was it stuck with him – the moment of hesitation when he had said 'Anderson and Mellors, go up to the top of that rise and see what you can see' instead of telling the sergeant to supervise unloading and going up himself. 'Yes,' he said, 'I wouldn't have minded going in with Dayan and his chaps.'

'You're getting on a bit for playing soldiers,' Tessa said. 'Old greysides!'

'Here, I say, steady on!'

Anne said: 'Daddy, what're we going to do today?'

Tessa said: 'We could go for a walk on the heath.'

'And all go down to the golf club for tea afterwards,' Colin suggested.

Jimmy said: 'Daddy, football.' Colin had bought James a blow football set for Christmas but had been unable to resist giving it to him earlier. 'We'll have a game in a little while. I want to look at the paper. Play with Anne till I'm ready.'

Anne said: 'I don't want to play with *him*.'

Jimmy said: 'And I wouldn't play with you for all the tea in China.'

Tessa said: 'Colin!'

Colin put the paper aside. 'All right, I'm coming. The world will have to wait. The Adler family has decided to play blow football.'

3

The afternoon was heavy as pewter. The great crowd in Trafalgar Square was wedded by the murkiness of the day. The crowd was quiet as it listened to the speeches. The figures on the rostrum (Francis Winter was there, with his

539

white hair brushed brilliantly back) alone moved with urgency, drawing now and then a cry of approval or a volley of applause from the audience. Paul and Susan walked from the park where Paul had left the car.

'It's like the end of the world,' Paul said.

All individuality seemed lost in the melancholy of the afternoon. A man slipped between the ranks of the people in the square, murmuring as he went, 'No War Over Hungary – excuse me – No War Over Hungary – excuse me – No War Over Hungary.' Paul and Susan edged past a group of young men in blue turtle-necked sweaters singing 'Rule, Britannia'. One of them was Stewart, Paul's old head-monitor. Podge was standing watching, not one of the group. Paul's mouth was filled with acid. He clenched his fists. Podge's moony face, with the same spectacles hooding the same chilly, sardonic blue eyes, was there for the smashing. Violence surged in Paul. One would walk up to Podge, smash his face in and then walk away through the crowd. The face was cream cheese in colour and then, with the smash of a fist, it would be red, red and black with blood. Paul clenched his fists and edged towards Podge. Susan hesitated and then went on into the crowd. 'With you in a minute,' Paul said. Podge's face was luminous with irony as he watched Stewart. To kill Podge! What a trivial incident in a day like this, when doom was coming, when death might come at any moment, when rockets might fly at any second, when oblivion was almost imminent, what a temptation to make a killing before one died. The world might end at any moment. Podge was eating a Crunchie bar, watching Stewart in his blue knitted muscles. Podge could be cracked open like a cockroach and spread white guts on the pavement and one could be away into the crowd. Podge bit a piece off his Crunchie bar. Paul was one away from him now.

A red beard jutted flame above the crowd. The large, red-furred hands held a banner above its head with the slogan: HANDS OFF THE MANCHESTER SHIP CANAL – HEADS OFF THE CABINET. 'Match-card,' Stan Halloran was calling, 'card of the match. Official programme, teams and places. Get your official programme here. The referee will blow up at five o'clock precisely. Card of the match.'

'Halloran, you great *lobbus*.'

'Benjamino! What brings you here today and gone tomorrow? Here, hold this, do you mind?' Stan handed his banner to a smiling man in the crowd. 'Thank God I've got rid of that bastard' – he winked at Ben. 'This chap Trotsky just handed it to me and went off without so much as by your leave.' Stan waved and smiled at the man with the banner. 'Come on, Ben, before the bugger realizes what a crap-heap he looks.'

'Quite like old times,' Ben commented with a pressed smile. 'Second Front now.'

'Happy days, Benjamino, happy days eaten slowly.'

'How's the show going?'

'Recognize the old catch-phrase there, do you?'

'Oh, yes,' Ben said. 'Dead up to date the boy is.'

'The world has taken me to its heart,' Stan Halloran said. 'And the stench is appalling.'

Ben said: 'Aha.'

'You seem to be in a sorry state this happy day, Benjamino. What's up? I always thought the Party thrived on misfortune.'

'What makes you so sure I'm still in the Party?'

'Benjamino, don't tell me you've quit the Party to end all Parties?'

'Let's say I've got other things on my mind.' Ben looked away. 'Susan's left me.'

'Susie? Left you? Christ, man, when?'

'Week now.'

'Poor old Benjamino. Jasus, I'm sorry to hear that, I am really. Why?'

'Some bloke.'

'Susie gone off with someone?'

Ben shrugged. 'No, just gone. You know what women are like.'

'It won't last, Benjamino,' Stan said. 'It won't last. She'll be back in no time, you'll see.'

'I don't know. I've – I don't know.'

'This is a right mess-up then,' Stan said, nodding at the crowd below the parapet.

'It could have been us,' Ben said. 'Eh, Stan? With old Halloran on the platform?'

'Comrades and friends, I take pleasure in announcing the People's Republic of Great Britain, President B. Simons, Esq., President.'

Ben said: 'We backed the wrong lot, boy.'

Stan put his arm through Ben's. 'Have the police been on to you at all, Benjamino?'

'Police? What about?'

'Apparently a certain Mr Fletcher has turned turtle.'

'Fletcher?'

'Our American comrade, Benjamino, don't tell me you've forgotten.'

Ben said: 'Oh yes. Aha. What's he done?'

'Turned turtle, gone bolshie, scapaed – I went over the wall for the NKVD – I'm surprised they haven't been on to you. They've been pestering the ballocks off me, I'll tell you.'

'Well,' Ben said, 'you're a suspicious character after all.'

'So you've left the Party, Benjamino?'

'Not officially.'

542

'I noticed you haven't been in the paper so much recently.'

'Still see the *Worker*, do you?'

'Where do you think I get me gags from, boy?'

'I'm a simple bloke, Stan, I never realized your programme was supposed to be funny.'

'Sharp. The bhoy's still sharp as a wet stone. Well, what else is new in people's circles?'

'We are waiting,' Ben said, 'to see how the situation develops.'

'Well, one thing's quite certain: your boys have done bloody well, eh, Ben?'

'My boys?'

'Israel. Gelded the Philistine again from all accounts.'

'They've been led up the garden, Stan, you know that as well as I do.'

'The Egyptians have been provoking them for years and they've given 'em a bash, I can't see the harm in that. If they go on taking the piss long enough they get a bucketful over their heads, I can't see the harm in it.'

Ben said: 'It's fighting the wrong battle.'

'Still, they're fightin' it damned well.'

'And they'll get pushed into the sea for their trouble.'

'You're being a traitor to your own people, Ben, talking like that.'

'They've got to be on the right side,' Ben said. 'There's no point in them being there if they aren't on the right side.'

'Ben, you missed your vocation; you should have been a Rabbi, lad.'

'And what about you, Stan?'

'League of Empire Loyalists, me boy. Join the lads in blue, blue and blue. All Irishmen are dyed in the potato imperialists really, you know that. Take the British Empah away from an Irishman and you've taken the wicket away from a fast bowler, if I may draw a stump from the old national game there.'

5

Paul was behind Podge. Stewart was still singing 'Rule, Britannia'. Podge twitched and half turned round as Paul hit him on the shoulder: 'Hullo, Reecers! What you doing here?'

'Same as you,' Paul said. 'Observing.'

'What do you think about it all?'

'Suez? I think it's absurd,' Paul said softly, aware of the blue knitted muscles around him. 'They can't hope to do any good.'

Stewart said: ''ush – simmer. "Land of Hope and Glory", everyone. Ready? "Land of – "'

'The man's serious,' Paul said. 'He'd really spill his guts for it, wouldn't he?'

'Wouldn't you?' Podge inquired.

'If I had to die,' Paul said, 'I'd like to die for you. In fact, old Podger, if things get any more out of control, I'll take care of you before I go myself.'

'To what do I owe the honour?'

'Didn't you know, Podge? The Jewish Old Benedictines have opened a special fund for you, boy. I'll make sure you get it some day, don't worry. It will take a concrete form – bricks.'

'I see you've had a novel published,' Podge said.

'How did you know that?'

'I read a review.'

'Did you? Where?'

'Oh, I don't know. Somewhere. I must get a copy. Is it good?'

'You get one,' Paul said. 'You'd like it.'

'I'll have to get you to autograph it.'

'No extra charge,' Paul said.

Podge said: 'No?'

Paul said: 'Well – um – cheerio. I must go and look for my woman. Don't forget about the book.'

Paul released the smile from his face, the reflection of Podge, and went into the crowd. This was the end of the world, dulled faces staring up at gesticulating monkeys on the platform, this was the end of the world, it might come at any moment, in the stab of a rocket, everyone knew that, and yet while the great P. Riesman solicited sales for his railway journey fiction, people could think of nothing better than this, to beg for peace, to implore for nothing to happen, and so long as they survived, they would go home again and never come out in such numbers and in such a way again until the next ghastliness loomed, then they would come again and beg for nothing to happen, thinking that they were contributing to peace, to life, to their children, to whatever fetish controlled their emissions into public life. Yet at the times when power was in their grasp they were indifferent. Only now, when whatever might happen would happen beyond them, in the cabinet room, in the Kremlin or wherever, only then did they dare to raise their voices, when they were sure they would not be lumbered with the responsibility of owning what they so loudly demanded. On one's death-bed one begged for life, in life desired nothing more vital than painless death. The people were betrayed into death by Paul Riesman and by every other writer whose books were published into the wilderness of life and who asked nothing more in the way of response than a few bob royalty. The British writer wanted nothing so well as to be *paid*, but unless one expressed something immediate to life, surely it would be better to pack up and get a proper job. The writer could break the dead isolation of every man, but only if books would become manuals of life, only if he could replace the old love-mush with a new and truer and wider community.

By reading people should become not cleverer, not smarter but readier for action, more capable of life. As for the writer, in him the life and the writing should be one, not by making writing his life but by living and writing as one person. If one believed in and was oneself in what one wrote, one stayed with people, one explained, one fought to gain not money but understanding, to create not one's own success but life. Such a writer would not be asked to entertain, for he would not be a docile comedian to amuse people when they came home from work, a man who played as long as the cash rolled in, but a man who pointed the way to life. The author must be there, even if laughed at and unwanted, to explain, to educate one by one as well as in books, explain not what to do, not how to obey, but how to stand up in life. Paul was prepared to admit that he had no place in the promised land, admit Jewishness as a special case somewhat overdone, but he would proclaim himself dedicated to seriousness, to making a fool of himself perhaps but only by overstating what had to be stated, that the state of man could be changed, had to be changed, not for what the writer was going to get out of it, but so that the writer should get nothing, so that the right thing might be said by everyone and the writer fall away and be needed no longer. Expression was a common gift of man; the writer was a freak, a man with an enlarged head whose function was, perhaps, to make other men realize that they had heads too. Paul nudged through the crowd with a growing awareness of his own age, that he was old, that he might never come to community with others, that it was going to be enough if time should last, to explain to people that they should begin to live, not only when their lives were threatened, as now, but at every moment, so that they might, on such occasions as these, cease to demand life and act alive. To demand life is to be dead. Paul did not know if he could ever act, whether his Jewish mania could ever leave him straight for life, but he knew this: two and two were still four, though shouted in the last torments of delirium. He knew the writer he should be. The illusion of being able to unite with timeless English Literature was frigid and immoral, like the effort to be only oneself, folding mirrors about oneself. There remained to find the true use of the voice, which was to speak oneself to others, to be an allegory for them.

6

Susan was alone in the crowd. She had lost Paul, had had no hold on him and almost welcomed losing him, and yet now she was alone and frightened that she had lost him. She was sorry for herself. She had done nothing wrong. She had done nothing wrong and Ben had cut her off. Now no one else would help her. What was the use of getting free if no one else wanted her? The outside world had promised so much and now, at the crux, it did not want her.

The news went through the crowd. In Hungary the Soviet troops had attacked. The news sifted through the crowd like blood darkening a flood. The crowd was breaking up, its unity of fear destroyed as the news came clearly through them that the guns were firing in Budapest. The integrity of the crowd was challenged, motives analysed; the crowd was cracked by the news.

The news came through in flashes, in backfires of excitement and shock, that the Russians were killing Hungary. The news came through among the crowd, glancing from head to head like Pentecostal fire, till the whole crowd crackled with news, except where at the head of the column (the statemen having departed for tea) men in mackintoshes were fighting with the police, horses' hooves sparking on the roadway of Whitehall. Other voices, other faces were in the crowd now, so that 'Eden Must Go' was a distant call. These were men ready to die, Europeans who knew death, matching Britons who wanted to be free of it. They beat through the crowd looking for action, fighting like madmen when Bryan Stewart said 'Who gives a damn about Hungary?' Saul Marowitz threw himself on Stewart, a man half as tall again as he, and grappled him to the ground, where Stewart began to bash his head against the road. 'Bloody foreigners!' Paul said: 'Get off, get off, you big slob, Stewart, go on, get off him.' Stewart said: 'Bloody Riesman! How are you?' 'Not so bad.' 'Bloody man wanted us to fight to save Hungary.' 'Maybe he was a Hungarian.' 'Well he ought to stay in Hungary then'. 'I'm not a bloody Hungarian,' Saul Marowitz breathed heavily. 'I'm a man.' 'Well you want to grow a bit, son.' Stewart winked at Paul who smiled and went off into the crowd again.

'What's happened?' Stan Halloran demanded. 'What's that?'

'The Russians have gone back into Budapest. The city's in flames.'

Ben said: 'What's happened?'

'The Red Army's gone back into Budapest. They're putting down the revolution.'

Stan said: 'The bastards. The filthy bastards.'

Ben said: 'They've gone back in.'

'That's it,' Stan said. 'That's it. Bejasus, Ben, you didn't get out a moment too soon.'

'I haven't got out,' Ben said. He moved forward, boisterously, forward into the crowd, to look for Susan. He didn't care what one called it now, intuition of love, anything, what mattered was that he wanted her back, no matter what she wanted, he would take her back. She was waiting for him, she had no real choice but to wait for him and now he would take her, no matter what his professions about marriage, she was his woman and he would have her. People could think what they liked. From now on he would

548

keep her. He would take her and he would have her. To hell with it, to hell with what people thought, to hell with the lumber of explanations and reasons. Stan Halloran's voice bawled over the crowd: 'Killer, you're a killer, you're a killer. Stop that man; he's a killer.' Ben turned and waved and winked to a man beside him and fought on to look for Susan. He could take her back again with a certain pretence gone, but back more firmly for that. He saw Susan now and she needed him. She saw him and she called out. People frowned or nodded but they paid no attention, not really being concerned. Ben's face was set. Susan half-smiled, half-cried, afraid perhaps. Ben gave nothing, coming forward at her through the indifferent crowd.

Susan said: 'Ben, be careful. Where're we going?'

'Back,' Ben said.

'Look – um – Paul's with me. He's somewhere. He'll be looking for me.'

'He'll be all right. You come with me, Susan.'

'How're the kids? Are they all right?'

'They're all right,' Ben said. 'My mum's there.'

'Well, thanks for the few kind words. How did you know I was here? Have you spoken to Julia?'

Ben said: 'Come on.'

'You don't have to shove me around,' Susan said.

'You're my old woman,' Ben said. 'You're with me now. Where you belong.'

'You know I've left Mac, I suppose?'

'Yes,' Ben said. 'I did find out.'

Susan said: 'I'm glad the kids are all right.'

'We're moving,' Ben said. 'We're moving from Archway.'

'We are? Where to?'

'I don't know yet, but somewhere. Somewhere more comfortable, more up to date; we're going into the big time, girl.'

'Big time, girl,' Susan sang. 'With your diamond ring.'

Ben said: 'You knew I'd find you here, didn't you?'

'Unless someone else did first.'

'No one else wants you, Susan.'

'Thanks very much.'

'Not the way I do. Sooner or later you had to come back to me.'

'Confident, aren't you?'

'You're my wife,' Ben said. 'Confidence doesn't come into it.'

'Thanks very much.'

'I'll see you right, girl, don't you worry. You'll be all right with me.'

Susan said: 'Ben, I – I don't want to stay in the Party.'

'Stay in the Party? I don't mind what you do about the Party.'

'Not after Hungary. You're not going to stay in, are you?'

Ben made a face and leered down at her. 'I *am* the Party,' he said.

'Help!' Susan said, in a very small voice.

7

Thornton Ashworth and Tom Wallace were standing on the far side of Whitehall from Downing Street when Paul saw them. He made straight towards them. 'I say, Thornton, Tom, hullo.'

Tom Wallace narrowed his eyes in his short-sighted way. Thornton Ashworth said: 'Paul! Hullo.'

Tom raised his hand in Caesarian salute. '*Hello*, how are you?'

Paul said: 'Two people I never expected to see here.'

'We're just passing through,' Thornton Ashworth said, producing cigarettes.

'Emerged from your ivory towers to observe the follies of mankind?'

'We're on our way to a Classical jamboree at Oxford,' Thornton agreed, 'and stopped to see the circus.'

'I see your book's out,' Tom Wallace said.

'Get you,' Paul said, 'fancy noticing that.'

Thornton Ashworth said: 'I hope it's not a *roman à clef*. I should hate to see us all depicted in our underwear.'

'The Senior Combinations Room,' Paul said. 'It's quite a temptation, I must say. No, it's all strictly made up, unfortunately. Watch out, though. If I get another chance, I'm finished with sedatives – I'm going to try tipping the patients out of bed instead.'

'Perhaps you'll write about all this one day,' Thornton said, with an airy wave towards the crowds among whom mounted policemen were bullocking about, 'and explain how it is that the world suddenly goes mad.'

'It's mad all the time,' Paul said, 'only you people are too well off to notice it.'

Thornton Ashworth said: 'I shouldn't advise you to try and support a wife and two children on my meagre emoluments.'

'It's not the emoluments that make you well off,' Paul said. 'It's the brocade lining in the old coffin there!'

'I think he's getting at us.'

Tom Wallace said: 'I think we shall have to pull out before the end of the high-wire act or we shall miss our train.' He watched closely as a girl with black stockings and mauve breasts was pushed back by the police. 'Much as I should like to stay.'

'What's the conference about?' Paul asked. 'At Oxford, I mean.'

'The meaning of the Non-Existent in the Sophist,' Thornton Ashworth said.

'Well,' Paul said, 'don't let me detain you. I can see you two boys must be indispensable to the discussion.' He pushed into the crowd, and though he was going a different way from the great mass, he was soon lost in it.

8

In the taxi, Susan said: 'I mean it, Ben, about leaving the Party. It'd be a farce to stay in now. Don't you agree?'

'No,' Ben said.

'I mean it's condoning things – after what's happened – '

'What's happened?'

Susan said: 'Well, I'm going to leave the Party anyway.'

'I'm not stopping you. You do what you want to do. Just as long as you stop with me.'

'Stop what?'

'Stop. Stay. We're going up in the world, girl. Don't you worry. I told you: I'll see you right.'

'Diminks?'

'Diminks and pearlminks and everythinkminks.'

'Better.'

'What kind of car has Paul got?'

'A Morris Minor.'

'Morris Minor, eh? I don't think much of that. I'd sooner have a Bentley, wouldn't you?'

'I'll believe it when I see it.'

'You'll see it all right.'

The taxi-driver said: 'No. 24, you said?'

'That's it.'

'Looks like they've come to pick you up, mate.'

Ben said: 'That's it, boy. I've come home to give myself up.'

'Want me to drive past?'

'No, I've had a good run for me money. I think I'll pack it in now.'

Susan said: 'Ben, you don't think they've really – '

Ben shrugged his shoulders. 'We shall see!'

The taxi pulled up. Superintendent Palmer had emerged from the police car and was standing by the garden gate, his pipe in his mouth. 'See you when you come out then,' the taxi-driver said. Superintendent Palmer rubbed his pipe bowl against the side of his nose. Susan put her arm through Ben's. 'Good afternoon, Mr Simons.'

'Afternoon.'

'Good afternoon, Mrs Simons. I hope this isn't an inconvenient moment – '

Susan said: 'I hope you haven't been waiting too long – '

'No, no, just a few minutes, that's all.'

'Oh well – that's lucky.'

Superintendent Palmer said: 'Mr Simons, I've called in connexion with certain investigations I have been making during the last few months on behalf of the American security authorities – '

'Aha.'

'I thought you should know that I have had instructions from my superiors to cease pursuing those inquiries. We are no longer making our files available to the Americans – '

'Good for you,' Ben said.

'Which does not of course mean that we shall destroy what we have already discovered – '

'What's that then?'

'But it does mean that we shall, for all practical purposes, leave this matter where it stands.' The superintendent frowned at his pipe and came up into a sad smile.

'Looks like international events have come to your assistance, doesn't it?'

'First as tragedy, then as farce,' Ben said. 'I told you there were advantages to being on the side of history.'

'I shouldn't rely too much on that, Mr Simons. We haven't quite given up the struggle yet.'

'No?'

'Off the hook doesn't mean out of mind, you know. It's not our intention to lose sight of you.'

'Aha. Well, thanks for calling round. Can't stop for tea, I suppose?'

'By the way,' said Palmer. 'I've – um – got something else I wanted to tell you. Something I've just heard about in the last couple of days.'

'Aha.'

'Since Hungary was opened up.'

'Opened up, yes?'

'That Miss Hilda Klein we were interested in –'

'What about her – ?'

The superintendent was looking at Susan. 'It appears she's dead, Mrs Simons.'

Susan said: 'Dead?'

'She was arrested four years ago in Budapest by the AVO.'

'The police,' Ben said.

'Someone who was arrested with her escaped to Vienna two nights ago. Apparently Miss Klein was arrested and tortured and then strangled, Mr Simons.'

'I see.'

'What for, Superintendent?'

'Oh, your friends aren't like us, you know; they don't need a reason for arresting people.'

'No, but –'

'Probably just because she'd been in London – knew how the other half lived. What do you think, Mr Simons?'

Ben said: 'We can't know. I don't know.'

'I'm sorry if I'm the bringer of sad news.'

'News,' Ben said.

'I thought you'd be interested. In view of what we know.'

'Very interesting, yes.'

'Pity we can't all go to the Promised Land, eh?'

'Sure,' Ben said.

The children were standing in the door of No. 24.

'Hullo,' Sarah called, 'hullo, Mummy.'

The superintendent said: 'Well, I'll leave you to it.'

'Aha, well thanks for coming round. You're welcome any time, you know, if you want to talk things over.'

554

'You're an interesting cove, Simons, I'll give you that.'

'You give it to me,' Ben said. 'And thanks again for coming.'

Jonathan said: 'Mummy, are you really home again? Is your business all finished?'

'Yes,' Susan said, 'all finished.'

Ben was at the gate, watching the police car drive off. It seemed a long path back to the house. Sarah called 'Daddy, Daddy, there's been a phone call for you, ever so urgent the man said. He said to phone as soon as you get back. I took the number.' Ben nodded and came down the long path to the house.

'Thanks, Sall.'

'Who it is, Ben?'

'Bill Ditchling.'

'Bill – ?'

'Deputy Editor up at the *Worker*. Better give him a buzz.'

Susan bit her nail and then went into the sitting-room where Ben's mother was. Jonathan said: 'Look! Mummy's home!'

Mrs Simons said: 'Yers, I can see.'

Ben came in to say: 'I've got to go out.'

'Oh, Ben, no.'

'Apparently they're threatening to break up the *Worker*.'

'Ben, you're not going?'

''Course I'm going.'

'Ben, you can't – ' She went into the corridor and shut the sitting-room door on the children. 'Ben, please, you can't – not now – '

'I've got to go, Susan.' He put on his coat. 'Do you think I'm going to stand by and let them smash everything we've built up? Do you really think that's what I ought to do?'

'But, Ben, what's the *good*?'

'It's there. It's what we've made. And I'm not going to let it go. See you later, girl.'

555

'Ben, you're helping the same people – the same people who killed Hilda – the girl – '

'What do you care? What does anyone care about who they're helping?'

'You don't realize what you're doing – '

'I know what I've *got* to do. When you know, you do it too.' Ben opened the front door. 'Otherwise leave me alone. Don't try to stop me until you know what you've got to do. And do it.'

9

'Today,' Paul said, 'the world's seen where our leaders lead us. And where we lead them. We've led them with all the lies that we've told each other; they've cheated us with all the cheating we've done each other. I'll never cheat you again, Julia, I promise you. I don't say I won't do things you don't like, but I won't be something that's false. We've had enough lies from everyone and the only way to stop them is to stop oneself. Today's the day that ought to teach the world what it's made itself. From now on I want to be true, as our child is true in you, and produce only what is right. There's only one thing we can give our children, the knowledge of the truth, by being true, by being true in front of each other, true in our work, true not in deadly fidelities but true as people. I want our child now because I know what I can say to it and what I can teach it, to stand up and be a man. We can't rely on other people's children. We can't rely on anyone except ourselves. We can't crawl into other people any more and live by them because today is what they do in our name: Hungary and Suez. The post-war twins, with the same parents, however much they shout at each other now. We've got to start again from the smallest individual and recreate a society where a man can be trusted to be a man, where people can stop lying and cheating and crawling because other people will back them up to do what's right. That's the writer's job – my job from now on – to show people how they can stand up and be something and let others be something. We've got to stop limiting each other; every lie runs through a people like a fever and distorts it. Each of us has to face and stop the lie wherever we see it, whenever we see it. We've got to stop the lie when it's small, before it's so big and powerful that opposing it is treason or counter-revolution or whatever you like to call it. We've got to hurry up and get our story straight and ourselves straight in our stories, however much people get hurt in the process. We've got to straighten up. We must say what must be said and be what we must be. It's too late today to stop what's been done up till today, but if we survive and live on, and then it happens again – whatever happens from this moment on – is our fault. As far as I'm concerned, from now on writing won't be a matter of nice stories for a railway journey, it'll be showing people how to arrive at the truth, not what the truth is, only each one knows that, but how to get to it, how to recognize it, in themselves and in others, not some special intellectual, only for Fellows of All Souls truth, but the truth that is themselves, what they are, how they act. People won't like it, they won't like looking at themselves and each other instead of the telly, listening to the truth instead of all the lying flattery they're used to; they'll say it hurts and it will. It's not what they want to see that I care about, it's what they've got to see. I'm not interested in entertainment; I'm interested in life and that's what I propose to write about, however painful it is. You won't like it; they won't like it; no one'll like it, but today it's the only way to write.'

After the War
Frederic Raphael

An epic novel of great scope and vision
from the author of *The Glittering Prizes*

When Michael introduces Joe to his sister, he warns her: 'Careful of this character - he's motorized mayhem.'

Michael Jordan, playwright, screen writer and director, grew up in the long shadow of the Second World War. Separated from his beautiful sister Rachel by wartime evacuation, they were like two only children. At prep school Michael meets Joe Hirsch, a refugee. Both Jewish – Joe, brash and uninhibited; Michael deferent to the England in which he grew up – their long, angry friendship and Rachel's life and loves form the kernel of this sweeping portrait of the postwar years.

From the seclusion of wartime Devon, to occupied Germany, and Paris, the action moves from showbiz London to Greece and Africa: but Israel provides a constant backdrop. When the threatened attack by the Arabs on Israel brings Michael, estranged from his wife, to his own year of decision, the irony of the masterly novel is manifest: since 1945 new wars have rendered that wonderful era 'after the war' systematically unattainable.

FONTANA PAPERBACKS